PULSE GENERATORS

PULSE GENERATORS

Edited by

G. N. GLASOE
PROFESSOR OF PHYSICS, RENSSELAER POLYTECHNIC INSTITUTE

J. V. LEBACQZ
ASSISTANT PROFESSOR OF ELECTRICAL ENGINEERING
THE JOHNS HOPKINS UNIVERSITY

OFFICE OF SCIENTIFIC RESEARCH AND DEVELOPMENT
NATIONAL DEFENSE RESEARCH COMMITTEE

NEW YORK
DOVER PUBLICATIONS, INC.

This Dover edition, first published in 1965, is an
unabridged and unaltered republication of the
work first published by McGraw-Hill Book Company, Inc., in 1948. It is made available through
the kind cooperation of McGraw-Hill Book Company, Inc.
This book was originally published as volume 5
in the Massachusetts Institute of Technology Radiation Laboratory Series.

Library of Congress Catalog Card Number 65-22726

Manufactured in the United States of America

Dover Publications, Inc.
180 Varick Street
New York, N. Y. 10014

PULSE GENERATORS

EDITORIAL STAFF

GEORGE B. COLLINS

G. NORRIS GLASOE

JEAN V. LEBACQZ

HOWARD D. DOOLITTLE

BARBARA DWIGHT

CONTRIBUTING AUTHORS

W. H. BOSTICK	A. S. JERREMS
J. R. DILLINGER	L. G. KERSTA
P. C. EDWARDS	H. H. KOSKI
O. T. FUNDINGSLAND	J. V. LEBACQZ
K. J. GERMESHAUSEN	R. S. STANTON
P. R. GILLETTE	H. J. WHITE

G. N. GLASOE

Foreword

THE tremendous research and development effort that went into the development of radar and related techniques during World War II resulted not only in hundreds of radar sets for military (and some for possible peacetime) use but also in a great body of information and new techniques in the electronics and high-frequency fields. Because this basic material may be of great value to science and engineering, it seemed most important to publish it as soon as security permitted.

The Radiation Laboratory of MIT, which operated under the supervision of the National Defense Research Committee, undertook the great task of preparing these volumes. The work described herein, however, is the collective result of work done at many laboratories, Army, Navy, university, and industrial, both in this country and in England, Canada, and other Dominions.

The Radiation Laboratory, once its proposals were approved and finances provided by the Office of Scientific Research and Development, chose Louis N. Ridenour as Editor-in-Chief to lead and direct the entire project. An editorial staff was then selected of those best qualified for this type of task. Finally the authors for the various volumes or chapters or sections were chosen from among those experts who were intimately familiar with the various fields, and who were able and willing to write the summaries of them. This entire staff agreed to remain at work at MIT for six months or more after the work of the Radiation Laboratory was complete. These volumes stand as a monument to this group.

These volumes serve as a memorial to the unnamed hundreds and thousands of other scientists, engineers, and others who actually carried on the research, development, and engineering work the results of which are herein described. There were so many involved in this work and they worked so closely together even though often in widely separated laboratories that it is impossible to name or even to know those who contributed to a particular idea or development. Only certain ones who wrote reports or articles have even been mentioned. But to all those who contributed in any way to this great cooperative development enterprise, both in this country and in England, these volumes are dedicated.

L. A. DuBridge.

Preface

WHEN the Radiation Laboratory was organized in the fall of 1940 in order to provide the armed services with microwave radar, one of the important technical problems facing this group was that of devising equipment capable of delivering high-power pulses to the newly developed cavity-magnetron oscillator. To be sure, some techniques for generating electrical pulses were available at this time. However, the special characteristics of these magnetrons and the requirements imposed by the operation of a microwave-radar system (high pulse power, short pulse duration, and high recurrence frequency) made it evident that new techniques had to be developed.

During the existence of the Radiation Laboratory the group assigned to the problem of pulse generation grew from a nucleus of about five people to an organization of more than ten times this number. The coordinated efforts of this group extended the development of pulse generators considerably beyond the original requirement of 100-kw pulses with a duration of 1 μsec and a recurrence frequency of 1000 pps. The development extended to both higher and lower powers, longer and shorter pulses, and lower and higher recurrence frequencies. Besides the improvement of existing techniques, it was necessary to devise entirely new methods and to design new components to provide satisfactory pulse generators for radar applications. The use of a lumped-constant transmission line (line-simulating network) to generate pulses of specific pulse duration and shape was carried to a high state of development. As a result of work both on transformers that could be used for short pulses and high pulse powers and on new switching devices, highly efficient and flexible pulse generators using line-simulating networks were available at the end of the war. Concurrent with the work at the Radiation Laboratory, a large amount of work was done at similar laboratories in Great Britain, Canada, and Australia, and at many commercial laboratories in this country and abroad.

The purpose of this volume is to present the developments in the techniques of pulse generation that have resulted from this work. These techniques are by no means limited to radar applications: they may be used with loads of almost any conceivable type, and should therefore be applicable to many problems in physics and engineering. The discussion of pulse-generator design and operation is divided into three principal parts. Part I is concerned with hard-tube pulsers, which are Class *C* amplifiers specifically designed for the production of pulses of short duration and high power; Part II presents the characteristics of the line-type pulser, which utilizes the line-simulating networks; Part III considers the design and characteristics of pulse transformers. Throughout this volume both the theoretical and the practical aspects of pulse-generator design are given in order to avoid restricting the available information to radar applications.

Although the major part of this volume is written by a few members of the Radiation Laboratory staff, many other individuals at the Radiation Laboratory and elsewhere have contributed their ideas in the preparation of this material, and we hereby acknowledge their contributions. Particular mention must be made of the work done by Miss Anna Walter in connection with many of the mathematical analyses. Her painstaking work in checking the mathematical derivations and making the long and tedious calculations necessary for many of the curves and numerical examples is gratefully acknowledged. We are glad to acknowledge also the work of Miss F. Newell Dutton, who processed the numerous pulse photographs that appear throughout the volume.

We are also indebted to the many people who have contributed their time freely in reading various chapters and sections of the manuscript, and who have made valuable suggestions for the improvement of the discussion. We wish to acknowledge the help received in this way from Mr. J. P. Hagen and his associates at the Naval Research Laboratory; Dr. J. E. Gorham and his associates at the Army Signal Corps Laboratory; Dr. F. S. Goucher, Mr. E. P. Payne, Mr. A. G. Ganz, Mr. A. D. Hasley, Mr. E. F. O'Neill, and Mr. W. C. Tinus of the Bell Telephone Laboratories; Mr. E. G. F. Arnott, Mr. R. Lee, Mr. C. C. Horstman, and Dr. S. Siegel and his associates at the Westinghouse Electric Corporation; Mr. H. W. Lord of the General Electric Company; Dr. A. E. Whitford of the Radiation Laboratory and the University of Wisconsin; and Dr. P. D. Crout of the Massachusetts Institute of Technology.

The preparation of the manuscript and the illustrations for this volume would have required a much longer time if we had not had the aid of the Production Department of the Office of Publications of the Radiation Laboratories. We wish to express our appreciation of the efforts of Mr. C. Newton, head of this department, for his help in getting the work done promptly and accurately.

The publishers have agreed that ten years after the date on which each volume in this series is issued, the copyright thereon shall be relinquished, and the work shall become part of the public domain.

CAMBRIDGE, MASS.,
June, 1946.   THE AUTHORS.

Contents

FOREWORD by L. A. DuBridge vii

PREFACE. ix

CHAP. 1.   INTRODUCTION 1

    1·1. Parameters Fundamental to the Design of Pulse Generators. . . 1
    1·2. The Basic Circuit of a Pulse Generator. 5
    1·3. Hard-tube Pulsers 6
    1·4. Line-type Pulsers 8
    1·5. A Comparison of Hard-tube and Line-type Pulsers. 13

PART I.   THE HARD-TUBE PULSER

CHAP. 2.   THE OUTPUT CIRCUIT OF A HARD-TUBE PULSER. . . . 21

    2·1. The Basic Output Circuit. 21

THE DISCHARGING OF THE STORAGE CONDENSER. 25

    2·2. The Output Circuit with a Resistance Load. 26
    2·3. The Output Circuit with a Biased-diode Load. 32

THE CHARGING OF THE STORAGE CONDENSER 51

    2·4. The Output Circuit with a High Resistance as the Isolating
        Element 52
    2·5. The Output Circuit with an Inductance or an Inductive Resistor
        as the Isolating Element 61

POWER TRANSFER TO THE LOAD 69

    2·6. Impedance-matching and Pulse-transformer Coupling to the Load 70
    2·7. The Effect of Stray Capacitance on the Pulser Power Output . . 76
    2·8. Output Power Regulation. 77
    2·9. Effects of Pulse-transformer Coupling to the Load 78

CHAP. 3.   VACUUM TUBES AS SWITCHES 90

    3·1. Required Characteristics 90
    3·2. The Characteristic Curves for Triodes and Tetrodes and their
        Importance to the Function of a Pulser Switch Tube. 98
    3·3. The Effect of Switch-tube and Load Characteristics on the
        Pulser Regulation 108

Chap. 4. DRIVER CIRCUITS. 119

    4·1. The Bootstrap Driver 120
    4·2. The Blocking Oscillator or Regenerative Driver 124
    4·3. The Multivibrator and Pulse-forming-network Drivers 132

Chap. 5. PARTICULAR APPLICATIONS 140

    5·1. The Model 3 Pulser—A Light-weight Medium-power Pulser for
          Airborne Radar Systems 140
    5·2. The Model 9 Pulser—A 1-Mw Hard-tube Pulser. 152
    5·3. A High-power Short-pulse Hard-tube Pulser. 160
    5·4. The Application of Pulse-shaping Networks to the Hard-tube
          Pulser 165

PART II. THE LINE-TYPE PULSER

Chap. 6. THE PULSE-FORMING NETWORK. 175

    6·1. The Formation and Shaping of Pulses 175
    6·2. Networks Derived from a Transmission Line 179
    6·3. Guillemin's Theory and the Voltage-fed Network 189
    6·4. Current-fed Networks 207
    6·5. Materials and Construction. 213
    6·6. Test Procedures 221

Chap. 7. THE DISCHARGING CIRCUIT OF THE LINE-TYPE PULSER 225

    7·1. General Properties of the Discharging Circuit 225
    7·2. Pulser Characteristics. 233
    7·3. Pulser Regulation and Efficiency. 244
    7·4. The Discharging Circuit and Pulse Shape. 255
    7·5. Computed and Actual Pulse Shapes 261

Chap. 8. SWITCHES FOR LINE-TYPE PULSERS. 273

The Rotary Spark Gap 275

    8·1. Electrical Considerations in the Design of Rotary Spark Gaps. . 276
    8·2. Considerations of Mechanical Design. 283
    8·3. Rotary-gap Performance 289

Enclosed Fixed Spark Gaps. 294

    8·4. General Operating Characteristics of Series Gaps. 296
    8·5. Trigger Generators. 304
    8·6. Division of Voltage Across Series Gaps 312
    8·7. General Considerations for Gap Design. 316
    8·8. The Cylindrical-electrode Aluminum-cathode Gap 318
    8·9. The Iron-sponge Mercury-cathode Gap. 327
    8·10. The Three-electrode Fixed Spark Gap 332

The Hydrogen Thyratron. 335

    8·11. General Operating Characteristics of the Hydrogen Thyratron 336
    8·12. The Anode Circuit. 344
    8·13.. The Grid Circuit. 349

CONTENTS   xiii

CHAP. 9. THE CHARGING CIRCUIT OF THE LINE-TYPE PULSER. . 355

INDUCTANCE CHARGING FROM A D-C POWER SUPPLY 356

9·1.   General Analysis of D-c Charging 356
9·2.   Practical D-c Charging Reactors. 364
9·3.   The Design of D-c Charging Reactors 372

INDUCTANCE CHARGING FROM AN A-C SOURCE. 380

9·4.   General Analysis of A-c Charging 380
9·5.   A-c Resonant Charging. 386
9·6.   A-c Nonresonant Charging 393
9·7.   Practical A-c Charging Transformers. 400
9·8.   The Design of High-reactance Transformers. 407
9·9.   Miscellaneous Charging Circuits. 414

CHAP. 10.   PERFORMANCE OF LINE-TYPE PULSERS 417

10·1.   Effects of Changes in Load Impedance 417
10·2.   Short Circuits in the Load. 423
10·3.   Open Circuits and Protective Measures. 431

PULSER PERFORMANCE WITH A MAGNETRON LOAD. 435

10·4.   Normal Operation of the Magnetron 435
10·5.   Magnetron Mode-changing 438
10·3.   Magnetron Sparking 441

CHAP. 11.   PARTICULAR APPLICATIONS 448

11·1.   A High-power Rotary-gap Pulser. 448
11·2.   A High-power Airborne Pulser. 454
11·3.   Multiple-network Pulsers. 463
11·4.   The Anger Circuit 468
11·5.   The Nonlinear-inductance Circuit 471
11·6.   Special-purpose Output Circuits 476
11·7.   Multiple-pulse Line-type Pulsers. 485
11·8.   Multiple-switch Circuit for Voltage Multiplication. 494

PART III.   PULSE TRANSFORMERS

CHAP. 12.   ELEMENTARY THEORY OF PULSE TRANSFORMERS . . 499

12·1.   General Transformer Theory 499
12·2.   Values of Elements in the Equivalent Circuit 510

CHAP. 13.   PULSE-TRANSFORMER DESIGN. 532

13·1.   General Pulse-transformer Design Considerations 532
13·2.   Design Methods. 536
13·3.   Typical Pulse-transformer Designs. 555

CHAP. 14.   EFFECT OF PULSE-TRANSFORMER PARAMETERS ON
            CIRCUIT BEHAVIOR. 563

14·1.   The Effect of Pulse-transformer Parameters on Pulse Shapes on
        Resistance and Biased-diode or Magnetron Loads 563

14·2.   The Effect of Pulse-transformer Parameters on the Behavior of
        Regenerative Pulse Generators. 575
14·3.   The Effect of Pulse-transformer Parameters on Frequency
        Response 591

CHAP. 15.   MATERIALS AND THEIR USES IN DESIGN 599

    CORE MATERIAL 599

        15·1.   D-c Properties and Test Results. 599
        15·2.   Pulse Magnetization 613
        15·3.   Energy Loss and Equivalent Circuits. 626
        15·4.   Additional Aspects of Pulse Magnetization 633
        15·5.   Techniques for Measuring Core Performance 639

    COIL MATERIAL 648

        15·6.   Insulation. 648
        15·7.   Wire. 655

APPENDIX A.   MEASURING TECHNIQUES 661

    OSCILLOSCOPIC METHODS. 662

        A·1.   Signal Presentation. 662
        A·2.   Pulse Measurements 667
        A·3.   Practical Considerations in Making Pulse Measurements 687
        A·4.   Voltage and Current Measurements in the Charging Circuit of a
               Line-type Pulser. 690

    METERING TECHNIQUES 692

        A·5.   Pulse Voltmeters. 692
        A·6.   The Average-current Meter. 701
        A·7.   Auxiliary Measuring Techniques. 706

APPENDIX B.   PULSE DURATION AND AMPLITUDE 710

        B·1.   Equivalent Rectangular Pulse by Conservation of Charge and
               Energy. 711
        B·2.   Equivalent Rectangular Pulse by Minimum Departure Areas . . 716
        B·3.   A Comparison of the Methods. 720

LIST OF SYMBOLS. 723

INDEX 729

CHAPTER 1

INTRODUCTION

By G. N. Glasoe

Microwave radar has required the development of pulse generators that are capable of producing a succession of pulses of very short time durations. The pulse generators of a radar system fall into two principal categories, namely, those that are associated with the transmitter and those that are used in the indicator and ranging circuits. The principal distinguishing feature of pulse generators of these two types is the output power level. The radar transmitter requires the generation of high-power and high-voltage pulses whereas the indicator and ranging circuits require pulses of negligible power and relatively low voltage. The purpose of this book is to record information that pertains to the basic principles underlying the design of power pulse generators. Although most of these principles have been developed primarily in the field of microwave radar, they are equally adaptable to a very large number of applications not associated with radar. The discussion is general, and reference to specific microwave-radar applications is made only when they serve as examples of attainable results. Specific design information is given for some of the practicable circuits that have been built and have proved to be satisfactory.

The most commonly used source of the high-frequency energy that is necessary for microwave radar has been the magnetron oscillator. The problem of power-pulse-generator design has, therefore, been greatly influenced by the characteristics of these magnetron oscillators. By virtue of this application many of the basic principles of pulse-generator design are better understood.

The power pulse generators used in the transmitters of radar systems have been variously referred to as "modulators," "pulsers," and "keyers." Since the function of these generators is to apply a pulse of voltage to an oscillator and thereby produce pulses of high-frequency energy to be radiated by the antenna, the term "pulser" is a descriptive abbreviation for pulse generator. Throughout this book, therefore, the term "pulser" will be used in preference to the terms "modulator" and "keyer."

1·1. Parameters Fundamental to the Design of Pulse Generators.— There are certain parameters of a pulser that are common to all types

1

and that affect the design. The most important of these parameters are pulse duration, pulse power, average power, pulse recurrence frequency, duty ratio, and impedance level. Before proceeding to the detailed discussion of pulser design, therefore, it is well to introduce the parameters by defining some terms and indicating the ranges which have been common in the microwave-radar field.

In its broadest aspects, the term "pulse duration" is the time during which a voltage or current maintains a value different from zero or some other initial and final value. The term "pulse shape" is used to refer to the form obtained when the pulse amplitude is plotted as a function of time. When referring to such a plot, it is convenient to discuss the details of a particular pulse shape in terms of the "leading edge," the "top," and the "trailing edge" of the pulse. If a pulse of voltage or current is truly rectangular in shape, that is, has a negligible time of rise and fall and is of constant amplitude for the intervening time interval, the pulse duration is simply the time elapsed between the deviation from and the return to the initial value. The term "negligible time" is, of course, relative and no strict boundaries can be attached. For most practical purposes, however, if the rise and fall times for a pulse are about a tenth or less of the pulse duration, the pulse is considered substantially rectangular. A current pulse of this type is required for a magnetron oscillator by virtue of the dependence of the output frequency on the current, which is called the "pushing factor." For pulses which are definitely not rectangular, the effective or equivalent pulse duration is either the time measured at some fraction of the maximum pulse amplitude that is significant to the particular application, or the time corresponding to a rectangular equivalent of the pulse in question. The interpretation of pulse duration is discussed in Appendix B, and when particular cases come up in the text they are considered in more detail.

The pulsers that have been designed for microwave-radar applications have pulse durations covering the range of 0.03 to 5 μsec. The design of a pulser for short pulse durations with substantially rectangular pulse shape requires the use of high-frequency circuit techniques since frequencies as high as 60 to 100 Mc/sec contribute to the pulse shape and the effects of stray capacitances and inductances become serious.

In the microwave-radar field the voltage required across the magnetron ranges from as low as 1 kv to as high as 60 kv. If a voltage pulse is applied to some type of dissipative load, a magnetron for example, there will be a corresponding pulse of current which depends on the nature of this load. The pulse current through the magnetron ranges from a few amperes to several hundred amperes. The combined considerations of short pulse duration and rectangularity therefore require that careful attention be given to the behavior of the pulser circuit and its components under conditions of high rates of change of voltage and current. The rate of change of voltage may be as high as several hundred kilovolts per microsecond, and the current may build up at the rate of hundreds to thousands of amperes per microsecond.

The product of the pulse voltage and the pulse current is the pulse power. When the voltage and current pulses are rectangular, the corresponding pulse power is unambiguous. When the pulses are irregularly shaped, however, the meaning of the term "pulse power" is not so clear because somewhat arbitrary methods are often used to average the product of voltage and current during the pulse. The peak power of a pulse is the maximum value of the product of the voltage and current. Thus, for rectangular pulses the peak power and the pulse power are the same, but for irregularly shaped pulses the peak power is greater than the pulse power.

In this connection there are two general types of load that are discussed most frequently, namely, the linear load, such as a pure resistance, and the nonlinear load, such as the magnetron. The magnetron load can be approximately represented as a biased diode with a dynamic resistance that is low and a static resistance that is about ten times higher. Static resistance is the ratio of the voltage across the load to the current through the load, whereas the dynamic resistance is the ratio of a small change in voltage to the corresponding change in current. When the dynamic resistance of the load is small, the magnitude of the pulse current varies greatly with only small variations of the pulse voltage, and for loads such as a magnetron, for example, the behavior of the pulser with a linear load is not necessarily a good criterion.

Since the pulse-power output of pulsers for microwave-radar application has ranged from as low as 100 watts to as high as 20 Mw, the average power output as well is important to the design. The average power corresponding to a particular pulse power depends on the ratio of the aggregate pulse duration in a given interval to the total time, and this in turn depends on the pulse recurrence frequency, PRF, which is the number of pulses per second (pps). If the pulse duration is τ and the time between the beginning of one pulse and the beginning of the next pulse is T_r, then

$$P_{av} = \left(\frac{\tau}{T_r}\right) P_{pulse} = \tau(\text{PRF})P_{pulse}.$$

A similar equation can be written in terms of the current if the pulse voltage is essentially constant during the time corresponding to the current pulse, thus

$$I_{av} = \left(\frac{\tau}{T_r}\right) I_{pulse} = \tau(\text{PRF})I_{pulse}.$$

Since the average current and the PRF are relatively easy to measure, this relation may be used to define a pulse current if the top of the pulse is irregular but the rise and fall times are negligibly small. It may also be used to define an equivalent pulse duration for a pulse shape that is trapezoidal and perhaps rounded at the top, but where some significance can be attached to a pulse-current measurement.

The ratio τ/T_r—or the product $\tau(\text{PRF})$—is commonly called the pulser "duty," "duty cycle," or preferably "duty ratio," and is expressed as a fraction or a percentage. Thus 1-μsec pulses repeated at a rate of 1000 pps correspond to a duty ratio of 0.001 or 0.1 per cent. Pulsers have been constructed with a duty ratio as high as 0.1, but for most radar applications a value of 0.001 or lower is most common. As with any power device, the over-all efficiency of a pulser is an important consideration in its design. This is particularly true when the average power output is high, that is, a combination of high pulse power and high duty ratio. This point is stressed in the discussion and is frequently a deciding factor in choosing one type of pulser in preference to another.

The pulse recurrence frequency affects the design of a pulser in ways other than from the standpoint of the power considerations. The pulser circuit may be considered to have a quiescent state that is disturbed during the pulse interval and to which it must return before the initiation of the next succeeding pulse. If the PRF is very high, the problem of returning the circuit to this quiescent state becomes of importance. Such things as time constants and deionization times may impose a limit on how small the interpulse interval can be without unduly complicating the design. This limit becomes especially important whenever it is necessary to produce a series of closely spaced pulses to form a code such as is used in radar beacons.

The choice of the internal impedance of the pulse generator depends on the load impedance, the pulse-power level, and practical considerations of circuit elements. Impedance-matching between generator and load is of prime importance in some cases, especially with regard to the proper utilization of the available energy and the production of a particular pulse shape. Impedance-matching is not always convenient with the load connected directly to the pulser output; however, matching can readily be attained by the use of a pulse transformer. By this means it is possible to obtain impedance transformations between pulser and load as high as 150/1, that is, a transformer with a turns ratio of about 12/1. The magnetrons which have been used in microwave radar have static impedances ranging from about 400 ohms to about 2000 ohms; in general, the higher the power of the magnetron, the lower its input impedance.

The impedance-transformation characteristic of the pulse transformer also provides a means of physically separating the pulser and the load.

Thus the power may be transmitted from the pulser to the load through a low-impedance coaxial cable, provided that pulse transformers are used to match impedances.   For most efficient power transfer such impedance-matching is necessary between pulser and cable and between cable and load.   In this way it has been possible to transmit high-power pulses of short duration over as much as 200 ft of cable without a serious loss in the over-all efficiency or a deterioration of the pulse shape.

The pulse transformer has another function that is important to pulser design, namely, it provides a means for reversing the polarity of a pulse. This feature of the pulse transformer together with the impedance-transformation property considerably extends the range of usefulness for pulsers of any type.

1·2. The Basic Circuit of a Pulse Generator.—The pulse generators discussed in this book depend on the storage of electrical energy either in an electrostatic field or in a magnetic field, and the subsequent discharge of a fraction or all of this stored energy into the load.   The two basic categories into which the largest number of pulser designs logically fall are (1) those in which only a small fraction of the stored electrical energy is discharged into the load during a pulse, and (2) those in which all of the stored energy is discharged during each pulse.   These two basic categories of pulsers are generally referred to as (1) "hard-tube pulsers" and (2) "line-type pulsers."

To accomplish this discharge, it is necessary to provide a suitable switch that can be closed for a length of time corresponding to the pulse duration and maintained open during the time required to build up the stored energy again before the next succeeding pulse.   In its simplest form, therefore, the discharging circuit of a pulser can be represented schematically as shown in Fig. 1·1.   The characteristics required for the switch will be different depending on whether or not all the stored energy is discharged into the load during a single pulse.   Some pulse-shaping will be necessary in the discharging circuit when all the energy is to be dissipated.

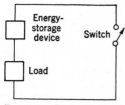

Fig. 1·1.—Basic discharging circuit of a pulser.

Since the charging of the energy-storage component of the pulser takes place in the relatively long interpulse interval, the discussion of pulsers may logically be divided into the consideration of the discharging circuit on the one hand, and the charging circuit on the other.   Power supplies for these pulsers are, in general, of conventional design and therefore usually need not be discussed, but wherever this design has bearing on the over-all pulser behavior, special mention is made of the fact.

1·3. Hard-tube Pulsers.—In general, the energy-storage device for these pulsers is simply a condenser that is charged to some voltage V, thus making available an amount of electrical energy $\frac{1}{2}CV^2$. The term "hard-tube" refers to the nature of the switch, which is most commonly a high-vacuum tube containing a control grid. The closing and opening of this switch is therefore accomplished by applying properly controlled voltages to the grid. Since only a small fraction of the energy stored in the condenser is discharged during the pulse, the voltage across the switch immediately after the pulse and during the charging interval is nearly the same as it is at the beginning of the pulse. It is therefore necessary that the grid of the vacuum-tube switch have complete control of the conduction through the tube. This required characteristic of the switch tube rules out the possibility of using known gaseous-discharge devices for this type of pulser.

It is generally desired that these pulsers produce a succession of pulses, and therefore some provision must be made to replenish the charge on the storage condenser. This is accomplished by means of a power supply which is connected to the condenser during the interpulse interval. The combination of the discharging and charging circuits of the pulser may be represented schematically as shown in Fig. 1·2. In order to avoid short-circuiting the power supply during the pulse interval, some form of isolating element must be provided in series with the power supply. This element may be a high resistance or an inductance, the particular choice depending on the requirements of over-all pulser design. The primary consideration is to keep the power-supply current as small as possible during the pulse interval. However, the impedance of this isolating element should not be so high that the voltage on the condenser at the end of the interpulse interval differs appreciably from the power-supply voltage.

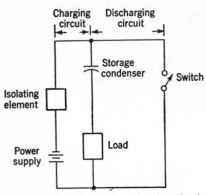

FIG. 1·2.—Charging and discharging circuit for a hard-tube pulser.

Because of the high pulse-power output, pulsers for microwave radar require switch tubes that are capable of passing high currents for the short time corresponding to the pulse duration with a relatively small difference in potential across the tube. Oxide-cathode and thoriated-tungsten-filament tubes can be made to pass currents of many amperes for the pulse durations necessary in the microwave-radar applications with a reasonable operating life expectancy. The cathode efficiency, that is, amperes of plate current per watt of heating power, is considerably less for the thoriated-tungsten filament than for the oxide cathode. For switch tubes with oxide cathodes it has been common to obtain about 0.3 to 0.5 amp/watt of heating power, although as much as 1 amp/watt has been obtained, whereas for thoriated-tungsten filaments this amount is generally less than 0.1 amp/watt. The tungsten-filament tube, however, is less subject to sparking at high voltages and currents and, within Radiation Laboratory experience, these tubes have not exhibited cathode fatigue, that is, a falling-off of cathode emission during long pulses. This cathode fatigue is sometimes a limitation on the longest pulse for which an oxide-cathode switch tube should be used.

In order to obtain a high plate current in these switch tubes, there must be a fairly high positive voltage on the control grid and therefore considerable grid current. In the case of a tetrode, there is a high screen-grid current as well   The duty ratio permitted in a given pulser is often limited by the amount of average power which the particular tube can dissipate.

The output circuit of a hard-tube pulser does not usually contain any primary pulse-shaping components, although its design, in combination with the load, has a marked effect on the ultimate shape of the pulse. In a pulser of this type, the pulse is formed in the driver circuit, the output of which is applied to the control grid of the switch tube. From the standpoint of over-all pulser efficiency, it is desirable that the switch tube be nonconducting during the interpulse interval. The control grid must therefore be at a voltage sufficiently negative to keep the tube cut off during this time, and consequently the output voltage from the driver must be sufficient to overcome this grid bias and carry the grid positive. For most designs of hard-tube pulsers, this requirement means that the driver output power must be a few per cent of the actual pulser output power.

The resistance of available vacuum tubes used as switches in hard-tube pulsers ranges from about 100 to 600 ohms. If the pulser is considered as a generator with an internal resistance equal to that of the switch tube, the highest discharge efficiency is obtained when the effective load resistance is high. Matching the load resistance to the internal resistance of the pulser results in an efficiency of 50 per cent in the output circuit and the switch tube must dissipate as much power as the load. Because of these considerations, the hard-tube pulser is generally designed with a power-supply voltage slightly greater than the required pulse voltage. This design practice has not been followed when the output voltage required is higher than the power-supply voltage that is easily obtainable. The power-supply voltage may be limited by available

components, size requirements, and other special considerations. A
pulse transformer may then be used between the pulser and the load to
obtain the desired pulse voltage at the load.

1·4. Line-type Pulsers.—Pulse generators in this category are referred
to as "line-type" pulsers because the energy-storage device is essentially
a lumped-constant transmission line.   Since this component of the line-
type pulser serves not only as the source of electrical energy during the
pulse but also as the pulse-shaping element, it has become commonly
known as a "pulse-forming network," PFN.   There are essentially two
classes, of pulse-forming networks, namely, those in which the energy for
the pulse is stored in an electrostatic field in the amount $\frac{1}{2}CV^2$, and those
in which this energy is in a magnetic field in the amount $\frac{1}{2}LI^2$.   The first
class is referred to as "voltage-fed networks" and the second as "current-
fed networks."   The voltage-fed network has been used extensively in
the microwave-radar applications in preference to the current-fed network because of the lack of satisfactory switch tubes for the latter type.

The pulse-forming network in a line-type pulser consists of inductances and condensers which may be put together in any one of a number
of possible configurations.   The configuration chosen for the particular
purpose at hand depends on the ease with which the network can be
fabricated, as well as on the specific pulser characteristic desired.   The
values of the inductance and capacitance elements in such a network can
be calculated to give an arbitrary pulse shape when the configuration,
pulse duration, impedance, and load characteristics are specified.   The
theoretical basis for these calculations and the detailed discussion of the
role of the various network parameters are given
in Part II of this book.

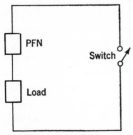

Fig. 1·3.—Discharging
circuit for a voltage-fed
network.

The discharging circuit of a line-type pulser
using a voltage-fed network may be represented
schematically as shown in Fig. 1·3.   If energy
has been stored in the network by charging the
capacitance elements, closing the switch will
allow the discharge of this energy into the load.
When the load impedance is equal to the characteristic impedance of the network, assuming the
switch to have negligible resistance, all of the
energy stored in the network is transferred to
the load, leaving the condensers in the network completely discharged.
The time required for this energy transfer determines the pulse duration
and depends on the values of the capacitances and inductances of the network.   If the load impedance is not equal to the network impedance, some
energy will be left on the network at the end of the time corresponding to
the pulse duration for the matched load.   This situation leads to complica-

tions in the circuit behavior and is to be avoided if possible by careful design and construction of the network to insure an impedance match with the load. The voltage appearing across a load that matches the impedance of a nondissipative voltage-fed network is equal to one half of the voltage to which the network is charged just before closing the switch.

The corresponding circuit for a current-fed network may be represented as shown in Fig. 1·4. In this case the switch acts to close the network-charging circuit and allows a current to build up in the inductance of the network. When this current is interrupted by opening the switch, a high voltage, whose magnitude depends on the load impedance and the current in the inductance, appears across the load. Impedance-matching between the load and a network of the current-fed type results in a division of current such that the load current is one half of that in the network just before the switch is opened.

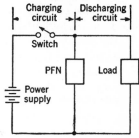

FIG. 1·4.—Charging and discharging circuit for a current-fed network.

The consideration of impedance-matching is of extreme importance in designing a line-type pulser because it affects the utilization of the energy stored on the network, as well as the ultimate shape of the voltage and current pulses at the load.   For these reasons, the nature of the load must be known before proceeding to the design of the pulser.   If the load is nonlinear, as in the case of a magnetron, it very often happens that the load characteristics can be taken into account only approximately, and the ultimate design of the network may have to depend on experimental tests with subsequent modifications to obtain the desired pulse shape.

Pulse-forming networks can be designed to have any value of characteristic impedance, but matters of practical convenience, such as the available size of inductances and condensers and the maximum permissible switch voltage, often dictate that this value be different from that required to match the impedance of the load. When the network impedance is different from the load impedance, the matched condition is attained by the use of a pulse transformer. Again, for reasons of engineering convenience, it has been common to apply the pulser output directly into one end of a coaxial cable, thus facilitating the physical separation of the pulser and the load.   The impedance of the cable matches that of the network, and a pulse transformer at the other end provides the impedance match to the load.   Since the cable that has been most available for applications of this type has a characteristic impedance of 100 ohms or less (commonly 50 ohms), most of the voltage-fed line-type pulsers for microwave radar have been designed for the 50-ohm level, thereby making the use of a pulse transformer a necessity with magnetron load. The pulse transformer therefore becomes an essential part of the discharging circuit in a low-impedance pulser used with high-impedance load, and as such its characteristics have an effect on the pulse shape and the over-all behavior of the discharging circuit. It is desirable and often necessary that the design of the pulse transformer and the design of the pulse-forming network be coordinated in order to obtain the most satisfactory pulser operation.

Since the impedance-transformation ratio for a transformer is equal to the square of the voltage-transformation ratio, the use of a low-impedance pulser with a load of higher impedance requires the use of a pulse transformer that gives a voltage stepup between pulser output and load input. Thus, when a line-type pulser with a 50-ohm voltage-fed network is used to pulse an 800-ohm load, for example, the voltage stepup ratio is about 4/1, and the current in the discharging circuit of the pulser becomes about four times the load current. Accordingly, the switch in the discharging circuit of a line-type pulser is required to pass very high pulse currents for high pulse power into the load. Since the switch is in series with the pulser output, its effective resistance must be small compared with the characteristic impedance of the pulse-forming network if high efficiency is desired.

When a pulser uses a voltage-fed network, the voltage across the switch falls to zero at the end of the pulse because the stored energy is completely discharged. This consideration, in conjunction with the high current-carrying capacity and low resistance required of the switch, suggests the use of a form of gaseous-discharge device, which must remain nonconducting during the interpulse interval if it is desired to apply a succession of pulses to the load. If it is also required that the interpulse intervals be of controlled duration, the switch must have a further characteristic which allows a positive control of the time at which conduction is initiated. These switch requirements can be met by rotary spark gaps, which depend on overvolting by a decrease in the gap length, or by fixed spark gaps, in which the discharge is initiated by an auxiliary electrode. A grid-controlled gaseous-discharge tube such as the thyratron is particularly well suited to this application since it is possible to start the discharge in a tube of this type at any desired time, within a very small fraction of a microsecond, by the application of proper voltage to the grid. Several grid-controlled hydrogen-filled thyratrons of different voltage and current ratings that cover the range of pulse-power output from a few kilowatts to almost two megawatts have been developed for this application. These hydrogen thyratrons have proved to be very practical switches for line-type pulsers because they fulfill adequately all the switch requirements mentioned above and have a stability against ambient temperature variations that is considerably better than that of the mercury thyratron. Hydrogen thyratrons that have a satisfactory operating life and yet can hold off 16 kv with the grid at cathode potential and carry pulse currents of several hundred amperes for a pulse duration of 2 μsec and a recurrence frequency of 300 pps have been developed and manufactured.

The grid-controlled high-vacuum tube is not well suited to serve as the switch in a low-impedance line-type pulser using a voltage-fed network because of its rather low cathode efficiency and relatively high resistance during the conduction period. An oxide-cathode high-vacuum tube that requires 60 watts of cathode-heater power, for example, can carry a pulse current of about 15 amp for a pulse duration of a few microseconds, and under these conditions, this tube presents a resistance of perhaps 100 ohms to the circuit. A hydrogen thyratron, on the other hand, with equivalent cathode-heater power can carry a pulse current of about 300 amp, presenting an effective resistance to the circuit of about one ohm.

As stated previously, a line-type pulser using a current-fed network requires a switch capable of carrying a current at least twice that desired in the pulser load. The further requirement that this switch must be capable of interrupting this current and withstanding high voltage during the pulse eliminates the gaseous-discharge type and points to the grid-controlled high-vacuum tube. The low current-carrying capacity of existing tubes has, therefore, been the principal deciding factor in choosing the voltage-fed network for line-type pulsers rather than the current-fed network.

Several different methods are used to charge a voltage-fed network in a line-type pulser. Since the general aspects of these methods are not appreciably affected by the discharging circuit, the requirements imposed on pulser design by the charging circuit can be considered separately. If the time allowed for the charging of the network is sufficiently long compared with the pulse duration, the charging cycle is simply that corresponding to the accumulation of charge on a condenser.

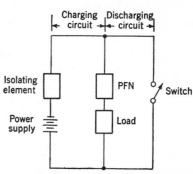

Fig. 1·5.—Charging and discharging circuit for a voltage-fed network.

Figure 1·5 indicates schematically the relation between the charging and discharging circuits of a pulser with voltage-fed network. For example, the network may be recharged from a d-c power supply through a high resistance, in which case the equilibrium voltage on the network can be nearly equal to the power-supply voltage. The requirement on the series-resistance isolating element in this charging circuit is simply that it must be large enough to allow only negligible current to be taken from the power supply during the pulse and the deionizing time for the switch, but not so large that the RC time constant becomes comparable to the interpulse interval. To get the highest network voltage from a given power-supply voltage with this arrangement, the length of the interpulse interval should be several times greater than the RC time constant in the charging circuit. This method of charging the network is inherently inefficient—its maximum possible efficiency is only 50 per cent.

Since the efficiency of the network-charging circuit with a resistance as the isolating element is very low, the use of a nondissipative element, such as an inductance, suggests itself. When a capacitance is charged through an inductance from a constant potential source, the voltage across the capacitance is in the form of a damped oscillation the first maximum of which is approximately equal to twice the supply voltage if the initial voltage across the capacitance and the current through the inductance are zero. This maximum occurs at a time equal to $\pi \sqrt{LC}$ after the voltage source is connected to the inductance-capacitance combination. The inductance to be used with a given network is, therefore, calculated by setting the interpulse interval equal to $\pi \sqrt{LC}$, where C is the network capacitance. This type of network charging is called "resonant charging." If the pulse recurrence frequency is less that $1/\pi \sqrt{LC}$, some current will still be flowing in the inductance at the beginning of each charging period and, under equilibrium conditions, this initial current will be the same for all charging cycles. The network will again be charged to approximately twice the power-supply voltage. This type of network charging is called "linear charging."

With careful design of the inductance, the efficiency of the charging circuit is as high as 90 to 95 per cent, and the power-supply voltage needs to be only slightly greater than one half of the desired network voltage, resulting in a great advantage over resistance charging. A factor of 1.9 to 1.95 between network and supply voltage can be obtained if the charging inductance is designed so that the quality factor Q of the charging circuit is high.

Resonant charging can also be done from an a-c source provided that the pulse recurrence frequency, PRF, is not greater than twice the a-c frequency. If the pulse recurrence frequency and the a-c frequency are equal, the network voltage attains a value π times the peak a-c voltage. This voltage stepup becomes greater as the ratio of a-c frequency to pulse recurrence frequency increases. The voltage gain soon becomes expensive, however, and it is not practical to go beyond an a-c frequency greater than twice the PRF.

1·5. A Comparison of Hard-tube and Line-type Pulsers.—Although it is not possible to give a set of fixed rules to be followed in determining the type of pulser best suited to a particular application, it is possible to give a few general comparisons of the two types which may aid in choosing between them. The comparisons made here concern such things as: power output and efficiency, pulse shape, impedance-matching, short interpulse intervals, high-voltage versus low-voltage power supply, the ease with which pulse duration and pulse recurrence frequency can be changed, time jitter, over-all circuit complexity, size and weight of the pulsers, and regulation of the pulser output against variations in input voltage. This list does not include all the possible points for comparison, but only those that are of primary importance in choosing between the two pulser types.

The over-all efficiency of the line-type pulser is generally somewhat higher than that of the hard-tube pulser, particularly when the pulse-power output is high. This is due in part to the fact that the hard-tube pulser requires a larger overhead of cathode-heating power. Furthermore, a high-vacuum-tube switch dissipates a greater portion of the available pulser power by virtue of its higher effective resistance than does a gaseous-discharge switch. The power required for the driver of the hard-tube pulser is not negligible and, since this component is not necessary in a line-type pulser, the over-all efficiency of the latter is thereby enhanced.

The pulse shape obtained from a hard-tube pulser can usually be made more nearly rectangular than that from a line-type pulser. This is particularly true when the network of the pulser has low impedance, and a pulse transformer must be used between the pulser and a nonlinear load such as a magnetron. In this case, small high-frequency oscillations are superimposed on the voltage pulse at the load. These oscillations make the top of the pulse irregular in amplitude. The amplitude of the corresponding oscillations on the top of the current pulse depends on the dynamic resistance of the load and, if this is small, these oscillations become an appreciable fraction of the average pulse amplitude. The hard-tube pulser is, therefore, generally preferred to the line-type for applications in which a rectangular pulse shape is important.

Impedance-matching between pulser and load has already been mentioned as an important consideration in the design of line-type pulsers. Usually, an impedance mismatch of ±20 to 30 per cent can be tolerated as far as the effect on pulse shape and power transfer to the load is concerned, but a greater mismatch causes the over-all pulser operation to become unsatisfactory. The load impedance of the hard-tube pulser, however, can be changed over a wide range without seriously affecting the operation. The principal limitation in the latter case is that, if the load impedance is too low, the required current through the switch tube is large and the power dissipated in the switch becomes a larger fraction of the total power, thus lowering the efficiency. In applications of the line-type pulser it is possible to effect an impedance match for any load by the proper choice of pulse transformer, but this procedure is somewhat inconvenient if, for example, it is desired to vary the power input to a nonlinear load between wide limits.

Switches of the gaseous-discharge type, which are commonly used in the line-type pulser, place a stringent limitation on the minimum spacing between pulses. After the pulse, the network must not charge up to any appreciable voltage until the deionization is complete, otherwise the switch will remain in the conducting state and the power supply will be short-circuited. For this reason, the interpulse interval must be several times as long as the switch deionization time when the gaseous-discharge type is used. The high-vacuum-tube switch in the hard-tube pulser does not present any similar limitations on the interpulse interval, but in this case the problem becomes one of designing the circuit with small RC and L/R time constants. It has been possible, for example, to construct hard-tube pulsers with 0.2-μsec pulses spaced 0.8 μsec between leading edges.

It has been stated in the preceding discussion of hard-tube pulsers that a high-voltage power supply is necessary for highest efficiency. This requirement is sometimes a very serious limitation on the design of such pulsers for high-pulse-power output. The low-impedance line-type pulser using resonant charging of the network, on the other hand, can be designed with a much lower power-supply voltage for a pulse-power output comparable to that of a hard-tube pulser. For example, a hard-tube pulser with a pulse-power output of 3 Mw has been built with a 35-kv power supply, whereas for a line-type pulser with d-c resonant charging of the network, the same power output is obtained with only about 14 kv from the power supply if a standard 50-ohm network is used. A line-type pulser using a-c resonant charging, on the other hand, requires an a-c power source giving a peak voltage of about 8 kv in order to provide a pulse-power output of 3 Mw. It should be stated, however, that in both of the line-type pulsers mentioned here the pulse-forming networks are charged to about 25 kv, but this voltage does not present such serious design problems from the engineering standpoint as the design of a power supply of equivalent voltage. It would have been advantageous to have a power-supply voltage greater than 35 kv for this 3-Mw hard-tube pulser, but a higher voltage was impractical because the pulser design was limited by the available components, in particular by the switch tube.

It is sometimes desirable to have a pulser capable of producing pulses of several different durations, the particular one to be used being selected by a simple switching operation. The pulse duration is determined in the driver of the hard-tube pulser, where this type of pulse selection is easily made since the switching can be done in a low-voltage part of the circuit. In the line-type pulser, however, the pulse duration is determined by the network and in order to change the pulse duration a different network must be connected into the circuit. This can be accomplished by a switching operation, but because of the higher voltage involved it is not so simple as in the hard-tube pulser. A further complication may arise in the line-type pulser since a change of network affects the characteristics of the charging circuit, and practical considerations of inductance charging therefore limit the ranges of pulse duration and pulse recurrence frequency that can be covered. The ease with which the pulse duration may be changed in a hard-tube pulser provides a flexibility that is difficult to obtain with a line-type pulser.

In many pulser applications it is important to have the interpulse intervals precisely determined. In hard-tube pulsers and some line-type pulsers, constant interpulse intervals are obtained by using a trigger pulse to initiate the operation of the pulser. These trigger pulses can be generated in a low-power circuit independent of the pulser, and it is a simple matter to design such a circuit so that the trigger pulses occur at precisely known time intervals. When the successive output pulses from the pulser start with varying time delay after the start of the trigger pulse, there is said to be time jitter in the output pulses. If the trigger pulses are used to initiate the operation of other apparatus, which is auxiliary to the pulser, this time jitter results in unsatisfactory over-all operation of the equipment. Hard-tube pulsers can be easily designed to make this time jitter negligible, that is, ≈ 0.02 μsec or less. The time jitter is also small in line-type pulsers that make use of a hydrogen thyratron as the switch. With line-type pulsers using the triggered spark gaps (series gaps), however, the time jitter is considerably greater, about 0.1 to 3 μsec depending on the gap design. Recent development of a triggered spark gap having a cathode consisting of spongy iron saturated with mercury has made it possible to obtain time jitter as small as 0.02 μsec with the series-gap switch. When a rotary spark gap is used as the switch in a line-type pulser, the interpulse intervals are determined by the rotational speed and the number of sparking electrodes. In this case time jitter refers to the irregularity of the interpulse intervals and may amount to as much as 20 to 80 μsec.

Because the circuit for the hard-tube pulser is somewhat more complex and requires a larger number of separate components than that of the line-type pulser, both the problem of servicing and the diagnosis of faulty behavior of the hard-tube pulser are more difficult. Because of the combination of fewer separate components and higher efficiency, a

line-type pulser can generally be designed for smaller size and weight than
a hard-tube pulser with equivalent pulse- and average-power output and
with comparable safety factors in the individual components.

Table 1·1.—Comparison of the Two Pulser Types

Characteristics	Hard-tube pulser	Line-type pulser
Efficiency..........	Lower; more overhead power required for the driver, cathode-heating, and for dissipation in the switch tube	High, particularly when the pulse-power output is high
Pulse shape..........	Better rectangular pulses	Poorer rectangular pulse, particularly through pulse transformer
Impedance-matching	Wide range of mismatch permissible	Smaller range of mismatch permissible (± 20 to 30%). Pulse transformer will match any load, but power input to nonlinear load cannot be varied over a wide range
Interpulse interval....	May be very short; as for coding beacons (i.e., < 1 μsec)	Must be several times the deionization time of discharge tube (i.e., > 100 μsec)
Voltage supply.......	High-voltage supply usually necessary	Low-voltage supply, particularly with inductance charging
Change of pulse duration	Easy; switching in low-voltage circuit	Requires high-voltage switching to new network
Time jitter..........	Somewhat easier to obtain negligible time jitter (i.e., < 0.02 μsec) than with a line-type pulser	High-power line-type pulsers with rotary-gap switch have an inherently large time jitter; with care in design and the use of a hydrogen thyratron or enclosed gaps of mercury-sponge type, a time jitter of 0.02 μsec is obtainable
Circuit complexity....	Greater, leading to greater difficulty in servicing	Less, permitting smaller size and weight
Effects of change in voltage	For design having maximum efficiency, $(\Delta P/P)$ output $\approx 6(\Delta V/V)$ input. By sacrificing efficiency in the design, $(\Delta P/P)$ output $\approx 0.5(\Delta V/V)$ input can be obtained	Better than a hard-tube pulser designed for maximum efficiency since $(\Delta P/P)$ output $\approx 2(\Delta V/V)$ input for a line-type pulser, independent of the design

The effect on the power output of a pulser resulting from a change in
the input voltage is sometimes of considerable importance to the particular application.   For a line-type pulser, the percentage change in output
power is about two times the percentage change in input line voltage, and

little can be done to change this ratio appreciably. In the case of the hard-tube pulser, however, this ratio may be controlled by the proper choice of the switch tube and its operating conditions. The percentage change in output power from a hard-tube pulser may be varied over the range of 0.5 to 6 times the percentage change in input line voltage. This advantage with the hard-tube pulser is gained only at the expense of lower efficiency, however, and the ratio is large when the discharging circuit is designed for maximum efficiency.

These comparisons between hard-tube and line-type pulsers are summarized in Table 1·1.

It should be evident from these general remarks concerning the relative merits of hard-tube and line-type pulsers that a perfunctory analysis of the requirements for a particular application cannot lead to an intelligent choice of the pulser type to be used. A detailed analysis requires a thorough understanding of the characteristics of pulsers in general, and of the two types in particular. It is the purpose of the following chapters, therefore, to present the available information on hard-tube and line-type pulsers in considerable detail in order that it may be of the greatest possible aid in the design of high-power pulse generators for any application.

PART I

THE HARD-TUBE PULSER

CHAPTER 2

THE OUTPUT CIRCUIT OF A HARD-TUBE PULSER

By G. N. Glasoe

2·1. The Basic Output Circuit.—As stated in Chap. 1, pulse-generator design and operation are discussed here from the standpoint of the basic circuit shown in Fig. 1·1, the essential elements of which are the reservoir for electrical energy, the switch, and the load. These components constitute the output circuit of the pulser, and their inherent characteristics, together with the circuit behavior, almost exclusively determine the pulse shape and amplitude. The power output from a pulser is usually required to be a succession of pulses occurring at more or less regular time intervals with a specified time duration for each pulse. The complete pulser circuit must therefore contain, in addition to the output circuit, a means of controlling the duration of the pulse and of replenishing the electrical energy in the reservoir during the interpulse intervals. Since the pulse shape and amplitude are usually the most important characteristics of the pulser output, it is logical to begin the discussion with a consideration of the output circuit.

The hard-tube pulser derives its name from the fact that the switch is a high-vacuum tube, the conduction through which can be controlled by the application of the proper voltage to a grid.   In its simplest form such a switch is a triode, but, as is shown later, a tetrode or pentode can often perform the switching function more satisfactorily. The choice of the tube to be used as the switch in a pulser designed for high pulse-power output depends on the capability of the tube to pass high peak currents and to stand off high voltages. The voltage drop across the switch tube must also be considered in connection with over-all pulser efficiency and allowable power dissipation in the tube, particularly if the duty ratio for the pulser is high.   The discussion of the design of hard-tube pulsers is therefore influenced to a considerable extent by the characteristics of the high-vacuum tubes that have been available.

Condenser as the Energy Reservoir.—The reservoir for electrical energy in a hard-tube pulser may be either a condenser or an inductance. The hard-tube pulsers for microwave-radar applications have most commonly been of the condenser type. The two possibilities may be represented schematically as shown in Fig. 2·1, where the load is indicated as a pure resistance. In Fig. 2·1a switch (1) is introduced only for convenience in the present discussion and is replaced by a high-impedance element in the more detailed discussion in the following sections.

Assume that the switch (1) in Fig. 2·1a is closed long enough to allow the condenser to become charged to the power-supply voltage. An amount of energy $\frac{1}{2}C_w E_{bb}^2$ is then available to be discharged into the load

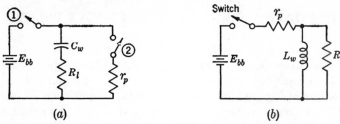

(a)   (b)

FIG. 2·1.—Basic hard-tube pulser circuits. (a) The condenser type. (b) The inductance type.

by opening switch (1) and closing switch (2). During this condenser discharge, the voltage across the load decreases with time according to the relation

$$V_l = E_{bb} e^{-\frac{t}{(R_l + r_p)C_w}} - V_p,$$

where t is measured from the instant the switch is closed, and $V_p = I_p r_p$ is the voltage drop in the switch. If the switch is closed for a time small compared with the time constant $(R_l + r_p)C_w$, only a small part of the total energy stored in the condenser is removed, and the voltage across the load and the current through the switch are very nearly constant. The load is therefore subjected to a voltage pulse of duration corresponding to the length of time the switch is kept closed. The capacitance that is necessary to keep the pulse voltage between the limits V_l and $V_l - \Delta V_l$ can easily be calculated if the pulse current and the pulse duration are specified. If the pulse duration τ is assumed to be small compared with the RC time constant of the discharging circuit, the change in voltage of the condenser during the pulse may be written

$$\Delta V_l = \frac{I_l}{C_w} \tau.$$

If switch (1) is closed again for the time between pulses, after opening switch (2), the energy in the condenser is replenished from the power supply. A repetition of this switching procedure produces a succession of identical pulses. The important point of this discussion is that the switch tube, represented by switch (2), carries current only during the pulse interval. Hence the average power dissipated in the switch tube is equal to $V_p I_p \tau/T_r$, where V_p is the tube drop, I_p is the plate current, τ is the pulse duration, and $T_r = 1/f_r$ is the recurrence interval.   The power dissipated in the switch tube is augmented slightly by replacing switch (1) by a high-impedance element, but for the present considerations this increase may be neglected.   Figure 2·2 shows a sketch of the condenser voltage as a function of time when switch (1) is replaced by a high resistance.

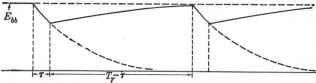

Fig. 2·2.—Idealized sketch of the time variation of the voltage on the storage condenser in a hard-tube pulser.

Inductance as the Energy Reservoir.—Consider next the pulser represented in Fig. 2·1b, in which an inductance serves as the electrical-energy reservoir.   When the switch is closed, a current builds up in the inductance according to the relation

$$i_L(t) = \frac{E_{bb}}{r_p}\left(1 - e^{\frac{r_p}{L_w}t}\right)$$

where r_p, the effective resistance of the switch, is considered to be small compared with R_l, and the resistance of the inductance is assumed to be negligibly small.   If the switch is opened at a time t_1, the initial current in the load resistance is $i_L(t_1)$ and decreases with time according to the relation

$$i_l(t') = i_L(t_1)e^{-\frac{R_l}{L_w}t'}$$

where t' is measured from the instant of opening the switch.   If $t_1 \gg L_w/r_p$, the initial voltage across the load is $E_{bb}R_l/r_p$.   A pulse is produced by keeping the switch open for the time interval desired for the pulse duration.   If this time is small compared with L_w/R_l, the current in the inductance, and hence that in the load, decreases only slightly during the pulse, and a large fraction of the energy initially stored in the inductance is still there at the instant the switch is closed.   As a result, the current in the switch at the start of the interpulse interval is almost as large as it was at the start of the pulse.   If a succession of pulses is obtained by repeating the switching procedure, the average current through the switch tube is nearly equal to the pulse current.

Comparison of a Condenser and an Inductance as the Energy Reservoir.—The pulse current through the switch tube for a given pulse power into a load is the same whether the electrical energy is stored in an inductance or in a capacitance.   Thus, the voltage drop across a given switch tube is comparable in the two cases.   The average power dissipated in the switch tube, however, is much higher when an inductance is used because the tube is conducting during the interpulse interval, whereas, when a capacitance is used, it is conducting only during the pulse interval. The idealized sketch shown in Fig. 2·3 indicates the current in the inductance as a function of time.

Fig. 2·3.—Idealized sketch of the time variation of current in the storage inductance of a hard-tube pulser.

Although the power-supply voltage required for a pulser with an inductance for energy storage is considerably less than the desired pulse voltage across the load, the switch tube must be capable of withstanding approximately the same voltage as when a capacitance is used.   In a pulser of the type shown in Fig. 2·1a, the maximum voltage across the switch tube is equal to the power-supply voltage, which must be greater than the load pulse voltage by an amount equal to the voltage drop in the tube.   The maximum voltage across the switch tube in the circuit of Fig. 2·1b is equal to the magnitude of the pulse voltage plus the power-supply voltage.   Pulsers of the two types that are designed to give the same output voltage and current for a particular load therefore require approximately the same characteristics for the switch tube.

If the effective resistance of the switch tube is reduced, the average power dissipation in the inductance pulser becomes a less serious matter. A tube of the gaseous-discharge type is capable of conducting a high current with a very small voltage drop across the tube, and hence introduces a low effective resistance into the circuit.   With conventional tubes of this type, however, once the gaseous discharge is initiated it cannot be extinguished by application of voltage to a grid.   For this reason, the known gaseous-discharge tubes are not practicable switches for the inductance pulser.

There is a method by which the energy dissipated in the switch tube can be reduced to a reasonable value in spite of the relatively high effective resistance of high-vacuum tubes.   The method is to allow all the energy stored in the inductance to be discharged into the load before the switch is closed again.   As a result, the pulse current drops to zero and the pulse shape, instead of being rectangular, has the form

$$i_l(t') = i_L(t_1)e^{-\frac{Rl_{l'}}{L_w}t'}.$$

The average power dissipation in the switch tube is kept small by closing the switch for only a short time interval before the start of the pulse. The current in the inductance as a function of time is shown in Fig. 2·4. The undesirable nonrectangular pulse can be transformed into a rectangular pulse by making the inductance a part of a current-fed pulse-forming network. This possibility is discussed in detail in Chap. 6, where it is shown that with such an arrangement the pulse current

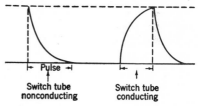

Fig. 2·4.—Inductance current as a function of time when all the energy stored in the inductance is discharged into the load.

in the load is only one half of the current built up in the inductance. The average power dissipation in the switch tube is therefore reduced at the expense of a higher pulse-current requirement on the tube.

Because of the preceding considerations and the characteristics of conventional high-vacuum tubes, the condenser was chosen as the electrical-energy reservoir for a hard-tube pulser. A detailed discussion of the pulse shape obtainable with such a pulser must involve the particular characteristics of the load and of the switch tube. There is invariably some distributed capacitance across the load which must be taken into account when considering the shape of the leading and trailing edges of the pulse. If, for example, the load is a biased diode, a conducting path must be provided in parallel with the load in order to allow the storage condenser to be recharged.

In the following sections the possible arrangements for the pulser output circuit are discussed, with emphasis on the effect of the various circuit parameters on the shape of the output pulse and on the efficiency of the discharging circuit.

THE DISCHARGING OF THE STORAGE CONDENSER

In Chap. 1 and in the preceding section, the use of a reservoir for electrical energy in a pulse generator has been emphasized and reasons have been given for choosing a condenser to serve as such a

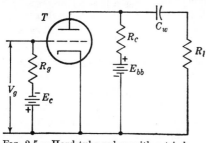

Fig. 2·5.—Hard-tube pulser with a triode as the switch tube.

reservoir in a hard-tube pulser. A pulser of this type is actually a Class C amplifier whose coupling condenser is considered to be the energy reservoir, as becomes evident when the circuit of Fig. 1·2 is redrawn with a three-element vacuum tube in the switch position, as shown in Fig. 2·5. By comparing the circuit of Fig. 2·5 with that of Fig. 1·2, it is seen that the discharging circuit consists of the condenser C_w, the load R_l, and the tube T. The charging circuit consists of the primary electrical-energy source E_{bb}, the isolating element R_c, the condenser C_w, and the load R_l. As with the Class C amplifier, in order to operate this circuit as a pulser the grid of the vacuum tube must be biased beyond cutoff so that the tube is normally nonconducting. The application of a voltage V_g of amplitude sufficient to overcome the grid bias causes the tube to conduct and a voltage to appear across the load R_l. There are two major differences, however, between the operation of such a circuit as a pulser and as a conventional Class C amplifier that make it desirable to deviate from the usual method of amplifier-circuit analysis in the discussion of pulser operation:

1. The ratio of conducting to nonconducting periods for the vacuum tube is considerably smaller in pulser operation than in amplifier operation. Thus, the pulser discussion is usually concerned with a ratio of the order of magnitude of 1/1000, whereas a conventional Class C amplifier involves a ratio slightly less than 1/2.

2. In pulser operation the shape of the voltage at the load is of fundamental importance.

The effects of the various circuit parameters on the pulse shape can best be discussed by considering the discharging circuit from the standpoint of transient behavior. In the following discussion of pulse shape, a linear load is represented by a pure resistance and a nonlinear load by a biased diode. When the biased diode is used, it is necessary to introduce a conducting path in parallel with the load in order to provide a recharging path for the storage condenser during the interpulse interval. The effect of this shunt element on the pulse shape is considered for the cases where it is a pure resistance or a combination of resistance and inductance.

2·2. The Output Circuit with a Resistance Load.—For the present discussion of the pulser discharging circuit, the switch tube is considered to function as an ideal switch, that is, as one requiring negligible time to open and close, in series with a constant resistance r_p. Actually, the particular tube characteristics and the shape of the voltage pulse applied to the grid by the driver modify these considerations somewhat, as discussed in Chap. 3. The simplest form for the discharging circuit is shown in Fig. 2·6. In this circuit the condenser C_s has been introduced to represent the shunt capacitance, which is the sum of the capacitance of the load, the capacitance of the switch tube, and the stray capacitance of the circuit wiring.

In order to discuss the effect of the circuit parameters on the pulse shape, it is necessary to find an expression for the voltage across the load as a function of time, that is, an equation for $V_{ba}(t)$. For the present discussion the storage condenser is considered to be charged to a voltage V_w that is very nearly equal to the power-supply voltage. It is further assumed that the capacitance of C_w is so large that the change in voltage during a pulse is negligibly small. The analytical expression for $V_{ba}(t)$

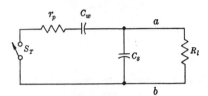

FIG. 2·6.—Discharging circuit of a hard-tube pulser with a resistance load and a shunt capacitance.

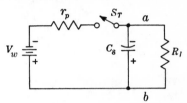

FIG. 2·7.—Equivalent output circuit for a hard-tube pulser with a resistance load. The charged storage condenser is replaced by a battery.

can be obtained by replacing the charged condenser C_w by a battery of voltage V_w, as shown in Fig. 2·7. The complete shape of the voltage pulse across the load resistance R_l is determined in two steps:

1. The switch S_T is closed at $t = 0$ and $V_{ba}(t)$ is evaluated over the time interval $0 \leqq t \leqq t_1$.
2. The switch S_T is opened at $t = t_1$ and $V_{ba}(t)$ is evaluated for $t \geqq t_1$.

The time interval during which the switch is closed essentially determines the pulse duration τ in many cases. It is sometimes desirable, however, to define pulse duration in a manner significant to the particular application and, although related to the time interval $0 \leqq t \leqq t_1$, τ may be either greater or smaller than this interval.

The expression for $V_{ba}(t)$ is found by solving the differential equations for the circuit subject to the initial conditions corresponding to the two steps indicated above. For this circuit and others to be discussed later, the Laplace-transform method[1,2] will be used to obtain the solution of the circuit equations. A further simplification in the analysis of a circuit such as that of Fig. 2·7 can be accomplished by replacing the voltage source by a current source.[2] This interchange of source makes it possible to write a single differential equation instead of the two simultaneous equations required for the two-mesh circuit. When the voltage source V_w and series resistance r_p are replaced by a current source I_w and

[1] H. S. Carslaw and J. C. Jaeger, *Operational Methods in Applied Mathematics*, 2nd ed., Oxford, New York, 1943.

[2] M. F. Gardner and J. L. Barnes, *Transients in Linear Systems*, Vol. I., Wiley, New York, 1942.

shunt conductance g_p such that

$$I_w = \frac{V_w}{r_p} = V_w g_p,$$

the circuit shown in Fig. 2·8 is equivalent to the circuit of Fig. 2·7. Using Kirchhoff's current law, the differential equation for this circuit when the switch S_T is closed is

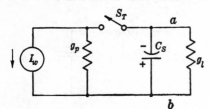

$$(g_p + g_l)V_{ba} + C_s\frac{dV_{ba}}{dt} = I_w. \quad (1)$$

Fig. 2·8.—Equivalent circuit for calculating the leading edge and top of the pulse for a hard-tube pulser with a resistance load, $I_w = g_p V_w$, $g_p = 1/r_p$ and $g_l = 1/R_l$.

The Laplace transform of a function $V(t)$ is written $V(p)$, and is defined by the equation

$$V(p) = \int_0^\infty V(t)e^{-pt}\,dt. \quad (2)$$

The Laplace transform for the circuit of Fig. 2·8 is then

$$(g_p + g_l)V_{ba}(p) + C_s[pV_{ba}(p) - V_{ba}(0)] = \frac{I_w}{p}, \quad (3)$$

in which $V_{ba}(0)$ is the initial voltage on the condenser C_s at the beginning of the time interval under consideration. The desired function $V_{ba}(t)$ is found by solving Eq. (3) for $V_{ba}(p)$ and evaluating the inverse Laplace transform, thus

$$V_{ba}(t) = \mathcal{L}^{-1}[V_{ba}(p)].$$

Let $V_1(t)_{0 \leq t \leq t_l}$ be the value of $V_{ba}(t)$ during the first step in the process of finding the pulse shape for the circuit of Fig. 2·6. Since the condenser C_s is assumed to be completely discharged at the instant of closing the switch, $V_{ba}(0) = 0$. The Laplace transform for $V_1(t)$ is obtained from Eq. (3) by putting $V_{ba}(0) = 0$.

$$V_1(p) = \frac{\dfrac{I_w}{p}}{C_s p + (g_p + g_l)}. \quad (4)$$

If the right-hand member of this equation is broken into partial fractions, there is obtained

$$V_1(p) = \frac{A}{p} + \frac{B}{p + \left(\dfrac{g_p + g_l}{C_s}\right)} \quad (5)$$

in which A and B are evaluated by standard methods, giving

$$A = \frac{I_w}{g_p + g_l} = \frac{V_w}{r_p} R_1$$

and

$$B = -\frac{I_w}{g_p + g_l} = -\frac{V_w}{r_p} R_1$$

where R_1 is the effective resistance of r_p and R_l in parallel. The inverse Laplace transform of $V_1(p)$ can then be written

$$V_1(t)_{0 \leq t \leq t_1} = \frac{V_w}{r_p} R_1 (1 - e^{-a_1 t}) \tag{6}$$

where

$$a_1 = \frac{g_p + g_l}{C_s} = \frac{1}{R_1 C_s}. \tag{7}$$

Equation (6) gives the shape of the leading edge of the voltage pulse across the load resistance R_l. If the switch is closed for a time $t_1 \gg R_1 C_s$, the voltage at the top of the pulse is

$$V_1(t)_{R_1 C_s \ll t \leq t_1} = \frac{V_w}{r_p} R_1. \tag{8}$$

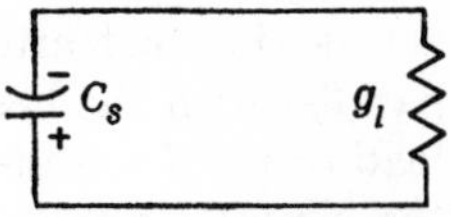

FIG. 2·9.—Equivalent circuit for calculating the trailing edge of the pulse for a hard-tube pulser with a resistance load.

The second step in determining the pulse shape involves calculating $V_{ba}(t)_{t \geq t_1}$ with the switch S_T open and the condenser C_s charged to the potential difference $V_1(t_1)$ given by Eq. (6). The equivalent circuit for this step is shown in Fig. 2·9. The Laplace-transform equation for this case is obtained from Eq. (3) by setting $I_w = 0$, $g_p = 0$, and $V_{ba}(0) = V_1(t_1)$ and letting $V_{ba}(t)_{t \geq t_1} = V_2(t)$.

Thus

$$V_2(p) = \frac{V_1(t_1)}{p + \dfrac{g_l}{C_s}} \tag{9}$$

from which

$$V_2(t)_{t \geq t_1} = V_1(t_1) e^{-a_2(t - t_1)} \tag{10}$$

where

$$a_2 = \frac{1}{R_l C_s}. \tag{11}$$

If $t_1 \gg R_1 C_s$, Eq. (8) may be used, and Eq. (10) becomes

$$V_2(t)_{t \geq t_1} = \frac{V_w}{r_p} R_1 e^{-a_2(t - t_1)}. \tag{11}$$

It is evident from Eqs. (6) and (10) that the stray capacitance across the output of a pulser—that is, across the load—has an important effect on the times of rise and fall of the pulse voltage. The most efficient hard-tube pulser is one in which the load resistance is considerably larger than the effective resistance of the switch tube, and hence the time constant

$$R_l C_s \gg \frac{R_l r_p}{R_l + r_p} C_s.$$

Under such conditions the time for the trailing edge of the pulse to return to zero, or the initial value, is greater than that required for the pulse voltage to build up to its maximum value. In order to produce as nearly rectangular a pulse as possible with a given resistance load, C_s must be kept small and r_p should be small.

The effect of the connection to the power supply indicated in Fig. 2·5 has been neglected in drawing the equivalent circuits for the pulser output circuit. Since the isolating element in series with the power supply usually has an impedance that is high compared with r_p, its effect on the leading edge of the pulse is small. For the calculations for the voltage across the load after the switch is opened, the isolating element is in parallel with the load and the shunt capacitance. Therefore, unless the load resistance is also small compared with that of the isolating element, the circuit element g_l in Fig. 2·9 must be considered as the sum of the conductances of the load and the isolating element.

From a practical standpoint, it is necessary to have some part of the output circuit at ground potential. The cathode of the switch tube is grounded, since the contribution to C_s introduced by the switch tube is best minimized in this way, and the voltage pulse at the load is therefore negative. In order to obtain a positive pulse at the load, the cathode of the switch tube must be insulated to withstand a high voltage, and consequently the capacitance of the filament-heating transformer also contributes to C_s. The presence of C_s results in an increase in the average power taken from the power supply for a given duty ratio and pulse power into the load, as is shown in Sec. 2·7.

The effect of the capacitance C_s and the conductance g_l on the voltage pulse across a resistance load is illustrated in the photographs of oscilloscope traces shown in Fig. 2·10. These pictures were obtained with a hard-tube pulser in which the capacitance of the storage condenser was 0.05 μf, the isolating element R_c was 10,000 ohms, r_p was approximately 150 ohms, and the pulse voltage at the load was 10 kv. Oscilloscope traces of the voltage pulse are shown for values of C_s equal to 50, 80, and 140 μμf and for R_l equal to 1000, 5000, and 10,000 ohms. Also shown in Fig. 2·10 are the plots of the pulse voltage as a function of time calcu-

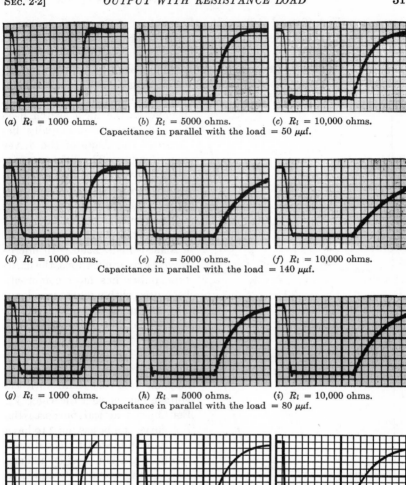

(a) R_l = 1000 ohms.   (b) R_l = 5000 ohms.   (c) R_l = 10,000 ohms.
Capacitance in parallel with the load = 50 μμf.

(d) R_l = 1000 ohms.   (e) R_l = 5000 ohms.   (f) R_l = 10,000 ohms.
Capacitance in parallel with the load = 140 μμf.

(g) R_l = 1000 ohms.   (h) R_l = 5000 ohms.   (i) R_l = 10,000 ohms.
Capacitance in parallel with the load = 80 μμf.

(j) R_l = 1000 ohms.   (k) R_l = 5000 ohms.   (l) R_l = 10,000 ohms.
Pulse shapes calculated from equivalent circuit (m) for shunt capacitance = 80 μμf.

FIG. 2·10.—Oscilloscope traces and calculated shapes for 10-kv voltage pulses obtained with a hard-tube pulser for various values of load resistance and shunt capacitance. Sweep speed: 10 div. = 1 μsec; vertical scale: 10 div. = 10 kv.

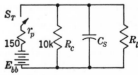

(m) Equivalent circuit for calculations.

lated from Eqs. (6) and (10) for the three values of R_l with $C_s = 80$ $\mu\mu$f. Since the 10,000-ohm isolating element is taken into account in these calculations, the value of g_l in Fig. 2·9 is the sum $(1/R_l) + (1/R_c)$. The calculated leading edge of the pulse differs slightly from the experimental value in that the observed time of rise is greater than the calculations indicate.   This difference occurs because the switch tube does not behave as the ideal switch used for calculations, principally because of the shape of the driver output pulse.   The difference is so small, however, that the calculated values give a reasonably good picture of the pulse shape to be expected from the pulser.

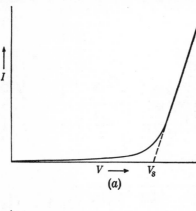

(a)

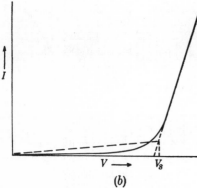

(b)

Fig. 2·11.—Current voltage characteristic of a magnetron.

2·3. The Output Circuit with a Biased-diode Load.—In microwave-radar applications, the hard-tube pulser has most commonly been used with a magnetron load. The current-voltage characteristic of a magnetron for a particular magnetic field is shown in Fig. 2·11. As indicated in these sketches, the current through a magnetron is very small until the voltage has reached the value V_s. For most practical purposes the I-V curve can be assumed to have the form indicated by the dotted line in Fig. 2·11a, that is, a sharp knee at the voltage V_s and zero current below this voltage. In some cases, however, the behavior of a magnetron is approximated better by the I-V characteristic indicated by the dotted lines of Fig. 2·11b.   This approximation involves the assumption that the magnetron presents a high dynamic resistance to the circuit for voltages below a critical value V_s and a low dynamic resistance above this voltage.   Whether the I-V characteristic sketched in Fig. 2·11a or b is to be used in any given case depends on the particular type of magnetron and the values of the circuit parameters.

For the I-V characteristic of Fig. 2·11a, the behavior of a magnetron as the load on a pulser is equivalent to that of an ideal diode, that is, one that has a linear I-V characteristic, in series with a battery of voltage V_s whose polarity is in opposition to that of the pulse voltage. For circuit analysis, it is possible to represent such a load as a biased resistance in series with a switch that is assumed to be closed only during the time when the magnitude of the pulse voltage is greater than V_s.

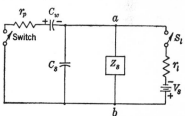

FIG. 2·12.—Discharging circuit of a hard-tube pulser with a biased-diode load and a recharging path for the storage condenser.

The biased-diode load is used to indicate the effect of nonlinear and unidirectional characteristics of the load on the output of a hard-tube pulser. The output circuit in this case is shown in Fig. 2·12. In this circuit r_l is the dynamic resistance of the load, V_s is the bias voltage, and S_l is a switch that is closed only when $V_{ba} \geqq V_s$. The shunt path indicated as Z_s must be provided with a load of this type in order to allow the charge on the storage condenser to be replenished after the pulse.

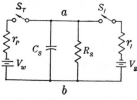

FIG. 2·13.—Equivalent output circuit for a hard-tube pulser with a biased-diode load and a resistance for the recharging path. The charged storage condenser is replaced by a battery.

Resistance for the Recharging Path.—The simplest form for Z_s is a resistance, and the corresponding equivalent circuit is shown in Fig. 2·13. The calculation of the complete pulse shape for this circuit involves four steps:

1. The switch S_T is closed at $t = 0$, S_l is open and $V_{ba}(t)$ is evaluated up to time $t = t_1$, such that $V_{ba}(t_1) = V_s$.

2. The switch S_T is closed, S_l is closed at $t = t_1$, and $V_{ba}(t)$ is evaluated over the time interval $t_1 \leqq t \leqq t_2$, where t_2 is the time at which S_T is opened.

3. The switch S_T is open, S_l is closed, and $V_{ba}(t)$ is evaluated over the time interval $t_2 \leqq t \leqq t_3$, where t_3 is the time at which $V_{ba}(t_3) = V_s$.

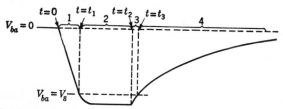

FIG. 2·14.—Sketch of pulse shape indicating the four steps necessary in the calculations for a hard-tube pulser with a biased-diode load.

4. Both switches are open and $V_{ba}(t)$ is evaluated for time $t \geqq t_3$. The procedure is represented in the diagram of Fig. 2·14.

The circuit equivalent to that of Fig. 2·13 with current sources in place of voltage sources is shown in Fig. 2·15. In this case $I_w = g_p V_w$

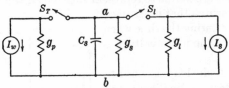

FIG. 2·15.—Equivalent circuit for calculating the pulse shape for a hard-tube pulser with a biased-diode load and a resistance for the recharging path.

and $I_s = g_l V_s$, where $g_p = 1/r_p$, $g_l = 1/r_l$ and $g_s = 1/R_s$. Using Kirchhoff's current law, the equation for this circuit with both switches closed is

$$(g_p + g_s + g_l)V_{ba} + C_s \frac{dV_{ba}}{dt} = I_w + I_s. \tag{12}$$

The pulse shape is obtained by solving this equation for $V_{ba}(t)$ using the initial conditions imposed by the four steps indicated above.

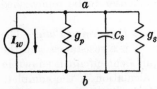

FIG. 2·16.—Equivalent circuit for Step 1 in the calculation of the pulse shape for a hard-tube pulser with a biased-diode load.

Step 1. The equivalent circuit for this case is shown in Fig. 2·16. Equation (12) reduces to

$$(g_p + g_s)V_{ba} + C_s \frac{dV_{ba}}{dt} = I_w \tag{13}$$

and the Laplace-transform equation then becomes

$$(g_p + g_s)V_1(p) + C_s[pV_1(p) - V_1(0)] = \frac{I_w}{p}, \tag{14}$$

where $V_1(p)$ is the Laplace-transform for $V_{ba}(t)$ in the time interval $0 \leq t \leq t_1$, t_1 being the time at which $V_{ba} = V_s$. Since it is assumed that C_s is initially uncharged, $V_1(0) = 0$. Solving Eq. (14) for $V_1(p)$,

$$V_1(p) = \frac{\dfrac{I_w}{p}}{C_s p + (g_p + g_s)}. \tag{15}$$

If the right-hand member of Eq. (15) is broken into partial fractions, there is obtained

$$V_1(p) = \frac{I_w}{(g_p + g_s)} \left[\frac{1}{p} - \frac{1}{\left(p + \dfrac{g_p + g_s}{C_s}\right)} \right]. \tag{16}$$

The inverse Laplace transform of this equation is

$$V_1(t) = \frac{I_w}{g_p + g_s}(1 - e^{-a_1 t}), \tag{17}$$

where

$$a_1 = \frac{g_p + g_s}{C_s}.$$

If Eq. (17) is expressed in terms of the parameters of the circuit of Fig. 2·13, and the fact that the voltage function is to be evaluated over a specific time interval is taken into account,

$$V_1(t)_{0 \leqq t \leqq t_1} = \frac{V_w}{r_p} R_1 (1 - e^{-\frac{1}{R_1 C_s} t}), \tag{18}$$

where

$$R_1 = \frac{R_s r_p}{R_s + r_p}.$$

Equation (18) gives the voltage at the pulser output as a function of time up to the time at which the magnitude of the voltage is equal to that of the load bias voltage V_s. At the time $t = t_1$, $V_1(t_1) = V_s$, the switch S_l is assumed to close, and the starting point for Step 2 is reached.

Step 2.   The equivalent circuit during the time interval $t_1 \leqq t \leqq t_2$ is that of Fig. 2·15 with both switches closed, and the Laplace transform of Eq. (12) is

$$(g_p + g_s + g_l)V_2(p) + C_s[pV_2(p) - V_2(t_1)] = \frac{I_w + I_s}{p}, \tag{19}$$

where $V_2(t)$ is the value of V_{ba} in the time interval $t_2 - t_1$, and $V_2(t_1) = V_s$ is the initial voltage on C_s at the start of this interval. The time t_2 is that at which switch S_T is to be opened. Solving Eq. (19) for $V_2(p)$, there is obtained

$$V_2(p) = \frac{V_s p + \dfrac{g_p V_w + g_l V_s}{C_s}}{p\left(p + \dfrac{G}{C_s}\right)}, \tag{20}$$

where G is written for $g_p + g_s + g_l$. Equation (20) may be written in the form

$$\begin{aligned} V_2(p) &= \frac{A_1}{p} + \frac{A_2}{p + \dfrac{G}{C_s}} + \frac{V_s}{p + \dfrac{G}{C_s}} \\ &= \frac{(g_p V_w + g_l V_s)}{G}\left(\frac{1}{p} - \frac{1}{p + \dfrac{G}{C_s}}\right) + \frac{V_s}{p + \dfrac{G}{C_s}}. \end{aligned} \tag{21}$$

The inverse Laplace transform of Eq. (21) for the time interval under consideration is

$$V_2(t)_{t_1 \le t \le t_2} = \frac{g_p V_w + g_l V_s}{G} [1 - e^{-\frac{G}{C_s}(t-t_1)}] + V_s e^{-\frac{G}{C_s}(t-t_1)}. \quad (22)$$

Let R_2 be the equivalent resistance for r_p, R_s, and r_l, in parallel such that

$$\frac{1}{R_2} = \frac{1}{r_p} + \frac{1}{R_s} + \frac{1}{r_l} = G. \quad (23)$$

Then Eq. (22) becomes

$$V_2(t)_{t_1 \le t \le t_2} = \left(\frac{V_w}{r_p} + \frac{V_s}{r_l}\right) R_2 [1 - e^{-\frac{1}{R_2 C_s}(t-t_1)}] + V_s e^{-\frac{1}{R_2 C_s}(t-t_1)}. \quad (24)$$

Equation (24) gives the pulse shape after the voltage has reached the value V_s and up to the time when switch S_T is opened. After some time $t_a < t_2$ such that

$$(t_a - t_1) \gg R_2 C_s,$$

the pulse voltage is very nearly constant, since the exponential terms become negligibly small, and Eq. (24) reduces to

$$V_2(t_a) = \left(\frac{V_w}{r_p} + \frac{V_s}{r_l}\right) R_2. \quad (25)$$

This relation, therefore, gives the voltage at the top of the pulse. The leading edge and top of the current pulse in the load are obtained from Eqs. (24) and (25) by calculating the current from the relation

$$I_l = \frac{V_2(t) - V_s}{r_l}. \quad (26)$$

From this equation it is evident that the current builds up from zero to its maximum value in the time required for the pulse voltage to build up

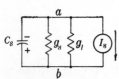

Fig. 2·17.—Equivalent circuit for Step 3 in the calculation of the pulse shape for a hard-tube pulser with a biased-diode load.

from the value V_s to $V_2(t_a)$, and that this time is less than that required for the voltage to build up from zero to V_s if V_s is nearly equal to V_w. The time constant for the current buildup is $R_2 C_s$. When the switch S_T is opened at $t = t_2$, the voltage across the pulser output starts to fall, and the shape of the pulse for the next time interval is found by the procedure outlined in Step 3.

Step 3. The next calculation for the voltage V_{ba} covers the time taken for the voltage to fall from the value $V_2(t_2)$ to V_s again. The equivalent circuit is determined by keeping switch S_T open and S_l closed as indicated in Fig. 2·17. The initial condition for this circuit is that the charge on

C_s must correspond to the voltage $V_2(t_2)$. Let the value of $V_{ba}(t)$ during the calculation be $V_3(t)$ and t_3 be the time such that $V_3(t_3) = V_s$. The Laplace-transform equation for this circuit is then

$$(g_s + g_l)V_3(p) + C_s[pV_3(p) - V_2(t_2)] = \frac{I_s}{p}. \tag{27}$$

Solving for $V_3(p)$,

$$V_3(p) = \frac{V_2(t_2)p + \dfrac{g_l V_s}{C_s}}{p\left(p + \dfrac{g_s + g_l}{C_s}\right)}. \tag{28}$$

In a manner similar to that used in Step 2, the inverse Laplace transform of Eq. (28) gives

$$V_3(t)_{t_2 \leq t \leq t_3} = \frac{g_l V_s}{g_s + g_l}[1 - e^{-\frac{g_s + g_l}{C_s}(t - t_2)}] + V_2(t_2)e^{-\frac{g_s + g_l}{C_s}(t - t_2)}. \tag{29}$$

If $g_s + g_l = \dfrac{1}{R_3}$,

$$V_3(t)_{t_2 \leq t \leq t_3} = \frac{V_s}{r_l}R_3[1 - e^{-\frac{1}{R_3 C_s}(t - t_2)}] + V_2(t_2)e^{-\frac{1}{R_3 C_s}(t - t_2)}. \tag{30}$$

At some time $t_3 > t_2$ the voltage $V_3(t)$ falls to the value V_s, at which time the switch S_l is assumed to open. The final step in the pulse-shape calculation is then reached.

Step 4. For this calculation both switches are open, and the initial charge on C_s corresponds to the voltage $V_3(t_3) = V_s$. The equivalent circuit is now reduced to the simple parallel combination of C_s and R_s as shown in Fig. 2·18.

The voltage $V_{ba} = V_4(t)_{t \geq t_3}$ can be written immediately,

$$V_4(t)_{t \geq t_3} = V_s e^{-\frac{1}{R_s C_s}(t - t_3)}. \tag{31}$$

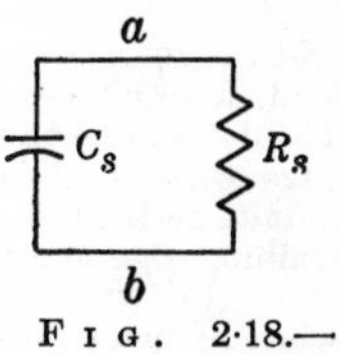

FIG. 2·18.— Equivalent circuit for Step 4 in the calculation of the pulse shape for a hard-tube pulser with a biased-diode load.

The complete calculation of pulse shape for a circuit such as shown in Fig. 2·12 consists of the four steps carried out as above. The composite picture of the pulse is obtained by plotting the four voltage functions $V_1(t)_{0 \leq t \leq t_1}$, $V_2(t)_{t_1 \leq t \leq t_2}$, $V_3(t)_{t_2 \leq t \leq t_3}$, and $V_4(t)_{t_3 \leq t}$ as calculated from Eqs. (18), (24), (30), and (31) respectively, and is of the form shown in Fig. 2·14.

The photographs of oscilloscope traces reproduced in Fig. 2·19a and b show the voltage and current pulses with a magnetron load. These traces were obtained with a hard-tube pulser in which $C_w = 0.05$ μf, $R_s = 10,000$ ohms, $C_s = 115$ $\mu\mu$f, $r_p = 150$ ohms, and the isolating element was a 10,000-ohm resistance. The characteristics of the magnetron were such that $r_{l'} = 200$ ohms and $V_s = 8.5$ kv. The voltage pulse shown in Fig. 2·19a has an amplitude of 10.5 kv, and the average amplitude of the magnetron current pulse is 10 amp. The voltage-pulse shape was also calculated from the equivalent circuit shown in Fig. 2·19g, in which the charged storage condenser is replaced by a battery and the voltage V_s is represented as a biasing battery. For a 10.5-kv pulse across the magnetron, the condenser voltage $V_w \approx 12$ kv; therefore,

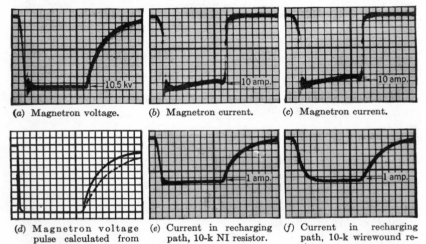

(a) Magnetron voltage.	(b) Magnetron current.	(c) Magnetron current.

(d) Magnetron voltage pulse calculated from equivalent circuit (g). (e) Current in recharging path, 10-k NI resistor. (f) Current in recharging path, 10-k wirewound resistor.

FIG. 2·19.—Oscilloscope traces and calculated voltage pulse for a hard-tube pulser with a magnetron load, a resistance recharging path and $C_s = 115$ μμf. The dotted line on the calculated pulse (d) is the trailing edge obtained with the magnetron assumed to be infinite resistance after S_l opens. The solid line is the trailing edge assuming an effective resistance of 8000 ohms for the magnetron, that is, switch S_M closes when S_l opens. Sweep speed: 10 div. = 1 μsec.

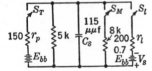

(g) Equivalent circuit for calculations.

$V_s \approx 0.7V_w$. The trailing edge of the voltage pulse indicated by dotted lines in Fig. 2·19d was calculated by assuming the *I-V* curve for the magnetron to be of the form shown in Fig. 2·11a, that is, that the magnetron becomes open-circuited as soon as the pulse voltage falls to the value V_s. On the basis of this assumption, the pulse voltage falls more slowly than it does on the oscilloscope trace. Another calculation was made by assuming that the magnetron presents an effective resistance of about 8000 ohms, instead of an infinite resistance, to the circuit for voltages less than V_s, corresponding to the *I-V* curve of Fig. 2·11b. The value of 8000 ohms was obtained by determining the effective magnetron resistance from the voltage and current pulses at several instants during the time the pulse voltage is dropping. The resistance in parallel with C_s during the fourth step in the calculations for the pulse voltage was therefore that of the 10,000-ohm charging path, the 10,000-ohm isolating element, and the 8000-ohm magnetron resistance in parallel. The pulse shape calculated under these conditions, shown as a solid line in Fig. 2·19d, agrees very well with the oscilloscope trace of F g. 2·19a.

In Fig. 2·19 the traces (e) and (f) were obtained for the current flowing in the recharging path during the pulse. A noninductive resistor was used for the trace (e) and an ordinary wire-wound resistor for trace (f). The magnetron current pulses corresponding to these two conditions are shown in Fig. 2·19b and c where no essential difference is observable.

It is evident from Eqs. (18) and (24) that the effect of R_s on the leading edge of the voltage pulse is small, provided that the switch-tube resistance and the dynamic resistance of the load are small. After the switch tube and the load have become nonconducting, however, the value of R_s has a marked effect on the trailing edge of the pulse. If the load is a nonlinear resistance, that is, if there is no bias voltage or switch S_l in the equivalent circuit, the trailing edge of the pulse is determined by the parallel resistance of R_s and r_l, and as r_l increases this effective resistance also increases. It is advantageous, therefore, for R_s to be as small as possible in order to have the pulse voltage drop quickly at the end of the pulse. Since R_s is in parallel with the load, some pulse power is lost in it, thus increasing the necessary power input to the pulser for a given load power. From the standpoint of pulser efficiency, it is desirable to have as large a value for R_s as possible. In choosing a value for R_s, a compromise must be made between the need for high efficiency and that for a steep trailing edge.

Inductance for the Recharging Path.—The power loss in the shunt element Z_s, which is necessary to provide a recharging path for the storage

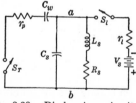

Fig. 2·20.—Discharging circuit of a hard-tube pulser with a biased-diode load and an inductive path for recharging the storage condenser.

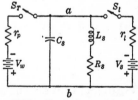

Fig. 2·21.—Equivalent output circuit for a hard-tube pulser with a biased-diode load and an inductive path for recharging the storage condenser. The charged storage condenser is replaced by a battery.

condenser, can be reduced by using an inductance in place of a resistance as just discussed. The output circuit of the pulser using an inductance for Z_s is shown in Fig. 2·20 for a biased-diode load. As before, the charged condenser C_w may be replaced by a battery, and the circuit becomes that shown in Fig. 2·21. The equivalent circuit for calculating the pulse voltage as a function of time is again set up by replacing the batteries by current sources, and the circuit of Fig. 2·22, in which the conductance g_s of Fig. 2·15 is replaced by the series L_sR_s combination, is obtained.

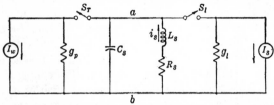

Fig. 2·22.—Equivalent circuit for calculating the pulse shape for a hard-tube pulser with a biased-diode load and an inductance for the recharging path.

In order to be able to write the Laplace-transform equation for this circuit, it is first necessary to find an expression for the Laplace transform of the current in the inductance in terms of V_{ba}. Considering this branch first,

$$V_{ba} = L_s \frac{di_s}{dt} + R_s i_s, \tag{32}$$

for which the Laplace-transform equation is

$$V_{ba}(p) = L_s[pi_s(p) - i_s(0)] + R_s i_s(p). \tag{33}$$

Solving for $i_s(p)$,

$$i_s(p) = \frac{V_{ba}(p) + L_s i_s(0)}{L_s p + R_s}. \tag{34}$$

The complete Laplace-transform equation for the circuit of Fig. 2·22 with both switches closed is, therefore,

$$(g_p + g_l)V_{ba}(p) + C_s[pV_{ba}(p) - V_{ba}(0)] + \frac{V_{ba}(p) + L_s i_s(0)}{L_s p - R_s}$$
$$= \frac{I_w + I_s}{p}, \tag{35}$$

where $V_{ba}(0)$ and $i_s(0)$ are the initial voltage on C_s and the initial current in L_s respectively. Solving Eq. (35) for $V_{ba}(p)$,

$$V_{ba}(p) = \frac{V_{ba}(0)p^2 + \left[V_{ba}(0)\dfrac{R_s}{L_s} + \dfrac{I_w + I_s}{C_s} - \dfrac{i_s(0)}{C_s}\right]p + \dfrac{(I_w + I_s)R_s}{C_sL_s}}{p\left\{p^2 + \left[\dfrac{R_s}{L_s} + \dfrac{(g_p + g_l)}{C_s}\right]p + \dfrac{1 + (g_p + g_l)R_s}{C_sL_s}\right\}}. \tag{36}$$

The calculation of the pulse shape in this case is again carried out in the four steps shown in Fig. 2·14, for which the four equivalent circuits are shown in Fig. 2·23.

The Laplace transform of $V_{ba}(t)$ is found from Eq. (36) by using the initial conditions and circuit parameters appropriate to the equivalent circuit in each step. The procedure is similar to the previous analysis for a resistive shunt element, but is complicated by the fact that the initial

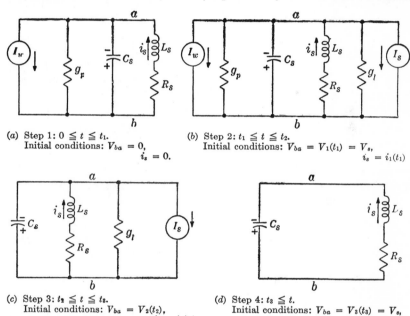

(a) Step 1: $0 \leqq t \leqq t_1$.
    Initial conditions: $V_{ba} = 0$,
    $\qquad\qquad\qquad\quad i_s = 0$.

(b) Step 2: $t_1 \leqq t \leqq t_2$.
    Initial conditions: $V_{ba} = V_1(t_1) = V_s$,
    $\qquad\qquad\qquad\quad i_s = i_1(t_1)$

(c) Step 3: $t_2 \leqq t \leqq t_3$.
    Initial conditions: $V_{ba} = V_2(t_2)$,
    $\qquad\qquad\qquad\quad i_s = i_2(t_2)$.

(d) Step 4: $t_3 \leqq t$.
    Initial conditions: $V_{ba} = V_3(t_3) = V_s$,
    $\qquad\qquad\qquad\quad i_s = i_3(t_3)$.

FIG. 2·23.—Equivalent circuits for the four steps in the calculation of the pulse shape for a hard-tube pulser with a biased-diode load and an inductive recharging path.

current in the inductance must be evaluated by using Eq. (34) in each step except the first. The algebraic expressions for $V_{ba}(t)$ become rather involved, and are not given in detail here.

Some general remarks can be made about the character of the pulse shape because the denominator of the Laplace-transform equation is of the same form for each of the four time intervals considered. The inverse Laplace transform

$$\mathcal{L}^{-1}[V_{ba}(p)] = V_{ba}(t)$$

has similar algebraic forms for each step. The term in braces in the denominator of Eq. (36) may be written in the form

$$p^2 + 2ap + b \qquad\qquad (37)$$

where

$$2a = \left[\frac{R_s}{L_s} + \frac{(g_p + g_l)}{C_s}\right],\tag{38}$$

and

$$b = \frac{1 + (g_p + g_l)R_s}{C_sL_s}.\tag{39}$$

This term may be put in a form more convenient for finding $\mathcal{L}^{-1}[V_{ba}(p)]$ by completing the square, thus

$$p^2 + 2ap + b = (p + a)^2 + \omega^2\tag{40}$$

where

$$\omega^2 = b - a^2.\tag{41}$$

The right-hand member of the Laplace-transform equation can be broken up into partial fractions with the result

$$V_{ba}(p) = \frac{A}{p} + \frac{B_1(p + a) + B_2}{(p + a)^2 + \omega^2},\tag{42}$$

where the terms A, B_1, and B_2 are evaluated by standard methods. The form of the inverse Laplace transform now depends on the following three conditions that can be placed on ω^2:

$$\left.\begin{array}{lll}
1. \text{ If } b > a^2, & \omega^2 > 0. \\
2. \text{ If } b = a^2, & \omega^2 = 0. \\
3. \text{ If } b < a^2, & \omega^2 < 0.
\end{array}\right\}\tag{43}$$

Condition 1. $\omega^2 > 0$. The inverse Laplace transform for Eq. (42) is

$$V_{ba}(t) = A + B_1e^{-at}\cos\omega t + \frac{B_2}{\omega}e^{-at}\sin\omega t.\tag{44}$$

Condition 2. $\omega^2 = 0$. The inverse Laplace transform for Eq. (42) is

$$V_{ba}(t) = A + B_1e^{-at} + B_2te^{-at}.\tag{45}$$

Condition 3. $\omega^2 < 0$. Let $\omega^2 = -k^2$, then the inverse Laplace transform for Eq. (42) is

$$V_{ba}(t) = A + B_1e^{-at}\cosh kt + \frac{B_2}{k}e^{-at}\sinh kt.\tag{46}$$

The Eqs. (44), (45), and (46) are of particular interest in connection with the calculation of the trailing edge of the pulse, that is, in Step 4 of Fig. 2·14. In this case the expressions for ω^2 and k^2 are

$$\omega^2 = \frac{1}{C_sL_s} - \frac{R_s^2}{4L_s^2}.\tag{47}$$

and

$$k^2 = \frac{R_s^2}{4L_s^2} - \frac{1}{C_s L_s}. \tag{48}$$

The trailing edge of the pulse is part of a damped oscillation if

$$\frac{R_s}{L_s} < \frac{2}{\sqrt{C_s L_s}}, \tag{49}$$

and is aperiodic if

$$\frac{R_s}{L_s} > \frac{2}{\sqrt{C_s L_s}}. \tag{50}$$

If condition (49) exists, the voltage across the pulser output oscillates at a frequency determined by Eq. (47) after the switch tube and the load become nonconducting. The voltage therefore passes through zero and reverses its polarity. This reverse voltage appearing at the pulser output is commonly referred to as the "backswing voltage." The period of the oscillation becomes smaller as R_s is decreased, and the trailing edge of the pulse becomes steeper as the ratio R_s/L_s is decreased relative to $2/\sqrt{C_s L_s}$. The damping of the oscillation depends on the exponential terms in Eq. (44) and, since the exponent is $R_s/2L_s$, a lower value for R_s/L_s causes a decrease in damping and hence a higher value for the backswing voltage. A high backswing voltage is very undesirable because it adds to the power-supply voltage at the plate of the switch tube, and increases the danger of flash-over and sparking within the tube.

The magnitude of the current that builds up in the inductance also has an effect on the rate at which the voltage drops at the end of the pulse, as is evident if the coefficients A, B_1, and B_2 are evaluated for the equivalent circuit of Step 4. From Eqs. (42) and (36) these values become

and

$$\left. \begin{array}{l} A = 0, \\ B_1 = V_3(t_3) = V_s, \\[2mm] B_2 = \dfrac{V_s R_s}{2L_s} - \dfrac{i_3(t_3)}{C_s}. \end{array} \right\} \tag{51}$$

When B_2 is negative, that is,

$$\left| \frac{i_3(t_3)}{C_s} \right| > \left| \frac{V_s R_s}{2L_s} \right|,$$

it is seen from Eq. (44) that, as $i_3(t_3)$ increases, the value of $V_4(t)$ decreases more rapidly for given values of the other parameters. The value of $i_3(t_3)$ increases with time up to a limiting value determined by the magnitude of R_s. As long as the current in the inductance continues to increase with time, therefore, the trailing edge of the pulse is steeper for the longer pulse durations than for the shorter ones.   The oscilloscope traces shown in Fig. 2·25 illustrate this behavior.

The oscillating voltage at the end of the pulse is undesirable not only because it produces backswing voltage, but also because it becomes of the same polarity as the forward pulse voltage on the return swing.   This post-pulse voltage may be large enough to cause appreciable current to flow in the load, and therefore is a secondary pulse.   When the damping introduced by the resistance of the inductance is small, it is necessary to increase the damping by connecting a diode across the pulser output in such a way that it is conducting only when there is backswing voltage. The equivalent circuit with a shunt diode is shown in Fig. 2·24.   The

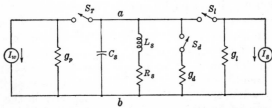

Fig. 2·24.—Equivalent circuit for calculating the pulse shape for a hard-tube pulser with a biased-diode load, an inductive recharging path, and a shunt diode to reduce the "backswing voltage."

diode is represented by the conductance g_d and switch S_d that is assumed to close only when the voltage V_{ba} is opposite in sign to the normal pulse voltage.   If g_d is large, the backswing voltage is negligibly small, and no post-pulse voltage appears with the same polarity as the pulse voltage.

The oscillating voltage after the pulse can also be avoided by making $R_s/L_s > 2/\sqrt{C_sL_s}$.   For this purpose, an inductance with high resistance, that is, an inductive resistor, must be used and, under such conditions, the voltage corresponding to the trailing edge of the pulse becomes aperiodic, as shown by Eq. (46).   The time of fall for the voltage decreases for smaller values of the ratio R_s/L_s, and the transition between the aperiodic and oscillating condition occurs when this ratio equals $2/\sqrt{C_sL_s}$. From a practical standpoint, such an inductive resistor is usually designed to have a ratio of R_s/L_s slightly less than the minimum for the aperiodic condition.   For this condition, the voltage is oscillatory, but the damping is high and the backswing voltage is correspondingly small.   The choice between a large value of R_s/L_s without a shunt diode or a small value of R_s/L_s with a shunt diode depends on the importance of having a small time of fall for the voltage pulse.

It is difficult to make a detailed analysis of the effect of the circuit parameters on the leading edge of the voltage pulse without actually carrying out the calculations for $V_{ba}(t)$ using numerical values for the circuit components. A very general statement can be made, however, to the effect that, as the switch-tube resistance or the shunt capacitance increases, the time of rise for the voltage pulse also increases. The effect of the shunt inductance on the leading edge of the pulse over a fairly wide range of values for the ratio R_s/L_s is rather small.

If there is a resistance in parallel with the shunt inductance, the times of rise and fall of the voltage pulse become shorter: the smaller the resistance, the smaller the rise and fall times. Such a resistance is introduced into the circuit when the connection to a power supply for recharging the storage condenser, as indicated in Fig. 2·5, is considered. In Sec. 2·4 it is shown that for good pulser design, the resistance R_c is large, but its effect on the trailing edge of the pulse is still appreciable.

A set of photographs of oscilloscope traces illustrating the effects of various circuit parameters, together with the pulse shapes calculated from the equivalent circuits discussed above, are shown in Figs. 2·25, 2·26, 2·27, and 2·28.

The oscilloscope traces reproduced in Fig. 2·25 were obtained with the magnetron and pulser used for the pictures of Fig. 2·19, replacing the resistance recharging path in the pulser by a 10-mh inductance and a shunt diode. In each case the magnetron voltage and current pulses and the current flowing in the 10-mh inductance are shown for pulse durations of 0.5, 1, and 2 μsec. The pulse voltage and pulse current were adjusted to 10 kv and 10 amp respectively for each pulse duration. The effect of the increase in current in the shunt inductance is shown in the more rapid fall of voltage as the pulse duration increases. The calculated values for the voltage pulses (j), (k), and (l) take into account the 10,000-ohm isolating resistance and an assumed equivalent resistance of 8000 ohms for the magnetron after the voltage has dropped to the value V_s.

The oscilloscope traces shown in Fig. 2·26 are for the 1-μsec pulse duration with a sweep speed about one tenth of that used for the traces of Fig. 2·25. The traces (a), (d), and (g) are the slow-sweep presentation of the 1-μsec pulses shown in Fig. 2·25, and indicate the effect of a good shunt diode, that is, one with high cathode emission. The traces (b), (e), and (h) were obtained with a shunt diode having lower cathode emission, and a small backswing voltage of about 1 kv is observable on the voltage pulse. The traces (d), (e), (g), and (h) show that the currents in the 10-mh inductance and in the shunt diode decrease more rapidly when the shunt diode has a higher effective resistance. When the shunt diode is removed from the circuit, a backswing voltage of about 6 kv appears after the voltage pulse, and the pulse shapes of Fig. 2·26c and f are obtained. The oscillation resulting from the use of the inductance for the recharging path is damped by the 10,000-ohm resistance of the isolating element that is in parallel with the discharging circuit for

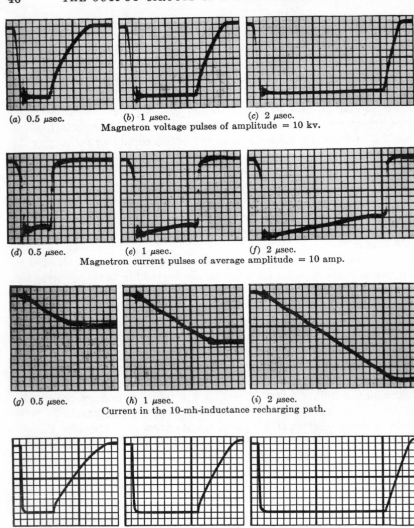

(a) 0.5 μsec.   (b) 1 μsec.   (c) 2 μsec.

Magnetron voltage pulses of amplitude = 10 kv.

(d) 0.5 μsec.   (e) 1 μsec.   (f) 2 μsec.

Magnetron current pulses of average amplitude = 10 amp.

(g) 0.5 μsec.   (h) 1 μsec.   (i) 2 μsec.

Current in the 10-mh-inductance recharging path.

(j) 0.5 μsec.   (k) 1 μsec.   (l) 2 μsec.

Voltage pulses calculated from the equivalent circuit (m).

FIG. 2·25.—Oscilloscope traces and calculated pulse shapes for a hard-tube pulser with a magnetron load, a 10-mh inductance as the recharging path, a shunt diode, and $C_s = 115$ μμf. Voltage pulses were calculated from the equivalent circuit (m) and S_T closed $0 < t < \tau$, S_l closed for $V_{ba} > 0.7E_{bb}$, S_M closed when S_l opens and until $V_{ba} = 0$, S_d closed for negative values of V_{ba}. Sweep speed: 10 div. = 1 μsec.

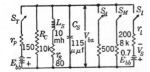

(m) Equivalent circuit for calculations.

the shunt capacitance. The calculated values for the current in the 10-mh inductance are plotted in Fig. 2·26i, assuming the effective resistance of the shunt diode to be 500 ohms. It can be seen that the calculated current in the inductance for the 1-μsec pulse agrees very well with the corresponding trace obtained when the good diode was used.

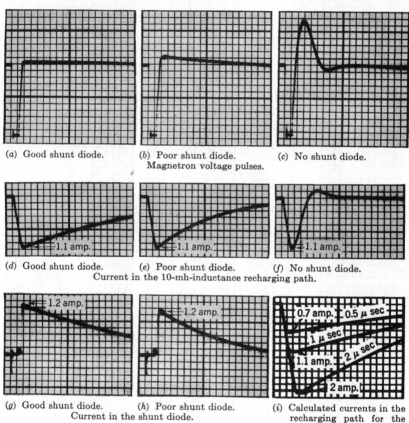

(*a*) Good shunt diode.   (*b*) Poor shunt diode.   (*c*) No shunt diode.
Magnetron voltage pulses.

(*d*) Good shunt diode.   (*e*) Poor shunt diode.   (*f*) No shunt diode.
Current in the 10-mh-inductance recharging path.

(*g*) Good shunt diode.   (*h*) Poor shunt diode.   (*i*) Calculated currents in the
Current in the shunt diode.   recharging path for the
                                                                circuit (*m*) of Fig. 2·25.

Fig. 2·26.—Oscilloscope traces and calculated recharging-path currents for a hard-tube pulser with a magnetron load and a 10-mh inductance as the recharging path. (*a*) and (*d*) are the slow-sweep-speed presentations corresponding to the 1-μsec pulses of Fig. 2·25. Horizontal scale = 1 μsec/div.

When an inductive resistor with a resistance of 7500 ohms and an inductance of 3 mh is used for the recharging path in the pulser, the oscilloscope traces appear as shown in Fig. 2·27. The small backswing voltage that appears after the pulse indicates that the value of R_s/L_s for this inductive resistor is slightly less than the value for critical damping. The magnitude of this backswing voltage is so small, however, that a

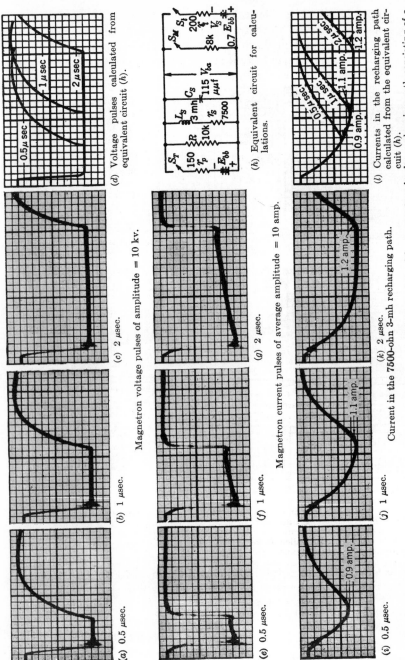

(d) Voltage pulses calculated from equivalent circuit (h).

(h) Equivalent circuit for calculations.

(l) Currents in the recharging path calculated from the equivalent circuit (h).

(a) 0.5 μsec.   (b) 1 μsec.   (c) 2 μsec.

Magnetron voltage pulses of amplitude = 10 kv.

(e) 0.5 μsec.   (f) 1 μsec.   (g) 2 μsec.

Magnetron current pulses of average amplitude = 10 amp.

(i) 0.5 μsec.   (j) 1 μsec.   (k) 2 μsec.

Current in the 7500-ohm 3-mh recharging path.

Fig. 2·27.—Oscilloscope traces and calculated pulse shapes for a hard-tube pulser with a magnetron load, a recharging path consisting of a 7500-ohm resistance in series with a 3-mh inductance, and shunt capacitance of 115 μμf. In the calculations the effective resistance of the magnetron was assumed to be 8000 ohms after S_l opens, that is, S_M closes when S_l opens.   Sweep speed: 10 div. = 1 μsec.

shunt diode is unnecessary. From a comparison of the voltage pulses of Fig. 2·27 with those of Fig. 2·25 it is seen that the voltage for the 0.5-μsec pulse drops at about the same rate in each case. At a pulse duration of 2 μsec, the voltage drops faster with the 10-mh inductance for the

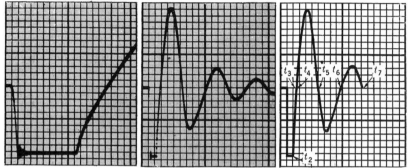

(a) 1μ sec = 10 div.   (b) 1μ sec = 1 div.   (c) Calculated for circuit (f).
Magnetron voltage pulses of amplitude = 10 kv.

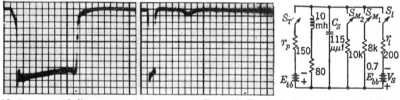

(d) 1μ sec = 10 div.   (e) 1μ sec = 1 div.   (f) Equivalent circuit for calculations.
Magnetron current pulses of average amplitude = 10 amp.

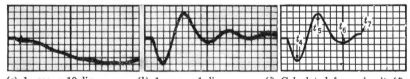

(g) 1μ sec = 10 div.   (h) 1μ sec = 1 div.   (i) Calculated from circuit (f).
Current in the 20-mh inductance recharging path.

FIG. 2·28.—Oscilloscope traces and calculated pulse shapes for a hard-tube pulser with a magnetron load, a 20-mh inductance as the isolating element, a 20-mh inductance as the recharging path, no shunt diode, and $C_s = 115\mu\mu f$. Voltage pulse and current in the 20-mh recharging path calculated from equivalent circuit (f) with the conditions: S_T opens at t_2, S_l opens at t_3, S_{M1} closed t_3 to t_4, all switches open t_4 to t_5, S_{M2} closed t_5 to t_6, all switches open t_6 to t_7.

recharging path than with the 3-mh 7500-ohm inductive resistor. The reason for this behavior is evident from a comparison of the currents in the recharging paths.

For the oscilloscope traces of Figs. 2·25, 2·26, and 2·27 the isolating element was a 10,000-ohm resistance. If an inductance having a low resistance is used for this isolating element, the damping of the oscillation that occurs after the switch tube becomes nonconducting is usually small, as shown by the pictures reproduced in Fig. 2·28. These pictures were obtained with the magnetron load, an inductance of 20 mh as the recharging path, and an identical inductance as the isolating element. Each of these inductances had a resistance of 160 ohms. The backswing voltage for this circuit becomes larger than the pulse voltage when there is no shunt diode, as can be seen in Fig. 2·28b. Since the damping in the circuit is small, the voltage swings back to the polarity of the main pulse and causes a small current to flow in the magnetron, as indicated by the trace (e). In calculating the voltage across the load as a function of time from the equivalent circuit shown in Fig. 2·28f, it is therefore necessary to introduce an effective resistance for the magnetron during the time when this post-pulse conduction occurs. The calculated values plotted in Fig. 2·28c and i were obtained by assuming the effective resistance of the magnetron to be 8000 ohms, and the magnitude of the voltage for the trailing edge of the voltage pulse was considered to be less than V_s but greater than zero. During the time corresponding to the backswing voltage, the magnetron is considered to be open-circuited, and hence to have an infinite resistance. When the post-pulse conduction occurs, the magnetron is assumed to appear as a 10,000-ohm resistance. The comparison of the plots for the load voltage and the current in the recharging path with the corresponding oscilloscope traces indicates good agreement between calculated and experimental values.

The assumptions made in the foregoing calculations with regard to the effect of the magnetron on the behavior of the pulser output circuit lead to reasonable agreement with the experimental data. This agreement may be considered a justification for the assumption that the shape of the I-V curve for a magnetron, shown in Fig. 2·11b, can be closely approximated by a high dynamic resistance for voltages less than V_s, and by a low dynamic resistance for voltages greater than V_s. If the load resistance is nonlinear, the functional relationship between r_l and V_{ba} must be taken into account in the calculations, and the analysis of pulse shape becomes considerably more complicated. Another complication arises if it is necessary to consider the variation of switch-tube resistance with the plate current in the tube.

At the start of this discussion of pulse shape as affected by pulser circuit parameters, it was assumed that the capacitance of the storage condenser was very large in order that the voltage across it could be considered constant during the pulse. It is stated in Sec. 2·1, however, that the storage-condenser voltage is less at the end than at the beginning of a pulse. This change in voltage depends on the magnitudes of the pulse current, the storage capacitance, and the pulse duration. As is shown in the following section, it is often impractical to have a storage capacitance that is large enough to keep this voltage change less than a few per cent of the initial condenser voltage. The actual pulse shape obtained from a hard-tube pulser of this type, therefore, does not have a flat top, but rather has a sloping top as indicated in the sketch of Fig. 2·29.

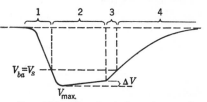

Since with a resistance load the pulse current has the same shape as the pulse voltage, the ratio $\Delta I/I_{max}$ is equal to the ratio $\Delta V/V_{max}$. If the load is a biased-

Fig. 2·29.—Sketch of the voltage pulse shape showing the effect of the drop in storage-condenser voltage during the pulse.

diode or magnetron with a low dynamic resistance, however, the ratio $\Delta I/I_{max}$ may be many times as great as the voltage ratio $\Delta V/V_{max}$. In Sec. 2·4 it is shown that

$$\frac{\Delta I}{I_{max}} = \frac{\Delta V}{V_{max}} \cdot \frac{V_{max}}{V_{max} - V_s}.$$

The effect of the drop in pulse voltage on the current in a load that has a low dynamic resistance can be seen in the oscilloscope traces shown in Figs. 2·19, 2·25, and 2·27. It is also evident that, if ΔV is large, it is possible for the pulse voltage to fall below V_s before the switch S_T is opened. As a result, the load current stops flowing before the end of the intended pulse interval.

If the switch-tube resistance increases with time during the conduction interval, the effect is similar to a change in voltage on the storage condenser. Such behavior of the switch tube is experienced with some oxide-cathode tubes, particularly for long pulses and high currents, and is referred to as cathode fatigue. It is very difficult to take into account the effect of cathode fatigue on the pulse shape, since it can vary so much from one tube to another of the same type. The magnitude of the cathode fatigue tends to increase as the tube gets older, but it is not uncommon for it to decrease during the first few hours of operation.

THE CHARGING OF THE STORAGE CONDENSER

The energy removed from the storage condenser during the pulse interval causes the potential difference across this condenser to be less at the end than at the beginning of the pulse. If the output of the pulser is to be a succession of identical pulses, it is necessary to provide some means by which the energy in the condenser can be replenished during the interpulse interval. This energy can be supplied by connecting the condenser to a primary electrical-energy source such as a battery or power supply during the interpulse interval. The ideal arrangement would be to make the charging and discharging cycles completely independent by using a switch as shown in Fig. 2·1a. The use of such a switch is impractical for pulses that recur at rates of several hundred to several thousand per second. The pulser must therefore be designed with a conducting path between the condenser and the power supply that has the least possible effect on the discharging of the condenser during the pulse interval.

One method that is used to isolate the power supply from the condenser-discharging circuit is shown in Fig. 2·5. In this method a resistance element is connected in series with the power supply. If this resistance is sufficiently high, the current that flows through the switch tube from the power supply is small enough to be neglected. When the switch tube is conducting for a very short time interval—that is, for short pulse durations—an inductance in series with the power supply can provide satisfactory isolation. This method has the disadvantage that the current from the power supply increases with time and, since this current flows through the switch tube, the tube drop during the pulse is also a function of time.

Although the reason for introducing the isolating element is to keep the current flowing from the power supply through the switch tube as small as possible, there are other points to be considered in choosing the particular element. Since the condenser is connected to the power supply in order to be recharged, the isolating element must not make the charging time constant so large that the condenser voltage at the end of the interpulse interval differs appreciably from the power-supply voltage. The connection to the power supply during the pulse interval has an effect on the leading edge and on the top of the pulse. The magnitude of this effect depends on the relative size of the impedances of the isolating element, the switch tube, and the load. When the switch is nonconducting, this isolating element is effectively in parallel with the pulser output circuit and therefore has an effect on the trailing edge of the pulse. These effects on the pulse shape can be taken into account in the analysis of the discharging circuit, as discussed in Secs. 2·2 and 2·3, by introducing the isolating element as an additional circuit parameter. The ultimate choice of the element is generally based on a compromise between these considerations.

2·4. The Output Circuit with a High Resistance as the Isolating Element.—The equivalent circuits for the pulser with a high resistance as the isolating element are shown in Fig. 2·30a and b. For reasons already stated, the resistance R_c is assumed to be very large compared with r_p. The analysis of the circuit behavior during the interpulse interval (that is, when switches S_T and S_l are open), is similar for the two circuits (a) and (b) if Z_s is a resistance. If Z_s is an inductance, the algebraic expressions become complicated, and circuit (a) is therefore used as the basis for the present discussion.

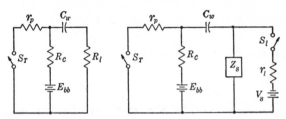

(a) Resistance load.   (b) Biased-diode load.

Fig. 2·30.—Hard-tube pulser circuits with a resistance as the isolating element in series with the power supply.

Assume that the switch S_T is open initially for a long time and therefore that the condenser C_w is charged to the voltage of the power supply. If the switch is then closed for a time τ and open for a time $T_r - \tau$, and this procedure is repeated, a succession of pulses is obtained with a recurrence frequency $f_r = 1/T_r$. During the time τ the condenser voltage decreases and during the time $T_r - \tau$ it increases. If the time $T_r - \tau$ is not many times greater than the time constant of the circuit, the condenser voltage is appreciably less than the power-supply voltage at the end of this interval. Equilibrium values for the condenser voltage at the beginning and at the end of the interval τ will be obtained if the switching procedure is repeated a sufficiently large number of times. This approach to equilibrium is shown diagramatically in Fig. 2·31.

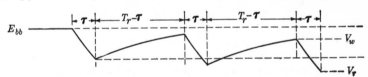

Fig. 2·31.—The voltage on the storage condenser of a hard-tube pulser as a function of time after the start of a series of regularly spaced pulses when a resistance isolating element is used.

It is of interest to obtain the value of V_w/E_{bb} for any given set of circuit parameters. Let V_w' be the value for the condenser voltage at the start and V_r' be the voltage at the end of any particular pulse, and let V_w and V_r be the equilibrium values of these voltages. During a charging interval the switch S_T is open, and the expression for the condenser voltage as a function of time is

$$V_C(t) = E_{bb} - (E_{bb} - V_r')e^{-\frac{t}{(R_c + R_l)C_w}}, \tag{52}$$

where t is measured from the start of the interpulse interval. The condenser voltage at the end of the interval is then

$$V'_w = E_{bb} - (E_{bb} - V'_\tau)e^{-\frac{(T_r - \tau)}{(R_c + R_l)C_w}}. \tag{53}$$

If it is assumed that $R_c \gg r_p$, the connection to the power supply may be neglected when considering a discharging (pulse) interval. The condenser voltage during this interval is thus

$$V_c(t') = V'_w e^{-\frac{t'}{(r_p + R_l)C_w}}, \tag{54}$$

where t' is measured from the start of the discharging interval. The condenser voltage at the end of this interval is then

$$V'_\tau = V'_w e^{-\frac{\tau}{(r_p + R_l)C_w}}. \tag{55}$$

For a continuous succession of pulses the equilibrium values of V'_w in Eqs. (53) and (55) must be equal and likewise the values of V'_τ. Solving these equations for V'_w, there is obtained

$$V_w = \frac{E_{bb}\left[1 - e^{-\frac{(T_r - \tau)}{(R_c + R_l)C_w}}\right]}{\left\{1 - e^{-\left[\frac{\tau}{(r_p + R_l)C_w} + \frac{(T_r - \tau)}{(R_c + R_l)C_w}\right]}\right\}}, \tag{56}$$

which may be written

$$V_w = E_{bb}\gamma. \tag{57}$$

A similar solution for V'_τ gives

$$V_\tau = E_{bb}\gamma e^{-\frac{\tau}{(r_p + R_l)C_w}}. \tag{58}$$

From Eq. (56) it is seen that the value of the ratio V_w/E_{bb} for a given set of circuit parameters increases as τ is decreased and T_r is increased. Also, for given values of τ and T_r, the condenser voltage approaches the power-supply voltage as R_c and C_w are decreased. By decreasing R_c, however, the current through the switch tube is increased. This increase is particularly undesirable in high-power pulsers where the load current and hence the switch-tube current are already large. The effect of variations in τ, T_r and C_w are illustrated in curves of Fig. 2·32. These curves were calculated from the exact expression for the equilibrium condenser voltage V_w, taking into account the effect of the power-supply connection on the discharging circuit. The equation for V_w is

$$V_w = \frac{E_{bb}r_p}{R_c + r_p}\left(1 + \frac{R_c}{r_p}\gamma'\right), \tag{59}$$

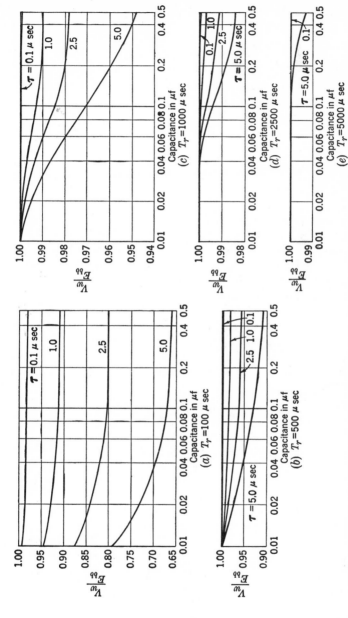

FIG. 2·32.—Ratio of the equilibrium condenser voltage at the start of the pulse to the power-supply voltage as a function of capacitance, pulse duration, and interpulse interval for $R_c = 10,000$ ohms, $R_l = 1000$ ohms, and $r_p = 100$ ohms.

and the voltage at the end of the pulse becomes

$$V_\tau = \frac{E_{bb}r_p}{R_c + r_p}\left(1 + \frac{R_c}{r_p}\gamma' e^{-\alpha\tau}\right),$$ (60)

where

$$\left.\begin{array}{l} \gamma' = \dfrac{1 - e^{-\beta(T_r - \tau)}}{1 - e^{-[\alpha\tau + \beta(T_r - \tau)]}}, \\[3mm] \beta = \dfrac{1}{(R_c + R_l)C_w}, \\[3mm] \alpha = \dfrac{R_c + r_p}{(R_c r_p + R_c R_l + R_l r_p)C_w}. \end{array}\right\}$$ (61)

If $R_c \gg r_p$,

$$\alpha \approx \frac{1}{(r_p + R_l)C_w},$$ (62)

and $\gamma' \approx \gamma$. Thus, for $R_c \approx 100 r_p$, the value of V_w calculated from Eq. (59) is about 1 per cent greater than the approximate value calculated from Eq. (56). In designing many pulsers, it is therefore sufficiently precise to calculate the equilibrium condenser voltage by neglecting the effect of the power-supply connection on the discharging circuit.

If only the charging circuit for the storage condenser is considered, an advantage is apparently gained by having the capacitance as small as possible. This supposition is contrary, however, to the conclusion reached by considering the discharging circuit. From Eqs. (59) and (60) the difference in the condenser voltage at the beginning and at the end of a pulse is

$$V_w - V_\tau = V_w\left[\frac{R_c\gamma'(1 - e^{-\alpha\tau})}{r_p + R_c\gamma'}\right].$$ (63)

Equation (63) may be reduced to the corresponding relation obtained from Eqs. (57) and (58) if $R_c \gg r_p$, namely

$$V_w - V_\tau = V_w[1 - e^{-\frac{\tau}{(r_p + R_l)C_w}}].$$ (64)

If $\tau \ll (r_p + R_l)C_w$, Eq. (64) may be written

$$V_w - V_\tau \approx \frac{V_w\tau}{(r_p + R_l)C_w}$$ (65)

Again, if $V_w - V_\tau$ is small, the change in load current during the pulse is small and

$$I_l \approx \frac{V_w}{r_p + R_l},$$

which leads to the approximation

$$V_w - V_\tau \approx \frac{I_l}{C_w}\,\tau. \tag{66}$$

This expression may be used to determine the magnitude of the capacitance required for a particular load current in order to keep the load voltage within certain limits during the pulse. In general, it is desired that the load voltage during the pulse be as nearly constant as possible, and therefore C_w must be large.

The same conclusion is reached if a corresponding analysis is made for a biased-diode load in the circuit of Fig. 2·30b. If it is assumed that the power-supply connection may be neglected in determining the condenser voltage during the pulse interval, the difference in condenser voltage at the beginning and at the end of the pulse is

$$V_w - V_\tau = (V_w - V_s)\,[1 - e^{-\frac{\tau}{(r_p + r_l)C_w}}]. \tag{67}$$

The relation (66) is obtained from Eq. (67) by the same reasoning used to obtain it from Eq. (64) using the approximation that

$$I_l' \approx \frac{V_w - V_s}{r_p + r_l}.$$

As may be seen from a consideration of the change in load current during a pulse, it is more important to keep the change in load voltage small for a biased-diode load than for a resistance load. Neglecting the power-supply connection again, the currents at the beginning and at the end of a pulse for a resistance load are,

$$
\left.
\begin{aligned}
(I_l)_0 &= \frac{V_w}{r_p + R_l} \\[2mm]
(I_l)_\tau &= \frac{V_\tau}{r_p + R_l}.
\end{aligned}
\right\} \tag{68}
$$

and

For the biased-diode load, the corresponding currents are

$$
\left.
\begin{aligned}
(I_l')_0 &= \frac{V_w - V_s}{r_p + r_l} \\[2mm]
(I_l')_\tau &= \frac{V_\tau - V_s}{r_p + r_l}.
\end{aligned}
\right\} \tag{69}
$$

and

The ratio of the change in current during the pulse to the current at the beginning of the pulse for the resistance load is therefore

$$\frac{(I_l)_0 - (I_l)_\tau}{(I_l)_0} = \frac{V_w - V_\tau}{V_w}, \tag{70}$$

and for the biased-diode load,

$$\frac{(I_l')_0 - (I_l')_\tau}{(I_l')_0} = \frac{V_w - V_\tau}{V_w - V_s}. \tag{71}$$

It is evident from Eqs. (70) and (71) that, for a given percentage change in load current, the ratio of the value of $V_w - V_\tau$ for a biased-diode load to that for a resistance load is

$$\frac{V_w - V_s}{V_w}.$$

The effect of the capacitance of the storage condenser on the current through the load during a pulse is illustrated by the curves of Fig. 2·33. These curves are plotted from the equation

$$\frac{(I_l)_0 - (I_l)_\tau}{(I_l)_0} = (1 - e^{-\alpha\tau}), \tag{72}$$

where α is the value given by Eqs. (61). From Eqs. (64) and (70) a similar expression is obtained in which $\alpha \approx 1/(r_p + R_l)C_w$, namely,

$$\frac{(I_l)_0 - (I_l)_\tau}{(I_l)_0} = [1 - e^{-\frac{\tau}{(r_p + R_l)C_w}}]$$

$$= \frac{V_w - V_\tau}{V_w}. \tag{73}$$

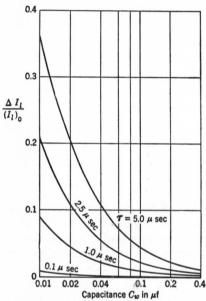

FIG. 2·33.—Ratio of the change in load current during a pulse to the load current at the start of the pulse for various values of pulse duration and storage capacitance. This ratio is approximately equal to the ratio of the change in condenser voltage during the pulse to the voltage at the start of the pulse. The curves are plotted for $R_l = 1000$ ohms, $R_c = 10,000$ ohms, and $r_p = 100$ ohms.

Curves of the type shown in Figs. 2·32 and 2·33 can be used to determine the best value for the capacitance of the storage condenser for given values of τ and T_r when $R_c \gg r_p$. A compromise must be made between the equilibrium condenser voltage and the amount of voltage drop that can be tolerated during the pulse for the particular pulser application.

From Eqs. (52) and (54) it is possible to calculate the time required for the condenser voltage to attain a value approaching V_w after the beginning of a succession of pulses. This time can best be expressed in

terms of the number of pulses such that $(V'_w)_n = kV_w$, with k some value
slightly greater than one.   The curves plotted in Fig. 2·34a and b give
the values of n as a function of the capacitance of the storage condenser
for $k = 1.01$ and 1.001 and for several values of τ and T_r.   If the value
V_w/E_{bb} is much less than 1.0, the number of pulses required to approach
the equilibrium value may affect the operation of loads with low dynamic

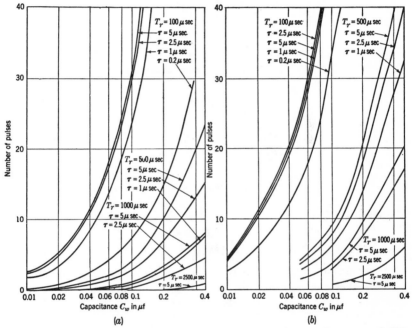

Fig. 2·34.—Number of pulses required for the storage-condenser voltage to reach kV_w
as a function of C_w for various values of τ and T_r, with $R_c = 10,000$ ohms, $R_l = 1000$ ohms,
and $r_p = 100$ ohms, (a) $k = 1.01$, (b) $k = 1.001$.

impedance such as the magnetron.   A large value of n indicates that the
current through the load is larger than the current obtained with continuous pulsing for a time that may be long enough to be deleterious to
the magnetron cathode.   This high current may also aggravate any
tendency for sparking to occur in the load.

In designing a hard-tube pulser with a resistance as the isolating
element, it is important to know how much average power will be dissipated in the resistor.   There are two major contributions to this power,
that from the current flowing in the resistance during the pulse interval
and that from the current flowing during the interpulse interval.   When
the switch tube is conducting, the current flowing in the isolating resist-

ance is

$$(i_c)_1 = \frac{E_{bb} - v_p}{R_c},$$

where $v_p = i_p r_p$ and i_p is the total instantaneous plate current in the switch tube. For most practical purposes, it may be assumed that v_p is constant during the pulse interval since its variation is usually small compared with $E_{bb} - v_p$. The current $(i_c)_1$ is therefore considered to be constant for a time τ, having the value

$$(I_c)_1 = \frac{E_{bb} - V_p}{R_c},$$

and the average power dissipated in R_c is then

$$P_1 = (I_c)_1^2 R_c \frac{\tau}{T_r}. \tag{74}$$

During the interpulse interval the amount of current flowing in R_c depends on the power-supply voltage and on the voltage on the storage condenser. Thus

$$(i_c)_2 = \frac{E_{bb} - V_C}{R_c}$$

where V_C is a function of time with the value given by Eq. (52), that is,

$$V_C(t) = E_{bb} - (E_{bb} - V_r)e^{-\frac{t}{(R_c + R_l)C_w}}. \tag{52}$$

In this equation the term R_l may be the value for either a resistance load or the recharging path if Z_s in Fig. 2·30b is a resistance. Substituting V_C from Eq. (52), the expression for $(i_c)_2$ becomes

$$(i_c)_2 = \frac{(E_{bb} - V_r)e^{-\frac{t}{(R_c + R_l)C_w}}}{R_c}. \tag{75}$$

The average power dissipated in R_c corresponding to this condenser-charging current is

$$P_2 = \frac{1}{(T_r - \tau)} \int_0^{(T_r - \tau)} (i_c)_2^2 R_c \, dt. \tag{76}$$

Using the value of $(i_c)_2$ in Eq. (75) and neglecting τ because, generally, $T_r \gg \tau$, the integration in Eq. (76) gives

$$P_2 = \frac{C_w(E_{bb} - V_r)^2(R_c + R_l)}{2R_c T_r}[1 - e^{-\frac{2T_r}{(R_c + R_l)C_w}}]. \tag{77}$$

The total power dissipation in the isolating resistance is the sum of the values for the pulse interval and that for the interpulse interval given by Eqs. (74) and (77). Thus

$$P_R = \frac{(E_{bb} - V_p)^2}{R_c} \frac{\tau}{T_r} + \frac{C_w (E_{bb} - V_r)^2 (R_c + R_l)}{2 R_c T_r} [1 - e^{-\frac{2T_r}{(R_c + R_l)C_w}}]. \quad (78)$$

In many cases the contribution of the first term of Eq. (78) to the power dissipation in the isolating resistance is several times larger than that of the second term. Consequently, the approximate value of P_R may be calculated somewhat more simply by taking advantage of the fact that the average condenser-charging current is approximately equal to the average load current. The average load current is the value of the pulse current multiplied by the duty ratio. Since the condenser-charging current as given by Eq. (75) is an exponential function of time, the rms and average values are nearly equal, provided that the time interval is not large compared with the time constant $(R_c + R_l)C_w$. It

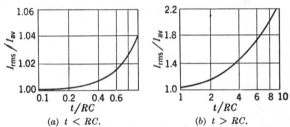

(a) $t < RC$.   (b) $t > RC$.

Fig. 2·35.—Ratio of rms to average current as a function of t/RC for a current of the form

$$i = \frac{E}{R} e^{-\frac{t}{RC}}.$$

is seen from the plot of I_{rms}/I_{av} versus $T_r/(R_c + R_l)C_w$ in Fig. 2·35 that, for $T_r = (R_c + R_l)C_w$, the rms current is only 1.04 times the average current. For the value of rms current determined in this way, the average power corresponding to Eq. (77) is

$$P_2 = I_{c rms}^2 R_c.$$

2·5. The Output Circuit with an Inductance or an Inductive Resistor as the Isolating Element.—The equivalent circuits for the pulser with resistance load and biased-diode load are shown in Fig. 2·36a and b. The analytical expressions for the equilibrium condenser voltages at the beginning and at the end of the pulse are considerably more complicated for these circuits than for those with a pure-resistance isolating element. A few general conclusions can be drawn, however, from a simplified analysis of the circuits of Fig. 2·36.

When the recharging circuit alone is considered and the switch S_T is open, the circuits of Fig. 2·36a and b, in which Z_s is a resistance, reduce to a simple series LCR-circuit as represented in Fig. 2·37. The initial conditions imposed on the equation for this circuit are (1) that the condenser is charged to a potential difference V_r, and (2) that a current i_0

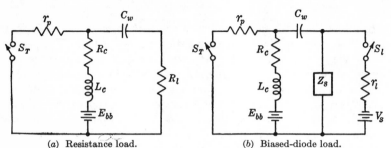

(a) Resistance load.   (b) Biased-diode load.

FIG. 2·36.—Circuits for hard-tube pulsers with an inductive isolating element in series with the power supply.

is flowing in the inductance. The Laplace-transform equation for the circuit is therefore

$$L_c[pI_c(p) - I_c(0)] + (R_c + R_l)I_c(p) + \frac{I_c(p)}{C_w p} = \frac{E_{bb} - V_r}{p}. \quad (79)$$

Let $(R_c + R_l) = R_c'$ and $I_c(0) = i_0$. Then, if Eq. (79) is solved for $I_c(p)$,

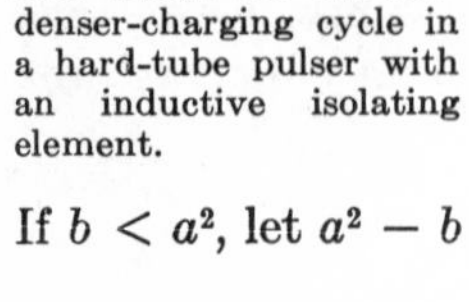

FIG. 2·37.—Equivalent circuit for the condenser-charging cycle in a hard-tube pulser with an inductive isolating element.

$$I_c(p) = \frac{\dfrac{E_{bb} - V_r}{L_c} + pi_0}{p^2 + \dfrac{R_c'}{L_c}p + \dfrac{1}{L_c C_w}}$$

$$I_c(p) = \frac{(p + a)i_0 + \dfrac{E_{bb} - V_r}{L_c} - ai_0}{(p + a)^2 + \omega^2}, \quad (80)$$

where $a = R_c'/2L_c$, $\omega^2 = b - a^2$, and $b = 1/L_c C_w$. If $b < a^2$, let $a^2 - b = k^2$, and Eq. (80) becomes

$$I_c(p) = \frac{(p + a)i_0 + \dfrac{E_{bb} - V_r}{L_c} - ai_0}{(p + a)^2 - k^2}. \quad (81)$$

Equations (80) and (81) give the Laplace transform of the current for the cases in which it is oscillatory and aperiodic respectively. The critically damped condition corresponds to $\omega^2 = k^2 = 0$. The inverse Laplace transform of Eq. (80) gives the time function for the current, thus

$$I_c(t) = \frac{(E_{bb} - V_r)e^{-at}}{L_c\omega} \sin \omega t + i_0 e^{-at}\left(\cos \omega t - \frac{a}{\omega} \sin \omega t\right). \quad (82)$$

Similarly for Eq. (81),

$$I_c(t) = \frac{(E_{bb} - V_r)e^{-at}}{L_c k} \sinh kt + i_0 e^{-at}\left(\cosh kt - \frac{a}{k} \sinh kt\right). \quad (83)$$

The voltage on the condenser expressed as a function of time is

$$V_C(t) = V_r + \frac{1}{C_w} \int_0^t I_c(t)\, dt, \quad (84)$$

so the integration of Eqs. (82) and (83) gives the expressions for the voltage on the condenser during the recharging interval. Thus, for the oscillatory case where $1/L_cC_w > R_c'^2/4L_c^2$, the condenser voltage is

$$V_C(t) = E_{bb} - e^{-at}\left[(E_{bb} - V_r)\left(\frac{a}{\omega} \sin \omega t + \cos \omega t\right) - \frac{i_0}{C_w\omega} \sin \omega t\right]. \quad (85)$$

Similarly, Eq. (84) and integration of Eq. (83) give the condenser voltage for the aperiodic case where $1/L_cC_w < R_c'^2/4L_c^2$, namely,

$$V_C(t) = E_{bb} - e^{-at}\left[(E_{bb} - V_r)\left(\frac{a}{k} \sinh kt + \cosh kt\right) - \frac{i_0}{C_w k} \sinh kt\right]. \quad (86)$$

For the critically damped case in which $1/L_cC_w = R_c'^2/4L_c^2$, the condenser voltage is

$$V_C(t) = E_{bb} - e^{-at}\left[(E_{bb} - V_r)(at + 1) - \frac{i_0}{C_w} t\right]. \quad (87)$$

Equations (85) and (86) can be written in a more convenient form by combining the sine and cosine functions in the one case and the sinh and cosh functions in the other. Thus Eq. (85) becomes

$$V_C(t) = E_{bb} - e^{-at}A \sin (\omega t + \varphi), \quad (88)$$

where

$$A = \sqrt{\left[\frac{(E_{bb} - V_r)a}{\omega} - \frac{i_0}{C_w\omega}\right]^2 + (E_{bb} - V_r)^2}$$

and

$$\varphi = \tan^{-1} \frac{E_{bb} - V_r}{\dfrac{(E_{bb} - V_r)a}{\omega} - \dfrac{i_0}{C_w\omega}}.$$

Similarly, Eq. (86) becomes

$$V_C(t) = E_{bb} - e^{-at}B \sinh (kt + \theta), \quad (89)$$

where

$$B = \sqrt{\left[\frac{(E_{bb} - V_\tau)a}{k} - \frac{i_0}{C_w k}\right]^2 - (E_{bb} - V_\tau)^2}$$

and

$$\theta = \tanh^{-1} \frac{(E_{bb} - V_\tau)}{\dfrac{(E_{bb} - V_\tau)a}{k} - \dfrac{i_0}{C_w k}}.$$

As the parameters L_c, C_w and R_c' are varied, the transition from the aperiodic to the oscillatory condition occurs when $L_c = \frac{1}{4}R_c'^2 C_w$; thus,

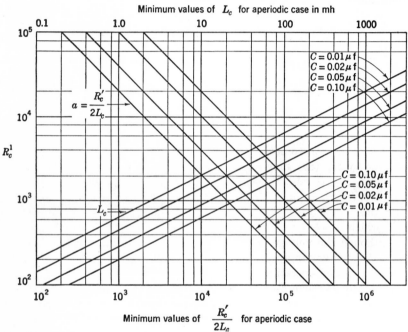

Fig. 2·38.—Values of L_c and $R'_c/2L_c$ necessary to critically damp the condenser-charging current in the circuit of Fig. 2·37.

if L_c is larger than this value, the condenser voltage and the power-supply current oscillates. Since, for the critical-damping case,

$$a = \frac{R_c'}{2L_c} = \frac{2}{R_c' C_w},$$

values of

$$\frac{R_c'}{2L_c} < \frac{2}{R_c' C}$$

correspond to the oscillatory condition. The curves of Fig. 2·38 give the maximum values of L_c and the minimum values of $R_c'/2L_c$ for aperiodic charging of the storage condenser for a range of R'_c and C_w values. When the oscillatory condition is satisfied, the voltage on the condenser reaches a maximum value that is greater than the power-supply voltage by an amount depending primarily on the initial current in the isolating inductance. It is evident from the circuits of Fig. 2·36 that a current in the inductance is built up during the pulse interval when S_T is closed, and that its magnitude depends on the pulse duration, the power-supply voltage, and the value of the inductance. If the pulse duration is small and the switch-tube resistance and the resistance associated with the inductance are small, the current can be calculated approximately from

$$i_0 = \frac{E_{bb}}{L_c} \tau.$$

The approximation is better the smaller the value of i_0 is, compared with the maximum possible value when t is very large, namely,

$$i_{\max} = \frac{E_{bb}}{R_c + r_p}.$$

It is of interest to note that the aperiodic charging of the condenser, as given by Eq. (89), may also cause the value of $V_C(t)$ to become larger than E_{bb}. If i_0 is large (actually, if $i_0/C_w k > (E_{bb} - V_r)a/k$), θ is negative, and there is some value of t for which $V_C(t) = E_{bb}$. For t greater than this value, $V_C(t)$ is greater than E_{bb}, reaching a maximum value after which it decreases and approaches the value E_{bb} asymptotically.

Although the voltage on the condenser may rise to a value greater than the power-supply voltage during the recharging interval, the resultant pulser operation is not necessarily unsatisfactory. If V_r is only slightly less than E_{bb} and i_0 is not large, the maximum value of $V_C(t)$ may not exceed E_{bb} by a dangerously large factor. The primary consideration is to determine that the maximum value of $V_C(t)$ does not exceed safe operating voltages for the condenser and the switch tube, and that sufficient damping is present to make the amplitude of oscillation negligibly small at the end of the interpulse interval.

For given values of R'_c and C_w it is reasonable to assume that the quantity $E_{bb} - V_r$ is independent of the value of L_c, provided that the resistance R_c is always small compared with R_l. Since, for small values of L_c, the charging is aperiodic with large values for i_0, the magnitude of B and θ in Eq. (89) may be strongly affected by this initial current in the inductance. As L_c is increased, the critically damped condition is approached and i_0 decreases, becoming less effective. A still further increase in L_c leads to the oscillatory condition, and a maximum value for the frequency, $\omega_{\max} = 1/R'_c C_w$, which occurs when $L_c = \frac{1}{2}R'^2_c C$.

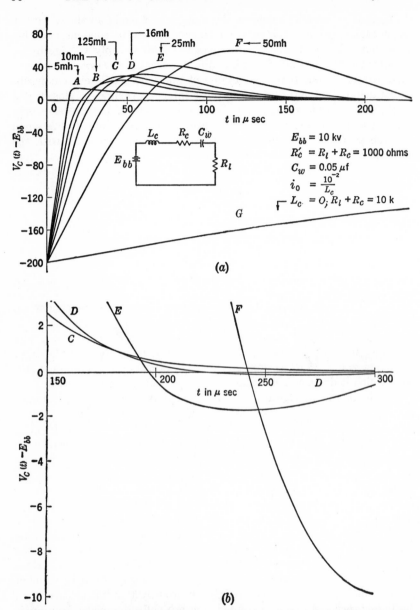

FIG. 2·39.—Storage-condenser voltage as a function of time during the recharging interval for an inductive element in series with the power supply; large values of R'_c/L_c. The portion of the curves C, D, E, and F beyond $t = 150\mu$ sec are plotted on expanded scales in (b) in order to show the transition from the aperiodic to the oscillatory conditions.

To illustrate the effect of the inductance of the isolating element on the charging of the storage condenser, the six curves shown in Fig. 2·39a have been plotted using the values of $[V_C(t) - E_{bb}]$ calculated from Eqs. (88) and (89) for various values of L_c. The calculations were made for $R'_c = 1000$ ohms, $E_{bb} = 10$ kv, and $C_w = 0.05$ μf in the circuit of Fig. 2·36a. Since the equations for $V_C(t)$ involve the terms $(E_{bb} - V_\tau)$ and i_0, it was also necessary to specify a particular pulse duration. For these calculations $\tau = 1$μsec was chosen, and the assumptions were made that $R_c \approx r_p$ for all values of L_c, and that the voltage on the storage condenser was equal to E_{bb} at the start of the pulse. The values of $(E_{bb} - V_\tau)$ and i_0 used in the calculations were therefore obtained from the relations.

$$(E_{bb} - V_\tau) \approx \frac{E_{bb}}{R'_c C_w} \tau$$

and

$$i_0 \approx \frac{E_{bb}}{L_c} \tau.$$

For the values of the circuit parameters given above, $(E_{bb} - V_\tau) = 200$ volts and $i_0 = 10^{-2}/L_c$ amp.

The curves A and B are obtained for L_c equal to 5 mh and 10 mh respectively. These values of L_c are less than the value for critical damping, so curves A and B are aperiodic. When $L_c = \frac{1}{4}R'^2_c C_w = 12.5$ mh, the curve C is obtained, which corresponds to the critically damped condition. Curves D, E, and F are oscillatory, with L_c equal to 16 mh, 25 mh, and 50 mh respectively. The value of 25 mh corresponds to $L_c = \frac{1}{2}R'^2_c C_w$, producing the maximum frequency for the oscillation. Portions of the curves C, D, E, and F are plotted in Fig. 2·39b with an expanded ordinate scale in order to show the details of the curves when L_c is larger than the value for critical damping. The curve G in Fig. 2·39a shows the effect of a 10,000-ohm noninductive resistance as the isolating element, and is included to emphasize the rapid buildup of the condenser voltage when an inductance is used.

The curves of Fig. 2·39 also apply for values of C_w other than 0.05 μf if R'_c, E_{bb}, and τ are not changed and a scale factor is introduced. With the scale factor $K \propto (E_{bb} - V_\tau)/R'_c$, the ordinate scale corresponds to $[V_C(t) - E_{bb}]/K$ and the abscissa scale is Kt. The condition is imposed that

$$\frac{(C_w)_2}{0.05\mu f} = \frac{(L_c)_2}{(L_c)_1} = \frac{1}{K},$$

where the values of $(L_c)_1$ are those that correspond to the curves of Fig. 2·39 for which $K = 1$. Thus, if $(C_w)_2 = 0.01$μf, the scale factor is 5 and $(L_c)_2$ for curve A, for example, is 1 mh. The curves C and E again correspond to the critically damped and the maximum-frequency conditions respectively.

To illustrate the effect of small damping on the charging of the storage condenser, the curves shown in Fig. 2·40 were calculated from Eq. (88). For the three curves A, B, and C a value of $R'_c/L_c = 10$ ohms per mh was used with $C_w = 0.05$ μf, $E_{bb} = 10$ kv, and $\tau = 1$ μsec. The values of L_c are 5 mh, 10 mh, and 20 mh, respectively, for the curves A, B, and C. The effect of adding some resistance in series with L_c is indicated by the curve A' for which $L_c = 5$ mh and $R'_c = 500$ ohms. These curves are

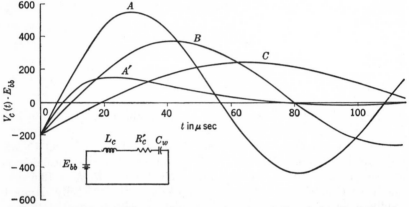

FIG. 2·40.—Storage-condenser voltage as a function of time during the recharging interval for an inductive element in series with the power supply; small values of R'_c/L_c. For curves A, B, and C the value of R'_c/L_c is 10 ohms per mh with $L_c = 5$ mh, 10 mh, and 20 mh respectively. For curve A', $L_c = 5$ mh and $R'_c = 500$ ohms. $E_{bb} = 10$ kv and $C_w = 0.05\mu$f for all curves.

indicative of the way in which the storage-condenser voltage varies during the interpulse interval if small inductances and small values of R_c/L_c are used both for the isolating element and for the recharging path Z_s of Fig. 2·36b.

There are two principal advantages to be gained by the use of an inductance as the isolating element. The possibility of having the condenser voltage equal to the power-supply voltage at the start of each pulse provides better utilization of the available power-supply voltage. Also, the power dissipated in the resistance associated with the inductance can be less than in the case of a high-resistance isolating element. In any pulser design, these advantages must be weighed against the undesirable possibility that the recharging of the condenser may be oscillatory, and also against the increase in current through the switch tube with time during the pulse interval. The latter consideration is perhaps the more serious, since it may cause a larger drop in pulse voltage during the

SEC. 2·5] AN INDUCTANCE AS THE ISOLATING ELEMENT   69

pulse than that which results from the change in the storage-condenser voltage.

The more rapid increase in the storage-condenser voltage during the interpulse interval, which is possible with the inductive isolating element, can be used to advantage in pulsers designed for closely spaced pulses, particularly if the interpulse intervals are of nonuniform duration, as in the case of pulse coding.

When an inductive element is used in parallel with the load in order to bring the trailing edge of the pulse down rapidly, as discussed in Sec. 2·3, this inductance becomes part of the recharging circuit as well. The current flowing in the inductance may be oscillatory and of sufficient magnitude to exert considerable influence on the initial conditions for the recharging cycle. It is therefore obvious that a complete analysis of the recharging of the storage condenser is too complex to permit as detailed conclusions to be drawn as are possible in the case of the resistive isolating element.

POWER TRANSFER TO THE LOAD

One of the important considerations involved in the design of a pulser is the magnitude of the pulse power to be delivered to the load. This pulse power is equal to the product of the voltage and current during the pulse. If the pulses of voltage and current are constant in amplitude for the pulse duration, the terms "pulse power" and "peak power" have the same significance. When the pulse amplitude is not constant during the pulse, the peak power refers to the maximum voltage-current product, and the pulse power is the product of an average amplitude for the voltage and current pulses. There are several possible methods by which this averaging may be done (see Appendix B). For the hard-tube pulser, the voltage and current pulses generally have a top that is relatively flat, and the meaning of "average pulse amplitude" is reasonably clear. For the present discussion the term "pulse power" refers to the average voltage-current product for pulses that do not deviate very much from constant amplitude.

It may be necessary to have some circuit elements in parallel with the load in order to change pulse shape or to provide a recharging path for the storage condenser, as shown in Secs. 2·2 and 2·3. Some power is dissipated in these shunt elements, and this power must be taken into account in designing a pulser for a given power output to a load. By careful design, however, it is generally possible to make the power loss small compared with the load pulse power. The present discussion of power transfer to the load on a hard-tube pulser is simplified by the assumption that any shunt losses may be considered as part of the pulser load.

It is evident from the circuit of Fig. 2·5 that the current through the switch tube is approximately equal to the current through the load. Also, the pulse voltage across the load is approximately equal to the power-supply voltage minus the voltage drop in the switch tube. These considerations are of fundamental importance in the design of a hard-tube pulser when a definite load impedance and pulse-power output are specified. The connection of the load to the pulser as indicated in the circuits discussed in Secs. 2·2 and 2·3 is referred to as a "direct-connection."

If the pulse power and the load impedance are specified, the requirements for the switch tube and the power supply are almost completely determined for the load directly connected to the pulser. Thus, if the pulse power is P_l and the load impedance is R_l, the pulse voltage is $V_l = \sqrt{P_l R_l}$ and the load current is $I_l = \sqrt{P_l/R_l}$. The switch tube must therefore be chosen so that the current I_l can flow without making the voltage drop in the tube too high. When the magnitude of this voltage drop is known, the required power-supply voltage is also known. The switch tube must also be capable of withstanding the power-supply voltage during the interpulse interval. The switch tubes that have been available for microwave-radar applications of hard-tube pulsers have had effective resistances ranging from about 50 ohms to several hundred ohms. Most of these tubes have a maximum current-carrying capacity that is determined by available cathode emission or by electrode power dissipation. For pulsers with low average power, the cathode emission determines the maximum current, and for pulsers with high average power, the allowable electrode power dissipation usually imposes the limit on the current. The effective resistance introduced into the puise circuit by the switch tube is relatively constant over the usable range of current, except for special design, such as operation on the flat portion of the pulse characteristic of a tetrode (see Chap. 3).

2·6. Impedance-matching and Pulse-transformer Coupling to the Load.—A hard-tube pulser may be considered as a generator with an internal impedance equal to the effective resistance of the switch tube. If the resistance of the load is high compared with the generator internal resistance, the efficiency is also high but the power delivered to the load is small compared with the maximum power that could be obtained. It is shown in most textbooks on electricity that the maximum power is delivered to a load when the load and generator resistances are equal. This condition means, however, that as much power is lost in the generator as is delivered to the load, and the efficiency is only 50 per cent. Since a maximum of 50 per cent efficiency can not be tolerated in most hard-tube-pulser applications, impedance-matching is seldom used.

Impedance-matching is important in the line-type pulsers to be discussed in Part II. Since for these pulsers the internal impedance is nondissipative, the above-mentioned difficulty for hard-tube pulsers is not encountered.   It is possible, however, to achieve some gain in hard-tube pulsers designed for low pulse-power output by changing the load impedance presented to the pulser.   In particular, it is possible to use a lower power-supply voltage for a given pulse power into a high-impedance load if a pulse transformer is used to transform the load impedance to a lower value at the pulser output terminals.   The details of pulse-transformer design and construction are given in Part III.

A brief discussion of the considerations involved in the use of a pulse transformer with a hard-tube pulser serves to indicate when such an arrangement is advantageous and to point out the limitations.   For this purpose, the hard-tube pulser is represented as a battery in series with the switch-tube resistance, as shown in Fig. 2·41.   The primary of the pulse transformer is connected to the pulser output terminals, and the load is connected across the secondary.   The secondary is considered to have n times as many turns as the primary, and the power-transfer

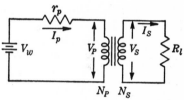

FIG. 2·41.—Equivalent circuit for a hard-tube pulser with pulse-transformer coupling to the load.

efficiency, η, of the transformer is assumed to be determined only by shunt losses.   This assumption is justified by experience with such transformers in the microwave-radar applications.   The following relations may then be written:

$$\frac{V_S}{V_P} = n \tag{90}$$

and

$$\frac{V_S I_S}{V_P I_P} = \eta, \tag{91}$$

thus

$$I_S = \frac{\eta I_P}{n}. \tag{92}$$

The power into the load is

$$P_l = \frac{V_l^2}{R_l} = \frac{V_S^2}{R_l}, \tag{93}$$

and

$$V_P = V_w - I_P r_p, \tag{94}$$
$$V_S = I_S R_l, \tag{95}$$

where the switch-tube current I_p is equal to the primary current I_P and the load current I_l is equal to the secondary current I_S.   Combining these relations, the expression for the load power becomes

$$P_l = \frac{V_w^2 n^2 \eta^2 R_l}{(R_l \eta + r_p n^2)^2}.$$ (96)

The condition for maximum power in the load, as governed by the transformer turns ratio, is obtained by differentiating Eq. (96) with respect to n and equating the result to zero; thus,

$$n_m^2 = \eta \frac{R_l}{r_p} \text{ for } (P_l)_{max},$$ (97)

and the maximum power is

$$(P_l)_{max} = \frac{V_w^2 \eta}{4 r_p}.$$ (98)

Equation (98) is the familiar result for a generator with matched load, except that in this case it is modified by the efficiency of the pulse transformer. This efficiency may be between 75 and 95 per cent, depending on the transformer construction.

TABLE 2·1.—COMPARATIVE VALUES FOR THE OPERATION OF A HARD-TUBE PULSER WITH A PULSE TRANSFORMER AND MAXIMUM POWER OUTPUT, AND FOR A DIRECT-CONNECTED LOAD*

With pulse transformer, maximum power output	No pulse transformer, load direct-connected
$\eta = 0.85$	
$n_m = \sqrt{\dfrac{R_l \eta}{r_p}} = 9.2$	
$V_l = \sqrt{P_l R_l} = 3.16 \times 10^3$ volts	$V_l = 3.16 \times 10^3$ volts
$I_l = \sqrt{\dfrac{P_l}{R_l}} = 0.316$ amp	$I_l = 0.316$ amp
$I_p = \dfrac{n_m}{\eta} I_l = 3.4$ amp	$I_p = I_l = 0.316$ amp
$V_w = \dfrac{2V_l}{n_m} = 700$ volts	$V_w = V_l + I_p r_p = 3.2 \times 10^3$ volts
Average P_p (switch tube) $= I_p^2 r_p \times 10^{-3} = 1.2$ watts	Average $P_p = I_p^2 r_p \times 10^{-3} = 0.1$ watts

* Test conditions:
        Load resistance, $R_l = 10,000$ ohms.
        Load pulse power, $P_l = 1$ kw.
        Switch-tube resistance, $r_p = 100$ ohms.
        Duty ratio = 0.001.

If the load resistance is greater than the switch-tube resistance, the maximum-power condition requires a stepup transformer, that is, $n > 1$. The voltage that appears across the load is then

$$V_l = \frac{V_w}{2} n_m,$$ (99)

and the switch-tube current is

$$I_p = \frac{n_m}{\eta} I_l. \tag{100}$$

The significance of these considerations is best brought out by comparing the values of the pulser parameters for the case of the direct-connected load on the one hand and that of the transformer-coupled load with maximum power output on the other hand. The results are given in Tables 2·1 and 2·2 for two values of load resistance and pulse power.

TABLE 2·2.—COMPARATIVE VALUES FOR THE OPERATION OF A HARD-TUBE PULSER WITH A PULSE TRANSFORMER AND MAXIMUM POWER OUTPUT, AND WITH A DIRECT-CONNECTED LOAD*

With pulse transformer, maximum power output	No pulse transformer, load direct-connected
$\eta = 0.85$	
$n_m = \sqrt{\dfrac{R_l \eta}{r_p}} = 2.9$	
$V_l = \sqrt{P_l R_l} = 10^4$ volts	$V_l = 10^4$ volts
$I_l = \sqrt{\dfrac{P_l}{R_l}} = 10$ amp	$I_l = 10$ amp
$I_p = \dfrac{n_m}{\eta} I_l = 34$ amp	$I_p = I_l = 10$ amp
$V_w = \dfrac{2V_l}{n_m} = 7 \times 10^3$ volts	$V_w = V_l + I_p r_p = 11 \times 10^3$ volts
Average P_p (switch tube) = 120 watts	Average P_p (switch tube) = 10 watts

* Test conditions:
  Load resistance, $R_l = 1000$ ohms.
  Load pulse power, $P_l = 100$ kw.
  Switch-tube resistance, $r_p = 100$ ohms.
  Duty ratio = 0.001.

Examination of these tables indicates that, with the 10,000-ohm load and 1-kw pulse power, the gain in using the pulse transformer is large as far as power-supply voltage is concerned. The switch-tube current is more than ten times the load current, but is still within the operating range of available tubes. The power dissipation of 1.2 watts in the switch tube is also not prohibitive. The question to be decided in this case is whether or not the reduction in power-supply voltage, from about 3 kv to 700 volts, is important enough to warrant the use of a switch tube that can pass a current of 3.4 amp with the additional power loss of approximately one watt.

For the 1000-ohm load and 100-kw pulse power, the increase in switch-tube current from 10 amp to 34 amp produced by using the pulse transformer and maximum power design is generally more serious than the factor of 10 increase in the previous case.   A relatively small tube[1] can be used to provide the 0.3 or 3.4 amp, whereas the increase in plate voltage from 700 volts to 3 kv may both increase the size of the tube and impose greater problems in its fabrication.   The increase in tube current from 10 amp to 34 amp, however, may necessitate the use of two or three tubes in parallel or the use of a larger cathode, which is generally a serious problem in tube manufacture.   For tubes that have been available for the microwave-radar applications, the gain introduced by the reduction of plate voltage from 11 kv to 7 kv does not offset the difficulties introduced by the increase in plate current.   The increase of more than 100 watts in power dissipation in the switch tube also imposes a more serious problem than the 1-watt increase for the 10,000-ohm load.

These examples show that the use of a pulse transformer to reduce the necessary power-supply voltage is not *a priori* always advantageous to pulser design.   However, the pulse transformer is not used only to give the maximum power output.   There are situations in which a small reduction in the necessary power-supply voltage may be warranted at the expense of slightly higher switch-tube current.   Under these conditions, it is necessary to use Eq. (96) for power output in terms of the circuit parameters in order to determine the design best suited to the available components.

The above design considerations lead to the minimum values of switch-tube current and power-supply voltage for a given load impedance and pulse power.   To these values must be added any contributions resulting from the connection between the charging circuit and the discharging circuit as discussed in Secs. 2·4 and 2·5.   These contributions can usually be kept small, but in some cases, such as a design for closely spaced pulses, it may be necessary to allow for increases of as much as 25 to 50 per cent above the minimum values.

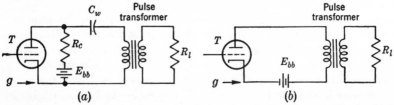

Fig. 2·42.—Two possible arrangements for the use of a pulse transformer with a hard-tube pulser.

A pulse transformer may be used with a hard-tube pulser in either of two ways.   The two possibilities, with a triode as the switch tube, are shown schematically in Fig. 2·42.   In Fig. 2·42a the primary of the pulse

[1] R. B. Woodbury, "Pulse Characteristics of Common Receiver Type Tubes," RL Report No. 704, Apr. 30, 1945.   See also tube data given in Chap. 3.

transformer takes the place of the load in the circuits of Sec. 2·2.   In the circuit of Fig. 2·42b the storage condenser is eliminated and the pulse-transformer primary is in series with the power supply and the switch tube.   It has been mentioned previously that, from a practical stand-point, some part of the circuit must be at ground potential, and reasons were given for connecting the switch-tube cathode, rather than the plate, to ground.   Thus, if point g is connected to ground in Fig. 2·42a, one end of the pulse-transformer primary is grounded, and the winding must be insulated only for the maximum pulse voltage.   If the cathode of the switch tube is connected to ground in the circuit of Fig. 2·42b, the primary of the transformer must be insulated for the d-c power-supply voltage. This voltage is greater than the pulse voltage by the amount of the voltage drop in the switch tube, which may amount to 10 to 20 per cent of the power-supply voltage.   The problem of providing adequate insula-tion for d-c voltages in such a transformer is somewhat more serious than for an equivalent pulse voltage.   This difficulty causes a transformer designed for the circuit in Fig. 2·42b to be somewhat inferior to a trans-former suitable for the circuit of Fig. 2·42a as regards the effect on pulse shape.   There is a greater deviation from a rectangular pulse shape at the load because of the less satisfactory ratio of leakage inductance to distributed capacitance in the transformer.   The transformer for circuit in Fig. 2·42b may also have a somewhat lower power-transfer efficiency.

There is a further argument in favor of the use of a storage condenser with pulse-transformer coupling to the load.   If the load is a magnetron or some other device that may exhibit sudden changes in impedance because of sparking or voltage breakdown, a high-voltage surge occurs at the plate of the switch tube.   This transient voltage may be sufficient to cause the switch tube to spark internally, thus vitiating the control of the grid over the tube conduction.   When the grid loses control, the time during which the switch tube is conducting may exceed the desired pulse duration by a large factor.   In the circuit of Fig. 2·42b this behavior causes more energy to be discharged into the load than that corresponding to the normal pulse, with the result that the sparking condition is aggra-vated.   In the circuit of Fig. 2·42a, the same sequence of events is not as serious, since the available energy in the storage condenser is considerably less than that in the filter condensers of a power supply.   Because of the inherent characteristics of a pulse transformer, it is actually possible to use a smaller capacitance for the storage condenser in the circuit of Fig. 2·42a than that necessary for a direct-connected load in order to obtain a given flatness for the top of the pulse.

If a pulser is designed to use a pulse transformer and no storage con-denser, the versatility of the unit is decreased.   A pulser of the type

shown in Fig. 2·42a can be used equally well with a direct-connected load
within the limits of its design. With a load substituted for the pulse
transformer in the circuit of Fig. 2·42b, the load or the switch tube must
be operated at high d-c potential with respect to ground.

2·7. The Effect of Stray Capacitance on the Pulser Power Output.—
When the duty ratio is high, the average-power considerations may out-
weigh the pulse-power requirements in governing the choice of components for the pulser. As has already been mentioned, the switch-tube
dissipation can impose a limit on the maximum allowable pulse current.
The choice of the capacitance for the storage condenser is also affected by
a high-duty-ratio requirement, but in different ways depending on
whether the high duty ratio is due to a long pulse duration, or to a high
recurrence frequency. Thus, if the pulse duration is long and the interpulse interval is also long, the storage condenser must have a high
capacitance in order to keep the pulse current as constant as possible
during the pulse. When the recurrence frequency is high, however, the
interpulse interval is small, and the condenser capacitance must be as
small as possible to best utilize the power-supply voltage, and it may
also be necessary to have a higher current from the power supply during
the pulse interval.

The stray capacitance in parallel with the pulser load becomes an
important consideration when the recurrence frequency is high and the
pulse voltage is large. This capacitance becomes charged during the
time required for the pulse voltage to build up, and its discharge starts
when the switch tube becomes nonconducting. The energy stored in
this capacitance, therefore, does not contribute to the pulse power in
the load except during the time corresponding to the trailing edge of the
pulse. The average-power loss that corresponds to the charging of this
capacitance is simply the energy stored per pulse multiplied by the
number of pulses per second, that is,

$$\text{PRF} \times \tfrac{1}{2}C_S V_l^2.$$

In the example used for the values of Table 2·2, a stray capacitance of
100 $\mu\mu$f introduces a loss of about 5 watts if the 0.001 duty ratio corresponds to a PRF of 1000 pps. At a PRF of 10,000 pps, however, this
power loss is 50 watts, which is one half of the average power delivered to
the load.

The current required to charge the stray capacitance also has an
influence on the pulse power for which the pulser is to be designed. If
it is desired to have a high rate of rise for the voltage pulse, the current-
carrying capabilities of the switch tube must satisfy the relation

$$I_C = C_s \frac{dV_l}{dt}.$$

If the value 100 $\mu\mu$f is again taken as an example, this current is 10 amp for $dV_l/dt = 100$ kv/μsec, which corresponds to a time of rise of 0.1μsec for a 10-kv pulse. In the example used for the values of Table 2·1, a switch tube capable of carrying 0.5 amp is adequate for the direct-connected load, but the maximum dV_l/dt is then 5 kv/μsec, corresponding to a time of rise of 0.6 μsec for a 3-kv pulse. Thus, the peak-current limitation for a particular switch tube may be high enough to satisfy the load pulse-power requirement and still limit the maximum rate of rise of the pulse voltage.

2·8. Output Power Regulation.—The change in output power from a hard-tube pulser, which is caused by a change in the power-supply voltage, may be expressed in terms of the switch-tube and load characteristics. This relation is of practical importance in pulser applications because it gives an indication of the stability of the power output as a function of the voltage input to the pulser. If the change in the power output is ΔP_l, the ratio $\Delta P_l/P_l$, expressed in terms of the ratio $\Delta E_{bb}/E_{bb}$ for the power-supply voltage and the circuit parameters, gives the regulation of the output power. Thus, for a given set of conditions, the regulation is determined by the relation

$$\frac{\Delta P_l}{P_l} = k\,\frac{\Delta E_{bb}}{E_{bb}}. \tag{101}$$

If k is large, the regulation is poor, that is, the percentage change in output power is large compared with the percentage change in power-supply voltage. Conversely, if k is small, the regulation is good.

The value of k in Eq. (101) depends on the pulser parameters and on the load characteristics. In order to find an expression for k, let it be assumed that a biased-diode load is used, and that the voltage on the storage condenser differs very little from the power-supply voltage. The power into the load is

$$P_l = V_l I_l \tag{102}$$

and

$$I_l = \frac{V_l - V_s}{r_l}, \tag{103}$$

where V_s is the bias voltage and r_l is the dynamic resistance of the load. The voltage across the load is

$$V_l = E_{bb} - I_l r_p, \tag{104}$$

where the effects of elements in parallel with the load and of the recharging circuit are neglected in considering the switch-tube current. Combining Eqs. (102), (103), and (104), the expression for the power becomes

$$P_l = \frac{(E_{bb}r_l + V_s r_p)(E_{bb} - V_s)}{(r_l + r_p)^2}. \tag{105}$$

Differentiating Eq. (105) with respect to E_{bb} and forming the ratio $\Delta P_l/P_l$, there is obtained

$$\frac{\Delta P_l}{P_l} = \frac{\Delta E_{bb}}{E_{bb}} \left[\frac{2\dfrac{r_l}{r_p} + \dfrac{V_s}{E_{bb}}\left(1 - \dfrac{r_l}{r_p}\right)}{\left(\dfrac{r_l}{r_p} + \dfrac{V_s}{E_{bb}}\right)\left(1 - \dfrac{V_s}{E_{bb}}\right)} \right]. \tag{106}$$

If the load dynamic resistance is equal to the switch-tube resistance and the bias voltage in the load is 0.8 times the power-supply voltage, Eq. (106) gives

$$\frac{\Delta P_l}{P_l} = \frac{\Delta E_{bb}}{E_{bb}} \times \frac{2}{1.8 \times 0.2} = 5.6\frac{\Delta E_{bb}}{E_{bb}}. \tag{107}$$

Thus, for these conditions, the percentage change in the output power is about six times as large as the percentage change in the power-supply voltage. Since the values chosen for this example are typical for the medium-power magnetrons used in microwave radar, this result is important in pulser applications with magnetron loads.

If the bias voltage is zero, that is, $V_s = 0$, Eq. (106) becomes

$$\frac{\Delta P_l}{P_l} = \frac{\Delta E_{bb}}{E_{bb}} \times 2. \tag{108}$$

The power regulation for a pure-resistance load is therefore considerably better than that for a magnetron or biased-diode load.

In the discussion of Chap. 3, it is shown that advantage may be taken of the characteristics of tetrodes as switch tubes in order to improve the power regulation for a hard-tube pulser. As in any power-generating device, however, improved regulation is obtained at the expense of additional power loss.

2·9. Effects of Pulse-transformer Coupling to the Load.—There are three principal advantages to be gained by coupling the output of a hard-tube pulser to a load by means of a pulse transformer. One of these has already been indicated in the discussion of Sec. 2·6, namely, that a transformation of the load impedance can be accomplished with a pulse transformer, that is, the impedance presented to the output of the pulser can be made either higher or lower than the load impedance. A gain in voltage, current, or power at the load can be obtained in this manner for given pulser and load characteristics. Another advantage is obtained by the use of two pulse transformers, a stepdown transformer at the pulser output terminals and a stepup transformer at the load, with a low-impedance cable between them. This arrangement facilitates the physical separation of the load and the pulser, which is a desirable engineering convenience in many cases. The third advantage of transformer coupling is that it provides a means of reversing the polarity of the pulse at the load. The use of two pulse transformers with different turns ratios for the stepup and stepdown transformers makes it possible to obtain all three of the advantages simultaneously.

In microwave applications, pulse transformers are used with hard-tube pulsers primarily because of the advantages to be gained by the physical separation of the load and the pulser. Serious difficulties arise in transmitting high pulse power and the correspondingly high pulse voltage more than a few feet from the pulser to the load. The use of stepdown and stepup pulse transformers makes it possible to transmit the pulse power at relatively low voltage over flexible coaxial cable for distances as great as several hundred feet. Associated with this added convenience, however, there is some power loss, some pulse-shape distortion, and sometimes increased backswing voltage. In any given case, therefore, it is necessary to weigh these disadvantages against the advantages. The purpose of this section is to indicate the extent to which the disadvantages may affect the design of the hard-tube pulser.

The theory of pulse transformers and the considerations involved in their design and construction are given in detail in Part III. There it is shown that the equivalent circuit for a pair of pulse transformers may be

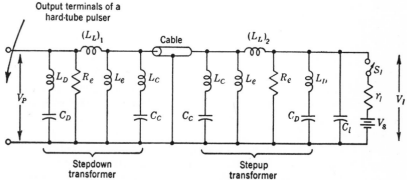

Fig. 2·43.—Equivalent circuit for a stepdown and a stepup pulse-transformer combination for a hard-tube pulser and a biased-diode load.

represented as in Fig. 2·43. The elements L_e, L_C, and C_C are associated with the low-voltage winding of the transformer, which is referred to as the primary, L_e being the effective shunt inductance and C_C the distributed capacitance of this winding. The so-called "charging inductance," L_C, is introduced to account for the nonuniform current distribution along the coil corresponding to the flow of charge into C_C. The element L_L is the leakage inductance, R_e represents the effective shunt loss in the transformer, and L_D and C_D have the same significance for the high-voltage or secondary winding that L_C and C_C have for the primary winding. The capacitance introduced by the load is represented by C_l.

In Sec. 14·1 it is shown that the leading edge of the pulse is affected principally by the elements L_L, R_e, and C_D, which cause the time of rise for the voltage pulse to be greater than it would be for a load direct-connected to the pulser. This effect may cause a rounding of the leading edge at the top of the pulse. With a pure-resistance load and no bias voltage, this increase in the time of rise for the pulse voltage becomes very noticeable. The best design of a pulse transformer for optimum pulse shape results when the static resistance of the load

$$R_l = \frac{V_l}{I_l} = \sqrt{\frac{\Sigma L_L}{C}},$$

where ΣL_L is the total leakage inductance of the two transformers plus the inductance of the cable (which is usually negligible), and

$$C = C_D + C_l.$$

Since the capacitance of the load is involved, it is necessary to have a knowledge of this parameter before designing the transformer.

When the load is a biased diode or a magnetron, the load current does not start to flow until the voltage V_l is greater than the bias voltage V_s. For a load that is direct-connected to the pulser, as discussed in Sec. 2·3, the load current builds up to the value

$$I_l = \frac{V_l - V_s}{r_l}$$

in a very short time, and $V_l = V_w$. The current I_l is referred to as the "normal load current." For the present, the cable between the pulse transformers is assumed to have negligible length. During the time required for the pulse voltage to build up to the value V_s, there is a current i_C flowing through the leakage inductance that corresponds to the flow of charge into the capacitances C_D and C_l. Thus, when the switch S_l is closed, there is a current flowing in L_L the magnitude of which may be greater than, equal to, or less than the normal load current. If the effective series inductance inherent in the load itself is small, the load current builds up to the value i_C in a negligibly short time after switch S_l closes. If i_C is larger or smaller than I_l, the current during the pulse interval decreases or increases respectively until the value I_l is reached. For $i_C = I_l$, the static resistance of the load must be equal to $\sqrt{\Sigma L_L/C}$. When $R_l > \sqrt{\Sigma L_L/C}$, the top of the current pulse droops, that is, the current decreases during the pulse, and when $R_l < \sqrt{\Sigma L_L/C}$, the top of the current pulse rises. The effect of L_e is to cause a small droop in the current pulse even for the optimum value of $\sqrt{\Sigma L_L/C}$. A series of oscilloscope traces that illustrates the foregoing statements is reproduced in Figs. 2·44 and 2·45.

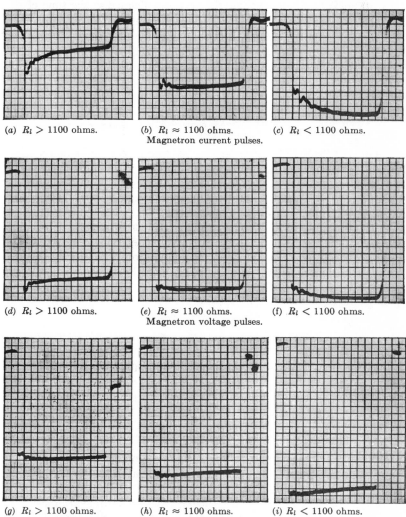

(a) $R_l > 1100$ ohms.   (b) $R_l \approx 1100$ ohms.   (c) $R_l < 1100$ ohms.
Magnetron current pulses.

(d) $R_l > 1100$ ohms.   (e) $R_l \approx 1100$ ohms.   (f) $R_l < 1100$ ohms.
Magnetron voltage pulses.

(g) $R_l > 1100$ ohms.   (h) $R_l \approx 1100$ ohms.   (i) $R_l < 1100$ ohms.
Voltage pulses at the input terminals of the stepdown transformer.

FIG. 2·44.—Oscilloscope traces for 2-μsec pulses of magnetron current, magnetron voltage, and pulser output voltage for a hard-tube pulser with pulse transformers and 6 ft of 50-ohm pulse cable. The 232AW stepdown and the 232BW stepup transformers, for which $\sqrt{\Sigma L_L/C} = 1100$ ohms, were used for these traces.

The effect produced by the effective shunt inductance and transformer losses may be seen by comparing the pictures of Figs. 2·44 and 2·45 for the cases where $R_l = \sqrt{\Sigma L_L/C}$. It is to be observed that the current pulse droop is greater for the 135AW-141BW transformer combination

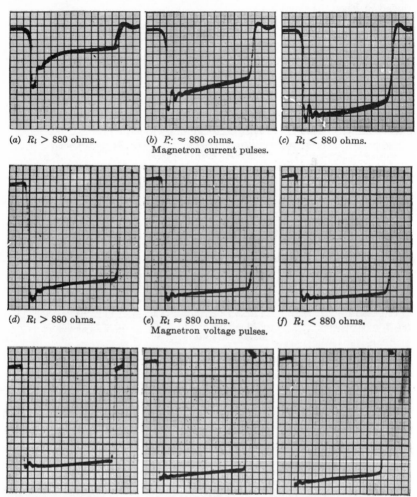

(a) $R_l > 880$ ohms.   (b) $R_l \approx 880$ ohms.   (c) $R_l < 880$ ohms.
Magnetron current pulses.

(d) $R_l > 880$ ohms.   (e) $R_l \approx 880$ ohms.   (f) $R_l < 880$ ohms.
Magnetron voltage pulses.

(g) $R_l > 880$ ohms.   (h) $R_l \approx 880$ ohms.   (i) $R_l < 880$ ohms.
Voltage pulses at the input terminals of the stepdown transformer.
FIG. 2·45.—Oscilloscope traces for 2-μsec pulses of magnetron current, magnetron voltage, and pulser output voltage for a hard-tube pulser with pulse transformers and 6 ft of 50-ohm pulse cable. The 135AW stepdown and the 141BW stepup transformers, for which $\sqrt{\Sigma L_L/C} = 880$ ohms, were used for these traces.

than for the 232AW-232BW combination. The latter pair of transformers have higher efficiency as determined by calorimetric measurements of power loss.

When the current in the leakage inductance is greater or less than the normal load current, the rate at which the pulse current decreases or

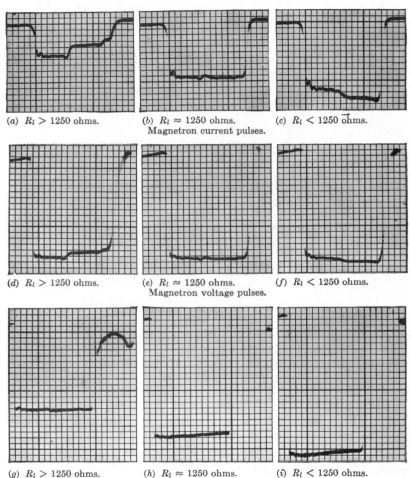

(a) $R_l > 1250$ ohms.   (b) $R_l \approx 1250$ ohms.   (c) $R_l < 1250$ ohms.
                           Magnetron current pulses.

(d) $R_l > 1250$ ohms.   (e) $R_l \approx 1250$ ohms.   (f) $R_l < 1250$ ohms.
                           Magnetron voltage pulses.

(g) $R_l > 1250$ ohms.   (h) $R_l \approx 1250$ ohms.   (i) $R_l < 1250$ ohms.
Voltage pulses at the input terminals of the stepdown transformer.

FIG. 2·46.—Oscilloscope traces for 2-μsec pulses of magnetron current, magnetron voltage, and pulser output voltage for a hard-tube pulser with the 232AW and the 232BW pulse transformers and 175 ft of 50-ohm pulse cable. The 50-ohm cable impedance is transformed to 1250 ohms at the output of the pulser and the input to the magnetron because the turns ratio for each transformer is 1 to 5. The transit time for the transformers and cable is 0.42μsec.

increases during the pulse depends on the time constant $\Sigma L_L/(r_p + r_l)$, where r_p is the internal resistance of the pulser. For the 232AW-232BW transformer combination and the magnetron used to obtain the oscilloscope traces of Fig. 2·44, this time constant is about 0.3 μsec, whereas for the 135AW-141BW combination it is about 0.18 μsec. This difference is observable in the pictures of Figs. 2·44 and 2·45.

Reflection Effects Caused by Impedance Mismatch with Long Cable.—Another effect is observed when the cable is so long that the time required for the pulse to travel from one transformer to the other is an appreciable fraction of the pulse duration. Discrete steps appear on the top of the current pulse as a result of an impedance mismatch between the load and the cable. Some photographs of oscilloscope traces showing this phenomenon are reproduced in Figs. 2·46 and 2·47 for the 232AW-232BW

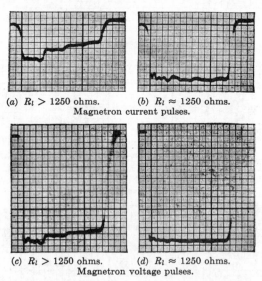

(a) $R_l > 1250$ ohms.   (b) $R_l \approx 1250$ ohms.
Magnetron current pulses.

(c) $R_l > 1250$ ohms.   (d) $R_l \approx 1250$ ohms.
Magnetron voltage pulses.

Fig. 2·47.—Oscilloscope traces for 2-μsec pulses of magnetron current and voltage for a hard-tube pulser using the 232AW and 232BW pulse transformers with 100 ft of 50-ohm pulse cable. The transit time for transformers and cable is 0.25μsec.

transformer combination and 175 ft and 100 ft of 50-ohm coaxial cable. These transformers have a turns ratio of 5/1 for the secondary and primary coils. Thus the 50-ohm impedance of the cable is transformed into an impedance of 1250 ohms at the high-voltage windings of the transformers.

The combination of pulse-transformer and cable may be considered as a transmission line of characteristic impedance $Z_0 = 1250$ ohms. If the impedance of the load is different from 1250 ohms, a voltage reflection occurs whose magnitude and sign depends on the reflection coefficient

$$\kappa = \frac{Z_l - Z_0}{Z_l + Z_0}.$$

Let V_P be the pulse voltage at the pulser output and let δ be the time required for the pulse to travel in one direction through the transformers and the cable.[1] If V_1 denotes the pulse voltage traveling from the pulser to the load, the magnitude of V_1 at the pulser is V_P. Because there is some attenuation of the pulse voltage in traversing the transformers and cable, the voltage appearing at the load end is kV_P, where $k < 1$. When $Z_l > Z_0$, the reflection coefficient at the load is positive, and the reflected voltage is

$$V_1' = kV_P \left(\frac{Z_l - Z_0}{Z_l + Z_0}\right). \tag{109}$$

This voltage therefore adds to the incident voltage at the load, producing an actual load voltage

$$(V_l)_1 = kV_P + V_1' = kV_P \left[1 + \left(\frac{Z_l - Z_0}{Z_l + Z_0}\right)\right]. \tag{110}$$

The load pulse voltage can be larger than the output voltage of the pulser, as in the first series of pulse pictures of Fig. 2·46.

The reflected voltage travels back toward the pulser, where it is again reflected. At the pulser the reflection coefficient

$$\kappa = \frac{Z_p - Z_0}{Z_p + Z_0},$$

where Z_p is the internal impedance of the pulser. For a hard-tube pulser Z_p is merely the switch-tube resistance r_p. Since, in general, Z_p is considerably less than 1250 ohms, the reflection coefficient is negative, and the polarity of the reflected voltage is opposite to that of the main-pulse voltage. At a time 2δ after the start of the pulse at the pulser output, the voltage at the input terminals of the stepdown pulse transformer is

$$V_P' = V_P + kV_1' + V_2, \tag{111}$$

where

$$V_2 = kV_1' \left(\frac{Z_p - Z_0}{Z_p + Z_0}\right). \tag{112}$$

The pulse voltage traveling away from the pulser toward the load is now $V_1 + V_2$, which is less than V_P because V_2 is of opposite polarity to V_1. At the time 3δ this new pulse voltage appears at the load, where a reflection again occurs such that

$$V_2' = k(V_1 + V_2) \left(\frac{Z_l - Z_0}{Z_l + Z_0}\right), \tag{113}$$

---

[1] The velocity of propagation in the cables used with pulsers for microwave applications is about 450 ft/μ sec. The observed time delay in the pictures of Fig. 2·46 is 0.42 μsec, indicating that the two transformers introduce a delay of about 0.03 μsec in addition to that of the cable.

and the load is subjected to a voltage

$$(V_l)_2 = k(V_1 + V_2) + V_2' = k(V_1 + V_2)\left[1 + \left(\frac{Z_l - Z_0}{Z_l + Z_0}\right)\right] \quad (114)$$

Since $(V_1 + V_2) < V_P$, the pulse voltage at the load changes suddenly at time 3δ from the value given by Eq. (110) to that given by Eq. (114), producing the first step that appears in the pictures of Fig. 2·46.

If the pulse duration is several times longer than 2δ, a succession of

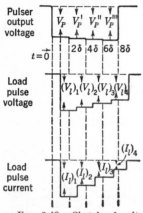

these steps occur as indicated in the sketch of Fig. 2·48. The successive steps become progressively smaller, as evidenced by the fact that $(I_l)_3$ and $(I_l)_4$ in Fig. 2·47 are almost equal. These pictures were obtained with the same transformers and magnetron, but with 100 ft of cable instead of the 175 ft used for the pulses shown in Fig. 2·46.

When the impedance of the load is less than that of the cable, the steps are in the opposite direction, as can be seen in the third series of pictures in Fig. 2·46. As a result of the change in load impedance during the time the pulse voltage is built up, reflections of short time duration occur. The effect of these reflections is evident from the second series of pictures in Figs. 2·46 and 2·47, in which the load and cable impedances are approximately equal. Small irregularities occur at the times corresponding to the steps in the other two series of pictures.

FIG. 2·48.—Sketch of voltage and current pulses indicating the steps resulting from an impedance mismatch between the load and the cable when two pulse transformers are used with a hard-tube pulser. The load impedance is greater than the cable impedance referred to the high-voltage windings of the transformers.

As an example of the foregoing discussion, the experimental and calculated values corresponding to the first series of pictures in Fig. 2·46 are given. The voltage at the pulser output is

$$V_P = 8.55 \text{ kv}$$

and that at the load is

$$(V_l)_1 = 9.36 \text{ kv}$$

Since

$$(I_l)_1 = 4.82 \text{ amp,}$$
$$(Z_l)_1 = \frac{9.36 \times 10^3}{4.82} = 1940 \text{ ohms.}$$

The reflection coefficient at the load is therefore

$$\frac{Z_l - Z_0}{Z_l + Z_0} = \frac{1940 - 1250}{1940 + 1250} = 0.216,$$

and the value of k may be determined with the aid of Eq. (110), that is,

$$k = \frac{9.36 \times 10^3}{8.55 \times 10^3 \times 1.22} = 0.9$$

The reflected voltage traveling toward the pulser is then

$$V_1' = 0.9 \times 8.55 \times 10^3 \times 0.216$$
$$= 1.65 \text{ kv.}$$

The reflected voltage, V_2, at the pulser is

$$V_2 = 0.9 \times 1.65 \times 10^3(-0.82) = -1.20 \text{ kv,}$$

where the reflection coefficient ($\kappa = -0.82$) is obtained by assuming the switch-tube resistance to be 125 ohms. The pulse voltage traveling toward the load after time 2δ is therefore

$$V_1 + V_2 = (8.55 - 1.20) \text{ kv} = 7.35 \text{ kv.}$$

When this voltage reaches the load at time 3δ, the reflected voltage is determined by a new load impedance, since the pulse voltage is less than the original value of 9.36 kv. In this case the new reflection coefficient is 0.346, and

$$(V_l)_2 = 0.9 \times 7.35 \times 10^3 \times 1.35 \text{ kv} = 8.90 \text{ kv.}$$

The dynamic resistance of the magnetron used for the pictures of Fig. 2·46 was determined experimentally to be 250 ohms, and the starting voltage V_s was 8.10 kv; thus

$$(I_l)_2 = \left(\frac{8.90 - 8.10}{250}\right) = 3.2 \text{ amp.}$$

This calculated value for the magnetron current after the first step agrees reasonably well with the value of 3.4 amp measured experimentally.

The above numerical example is given to justify the previous argument explaining the presence of the steps in the load current and voltage pulses when a long cable is used between the transformers. It is possible to derive relationships from which the load current and voltage may be calculated for the successive steps. To do this, it is necessary to know the load pulse voltage and current before the first reflection is effective, the dynamic resistance and bias voltage for the load, the cable impedance referred to the secondary of the transformers, and the pulser internal resistance. If the attenuation factor k is known from auxiliary experiments, the initial pulse voltage and current at the load need not be known, and the pulse voltage at the pulser output terminals can be used as the starting point for the calculations.

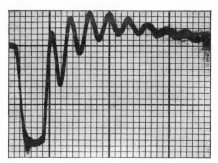

(a) 0.5-μsec voltage pulse.

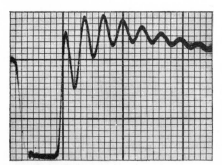

(b) 1-μsec voltage pulse.

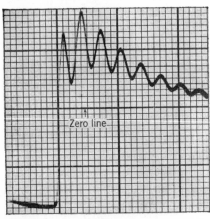

(c) 2-μsec voltage pulse.

Fig. 2·49.—Oscilloscope traces of voltage pulses showing oscillations superimposed on the general backswing voltage that is characteristic of the use of pulse transformers with a hard-tube pulser. Pulse amplitude ≈ 11 kv.

In the pulse pictures of Figs. 2·44 and 2·45, the steps resulting from reflections are not resolved since the transit time for the transformers and the 6-ft cable is only about 0.04 μsec as compared with 0.42 μsec for the 175-ft cable and 0.25 μsec for the 100-ft cable. The effect of the reflections is present, however, even for the short cable, and is superimposed on the current pulse droop or rise resulting from a value of R_l different from $\sqrt{\Sigma L_L/C}$. In order that neither of the two effects occur, the pulse transformers must be designed so that the normal load impedance matches the cable impedance, and at the same time is equal to $\sqrt{\Sigma L_L C}$.

In the pulse pictures of Figs. 2·44, 2·45, 2·46, and 2·47 there are small oscillations superimposed on the top of the current and voltage pulses. These oscillations are due to the shock excitation of the circuit containing the elements L_D and C_D. Their amplitude is greater with some transformers than with others, as can be seen by comparing the pictures in Fig. 2·44 with those of Fig. 2·45.

Backswing Voltage.—It was indicated in Sec. 2·3 that the voltage at the pulser output terminals reverses its polarity at the end of the pulse when there is an inductance in parallel with the load. This backswing voltage is inherent in pulsers using pulse transformers. In this case it is due to the current built up in the shunt inductance L_e during the pulse.

It is shown in Sec. 14·1 that the amplitude and duration of the backswing voltage depends on L_e, R_e, C, and i_{L_e}, the current flowing in L_e at the instant the switch-tube becomes nonconducting. For any given pulse transformer the maximum amplitude of the backswing voltage increases as the pulse duration is increased.

When it is necessary to use a pulse transformer for a range of pulse durations, a compromise must be made between a high backswing voltage for the longest pulse and a slow rate of fall for the shortest pulse. The slow rate of fall is not serious if the backswing voltage is aperiodic. However, there are high-frequency oscillations superimposed on the general backswing voltage because of the current flowing in the leakage inductance at the end of the pulse, and the presence of the capacitances C_D and C_l. For short-pulse operation these oscillations may be large enough to cause the load voltage to swing over to normal pulse polarity again and cause some load current to flow. In microwave-radar applications this occurrence may cause some post-pulse energy to be radiated, leading to confusion with the echoes from nearby objects. The form and amplitude of the oscillations is indicated in the oscilloscope traces reproduced in Fig. 2·49. When the load is unidirectional, these oscillations are damped only by the transformer losses represented by the shunt resistance R_e.

A high backswing voltage is to be avoided in the operation of a hard-tube pulser, as is stated in Sec. 2·3. Since the voltage appearing across the switch tube is the sum of the power-supply and the backswing voltages, a high backswing voltage may seriously aggravate any tendency for the switch tube to spark. However, a shunt diode may be used to prevent the backswing voltage from becoming effective.

CHAPTER 3

VACUUM TUBES AS SWITCHES

By G. N. Glasoe

3·1. Required Characteristics.—The switch used in a pulser with a condenser as the electrical-energy reservoir is a high-vacuum tube rather than a gaseous-discharge tube when only a small part of the stored energy is discharged during a pulse, hence, the name "hard-tube pulser." The reasons for this choice of switch are mentioned briefly in Chaps. 1 and 2. The purpose of this section is to elaborate upon them, and to discuss the characteristics required of the switch tube for satisfactory pulser operation. The following sections of this chapter consider the inherent characteristics of available high-vacuum tubes with particular reference to switch-tube operation.

As is evident from the discussion of the pulser output circuit in Chap. 2, there are four major considerations that determine the properties a tube must have in order to function satisfactorily as the switch:

1. Current. During the pulse interval the switch must conduct a current that, under the most favorable conditions, is slightly larger than the pulse current at the output terminals of the pulser.
2. Effective resistance. The switch is in series with the pulser load during the pulse interval. For maximum efficiency, therefore, the effective resistance of the switch must be as small as possible, that is, the potential difference across the switch tube, called the "tube drop," must be small during the conduction period.
3. Voltage. During the interpulse interval the switch must be able to withstand the power-supply voltage, which is slightly larger than the pulse voltage at the pulser output terminals. (If backswing voltage is present, it must be added to the power-supply voltage for this consideration.) The current through the switch during this interval must be negligibly small.
4. Transition from the conducting to the nonconducting state. It must be possible to change the switch from the conducting to the nonconducting state, and vice versa, in a negligibly short time. This transition must be possible while the power-supply voltage is applied to the switch terminals.

The characteristics of a gaseous-discharge tube such as the thyratron satisfy the current and tube-drop requirements better than those of conventional high-vacuum tubes. The thyratron can be kept nonconducting if the grid is near cathode potential, or somewhat negative with respect to the cathode, before the plate voltage is applied. Once the gas is ionized, however, and the tube is conducting, the nonconducting state cannot be attained again without first removing the plate voltage for a time long enough to allow complete deionization of the gas. It is this feature of available thyratrons that prevents their use as switches in pulsers of this type. A similar objection can be raised against the use of triggered spark gaps.

In contrast to the thyratron, it is possible to control the conduction through a high-vacuum tube merely by changing the voltage of the control grid with respect to the cathode. The voltage on the grid of a high-vacuum tube has a large effect on the tube drop and the plate current, but in order to make the best use of the available electron emission from the cathode it is necessary to apply a high positive voltage to the grid, hereafter referred to as the "positive grid drive." This positive grid drive causes a grid current to flow, and requires power to be delivered to the grid during the pulse interval.

For a given cathode material, size, and temperature the positive grid drive that is necessary to obtain a particular plate current depends on the number and disposition of electrodes in a high-vacuum tube. The plate current in a triode is given by[1]

$$I_p = k \left(E_{g_1} + \frac{V_p}{\mu} \right)^{3/2}$$

where E_{g_1} is the grid voltage, V_p is the plate voltage, μ is the amplification factor, and k is a constant sometimes referred to as the perveance. This relation indicates that the influence of the plate voltage on the plate current is increased by decreasing μ. A low value of μ, however, is inconsistent with the need for a low cutoff bias. In a tetrode the space current (the sum of the plate and screen-grid currents) is influenced very little by the plate voltage, and is given by

$$I_s = k' \left(E_{g_1} + \frac{E_{g_2}}{\mu_{sg}} \right)^{3/2},$$

where E_{g_1} is the control-grid voltage, E_{g_2} is the screen-grid voltage,

$$\mu_{sg} = \left(\frac{dE_{g_2}}{dE_{g_1}} \right)_{I_s \text{ constant}}$$

[1] F. E. Terman, *Radio Engineers' Handbook*, McGraw-Hill, New York, 1943, Sec. 4, par. 6.

is an amplification factor analogous to that of a triode, and k' is a constant depending on the electrode geometry. As indicated by this relation the tetrode is preferable to the triode because a reasonable cutoff bias can be obtained with a low value of μ_{sg}, and the required positive grid drive is therefore less because of the effect of the screen-grid voltage on the plate current. The choice of the particular tube to serve as the switch in a given pulser design requires some compromise between the necessary positive grid drive, the grid power, the cathode-heating power, the effective tube resistance, the ability to withstand high voltage, and the physical size of the tube.

In order to maintain the nonconducting condition in the high-vacuum tube, it is necessary to apply a sufficiently large negative bias voltage to the grid. The transition from the nonconducting to the conducting state is then accomplished by removing or neutralizing this bias voltage and supplying enough voltage to carry the grid positive. The time required for this transition depends on the rapidity with which the grid voltage can be changed, which in turn depends on the associated circuit and the grid capacitance. Since the total change in grid voltage during the pulse, called the "grid swing," is the sum of the bias voltage and the positive grid drive, it is desirable that the required bias voltage be as small as possible. For this reason, a switch tube having a sharp cutoff is generally used in order to have a negligible amount of current flowing through the tube during the interpulse interval.

For example, in a pulser designed to deliver 100-kw pulses to a load at 0.001 duty ratio, suppose that the plate voltage on the switch-tube during the nonconducting interval is 11.5 kv. If the unbiased current through the tube is 1 ma, the average power dissipated in the tube is 11.5 watts. The switch-tube current during the pulse is about 10 amp, and for available high-vacuum tubes the tube drop is about 1.5 kv. Thus, the average power dissipated in the tube during the pulses is 15 watts. Although the 1-ma plate current during the interpulse interval is only one-ten-thousandth of the pulse current, the corresponding tube dissipation is almost equal to that resulting from the pulse current. If the tube does not have a sharp cutoff, it may therefore be necessary to use a very high bias voltage in order to keep the tube dissipation small during the interpulse interval. This high bias voltage increases the required grid swing and input power and makes the grid-driving circuit more complicated.

The desirability of using a switch tube that is nonconducting during the interpulse interval arises from the consideration of average power. For a conduction period corresponding only to the pulse interval, it is possible to use a smaller tube for a given output pulse power and duty ratio. For this reason, it has been possible to use available high-vacuum tubes as switches for pulsers having a high pulse-power output.

Some Switch-tube Characteristics Affecting Pulser Design and Circuit Behavior.—For microwave-radar applications, it has been necessary to design hard-tube pulsers within the limits imposed by commercially available high-vacuum tubes. These tubes have generally been designed for c-w oscillator or amplifier service, and not for pulse applications, and their voltage and current ratings are accordingly based on satisfactory operation in conventional oscillator and amplifier circuits. The upper limits for these ratings are usually determined by the allowable power dissipation for the tube elements. It is not surprising, therefore, that experience with these tubes has proved that they may be used as pulser switch tubes with plate voltages and pulse currents many times greater than the maximum values given in the normal tube ratings. A separate set of specifications has been developed for some tubes that gives the allowable values of plate voltage and plate current that are applicable to pulse operation.

The maximum allowable plate voltage for pulse operation generally depends on the tendency for sparking to occur between the tube elements. The ability of a tube to withstand a high plate voltage with the grid biased beyond cutoff depends on the tube construction and the nature of the tube elements, particularly the cathode. One of the first tubes used successfully in a high-power pulser for microwave radar was the Eimac 304TH. This tube has a rating of 3 kv for oscillator use (that is, 6 kv peak), but it has been used as a switch tube with as much as 15 to 20 kv applied to the plate during the interpulse interval.

The cathode of the 304TH is a thoriated-tungsten filament that requires 125 watts of heater power, and the plate and grid are such that they can be very thoroughly outgassed during the evacuating process. The pulser design is limited, however, by the pulse current that can be obtained with this tube for a reasonable positive grid drive. The tube was successfully used with a pulse plate current of about 6 amp, but the necessarily high bias voltage makes the required grid swing about 1300 volts.

Another tube that has been widely used as an oscillator and amplifier and has proved to be a useful switch tube is the RCA 829 beam tetrode. This tube has a maximum plate-voltage rating of about 750 volts and a d-c plate-current rating of about 200 ma. The tube has an indirectly heated oxide-coated cathode that requires 14 watts of heater power. In pulser circuits it has been possible to use this tube satisfactorily with a plate voltage as high as 2 kv and a pulse plate current of several amperes. The plate-voltage rating for this tube is limited because of internal sparking at relatively high plate voltages. This sparking is considered to be caused by foreign matter introduced into the tube by the mica sheets used to space and support the plates.   By removing the mica and using ceramic spacers for the plates, it was possible to place a rating of 5 kv on the tube.   It was then found, however, that the ceramics tend to limit the operation of the tube in a high-frequency oscillator, and therefore two tube types were designated.   The tube suitable for normal high-frequency oscillators and amplifiers was called the 829B, and that for pulser applications was designated the 3E29.   The 829B can be used up to a plate voltage of about 2 kv and a pulse plate current of about 2 amp, whereas the 3E29 is rated at a plate voltage of 5 kv and a pulse plate current of 8 amp.   The 829B and 3E29 tubes are almost identical in construction, and the difference in ratings corresponds to limitations of the tests to which the tubes are subjected by the manufacturer.

Experience with commercial tubes has shown that those having a thoriated- or a pure-tungsten filament can be operated at a plate voltage considerably higher than that at which tubes having oxide cathodes can be operated.   A partial explanation lies in the fact that it is difficult to outgas a tube with an oxide cathode to the extent possible with one having a tungsten filament.   Also, the oxide-cathode tube is apt to have small particles of the oxide material on various parts of the tube elements, and these increase the tendency for a spark to occur.   Tungsten-filament tubes have been used with plate voltages in excess of 35 kv, but about 20 kv have been the limit with available oxide-cathode tubes.   The 715B is an oxide-cathode tube, with aligned grids, which was developed in the Bell Telephone Laboratories primarily for pulser applications and was manufactured by the Western Electric Company and by the Raytheon Company.   This tube has a plate-voltage rating of 15 kv and a pulse-plate-current rating of 15 amp.   The 5D21 tube is identical in construction to the 715B, but has a plate-voltage rating of 20 kv.   This increase in the maximum safe plate voltage was made possible by a more careful processing of the tube, and by tube selection in the final testing of completed tubes.   It is not meant to imply here that 20 kv is a practical upper limit for tubes with oxide cathodes; improvement in the tube manufacture will undoubtedly raise the allowable plate voltage for nonsparking operation in pulser applications.

The nature of the sparking in tubes with an oxide cathode is such that it is difficult to correlate cause and effect.   Some tubes spark violently when subjected to a steady high plate voltage with the grid biased beyond cutoff.   When these tubes are used as the switch in a pulser and made alternately conducting and nonconducting, however, the plate voltage may sometimes be increased without sparking to as much as 25 per cent above the limit for a steady-state operation.   The explanation is somewhat difficult to determine because the interpulse interval may be 99.9

per cent of the total time.   On the other hand, some tubes show just the reverse behavior, having a greater tendency to spark during pulsing operation.   In general, however, tubes with oxide cathodes spark more as the pulse duration is increased.   There is also some evidence that an increase in the pulse plate current may cause a tube to spark more readily.

Sparking in the switch tube of a pulser has two principal deleterious effects.   When a spark occurs in a tube having an oxide-coated cathode, it frequently dislodges some of the cathode material and thereby reduces cathode emission.   Prolonged sparking, therefore, can seriously shorten the useful life of the tube.   The second effect is related to the functioning of the tube as a switch and is independent of the nature of the cathode. A spark that occurs during the interpulse interval is equivalent to the removal of the grid bias, and the tube becomes a closed switch.   The energy from the storage condenser is thus discharged into the load at a time when there should be no output power from the pulser.   Since the duration of the spark can be considerably longer than that of the normal pulse, a succession of such sparks can produce an abnormally high average current, which may be detrimental to the load or to the pulser power supply.   Since some form of overload protection is usually incorporated into the pulser, persistent sparking in the switch tube causes an aggravating disruption of pulser operation.

The pulse plate current that can be obtained with an oxide cathode is about three to five times as large as that which can be obtained with a thoriated-tungsten filament for the same cathode-heating power.   Table 3·1 shows the pulse current that has been obtained for several tubes used in pulsers for microwave-radar systems.

Figure 3·1 is a photograph of these tubes and shows their relative sizes. The figures given in the pulse current column of Table 3·1 are based on

TABLE 3·1.—COMPARISON OF SEVERAL HIGH-VACUUM TUBES USED AS SWITCHES IN HARD-TUBE PULSERS

Tube	Type of cathode	Cathode-heating power, watts	Max. plate voltage, kv	Pulse current, amp	Amp/watt
3D21	Oxide	10	3.5	5	0.5
3E29	Oxide	14	5	8	0.57
715B	Oxide	56	15	15	0.27
304TH	Th-W	125	15	6	0.05
6C21	Th-W	140	30	15	0.11
6D21	Th-W	150	37.5	15	0.10
527	Th-W	770	30	60	0.08

experience with the tubes, and correspond to reasonable values of positive grid drive, tube drop, and operational life. To obtain satisfactory switch-tube operation with a high plate voltage it is necessary to accept

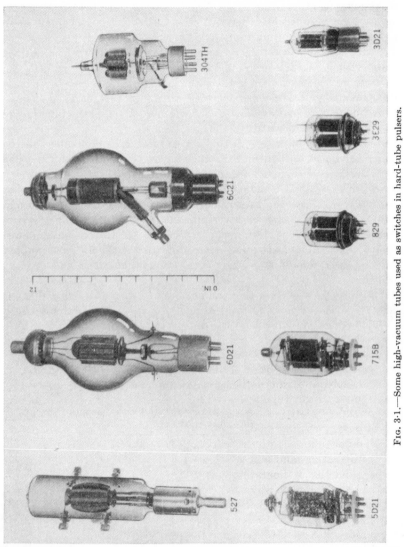

FIG. 3·1.—Some high-vacuum tubes used as switches in hard-tube pulsers.

the disadvantage inherent in the high cathode-heating power required for tungsten filaments.

As has been mentioned, it is usually necessary to drive the grid of a tube positive in order to obtain the required plate current. The grid current associated with tube operation of this type causes a certain amount of power dissipation in the grid. During the outgassing process in tube manufacture, some of the material that is always vaporized from the cathode may settle down on the grid wires. Since this vaporized material contains thorium from the thoriated filaments and barium from the oxide cathodes, it lowers the work function of the grid-wire material. Thus, when the grid becomes heated, there is a greater tendency for the emission of primary electrons from the grid. The emission of secondary electrons may also be enhanced. Electron emission, whether primary or secondary, is very undesirable for proper tube operation, and can vitiate the control of plate current by the externally applied grid voltage. Various methods have been used to minimize this contamination of the grid. Gold plating and platinum plating of the grid wires have both been fairly successful in this connection. The practical difficulty, in many instances, is the evaporation of the plated material during the processing of the tube, which may progress to such an extent that the operational life of the tube is materially shortened. Since it is almost impossible to detect this evaporation in a tube by tests in the manufacturing plant, the best safeguard seems to be the rigid control of the processing schedule, correlated with life tests on completed tubes.

Oxide cathode tubes have exhibited a behavior that was never observed at the Radiation Laboratory with thoriated-tungsten-filament tubes, namely, cathode fatigue. As a result of cathode fatigue, some tubes show a marked decrease in plate current during a pulse. This decrease may be as much as 40 to 50 per cent during a 2-μsec pulse. The phenomenon seems to be correlated with inherent cathode activity, but the wide spread of values obtained with tubes of a given type indicates that the reason for this fatigue is probably complex. Some tubes that exhibit cathode fatigue to a marked extent when they are first put into operation tend to improve with age for a short time and then become worse, other tubes show a progressive deterioration from the very beginning of operation, and still others may never exhibit the fatigue during many hundreds of hours of operation. Cathode fatigue is probably related in a complex way to the method of processing and inherent characteristics of the cathode material, and to the manner in which the material is activated in the completed tube.

In most microwave-radar applications of hard-tube pulsers, the ability to withstand a high plate voltage and to conduct a high pulse current have been the major considerations in the choice of the switch tube because the duty ratio is of the order of magnitude of 0.001, and average-power considerations are therefore not important. When the duty ratio becomes high, however, the average power dissipated in the switch tube may govern the choice of the tube to be used. It may then be advisable to use two or more tubes in parallel, rather than a single larger tube. Pulsers with as many as six tubes in parallel have given completely satisfactory operation. The most serious difficulty encountered in such an arrangement is usually the difference in the plate current for tubes of the same type corresponding to a given positive grid drive and tube drop. If the tubes are very different in this respect, the total plate current is nonuniformly distributed between the tubes. A fairly large factor of safety must be allowed in the power dissipation and the pulse current required of each tube when assuming equal current distribution.

3·2. The Characteristic Curves for Triodes and Tetrodes and Their Importance to the Function of a Pulser Switch Tube.—As with any application of vacuum tubes, the functional relationships between the various tube parameters such as plate current, plate voltage, grid voltage (or voltages), and grid current (or currents) are important in the proper choice of the operating conditions for a switch tube. In general, these relationships are difficult to express analytically, for a wide range of values, and graphical representations given by the so-called "characteristic curves" are used instead. These curves are plotted for corresponding values, obtained experimentally, of any two of the tube parameters, holding all others constant. A third parameter may be introduced by plotting a family of curves, each one of which corresponds to a particular value for this third parameter. (Each curve of such a family is actually the boundary of the intersection of a plane with the surface generated by plotting the corresponding values of the three quantities along the axes of a rectangular-coordinate system.[1])

For conventional oscillator and amplifier applications, the static characteristics for a tube are usually adequate. The data for such curves are obtained by applying d-c voltages to the plate and to the grid or grids, and measuring the d-c plate and grid currents. For the operation of a pulser switch tube during the pulse interval, however, the range of values for the plate current and the control-grid voltage given in the static characteristics is generally too small. The limiting values of these quantities are usually imposed by the average power dissipation allowable in the tube elements. In order to extend the range of values, it is necessary to apply a pulse voltage to the control grid and to measure the pulse plate and grid currents with d-c voltage applied to the plate, and, in the case of a tetrode, to the screen grid as well. The curves plotted from data obtained in this way are referred to as the "pulse characteristics." In the following discussion the pulse characteristics are those obtained

---

[1] E. L. Chaffee, *Theory of Thermionic Vacuum Tubes*, 1st ed., McGraw-Hill, New York, 1933.

with 1-μsec voltage pulses applied to the control grid at a recurrence frequency of 1000 pps.

Plate-current—Grid-voltage Characteristics.—During the interpulse interval the switch tube is nonconducting; therefore, the tube characteristic of interest is the curve showing the plate current as a function of negative grid voltage. As mentioned in the preceding section, the plate voltage during this interval can exceed the normal tube rating in many cases. It is necessary, in such cases, to extend these curves in order to include the higher plate voltages required for pulser operation. Since the interpulse interval may be very long compared with the pulse duration, the data for such curves must be obtained in the manner used for the static characteristics of the tube. The shape of these curves in the region of small plate current is particularly important to pulser design. As pointed out previously, a plate current as small as 1 ma can cause an appreciable amount of power dissipation in the switch tube for a high-power pulser. A plate current of this magnitude can often be the result of leakage current in the tube. This leakage current may be due to a bent grid wire or to a grid structure that is improperly placed so that it fails to screen a small portion of the cathode from the plate. When this condition exists, there is a small residual plate current that is relatively unaffected by an increase in negative grid voltage. This effect is indicated by the two curves sketched in Fig. 3·2, in which

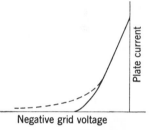

Negative grid voltage

FIG. 3·2.—Plate-current—grid-voltage characteristic of a high-vacuum tube showing the effect of leakage current resulting from improper grid structure.

the solid line represents the normal tube characteristic and the dotted line shows the behavior when leakage current is present.

The negative grid voltage necessary to make the plate current equal to some arbitrarily chosen small value is called the cutoff bias voltage, or simply the cutoff bias. The particular value of plate current chosen for cutoff depends on the application, and often on the shape, of the characteristic. For switch-tube applications, a good choice is the maximum plate current that is allowable during the interpulse interval. There are three aspects of the tube cutoff that should be considered in connection with pulser design. First, it is desirable to have as small a cutoff bias as possible because the required negative grid voltage must be added to the positive grid drive in order to determine the necessary grid swing. The second aspect is the range of cutoff bias voltage for different tubes of a given type. If this range is large, provision must be made for a bias voltage considerably higher than that needed for an average tube in order to insure a small plate current for all tubes. This increase is a serious matter when the necessary minimum bias voltage is already large. The third aspect is the variation of cutoff bias with plate voltage and, in the case of a tetrode, with screen-grid voltage as well. The pulser must be designed to provide a bias voltage large enough to be effective for the highest plate and screen-grid voltages that may be encountered in the operation of the pulser, particularly when the pulser is designed to have different output powers for various applications. In the operation of a hard-tube pulser, the output power can most readily be varied by changing the power-supply voltage.

Because of the effect of the screen grid, the cutoff bias for a tetrode is usually less than that necessary for a triode having comparable cathode emission, as illustrated by the curves of Figs. 3·3a and b. As indicated in Table 3·1, the 6C21 triode and the 6D21 tetrode are almost identical with respect to cathode-heating power and pulse plate current, and both have thoriated-tungsten filaments. The 304TH triode has a thoriated-tungsten filament, whereas the 5D21 tetrode has an oxide-coated cathode and is capable of more than twice the pulse plate current obtainable with the 304TH. The values of screen-grid voltages corresponding to the curves for the tetrodes are approximately those that have been used in microwave-radar applications. The ranges of cutoff bias voltages shown on the

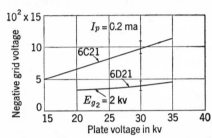

(a) The 6C21 triode and the 6D21 tetrode.

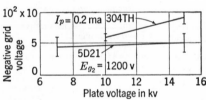

(b) The 304TH triode and the 5D21 tetrode.
FIG. 3·3.—Variation of cutoff bias with plate voltage.

curves of Fig. 3·3 are based on data taken for a large number of tubes, and are fairly representative; a small percentage of tubes may be found to have cutoff values lying outside of the ranges shown, but normally such tubes are apt to be inferior in other respects and should be rejected in the final tests by the manufacturer.

The cutoff bias of a tetrode is a function of the screen-grid voltage as well as the plate voltage, as is indicated by the curves of Fig. 3·4 for the 5D21 tetrode. The effect of screen-grid voltage is an added complication in the use of a tetrode as a pulser switch tube. However, the maximum bias voltage required for a tetrode is smaller than that required for a comparable triode, even when taking into account the possible variation in screen-grid voltage, by an amount that is large enough to give preference to the tetrode.

Plate-current–Plate-voltage and Grid-current–Plate-voltage Characteristics.—It has already been mentioned that a higher plate current can be used with pulse operation of available high-vacuum tubes, and that, consequently, the range of values must be extended beyond those of the ordinary static characteristics. This extension is accomplished by applying the pulse voltage to the control grid and measuring the resulting pulse plate and grid currents. The measurements of the pulse plate current are made by using the tube as the switch in a hard-tube pulser with a noninductive resistance of known low value as the load. The pulse voltage developed across this resistance by the pulse current can be measured with the aid of a synchroscope, as described in Appendix A. The plate voltage or tube drop corresponding to the pulse current is the difference between the power-supply voltage (measured with a d-c voltmeter) and the load pulse voltage. For high values of plate voltage the load voltage may be neglected, since about 50 volts is adequate for the precision required in such measurements. For low plate voltage, however, the correction for load voltage should be made in order that the curves may be used properly. If the voltage pulse across the resistance load is rectangular in shape, and the pulse duration and pulse recurrence frequency are accurately known, the average power-supply current can be used to calculate the pulse current with reasonable precision. The principal error introduced in this

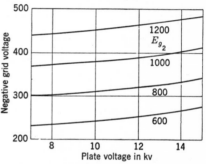

FIG. 3·4.—Variation of cutoff bias with screen-grid and plate voltages for the 5D21 tetrode, $I_p = 0.2$ ma.

procedure is due to the contribution to the average power-supply current resulting from the recharging of the storage condenser.

The pulse grid voltage can also be measured with the use of a synchroscope. Since it is the value of positive grid voltage that is important, the negative bias voltage must be subtracted from the pulse-voltage measurement. The latter is a rather difficult measurement to make with high precision because of the self-bias generated in the grid circuit. The preferred way of measuring this positive grid voltage has been with a positive peak voltmeter. The precision that can be obtained in such a measurement depends on the flatness of the top of the grid-voltage pulse. For pulse-characteristic measurements, it is necessary to be able to view the grid pulse on a synchroscope in order to make the top of the pulse as flat as possible. If a spike is present on the top of the pulse, the peak-voltmeter reading may correspond to the spike maximum, thus giving an erroneous reading of the positive grid voltage. The pulse grid current is difficult to measure, and has usually been obtained from the average grid current and the measured duty ratio. Although this procedure is lacking in precision, it has been adequate for pulser applications in microwave-radar systems.

In order to obtain the data necessary for the pulse characteristics of small tubes of the receiver type, a circuit was devised which made it possible to read pulse voltages and currents directly on ordinary d-c meters.[1] This circuit uses pulse voltmeters to measure pulse voltages, and the pulse currents are obtained by measuring the pulse voltages across precision noninductive resistors connected in series with the grids and the plate of the tube under test. A block diagram of this circuit is shown in Fig. 3·5, and a schematic diagram in Fig. 3·6.

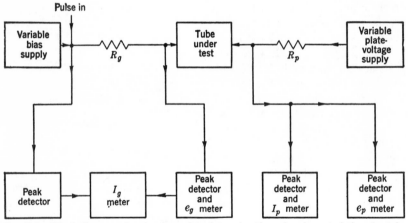

Fig. 3·5.—Block diagram of a circuit used to determine the pulse characteristics of a tube of the receiver type.

The pulse characteristics for several tubes are shown in Figs. 3·7–3·11. From curves such as these, the effective resistance of the tube and the grid-driving power can easily be determined for the pulse current corresponding to the pulser output power. One of the first hard-tube pulsers to be used extensively in a microwave-radar system used two Eimac 304TH tubes in parallel as the switch. A pulse-power output of about 150 kw with a pulse voltage of 12 to 13 kv was required for this

[1] R. B. Woodbury, "Pulse Characteristics of Common Receiver Type Tubes," RL Report No. 704, Apr. 30, 1945.

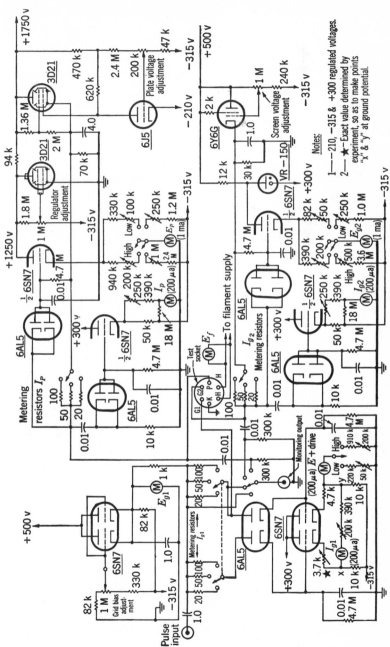

FIG. 3·6.—Schematic diagram of a circuit used to determine the pulse characteristics of a tube of the receiver type.

pulser. The 304TH was found to withstand the high plate voltage during the interpulse interval. The curves of Fig. 3·7 indicate the reason that two tubes in parallel were needed to carry the pulse current. From

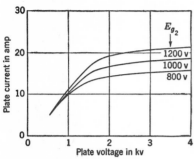

(a) 5D21 (WE) and 715B (WE and Raytheon), $E_{g_1} = +200$ volts

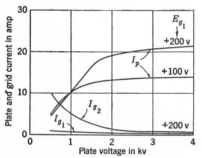

(b) 5D21 (WE) and 715B (WE and Raytheon), $E_{g_2} = 1200$ volts

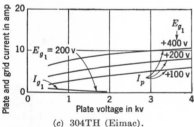

(c) 304TH (Eimac).

FIG. 3·7.—Pulse-characteristic curves for the 5D21 and 715B tetrodes and the 304TH triode.

these curves it is seen that a positive grid drive in excess of 400 volts is required to obtain a pulse plate current of 12 amp, and that, under these conditions, it is necessary to operate the tube with a tube drop of 4 to 5 kv. For two tubes in parallel, however, the required pulse plate current can be obtained with a positive grid drive of about 200 volts and a tube drop of about 2 kv. The low grid-driving power necessary to operate the 304TH as the pulser switch tube was an additional reason for its selection. One of the most undesirable features is the high cathode-heating power required, 125 watts for each of the two tubes.

After the 715B tube was developed by the Bell Telephone Laboratories, it was possible to construct a hard-tube pulser for 150-kw power output with a higher over-all efficiency and more satisfactory pulser operation. The curves for this tube are shown in Fig. 3·7, where it can be seen that a pulse current of 15 amp can be obtained with a tube drop of about 1.5 kv and a positive grid drive of 200 volts. In this case also, the grid-driving power is small because a grid current of less than 1 amp is necessary. Since the cathode-heating power for the 715B is 56 watts, a saving of

about 200 watts is effected when this tube is used in preference to two 304TH tubes. Also, slightly less power is dissipated in the 715B tube than in two 304TH tubes because of the lower tube drop. The power dissipation resulting from the screen-grid current is not suf-

ficient to offset the decrease in plate dissipation.   The screen-grid voltage, required because the 715B is a tetrode, can generally be obtained
from the power supply for the driver circuit, and the pulser design is not
further complicated.

In addition to the positive grid drive and the tube drop necessary in
order to obtain a given value of plate current, the shape and disposition
of the characteristic curves as a function of grid voltage are also important

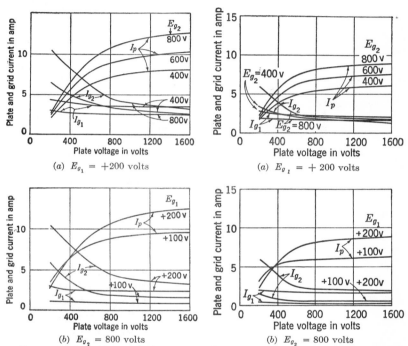

(a) $E_{g_1} = +200$ volts

(a) $E_{g_1} = +200$ volts

(b) $E_{g_2} = 800$ volts

(b) $E_{g_2} = 800$ volts

FIG. 3·8.—Pulse-characteristic curves
for the two sections of the 829 beam tetrode
(RCA, NU, Kenrad, Raytheon).

FIG. 3·9.—Pulse-characteristic curves for
the 3D21 beam tetrode (Hytron).

to pulser operation.   The effect of variation in grid voltage on the output
pulse of the pulser may be illustrated by drawing the load line on the
plate-current–plate-voltage diagram.   In Fig. 3·12 a family of characteristic curves is drawn for a tetrode such as the 715B for constant screen-
grid voltage.   Two load lines are drawn on this diagram.   Line (1)
corresponds to a low-resistance load in series with a bias voltage, such as
the dynamic resistance of a magnetron or biased diode, line (2) corresponds to a high-resistance load of the same magnitude as the static
resistance of the biased diode for the operating point O_p.   From this
diagram it is evident that a change in grid voltage corresponding to the

curves *A*, *B*, and *C* has a negligible effect on the operating point for the switch tube. The only change in the operating point is due to the slight shift of the curves toward lower plate voltage as the grid voltage is lowered. This effect is observable in the tetrode characteristics shown in Figs. 3·7, 3·8, and 3·9, and is caused by the smaller grid currents that correspond to the lower values of positive grid drive. The load voltage

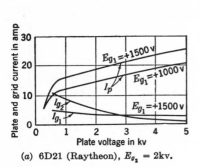

(a) 6D21 (Raytheon), $E_{g_2} = 2$kv.

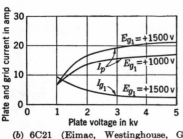

(b) 6C21 (Eimac, Westinghouse, GE, Machlett).

Fig. 3·10.—Pulse-characteristic curves for the 6D21 tetrode and the 6C21 triode.

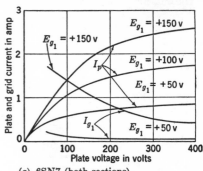

(a) 6SN7 (both sections).

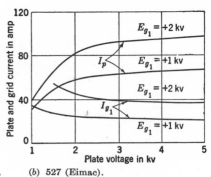

(b) 527 (Eimac).

Fig. 3·11.—Pulse-characteristic curves for the 6SN7 and 527 triodes.

and the load current therefore remain very nearly constant even though the grid voltage may change within this range during the pulse. Therefore, if adequate positive grid drive is provided to keep the operating point for the tube somewhat below the knee of the characteristic curve, irregularities in the top of the grid voltage pulse are not observed on the pulser output pulse. This consideration is of considerable importance to the design of the driver circuit.

If the initial operating point corresponds to the curve *C* of Fig. 3·12 and the grid voltage changes over the range *C* to *E*, a different situation obtains. In this case both the load voltage and the load current are affected.   For the low-resistance load the change in voltage is ΔV_1 and the change in current ΔI_1.   Similarly, for the high-resistance load the corresponding changes are ΔV_2 and ΔI_2.   Because of the slight upward slope of the characteristic curves above the knee, the change in current is greater for the low-resistance load and the change in voltage is less. When the pulser switch tube is operated in this manner, irregularities in the grid-voltage pulse are transferred to the load pulse.

When the characteristic curve of the switch tube does not have a knee as shown in Fig. 3·12, the shape of the grid-voltage pulse must be controlled more carefully in order to obtain a flat-topped pulse at the

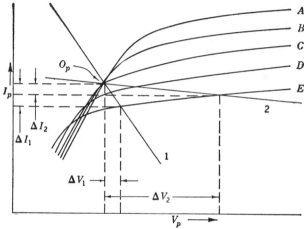

FIG. 3·12.—Family of plate-current—plate-voltage curves with load lines corresponding to a low and a high resistance showing the effect of a change in grid voltage on the operating point of a pulser switch tube; A, B, C, D, and E are curves for different values of E_{g_1} with E_{g_2} = constant.

load.   As an example, see the curves for the 304TH tube in Fig. 3·7. There are triodes that exhibit a knee in the characteristic, as shown by the curves for the 6C21 and the 527 in Figs. 3·10 and 3·11.   If these curves are compared with those for the tetrodes in Figs. 3·7, 3·8, and 3·9, however, it is seen that the curves for different grid voltages are separated by a greater amount below the knee.   The change in the operating point that results from a change in grid voltage is not as great as that resulting from operation above the knee of the characteristic curve.   For a 6D21 tetrode this knee occurs at such a low current that the tube is usually operated well above the knee.   Because of the greater slope of the upper portion of the curves for this tube, the variation in grid voltage does not have as great an effect as it does for comparable operation of the 6C21 triode.

A comparison of the curves for the 6C21 and the 6D21 in Fig. 3·10 with the curves for the 5D21 and 715B in Fig. 3·11 indicates that the latter tubes are better from the standpoint of plate current and grid-driving power. The only reason for using a 6C21 or a 6D21 as a pulser switch tube is the fact that they can stand a higher plate voltage than can the 5D21 or 715B. This comparison illustrates the increased difficulty involved in designing a hard-tube pulser for a power-supply voltage in excess of 20 kv with existing high-vacuum tubes. When pulse power of the order of magnitude of several megawatts is wanted, however, this disadvantage must be accepted until better tubes are available. A 1-Mw hard-tube pulser using three of the 6C21 tubes in parallel as the switch has been built and used extensively. This pulser has a pulse output of 25 kv at 40 amp. The 6D21 was used in a pulser designed to have an output of 3 Mw, 30 kv at 100 amp. In this case five tubes were used in parallel. The highest power hard-tube pulser built at the Radiation Laboratory used six 527 tubes as the switch. This pulser had an output of about 25 kv at 400 amp, and a grid-driving power of about 700 kw.

An effect similar to that resulting from variation in grid voltage is observed if the screen-grid voltage of a tetrode is allowed to change. The effect is illustrated by the family of curves for the tetrodes in Figs. 3·7, 3·8, and 3·9 in which the control-grid voltage is constant and the screen-grid voltage is varied. For satisfactory operation of a tetrode as the switch tube, therefore, the voltage of the screen grid must not be allowed to change during the pulse. Because of the flow of pulse current to the screen grid and the plate-to-screen capacitance, it is necessary to provide a large bypass condenser between the screen grid and the cathode. For most effective operation, this condenser must be connected as close to the tube element as possible.

The curves for the 829 beam tetrode shown in Fig. 3·8 illustrate another consideration in the operation of a tetrode as the switch tube. For a given pulse plate current and tube drop it is advantageous to use the highest possible screen-grid voltage and the lowest possible positive grid drive. The curves of Fig. 3·8 indicate that the control-grid current decreases as the screen-grid voltage is increased for a given positive grid-drive voltage. Since the screen-grid current increases with the screen-grid voltage, some compromise must usually be made between the two grid voltages for most efficient tube operation.

The shape of the characteristic curves has another effect on pulser operation. If the grid voltages are held constant, there is still the possibility of changing the operating conditions by varying the power-supply voltage. This effect is discussed in detail in the following section.

3·3. The Effect of Switch-tube and Load Characteristics on the Pulser Regulation.—The characteristics of the switch tube in a hard-tube pulser may be utilized to a certain extent to minimize the change in load current resulting from a change in the power-supply voltage. This power-supply voltage may vary because of changes in either the input voltage to the pulser or the average current from the power supply. The change in average current may be brought about by variations in the duty ratio that occur as a result of changes in either the pulse duration or the pulse recurrence frequency. The discussion of this section shows the way in which this regulation depends on the characteristics of the load and the switch tube.

Those features of a hard-tube pulser that are essential in this discussion are shown schematically in Fig. 3·13. In this circuit S_T and r_p represent the switch tube, E_{bb} is the power supply, R_c is the isolating

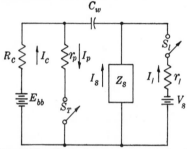

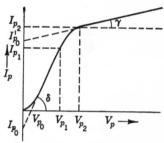

FIG. 3·13.—Equivalent circuit of a hard-tube pulser with a biased-diode load.

FIG. 3·14.—Current-voltage characteristic of a high-vacuum switch tube.

resistor, C_w is the storage condenser, Z_s is the condenser-recharging path that is necessary when the load is unidirectional, and r_l, S_l, and V_s represent the load. The considerations are restricted to the voltages and currents that correspond to the top of a pulse when the pulsing is continuous, and to pulse durations that are considered small compared with the interpulse interval.

The plate-current–plate-voltage characteristic of the switch tube may be represented as shown in Fig. 3·14. For the purposes of the present discussion, the I_p-V_p curve is very nearly a straight line above some current value I_{p_2}, and for the greater part of the curve below some current I_{p_1}. The knee of such a curve, already referred to in the preceding section, is the region between I_{p_1} and I_{p_2}. Two tube resistances may be defined, one for the operation of the switch tube below the knee, and the other for the operation above the knee. Thus

$$r_p = \frac{1}{\tan \delta} = \left(\frac{dV_p}{dI_p}\right)_{I_p < I_{p_1}} \tag{1}$$

and

$$r'_p = \frac{1}{\tan \gamma} = \left(\frac{dV_p}{dI_p}\right)_{I_p > I_{p_2}}. \tag{2}$$

For a tetrode, two families of characteristic curves may be drawn, one for E_{g_2} constant and the other for E_{g_1} constant. It is evident from the tetrode curves shown in Figs. 3·7, 3·8, and 3·9 that the values of r'_p for various values of the grid voltages are essentially the same. The value of r_p, however, does change somewhat with variations in either of the grid voltages. The change is small, and is neglected in this discus-

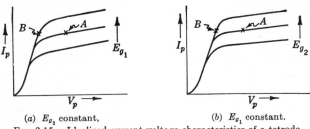

(a) E_{g_2} constant,   (b) E_{g_1} constant.

FIG. 3·15.—Idealized current-voltage characteristics of a tetrode.

sion. The idealized curves for a tetrode are sketched in Fig. 3·15. The curves of Fig. 3·15a may also be considered applicable to a triode. The value of r_p is more dependent on E_{g_1} in a triode than it is in a tetrode, but the characteristic curves shown in Figs. 3·10 and 3·11 indicate that r'_p is practically independent of E_{g_1}.

The most general load that can be considered is one having a non-linear current-voltage characteristic as sketched in Fig. 3·16. The

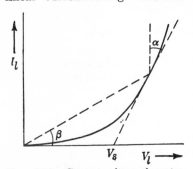

FIG. 3·16.—Current-voltage characteristic of a nonlinear load.

magnetron or biased-diode load discussed in Chap. 2 is a special case of the nonlinear load in which the current below V_s is considered negligibly small and the I-V curve above V_s is linear. Compare Fig. 3·16 with Fig. 2·11. In discussing the effect of the load characteristics on the pulser regulation, it is not necessary to restrict the argument to this special case since only the values of V_l and I_l at the top of the pulse are being considered. It is assumed, however, that the range of voltage and current values is so small that the I-V curve may be considered linear at the operating point.

The static resistance of the load is given by

$$R_l = \frac{V_l}{I_l} = \frac{1}{\tan \beta} \qquad (3)$$

and the dynamic resistance is

$$r_l = \frac{dV_l}{dI_l} = \tan \alpha. \tag{4}$$

For a small range of values about a particular operating point, the following relationships hold approximately:

$$V_l = V_s + r_l I_l \tag{5}$$

and

$$I_l = \frac{V_l - V_s}{r_l}. \tag{6}$$

By using the above relations for the switch-tube and load characteristics, and referring to the pulser circuit of Fig. 3·13, it is possible to derive the relationships that express the load operating voltage and current in terms of these characteristics and the circuit parameters. In particular, there are two operating conditions for the switch tube to be considered, namely, (1) operation above the knee of its characteristic curve corresponding to the point marked A in Fig. 3·15 (type A operation), and (2) operation below the knee corresponding to the point B indicated in Fig. 3·15 (type B operation).

Operation of the Switch Tube above the Knee of the I_p-V_p Curve.—As stated previously, the power-supply voltage E_{bb} varies principally because of changes in line voltage and duty ratio. Variation of the line-voltage input to the pulser causes a change in all the voltages in the pulser, and therefore changes the voltages applied to the grids as well as the plate voltage of the switch tube. As indicated in Fig. 3·15 changes in the grid voltages cause the value of the intercept I'_{po}, indicated in Fig. 3·14, to change. Therefore, in considering the effect of line-voltage changes on the operating conditions for the load, the variation in I'_{po} must also be taken into account. The change in operating values for the load and switch tube that results from the simultaneous variation of E_{bb} and I'_{po} may be written as follows:

$$dI_l = \frac{\partial I_l}{\partial E_{bb}} dE_{bb} + \frac{\partial I_l}{\partial I'_{po}} dI'_{po}, \tag{7}$$

$$dV_l = \frac{\partial V_l}{\partial E_{bb}} dE_{bb} + \frac{\partial V_l}{\partial I'_{po}} dI'_{po}, \tag{8}$$

$$dV_p = \frac{\partial V_p}{\partial E_{bb}} dE_{bb} + \frac{\partial V_p}{\partial I'_{po}} dI'_{po}. \tag{9}$$

Referring to Fig. 3·14 and the definition of r'_p given by Eq. (2) the plate current for the switch tube is given by

$$I_p = I'_{po} + \frac{V_p}{r'_p}. \tag{10}$$

Considering the pulser circuit of Fig. 3·13, the plate current is

$$I_p = I_l + I_c + I_s. \tag{11}$$

As discussed in Chap. 2, the voltage across the condenser, V_w, is never very different from E_{bb} if the capacitance is sufficiently large. For steady pulsing the condenser voltage is slightly less than the power-supply voltage, but for the purpose of this discussion it is reasonable to neglect this difference and to assume that $V_w = E_{bb}$. The voltage across the load with switches S_T and S_l closed is, therefore,

$$V_l = V_w - V_p = E_{bb} - V_p. \tag{12}$$

The currents I_s and I_c in Eq. (11) can be expressed in terms of V_l, thus,

$$I_s = \frac{V_l}{Z_s} \tag{13}$$

where Z_s is the effective impedance of the condenser-recharging path. Also

$$I_c = \frac{E_{bb} - V_p}{R_c} = \frac{V_l}{R_c}. \tag{14}$$

Thus from Eqs. (6), (10), (11), (12), (13), and (14), the expression for the load current becomes

$$I_l = \frac{E_{bb} - V_s\left[1 + \frac{r'_p}{R_c} + \frac{r'_p}{Z_s}\right] + I'_{po}r'_p}{r_l + r'_p + \frac{r'_p r_l}{R_c} + \frac{r'_p r_l}{Z_s}}. \tag{15}$$

From Eqs. (6) and (15),

$$V_l = \frac{E_{bb}r_l + V_s r'_p + I'_{po}r_l r'_p}{r_l + r'_p + \frac{r'_p r_l}{R_c} + \frac{r'_p r_l}{Z_s}}. \tag{16}$$

From Eqs. (12) and (16),

$$V_p = \frac{E_{bb}\left[r'_p + \frac{r'_p r_l}{R_c} + \frac{r'_p r_l}{Z_s}\right] - V_s r'_p - I'_{po}r'_p r_l}{r_l + r'_p + \frac{r'_p r_l}{R_c} + \frac{r'_p r_l}{Z_s}}. \tag{17}$$

It is seen from Eqs. (7) and (15) that the variation of load current can be made zero if

$$dI'_{po} = -\frac{dE_{bb}}{r'_p}. \tag{18}$$

The characteristic curves for tetrodes shown in Figs. 3·7, 3·8, and 3·9 and sketched in Fig. 3·15 indicate that it is possible to satisfy this relation. For a particular tetrode and for moderate changes in grid voltages, the following relations are approximately true:

$$dI'_{po} = (k_1 dE_{g_1})_{E_{g_2} \text{const}},$$ (19)

and

$$dI'_{po} = (k_2 dE_{g_2})_{E_{g_1} \text{const}}.$$ (20)

If the characteristic curves for the switch tube are known and the values of k_1 and k_2 therefore determined, it is possible to devise a control circuit that changes the grid voltages, as E_{bb} varies, in such a way as to satisfy Eq. (18). Since the voltage outputs of the grid and plate power supplies may depend on the input line voltage to approximately the same degree such a control circuit should not be very complicated if the duty ratio remains constant. When the duty ratio changes, however, the average currents also change, and the added factor of inherent regulation in these power supplies has to be considered, which complicates the design of the control circuit considerably.

For a low-power pulser using a tetrode switch tube, grid voltages of only a few hundred volts are generally required. Power supplies that are electronically regulated against variations in input voltage and output current can easily be built for these voltages. It is not economical, however, to construct a high-voltage power supply with similar regulation. The changes in load and switch-tube operating values that are due to variations in the high-voltage power supply only may be obtained from Eqs. (15), (16), and (17) by differentiating with respect to E_{bb}. Since the denominator of each of these expressions is the same, let

$$D = r_l + r'_p + \frac{r'_p r_l}{R_c} + \frac{r'_p r_l}{Z_s}.$$ (21)

Then

$$\frac{\partial I_l}{\partial E_{bb}} = \frac{1}{D},$$ (22)

$$\frac{\partial V_l}{\partial E_{bb}} = \frac{r_l}{D},$$ (23)

and

$$\frac{\partial V_p}{\partial E_{bb}} = \frac{r'_p + \frac{r'_p r_l}{R_c} + \frac{r'_p r_l}{Z_s}}{D}$$ (24)

$$= \frac{D - r_l}{D}.$$ (25)

The Eqs. (15), (16), and (17) do not explicitly involve time. If the condenser-recharging path Z_s is an inductive resistor, however, the time measured from the start of the pulse is included because, for this case,

$$Z_s = \frac{R_s}{1 - e^{-\frac{R_s}{L_s}t}},$$

where R_s is the resistance and L_s is the inductance of the element. Three cases are of interest in this connection:

1. When the recharging path is a wire-wound resistor whose inductance is not negligible. In general, $L_s/R_s \ll t$ where $t_{max} = \tau$ (the pulse duration), so $Z_s \approx R_s$.
2. When the recharging path is an inductance coil of low ohmic resistance such that $L_s/R_s \gg t$ where $t_{max} = \tau$. Expanding $e^{-\frac{R_s}{L_s}t}$ and using only the first two terms, $Z_s = L_s/t$.
3. When the recharging path is a combination of inductance and resistance for which $L_s/R_s \approx \tau$. If, for a particular value of τ, $L_s/R_s = \tau$, then $Z_s = R_s/0.63$.

When the recharging path is an inductance having low resistance Condition 2 obtains, and the load current decreases during the pulse, as is evident from Eq. (15) in which the term r_p'/Z_s increases with time. For long pulses, that is, with a duration of 2 μsec or more, this effect may become prominent. This decrease in load current during the pulse occurs in addition to the change in load current given by Eq. (22). Other effects already discussed, such as the drop in voltage across the storage conaenser and the possible change in cathode emission in the switch tube, can also cause the load current to change during a pulse.

Operation of the Switch Tube below the Knee of the I_p-V_p Curve.—The switch tube is now operated at point (B) indicated in Fig. 3·15. If Fig. 3·14 is again referred to, it is evident that the relationships derived above also apply to this case, when r_p is substituted for r_p' and I_{po} is substituted for I_{po}'. The value of I_{po} may be expressed in terms of V_{po}, thus

$$I_{po} = -\frac{V_{po}}{r_p}. \tag{26}$$

With these changes, the Eqs. (15), (16), and (17) become

$$I_l = \frac{E_{bb} - V_s\left[1 + \dfrac{r_p}{R_c} + \dfrac{r_p}{Z_s}\right] - V_{po}}{r_l + r_p + \dfrac{r_p r_l}{R_c} + \dfrac{r_p r_l}{Z_s}}, \tag{27}$$

$$V_l = \frac{E_{bb}r_l + V_s r_p - V_{po}r_l}{r_l + r_p + \dfrac{r_p r_l}{R_c} + \dfrac{r_p r_l}{Z_s}}, \tag{28}$$

and

$$V_p = \frac{E_{bb}\left[r_p + \frac{r_p r_l}{R_c} + \frac{r_p r_l}{Z_s}\right] - V_s r_p + V_{po} r_l}{r_l + r_p + \frac{r_p r_l}{R_c} + \frac{r_p r_l}{Z_s}}. \tag{29}$$

In general, V_{po} is so small compared with E_{bb} that it may be neglected.

When the switch tube is operated below the knee of the I_p-V_p characteristic curve, it is evident that changes in line-voltage input to the pulser affect the operating values for the load only because of the resulting change in the power-supply voltage, since all the terms in Eqs. (27), (28), and (29) except E_{bb} are independent of the pulser input voltage. The pulser regulation is therefore obtained simply by differentiating these equations with respect to E_{bb} without considering the variation of grid voltages. The resulting expressions are identical with Eqs. (22) to (25) when r_p is replaced by r_p'.

Examples of the Two Types of Switch-tube Operation.—The order of magnitude of the effect of variations in the high-voltage power supply on the operating values for the load and switch tube is illustrated by the following typical values for two pulser-load combinations. As an example of a medium-power combination, the operation of a pulser is considered with a 715B switch tube and a 725A magnetron as the load. The 2J41 magnetron operated with a pulser using a 3D21 switch tube is an example of a low-power combination. Data are given for the two types of switch-tube operation in each case. The term "type A operation" refers to operation of the switch tube above the knee of the I_p-V_p curve, and the term "type B operation" refers to operation below the knee of the curve.

For type A operation of the 715B tube, the applied screen-grid voltage is about 1000 volts, and the positive grid drive must be about 100 volts in order to obtain a current of 10 amp through the 725A magnetron. With a magnetic field of about 5000 gauss the voltage across this magnetron is approximately 11 kv for a 10-amp current pulse. In order to obtain the same operating conditions for the magnetron with type B operation of the 715B, the screen-grid and control-grid voltages must be raised to about 1200 volts and 150 to 200 volts respectively.

The normal operating voltage and current for a 2J41 magnetron are about 2.5 kv and 1 amp. The 3D21 switch tube in a pulser operating with this magnetron requires about 300 volts on the screen grid and a 25-volt positive grid drive for type A operation. For type B operation of the 3D21, these grid voltages must be increased to about 400 volts and 50 volts respectively.

Values of pulser and switch-tube parameters considered typical for the above-stated operating conditions are given in Table 3·2. The values of the quantities $\partial I_l/\partial E_{bb}$, $\partial V_l/\partial E_{bb}$, and $\partial V_p/\partial E_{bb}$ that have been calculated from these data and from Eqs. (22), (23), and (25) are also tabulated. It is to be noted that the quantities $r_p r_l/R_c$ and $r_p r_l/Z_s$ may be neglected for all practical purposes, since their sum is only one or two per cent of the sum $(r_p + r_l)$. A negligible error would therefore have been introduced for these examples if the switch-tube current had

TABLE 3·2—VALUES CALCULATED FROM EQS. (22), (23), AND (25) FOR TYPICAL OPERATING CONDITIONS FOR TWO PULSER-LOAD COMBINATIONS

	715B switch tube, 725A magnetron,		3D21 switch tube, 2J41 magnetron	
	type A operation	type B operation	type A operation	type B operation
R_c	10,000 ohms	10,000 ohms	15,000 ohms	15,000 ohms
Z_s	(1) 10 mh (2) (7500 ohms + 3 mh)	(1) 10 mh (2) (7500 ohms + 3 mh)	15,000 ohms + 5 mh 15,000 ohms + 5mh	15,000 ohms + 5 mh 15,000 ohms + 5 mh
r_p'	2500 ohms	....	3500 ohms	....
r_p	....	100 ohms	....	75 ohms
r_l	125 ohms	125 ohms	200 ohms	200 ohms
$\dfrac{r_p' r_l}{R_c}$	31 ohms	....	47 ohms	....
$\dfrac{r_p' r_l}{Z_s}$	for $t = 10^{-6}$ sec (1) 31 ohms (2) 46 ohms	....	for $t = 10^{-6}$ sec 44 ohms	....
$\dfrac{r_p r_l}{R_c}$	....	1.25 ohms	....	1 ohm
$\dfrac{r_p r_l}{Z_s}$	....	for $t = 10^{-6}$ sec (1) 1.25 ohms (2) 1.5 ohms	....	for $t = 10^{-6}$ sec 1 ohm
$\dfrac{\partial I_l}{\partial E_{bb}}$	$3.7 \times 10^{-4} \dfrac{\text{amp}}{\text{volt}}$	$4.4 \times 10^{-3} \dfrac{\text{amp}}{\text{volt}}$	$2.6 \times 10^{-4} \dfrac{\text{amp}}{\text{volt}}$	$3.6 \times 10^{-3} \dfrac{\text{amp}}{\text{volt}}$
$\dfrac{\partial V_l}{\partial E_{bb}}$	0.047	0.55	0.052	0.72
$\dfrac{\partial V_p}{\partial E_{bb}}$	0.95	0.45	0.95	0.28

been assumed to be equal to the load current.   It is also evident that, for the type A operation of the switch tube, the value of r_l may also be neglected in the denominator of the expressions (22), (23), and (25) without causing serious error in the calculated pulser regulation.

These examples indicate that the change of load current that is due to the variation of the high-voltage supply is decreased by a factor of about 10 if the switch tube is operated above rather than below the knee of the I_p-V_p characteristic.   It must be remembered, however, that in order to realize this gain, the screen-grid voltage and the positive grid drive must not be allowed to change.   As pointed out in the previous section, when the load line crosses the switch-tube characteristic above the knee, the shape of the control-grid voltage pulse is transferred to the load pulse.   In order to take advantage of the better regulation against power-supply variations, and thus to realize an output-pulse amplitude that is constant throughout the pulse duration, the control-grid pulse must have a flat top.   The particular application to which a pulser is to be adapted generally determines the type of switch-tube operation that is desirable.

Some pulser applications require that the operating conditions for the load must not change even though the duty ratio may vary over wide limits.   For such a pulser, either the high-voltage power supply must be regulated for a large variation in the average current delivered, or the regulation must be obtained by type A operation of the switch tube, in which case the voltage across the switch tube changes by almost the same amount as the power-supply voltage.   It is therefore necessary to adjust the pulser voltages so that the lowest value of E_{bb} to be expected in the operation does not cause the tube drop, V_p, to fall below the value V_{p_2} indicated in Fig. 3·14.

For a pulser designed to operate at constant duty ratio, the variation in power-supply voltage produced by the change in average current is less important than that caused by changes in the line voltage.   It must be decided, therefore, whether or not the improved regulation provided by type A operation of the switch tube compensates for the difficulty of regulating the grid-voltage power supplies.   If the effect of line-voltage variation is not serious, there are some advantages to be gained by operating the switch tube below the knee of the I_p-V_p curve.   Besides the smaller effect of change in grid voltage mentioned in the previous section, there is also the advantage that a lower power-supply voltage is required, as can be seen from the relative positions of points A and B in Fig. 3·15.

When the load has a dynamic resistance that is low compared with its static resistance, the variation of load current is generally of more interest than the variation of load voltage.   (In the operation of a magnetron the oscillation frequency is a function of the magnetron current. The change of frequency, f, caused by current change is referred to as the "pushing figure" of the magnetron, and is generally expressed as the value of $\partial f/\partial I_m$, where I_m is the magnetron current.) For a magnetron load, the ratio dI_l/I_l is often more significant than the value of dI_l. From the equations developed in the preceding discussions it is possible to express the ratio dI_l/I_l in terms of the ratio dE_{bb}/E_{bb}. Thus Eq. (22) gives

$$dI_l = \frac{dE_{bb}}{D}. \tag{22}$$

Dividing by the value of I_l given by Eq. (27) for type B operation,

$$\frac{dI_l}{I_l} = \frac{dE_{bb}}{E_{bb}} \times \frac{E_{bb}}{E_{bb} - V_s\left[1 + \frac{r_p}{R_c} + \frac{r_p}{Z_s}\right]}. \tag{30}$$

For type B operation of the 715B switch tube, a 725A magnetron operating at 11 kv and 10 amp, and the data given in Table 3·2,

$$V_s = 9750 \text{ volts}$$

and

$$E_{bb} = 12 \text{ kv.}$$

With these data, Eq. (30) gives

$$\frac{dI_l}{I_l} \approx \frac{dE_{bb}}{E_{bb}} \times 6.$$

This value is the same as that obtained in Sec. 2·8 by the use of Eq. (2·106) assuming that $r_l = r_p$. Thus, the variation in load current leads to very nearly the same regulation factor as the variation in load power when the dynamic resistance of the load is small.

If the high-voltage power supply has very good regulation, the percentage change in the input line voltage and in the power-supply voltage is almost the same. The percentage change in load current is therefore about six times the percentage change in input line voltage for an average magnetron load. For a pure-resistance load, $V_s = 0$, and the percentage change in load current is equal to the percentage change in input line voltage.

CHAPTER 4

DRIVER CIRCUITS

By G. N. Glasoe

In the preceding discussion of the hard-tube pulser circuit, it is assumed that there is an available means of making the switch tube conducting for a controlled length of time that corresponds to the desired pulse duration. The control of the pulse duration can be accomplished by the application of the proper voltage to the grid of a high-vacuum tube. The circuit that performs this function is called the "driver," and is an essential part of a hard-tube pulser.

In the discussion of switch-tube characteristics in Chap. 3 it is pointed out that, in order to obtain the necessary plate current, the grid of the switch tube must be at a positive potential relative to the cathode during the pulse. Since this grid must be maintained at a high negative voltage during the interpulse intervals, the output voltage of the driver must equal the sum of the bias and positive grid-drive voltages. This required voltage output is called the "grid swing," and may vary from about a hundred volts to several kilovolts depending on the switch-tube characteristics. The pulse-power output of the driver is, therefore, the product of this grid swing and the grid current in the switch tube. For very high power pulsers, for example, the one using six 527 tubes in parallel mentioned in Sec. 3·2, the driver output power may amount to as much as ten per cent of the pulser output power. In general, however, it is more nearly of the order of magnitude of one per cent of the pulser output power.

The pulse duration is entirely determined by the characteristics of the driver circuit for a hard-tube pulser. The circuit should, therefore, be designed so that all the pulses, in a long succession, are identical, and their duration can be determined accurately. For such a succession of pulses, it is generally desired that the interpulse intervals, as well as the pulses, be of controlled duration. The control of the interpulse intervals is usually accomplished by constructing the driver circuit in such a way that it does not produce an output pulse until it has received the proper impulse at its input terminals. These impulses are called trigger pulses, and are produced by some form of auxiliary timing circuit that has a negligible power output. In order to keep the pulser design as versatile as possible, this trigger generator is ordinarily not a part of the pulser, and is commonly used for other functions in addition to starting the action of the driver. One of the principal advantages of the hard-tube pulser over the line-type pulser is that the pulse duration is determined in a relatively low power circuit. For this reason, the driver circuit can be designed so that the pulse duration and the interpulse interval may be changed readily over a wide range of values without necessitating any major changes in the circuit. A given design of a hard-tube pulser may therefore be adapted to a large variety of applications with little difficulty; therefore, a pulser of this type is particularly suitable for research and development work where the specific values of pulse duration, interpulse interval, and output power desired are not definitely known.

There is an inevitable time delay between the start of a trigger impulse and the start of the pulse at the pulser load. When this time delay varies in a random manner from pulse to pulse, there is said to be "time jitter" in the output pulses. This time jitter causes unsatisfactory operation when the functioning of auxiliary circuits depends on both the trigger impulses and the pulser output pulses.

4·1. The Bootstrap Driver.—Many circuits that are available for generating voltage pulses are incapable of delivering enough power to drive the grid of a pulser switch tube. The obvious procedure is there-

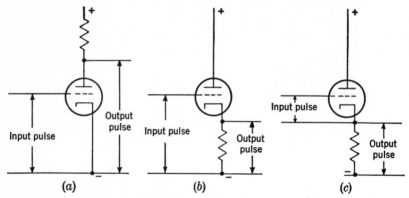

Fig. 4·1.—(a) Plate coupling; requires "on" tube for a positive output pulse. (b) Cathode follower; requires "off" tube for positive output pulse, voltage gain less than one. (c) "Bootstrap" cathode follower; requires "off" tube for positive output pulse, voltage gain greater than one

fore to design an amplifier with a power gain sufficient to deliver the requisite power. Several stages of amplification may be necessary, and the problem of maintaining good pulse shape becomes rather serious. The so-called "bootstrap driver" was devised to generate a pulse at a low-power level, and to amplify it with a minimum number of tubes and circuit elements. Although with the development of satisfactory pulse

transformers this circuit has become obsolete, it is discussed here because
it was one of the first uses of the pulse-forming network as a means of
determining pulse duration.

Since the driver output pulse must be positive, the coupling to the
plate of an amplifier tube, as indicated in Fig. 4·1, requires that the tube
be conducting during the interpulse interval and nonconducting during
the pulse interval.   When it is considered that the output pulse must
supply a current of the order of magnitude of several amperes to the grid
of the switch tube, it is obvious that such plate coupling is very wasteful
of power.   The cathode follower provides a means of getting a positive
output pulse with a normally "off" tube, as is indicated in Fig. 4·1b.
The disadvantage of this arrangement is that the ratio of the voltage
output to the voltage input is less than one.   The arrangement of Fig.
4·1c, however, provides both a voltage and a power gain greater than
one.   However, the circuit generating the input pulse must be able to
rise or fall in potential as the potential of the cathode rises or falls as a
result of the flow of current in the cathode resistor.

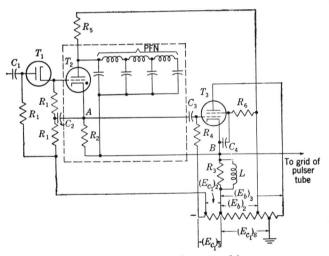

FIG. 4·2.—Circuit for a bootstrap driver.

The complete circuit of a bootstrap driver is shown in Fig. 4·2   The
pulse is generated in the part of the circuit that is enclosed in the dotted
lines.   This pulse generator is merely a low-power line-type pulser in
which the pulse-forming network, PFN, determines the pulse duration
(see Part II for the detailed discussion of line-type pulsers).   The gaseous-discharge tube T_2 is the switch tube, and the resistance R_2, in parallel
with the input resistance of the amplifier tube T_3, is the pulser load.

In the quiescent state of this driver circuit, the reference potential for all voltages is determined by the grid-bias voltage required for the switch tube in the pulser output circuit. In Fig. 4.2 this voltage is indicated as $(E_{c_1})_s$. Thus, the plate voltages for the two tubes are $(E_b)_2$ and $(E_b)_3$, and the grid voltages are $(E_{c_1})_2$ and $(E_{c_1})_3$ for tubes T_2 and T_3 respectively. The grid voltages are adjusted to be sufficiently negative to keep the two tubes nonconducting. When tube T_2 is nonconducting, the PFN is charged to a potential difference equal to $(E_b)_2$.

The operation of this circuit is initiated by applying a positive trigger voltage to the grid of T_2 through the capacitance C_1 and the diode T_1. When this grid is raised in potential relative to the cathode, the gas in the tube becomes conducting, and the PFN is connected directly across the resistance R_2. The point A is thus raised in potential relative to point B by an amount depending on the characteristic impedance of the PFN and on the effective resistance between A and B. In general, an attempt is made to match these impedances so that one half of the network voltage appears across R_2. By virtue of the coupling capacitance C_3, the grid of T_3 is raised in potential along with point A. The resistance R_4 must be large enough to decouple the grid from the bias-voltage supply during the pulse. If the potential difference across R_2 is greater than the bias voltage $(E_{c_1})_3$, the grid of T_3 becomes positive with respect to the cathode (point B in Fig. 4.2). Tube T_3 is thus made conducting, and a current flows in the cathode resistance R_3. This current causes the point B to rise in potential and, if the current is large enough, the grid of the pulser switch tube becomes sufficiently positive with respect to ground to make the plate current sufficient to obtain the required pulser output current. It is to be observed that, as the point B starts to rise in potential because of conduction in tube T_3, all the parts of the pulse-generating circuit must also rise in potential. The circuit is referred to as a bootstrap driver, since it is raised in potential by its "bootstraps," so to speak.

The duration of the pulse from this circuit is determined by the time required for a voltage wave to travel down the PFN and return. When this time has elapsed, the network is completely discharged (if the PFN impedance is matched by the resistance between A and B), and the potential difference across R_2 falls suddenly. This drop in potential cuts off the current in both T_3 and its cathode resistor, thus removing the grid drive from the pulser switch tube.

The bootstrap action of this circuit has important consequences that must be taken into account in the design. When point B rises in potential, it causes the cathode of the gaseous-discharge tube to rise with it; therefore, the life of this tube is seriously affected if the grid can not also rise in potential. In order to permit the potential of the grid to increase, the capacitance C_2, shown in Fig. 4.2, is added. The capacitance C_1 and diode T_1 are introduced to decouple effectively the grid of T_2 from the trigger-pulse-generating circuit during this action.   The network of resistances R_1 provides decoupling between the trigger input and the bias supply, and allows the circuit to return to its quiescent state during the interpulse interval.   The resistance R_5 provides decoupling between the pulse-generating circuit and the power supply during the pulse.   The value of this resistance should be as large as is possible without seriously reducing the voltage on the PFN at the end of the interpulse interval.

Another consequence of the bootstrap action is that the stray capacitance of the circuit to ground (wiring, components, filament transformers, etc.) must be kept as small as possible.   As the circuit rises in potential, this stray capacitance must be charged, and, unless it is small, the pulse shape is seriously distorted.   At the end of the pulse the charge on this stray capacitance must leak off, and, as indicated in Chap. 2, if the RC time constant for the discharge is large, the trailing edge of the pulse falls slowly.   In order to make the voltage drop more rapidly at the end of the pulse, the inductance L is introduced in parallel with the cathode resistance R_3.

This circuit was used successfully to drive the grids of two 304TH tubes in parallel as the pulser switch tube.   A bias voltage of about -1000 volts and a positive grid drive of $+300$ to $+400$ volts were necessary.   Thus, the voltage developed across the cathode resistance R_3 had to be about 1300 to 1400 volts.   This voltage was obtained with $(E_b)_3$ equal to 1550 volts when an 829 beam tetrode was used as the tube T_3.   The gaseous-discharge tube T_2 was either an 884 or a 2050, the performance of the latter being somewhat more satisfactory.   The voltage $(E_{c_1})_2$ for either of these tubes was critical: if it were too large or too small, the tube would tend to remain conducting.   The value of $(E_{c_1})_2$ usually had to be adjusted for the particular tube being used.   For this application, the circuit was designed to give three different pulse durations, $\frac{1}{2}$, 1, and 2 μsec.   By the use of a selecting switch, any one of three different networks could be connected into the circuit.   For the high recurrence frequency (2000 pps) used with the shortest pulse, the PFN did not become charged to the full value of $(E_b)_2$ if R_5 were very large.   On the other hand, reducing R_5 made it more difficult to prevent tube T_2 from becoming continuously conducting.   With careful adjustment of the circuit voltages and the values of the circuit elements, however, it was possible to obtain satisfactory operation at 4000 pps.   The particular gaseous-discharge tube to be used had to be selected carefully, since the long deionization time for some tubes did not allow the charge on the PFN to accumulate fast enough to produce the full network voltage before the initiation of the next pulse.   The values finally used were

$(E_b)_2 = 500$ to 600 volts and $R_5 \approx 0.6$ megohm. The characteristic impedance of the PFN was about 1500 ohms, and R_2 ranged from 1500 to 2500 ohms. The other values of the circuit components were as follows: $C_1 = 0.005$ µf, $C_2 = C_3 = C_4 = 0.01$ µf, $R_1 = 100,000$ ohms, $R_3 = 1000$ ohms, $R_4 = 25,000$ ohms, $R_6 = 30,000$ ohms, $L = 2.5$ mh.

4·2. The Blocking Oscillator or Regenerative Driver.—With the development of transformers capable of passing pulses of short duration, it became possible to design a driver circuit using a single tube. A circuit of this type was used extensively in pulsers with medium-power output (150 to 250 kw) for airborne microwave-radar systems, and became known as the blocking-oscillator driver. This name was given to the circuit because of a similarity between it and the blocking oscillators used to produce pulses in television applications. The driver circuit is not an oscillator in the same sense as the circuit used in television, and may more properly be referred to as a "regenerative pulse generator." This term is not exclusively distinctive, however, since there is a large class of circuits, such as the multivibrator for example, which could go by the same name. The particular type of circuit discussed here is called a "regenerative driver" in an attempt to avoid confusion with the circuit used in television.

There are two essential differences between the regenerative driver and the conventional blocking oscillator:

1. The regenerative driver can be kept in its quiescent state for an indefinite length of time, and starts its operating cycle only when the proper impulse is applied to the input terminals.
2. The output pulse is almost constant in amplitude throughout the pulse duration, as a result of the circuit and tube characteristics.

There is still a third difference that is not always essential, namely, that the pulse duration from a regenerative driver is usually determined by a line-simulating network, whereas that from most blocking oscillators is determined by a parallel *LC*-combination.

A regenerative driver circuit arrangement which incorporates an iron-core pulse transformer together with a line-simulating network in the grid circuit of a vacuum tube is shown schematically in Fig. 4·3. As discussed later, the range over which the pulse duration may be varied, by changing the network parameters, depends on the pulse transformer characteristics. Because of the line-simulating network, the circuit has sometimes been referred to as a "line-controlled blocking oscillator." The triggering pulse for this circuit is introduced directly onto the grid; this arrangement is called "parallel triggering" in contrast to the method of series triggering shown in the circuit of Fig. 4·4. The latter circuit has been widely used in pulsers for microwave-radar systems, and the regenerative feature is therefore discussed from the standpoint of Fig. 4·4 rather than the earlier arrangement of Fig. 4·3. The series-triggering arrangement proved to be somewhat more stable and less critical in regard to the values of circuit parameters than the parallel-triggering circuit.

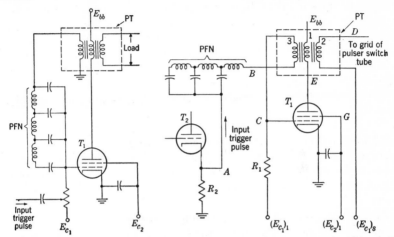

FIG. 4·3.—Circuit of a regenerative driver with parallel triggering.   FIG. 4·4.—Circuit for a regenerative driver with series triggering.

The circuit of Fig. 4·4 consists of a tube T_1, pulse transformer PT, line-simulating network PFN, and power supplies for the tube-element voltages. The tube T_1 is represented as a tetrode, but triodes can be used as well. The grid voltage for the tube is sufficiently negative to keep the tube nonconducting when the full values of plate and screen grid voltages are applied. The operating cycle of this circuit is initiated by applying a positive trigger pulse to one terminal of the PFN. This trigger voltage raises the potential of the line, the transformer winding (3), and the grid of T_1 to a value sufficient to start a flow of plate current in the tube. Because of the flow of plate current, the voltage at the plate of T_1 falls, causing a potential difference to appear across the primary winding (1) of the transformer. A voltage therefore appears simultaneously across the other two windings, (2) and (3), of the transformer. The grid of T_1 is connected to the winding (3) in such a way that the voltage on this winding raises the potential of the grid. A regenerative action is thereby started, which continues until grid current starts to flow.

The voltage across the grid winding of the transformer is divided between the PFN, the grid-cathode resistance of T_1, and the output resistance of the trigger generator. A cathode-follower output is gener-

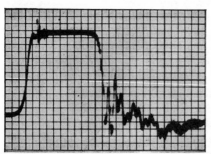

ally used for the trigger generator in order to ensure a relatively low effective resistance. The voltage appearing across the PFN starts a voltage wave traveling toward the open end, where it is reflected and returns toward the transformer end. When this cycle is completed the PFN is fully charged, and the potential of the grid of T_1 starts to fall abruptly. The plate current in the tube then begins to fall, reducing the voltage across winding (1). This process results in a reduction in the voltage across winding (3) that makes the grid still more negative, and causes a regenerative shutoff of the plate current. The voltage across the grid winding then disappears, and the PFN discharges through the resistances R_1 and R_2, driving the grid below cutoff. The bias voltage $(E_{c_1})_1$, keeps the tube nonconducting until the next trigger pulse starts another cycle.

The above description of the action of a regenerative driver is very qualitative. The analysis of the effect of transformer and tube characteristics on this circuit is extremely difficult. An approximate analysis has been made with a simplified circuit for the effects introduced by the pulse-transformer parameters. This analysis is given in Sec. 14·2.

In the action of the regenerative-driver circuit a voltage is induced across the winding (2). This winding is connected between the bias supply and the grid of the pulser switch tube. In order for this circuit to function as the driver for the switch tube, the voltage appearing across this transformer winding must be equal to the required grid swing. The load introduced by the grid circuit of the switch tube has a strong influence on the flatness of the top of the voltage pulse appearing at the grid. If the load on winding (2) is small, the voltage pulse generally has oscillations of appreciable magnitude superimposed on its top. Since switch tubes of a given type vary considerably in their grid-voltage–grid-current characteristics, it is sometimes necessary to introduce resistors across one or more of the transformer windings to damp out the oscillations. These oscillations are the result of the inherent leakage inductance and distributed capacitance of the transformer, and they may therefore be minimized to some extent by careful transformer design. The oscilloscope trace reproduced in Fig. 4·5

Fig. 4·5.—Voltage pulse at the grid of a 715B tube obtained from a regenerative driver using an 829 tube. Sweep speed: 10 div. per μsec; pulse amplitude: 1000 volts.

indicates the character of the pulse obtained at the grid of a 715B switch tube from a regenerative driver using an 829 beam tetrode.

Both the maximum and the minimum pulse durations obtainable with a given regenerative driver are dependent on the pulse-transformer characteristics. The maximum is determined by the magnetizing current and core saturation. When the magnetization of the transformer core approaches saturation, the magnetizing current increases very rapidly, increasing the tube drop and thereby reducing the voltage across winding (1), and hence across winding (3). This decrease in voltage causes the regenerative shutoff to start before the PFN is fully charged. The pulse may be terminated by this same process, even if the transformer core does not become saturated, if the magnetizing current becomes too great. The minimum obtainable pulse duration is determined by the inherent inductance and capacitance of the circuit (including the transformer), exclusive of the pulse-forming network. For intermediate values of pulse duration, the duration of the output pulse corresponds reasonably well with the calculated value based on the inductance and capacitance of the network. Thus, if L_N is the total inductance and C_N is the total capacitance of the network, the time required for a voltage wave to travel from one end to the other is $\sqrt{L_N C_N}$ and the pulse duration $\tau = 2\sqrt{L_N C_N}$.

It has been possible to design regenerative drivers in which the pulse duration may be varied over a wide range merely by changing the constants of the PFN. With an 829 tube and a GE 68G627 pulse transformer, satisfactory operation can be obtained in this manner over the range 0.5 μsec to 5 μsec. The relatively low voltages involved in the circuit make it possible to change from one pulse duration to another by means of small remote-controlled relays. It is thus feasible to adapt a single design to a number of different applications.

The range of pulse duration may be extended beyond 5 μsec merely by connecting the corresponding windings of two pulse transformers in series. In this way the circuit has been made to operate satisfactorily at 10 μsec. A second transformer can also be introduced with the aid of small relays, which thus provides a range from 0.5 μsec to 10 μsec with no major change in the circuit.

The lower limit of the range in pulse duration that can be obtained with a given 68G627 pulse transformer is considerably less than 0.5 μsec. Below this value, however, the inevitable small variations in transformer parameters from one unit to another begin to have a greater effect. With any given unit, it is possible to construct a pulse-forming network that produces a 0.25-μsec output pulse from the driver. Although the same PFN in another circuit with a different transformer may produce a pulse duration as much as 50 per cent greater, the 0.25-μsec pulse duration can generally be obtained by adjusting the constants of the PFN. It is, therefore, possible to have the range 0.25 μsec to 10 μsec available from such a driver if the PFN's for the shortest pulses are properly adjusted for each individual case.

When the desired range of pulse durations does not extend higher than about 1 μsec, a smaller pulse transformer than the 68G627 can be used. The Utah OA18 transformer has been found satisfactory for the shorter pulses. Using this pulse transformer, it has been possible to use pulse durations as short as 0.1 μsec with no serious difficulty. When very short pulse durations are desired, the shape of the trigger pulse becomes important for reasons that are discussed below.

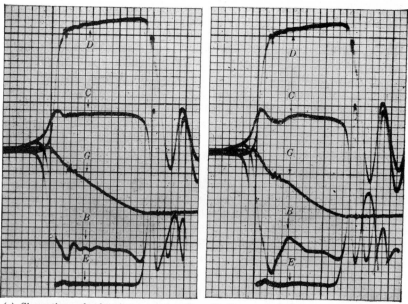

(a) Six-section pulse-forming network with $Z_N = 1000$ ohms.

(b) Two-section pulse forming network with $Z_N = 1000$ ohms.

Fig. 4·6.—Oscilloscope traces of the pulse shapes occurring at various points in a regenerative-driver circuit with a GE 68G627 pulse transformer and an 829 tube. The letters correspond to the labelling on the circuit diagram of Fig. 4·4. Sweep speed $\approx$ 10 div. per μsec.

It has been found experimentally that, with some transformers and tubes, it is possible to maintain a reasonably good pulse shape for pulse durations as long as 2 μsec and as short as 0.1 μsec by reducing the network to a single inductance and a single condenser. The pulse shape is not as good as that obtained from a multisection line, but, with a switch tube such as the 715B, the pulser output pulse can be made considerably more rectangular than the grid-driving pulse. (Compare Fig. 4·5 with Figs. 2·25, 2·26, 2·27, and 2·28.) The possibility of simplifying the network in this way has made it possible to adjust the pulse duration as much as ±20 per cent by varying the inductance of the single coil.   This inductance may be varied either by means of a slug of magnetic material, which may be moved in or out of the inductance coil, or by moving a piece of copper toward or away from the end of the coil.   Oscilloscope traces of the voltage pulses appearing at various points in the circuit of Fig. 4·4 are reproduced in Fig. 4·6a and b.   These two pictures indicate that the output pulse from the driver is the same whether a two-section or a six-section pulse-forming network is used to determine the pulse duration.

The characteristic impedance $Z_N = \sqrt{L_N/C_N}$ of the PFN used in a regenerative driver circuit has an effect on the circuit behavior.   It has been found experimentally that there is a range of values of Z_N that allows satisfactory operation.   The extent of this range, however, varies with the particular combination of tube and pulse transformer.   With an 829 tube and a GE 68G627 transformer the mean value of Z_N for this range is about 1000 ohms, and the operation does not become seriously affected until Z_N is reduced to about 500 ohms or increased to about 1500 ohms.   At the high impedance values the pulse duration may be too short, and there is sometimes a tendency for several short pulses to occur in the time corresponding to the normal pulse duration.   At the low impedance values the pulse duration tends to become longer than it should be, and is finally limited by the transformer characteristics These effects are illustrated in the oscilloscope traces reproduced in Fig 4·7a, b, and c.

As the desired pulse duration becomes shorter, the total capacitance of the PFN becomes smaller, and the magnitude of the trigger pulse that appears at the grid of the tube for a given input trigger pulse also becomes smaller.   If the trigger-pulse amplitude at the grid becomes sufficiently small, the regenerative action may not start.   Thus, for a low-capacitance line or a slow-rising trigger pulse, there can be an uncertainty in the time at which the regeneration starts.   This effect is indicated by the sketches of Fig. 4·8 for a given network capacitance and for both a fast- and a slow-rising trigger pulse.   Time jitter, that is, the uncertainty in the starting time for the grid pulse shown in Fig. 4·8b, is observed when a succession of pulses is desired.   The effect shown in Fig. 4·8b is also obtained when the capacitance of the PFN is very small, even though the trigger-pulse voltage may rise fast enough for satisfactory operation with longer pulse durations.   When this situation exists, it can generally be corrected by introducing a trigger amplifier and sharpener between the trigger generator and the driver input.

The time delay between the start of the trigger pulse and the start of the driver output pulse also depends on the rate of rise of the voltage pulse appearing at the grid of the driver tube.   For a given tube and

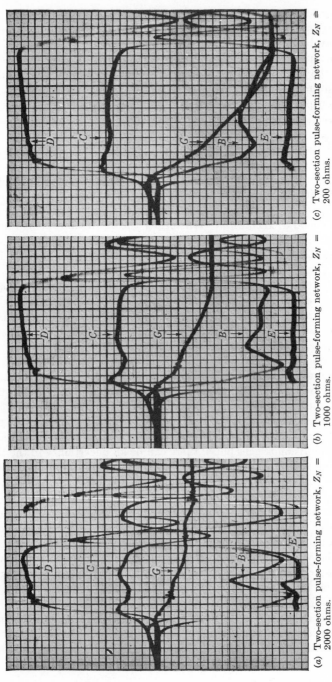

(a) Two-section pulse-forming network, Z_N = 2000 ohms.

(b) Two-section pulse-forming network, Z_N = 1000 ohms.

(c) Two-section pulse-forming network, Z_N = 200 ohms.

FIG. 4·7.—Oscilloscope traces of the pulse shapes occurring at various points in a regenerative-driver circuit with a GE 68G627 pulse transformer and an 829 tube. The letters correspond to the labeling in the circuit diagram of Fig. 4·4. Sweep speed ≈ 10 div. per μsec.

given circuit voltages, this time delay remains very nearly constant over long periods of time. The actual value of this time delay is a complicated function of the tube characteristics, the bias voltage, and the rate of rise of the trigger-pulse voltage.

For a few pulser applications, for example, for pulse-coding in radar beacons, it is required that some of the interpulse intervals be comparable with the pulse duration. When it is necessary to have successive pulses of about 1-μsec duration follow each other at intervals as short as 10 to 15 μsec, special attention must be given to the driver design. The regenerative driver is readily adaptable to this application. By referring to the circuit of Fig. 4·4, it may be seen that the voltage of the grid of T_1 becomes considerably more negative than the bias voltage at the end of

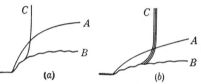

FIG. 4·8.—Sketch made from oscilloscope traces showing the effect of fast- and slow-rising trigger pulses on the start of regeneration in a regenerative driver. Curve *A* is the trigger pulse at the input to the PFN. Curve *B* is the trigger pulse at the grid of the driver tube. Curve *C* is the grid voltage after regeneration starts.

the pulse because of the discharging of the PFN through the resistances R_1 and R_2. The time constant of this discharge is therefore dependent on the capacitance of the network and on the values of these resistances. Since R_1 serves to decouple the grid from the bias power supply during the pulse, it cannot be reduced in value without affecting the grid voltage at that time. The obvious alternative is to use a small inductance in combination with a small resistance in place of the high resistance R_1. For pulses with durations of the order of magnitude of 1 μsec, this inductance can be about 1 mh. A driver having an inductance of 0.5 mh in series with a resistance of 5000 ohms in place of R_1 and an 829 for T_1 produces satisfactory 2-μsec pulses at a recurrence frequency of 80 kc/sec.

The regenerative-driver design has proved to be a versatile one for use with a hard-tube pulser. In addition to the available flexibility in pulse duration and interpulse interval, it is also possible to accomplish some changes in pulse shape. For one particular application it became necessary to reduce the rate of rise of the output pulse at the magnetron load. Although this reduction can be effected in the output circuit, as indicated in Chap. 2, it was easier in this case to make the change in the driver circuit. The requisite change in rate of rise of the output voltage pulse was obtained by introducing a small inductance in series with the plate of the tube in the driver. When such an inductance is used alone, large oscillations are superimposed on the pulse. They may be damped out, however, by inserting a resistance in parallel with the inductance.

A regenerative driver using a single 829 tetrode provides a power output and grid swing that are sufficient to drive the grids of two 715B or 5D21 tubes in parallel. This power output is 2 to 3 kw with a grid swing of about 1000 volts. The power output of the pulser is about 250 to 300 kw.

4·3. The Multivibrator and Pulse-forming-network Drivers.—Multivibrators are used extensively to generate pulses at low-power levels. Several arrangements of the multivibrator circuit are discussed in Vol. 19 of the Radiation Laboratory Series. For microwave-radar systems, the so-called "biased multivibrator" has been adapted for use as the pulse generator in the driver of a hard-tube pulser. This circuit is suitable for driver application because it has a single stable state. It is therefore possible to obtain an output pulse from a biased multivibrator only when the proper triggering impulse is applied to one of the tubes, and the length of the interpulse intervals can be determined by a timing circuit that is independent of the pulser.

A driver circuit utilizing a biased-multivibrator as the pulse generator has been devised for a 1-Mw hard-tube pulser (described in detail in Sec. 5.2). The switch in this pulser consists of three 6C21 triodes in parallel. It is evident from the discussion of switch tubes in Chap. 3 that the driver for such a pulser must deliver a pulse power of about 15 kw to the three 6C21 grids. The grid-voltage swing required for 1-Mw power output from the pulser is about 2.5 to 3 kv. Since it is impracticable to try to obtain this much power at the output of the multivibrator, it is necessary to use amplification.

The shape and duration of the output pulse from a multivibrator depends on the load and on the values of the circuit elements and tube voltages. In practice, some variation must usually be expected in these parameters, and it is therefore necessary to allow sufficient latitude in the circuit design to accommodate a reasonable range of values. The most serious aspect of this characteristic of the multivibrator in the driver application is the possible variation of pulse duration. In this driver the difficulty was avoided by introducing an auxiliary means for determining the pulse duration, which consisted of a delay line connected between the output of the driver and the input of the amplifier following the multivibrator.

The block diagram of this driver circuit, shown in Fig. 4·9, indicates the way in which the pulse duration is determined. The multivibrator pulse generator is constructed so that the pulse fed into the amplifier at B is of longer duration than the pulse desired at the output of the driver.

When the leading edge of the pulse reaches A, a voltage wave starts to travel from A to B through the delay line.   This voltage wave reaches B after a time determined by the constants of the delay line.   If the pulse fed into the amplifier at B is positive and the pulse voltage at A is negative, it is possible to neutralize the positive voltage at the amplifier input, and thereby to terminate the pulse appearing at A.   The pulse duration at the driver output is thus fixed by the time it takes a voltage wave to travel the length of the delay line, independent of the multivibrator output.   This arrangement has been expressively called the "tail-biting" circuit.

In order to insure that only one pulse appears at the driver output for each trigger pulse, the output pulse of the multivibrator must not

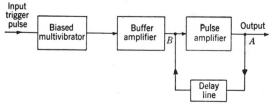

FIG. 4·9.—Block diagram of the driver for a hard-tube pulser using a multivibrator pulse generator.

last longer than twice the transit time for the delay line.   For pulse durations of about a microsecond, this latitude for the multivibrator output is ample.   When the desired pulse duration is very short, however, more care must be exercised in the design of the circuit.   The buffer amplifier is introduced to minimize the effect of loading on the output pulse shape and pulse duration obtained from the multivibrator.   If the amplifier is carefully designed, the shape of the pulse at the driver output can be considerably better than that fed into the amplifier, and the dependence of driver output on multivibrator output is further reduced.

A simplified schematic diagram for this driver circuit is shown in Fig. 4·10.   The biased multivibrator, which consists of the two halves of a 6SN7, delivers a negative pulse to the grid of the normally "on" buffer amplifier tube, a 6L6.   A positive pulse is then obtained at the grid of the first 3E29 amplifier.   The negative pulse that appears at the plate of this 3E29 is inverted by means of a pulse transformer, and the resulting positive pulse is applied to the grids of two 3E29 tubes in parallel.   The negative pulse obtained at the plates of these tubes is also inverted by a pulse transformer in order to give a positive pulse at the grids of the 6C21 tubes.   A part of the negative pulse at A is impressed across the end of the delay line by means of the voltage divider consisting of R_1 and R_2.   After traversing the delay line, this negative pulse appears at B

with amplitude sufficient to neutralize the positive pulse output from the 6L6. This negative pulse lasts for a time corresponding to the pulse duration at point A and, if this time plus the delay time is greater than the duration of the pulse from the multivibrator, the bias voltage maintains the 3E29 nonconducting when the pulse is over.

The pulse duration from this driver may be varied by changing the length of the delay line between points A and B. The switch S_1, indicated in Fig. 4·10, is provided to facilitate this change. The switch S_2

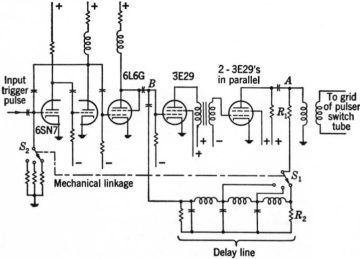

Fig. 4·10.—Simplified schematic diagram of the driver for a hard-tube pulser using a multivibrator pulse generator and a delay line to determine pulse duration.

is mechanically coupled with S_1 in order to change the pulse duration at the multivibrator output at the same time that the length of the delay line is changed. The constants in the multivibrator circuit are chosen so that the pulse delivered to the amplifier is about 25 to 40 per cent longer than the pulse duration desired from the driver.

The operation of this driver requires two of the tubes, the 6L6 and one half of the 6SN7, to be conducting during the interpulse interval. When the pulser is being operated at a low duty ratio, where the interpulse interval is about 1000 times as long as the pulse interval, it is desirable to have the power dissipated by these normally "on" tubes as small as possible. The multivibrator power output should be kept small for this reason also, and the necessary output power from the driver must be provided by pulse amplification.

Another driver circuit making use of a biased multivibrator has been devised for the 200-kw hard-tube pulser of a microwave-radar system used in aircraft.   The switch in this pulser consists of two 5D21 tetrodes in parallel.   In this driver, the multivibrator serves a somewhat different purpose than it does in the circuit just discussed.   The pulse shape and pulse duration are determined in this driver by a current-fed net-work (see Part II for the detailed discussion of pulse-forming networks). The function of the multivibrator is to start and stop the current in this network.   This circuit should, therefore, more properly be referred to as a "pulse-forming-network driver" rather than a "multivibrator driver."

The operation of this driver circuit is best discussed with reference to the circuit diagram shown in Fig. 4·11.   The two tubes, 6AG7 and 3E29,

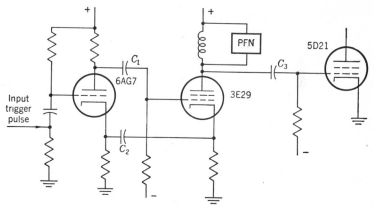

FIG. 4·11.—Driver for a hard-tube pulser using a biased multivibrator with one stable state and a current-fed network for pulse-shaping.

and associated circuit elements constitute a cathode-coupled biased multivibrator.   The values of the circuit elements and voltages are such that the 6AG7 is normally conducting and the 3E29 is nonconducting. A negative trigger pulse applied to the grid of the 6AG7 makes this tube nonconducting, and the plate rises in potential.   As a result, the grid of the 3E29 is raised in potential by virtue of the coupling capacitance C_1, and plate current starts to flow.   The current flowing in the cathode resistance of the 3E29 then raises the potential of the cathode of the 6AG7 through the medium of the coupling capacitance C_2, keeping this tube in the nonconducting state.   The 3E29 remains conducting until the potential of the 6AG7 cathode falls sufficiently to allow this tube to become conducting again.   The time required for the cycle to be completed is determined by the time constant of the capacitance C_2 and the cathode resistance.

A current-fed network is connected in series with the plate of the 3E29.   In its simplest form, such a network is a short-circuited line-simulating network, as indicated in Fig. 4·12a.   The configuration

actually used for one of the networks in this driver is shown in Fig.
4·12b.   The network of Fig. 4·12b is used in preference to that of Fig.
4·12a in order to obtain a better pulse shape.   During the time that the
3E29 is conducting, current builds up in the inductance of the network,
thus storing energy in the amount $\frac{1}{2}LI^2$.   When the 3E29 suddenly
becomes nonconducting at the end of the multivibrator operating cycle,
the network begins to discharge through the load presented by the grid
circuit of the switch tube.   A positive voltage pulse is thus started at
the plate of the 3E29 and the grid of the pulser switch tube.   If the net-

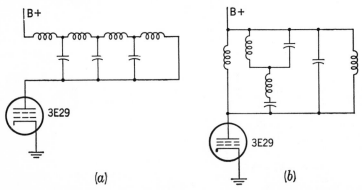

Fig. 4·12.—Current-fed networks used to form the pulse in the driver circuit shown in
Fig. 4·11.

work is well designed and the load presented by the grid circuit of the
switch tube matches the characteristic impedance of the network, the
pulse voltage drops to zero when the energy stored in the inductance is
completely discharged.   The construction of the network therefore
determines both the shape and the duration of the driver output pulse.

The pulse duration obtained from this driver may be changed by
connecting different pulse-forming networks into the circuit.   In one
pulser design, which was widely used in airborne microwave-radar
systems, three pulse durations can be selected by remote-controlled
switching of networks.   For all three of these pulse durations, $\frac{1}{2}$, $1\frac{1}{8}$, and
$2\frac{1}{4}$ μsec, the conducting period for the 3E29 is the same.   In this particular case, the multivibrator is designed to allow 4.5 μsec for the buildup of
current in the network.   A considerable range of pulse duration at the
driver output may therefore be obtained without changing the constants
of the multivibrator circuit.

The time delay between the start of the trigger pulse and the start
of the driver pulse is inherently longer with this circuit than for those
previously discussed because of the time required for current to build
up in the inductance of the pulse-forming network.   The dependence of

the pulse duration of the multivibrator output on the circuit voltages affects this time delay.   If, for any reason, the voltages applied to the tubes of the multivibrator are subject to random variations, the change in time delay appears as time jitter in the output pulse.

Because of the effect just mentioned, a later version of this driver incorporated a modification of the multivibrator circuit such that the 6AG7 tube is returned to the conducting state by the positive pulse obtained by connecting a short-circuited delay line in parallel with the trigger input as shown in Fig. 4·13.   For this modification, indicated

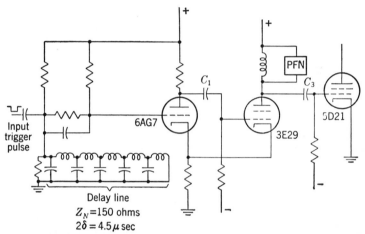

Fig. 4·13.—Driver for a hard-tube pulser using a biased multivibrator with one stable state and one quasi-stable state.   The pulse-shaping is obtained with a current-fed network.

in Fig. 4·13, the coupling capacitance between the cathodes of the two tubes is removed, and a direct connection is made in its place.   The two tubes have, therefore, a common cathode resistor.   The behavior of this circuit when a negative trigger pulse is applied to the grid of the 6AG7 is the same as that for the circuit of Fig. 4·11.   The 3E29 is changed from the conducting to the nonconducting state by the positive pulse at the 6AG7 grid, and, because it is again desired to have 3E29 conducting for 4·5 μsec, the delay line is constructed so that it has a two-way transit time of 4·5 μsec.   This circuit, as well as the earlier version, has a single stable state, but, because of the long time constants in the grid circuits, the state in which the 3E29 is conducting can be considered quasi-stable as far as the circuit operation is concerned.   The principal advantages of this arrangement over the previous one are a smaller dependence of circuit behavior on the 3E29 characteristics, and the possibility of better control over the length of the PFN-charging period.

For reasons already mentioned, it is desirable to have the normally "on" tube of the multivibrator dissipate as little power as possible. It is also desirable to keep the conducting period for the 3E29 short in order to maintain a high over-all efficiency.

A pulse-forming-network driver can also be designed with a voltage-fed network. In this case the driver is a line-type pulser of the type described in detail in Part II of this volume. Although the pulse generator used in the bootstrap driver, discussed in Sec. 4·1, is such a line-type pulser, the output power is too small for the driver function, and it is necessary to provide amplification. The subsequent development of pulse-forming networks and satisfactory gaseous-discharge tubes capable of handling high pulse power has eliminated the necessity of amplification. With the 3C45, 4C35, and 5C22 hydrogen thyratrons it is now possible to design line-type pulsers having a range of pulse-power output from a few kilowatts to several megawatts.

The schematic circuit for one possible arrangement of a pulse-forming-network driver using a voltage-fed network is shown in Fig. 4·14. The

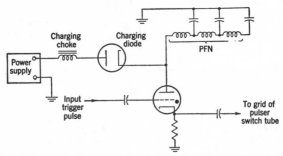

Fig. 4·14.—Pulse-forming-network driver for a hard-tube pulser.

PFN is charged during the interpulse interval from the d-c power supply through an inductance and a diode in series. The output pulse is initiated by the application of a positive trigger pulse to the grid of the gaseous-discharge switch tube. When the tube is conducting, the PFN discharges into the load, which consists of the cathode resistor and the grid circuit of the high-vacuum switch tube of the pulser output circuit. The pulse shape and the pulse duration are determined by the characteristics of the PFN and its discharging circuit. The reader is referred to Part II for further details concerning the operation of line-type pulsers.

When the pulser application requires only one pulse duration and recurrence frequency, it is unnecessary to have a diode in the charging circuit of the network. With the diode, however, it is possible to change recurrence frequency over a considerable range, and the pulse duration may be changed by connecting different networks into the circuit.

By using a pulse transformer, it is possible to connect the cathode of the gaseous-discharge tube to ground, as shown in Fig. 4·15, and thus to eliminate the need for a filament transformer with high-voltage insulation.

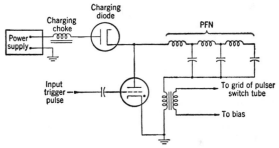

Fig. 4·15.—Pulse-forming-network driver with pulse-transformer coupling to the grid of the high-vacuum switch tube.

A possible disadvantage is that the introduction of the pulse transformer may result in a somewhat poorer pulse shape at the grid of the high-vacuum switch tube.

CHAPTER 5

PARTICULAR APPLICATIONS

By G. N. Glasoe

5·1. The Model 3 Pulser—A Light-weight, Medium-power Pulser for Airborne Radar Systems.—The original specifications for this pulser, based on the requirements for a light-weight airborne search radar, ASV, and an aircraft-interception radar, AI, were formulated in the winter of 1941. By the summer of 1945 this pulser had been incorporated into six different radar systems and their various modifications. The pulser was manufactured in very large numbers by the Stromberg-Carlson Company and the Philco Corporation. A revised model of the pulser, Mark II, in which improvements were made in engineering and manufacturing details, was manufactured during the last year of the war. A few circuit modifications were also incorporated as a result of the experience gained in the operation of the original version, Mark I. The revised pulser was designed to meet the requirement that it be physically and electrically interchangeable with the original unit. The stringent requirements placed on the size and weight of this pulser resulted in some departures from accepted engineering practices. Improvements in techniques and in the design and manufacture of components, however, warranted such departures, and extensive laboratory tests proved their feasibility. Because of the small size of this pulser compared with others that had previously been constructed for an equivalent power output, the unit was facetiously referred to as the "vest-pocket pulser."

The Model 3 pulser was designed to meet the following specifications:
Output pulse power: 144 kw (12 kv at 12 amp).
Duty ratio: 0.001 maximum.
Pulse duration: 0.5, 1.0 and 2.0 μsec. (Remote control of pulse selection.)
Size: must fit into a cubical space 16 in. on a side.
Weight: preferably no greater than 60 lbs.
Ambient-temperature range: −40 to +50°C. (External fan to be provided with ambient temperature above +30°C.)
Altitude: must operate satisfactorily at 30,000 ft.
Input voltages: 115 volts at 400 to 2000 cycles/sec and 24v d-c. (The a-c frequency range was changed to 800 to 1600 cycles/sec when the revised pulser was being designed.)

The design of a pulser to meet these specifications was undertaken before satisfactory pulse transformers and line-type pulsers were developed. The design, of necessity, included the high-voltage power supply associated with a hard-tube-pulser design. The combined size, weight, and altitude specifications therefore required that the pulser be housed in an airtight container in order to maintain atmospheric pressure around the high-voltage parts of the circuit, regardless of the reduced external pressure at high altitude. The need for an airtight housing complicated the problem of heat dissipation. Because the lack of ventilation and the high external temperature caused the components to operate at high temperatures, it was imperative that the over-all efficiency be as high as possible. The size and weight specifications imposed the necessity of using small components, resulting in small factors of safety. The completed pulser unit was mounted on a square base 15 in. by 15 in. by 4½ in. The airtight housing was a cylinder having a diameter of 15 in. and a dome-shaped end of dimensions such that the over-all height was 11½ in. The combined heights of the base and housing were 16 in. A space under the base was provided for mounting a magnetron, TR tube, preamplifier, and miscellaneous parts associated with the r-f components. The original unit manufactured by Stromberg-Carlson weighed 64 lb, and the Philco unit weighed 60 lb. The revised pulser, which was manufactured by Stromberg-Carlson, weighed 53 lb. Photographs of the Stromberg-Carlson pulser are reproduced in Figs. 5·1 and 5·2, and the schematic diagrams for these two units are shown in Figs. 5·4 and 5·5.

The control circuit and connections to the primary power source are omitted for the sake of clarity.

The Output Circuit.—The original plans for the Model 3 pulser called for its operation with the 2J21 and 2J22 magnetrons. The 725A magnetron, which was developed later, replaced the 2J21 as soon as it became available. From a knowledge of the operating characteristics of these magnetron oscillators, it was decided that the output voltage pulse obtained from the pulser could be allowed to drop as much as 2 per cent during a 1-μsec pulse without seriously affecting the frequency of the magnetron output. The minimum capacitance of the storage condenser to be used in the pulser was, therefore, determined from the relation $\Delta V_l = I_l \, \Delta t / C_w$, as indicated in Chap. 2. For a pulse voltage of 12 kv and a pulse current of 12 amp, the capacitance of the storage condenser is

$$C_w = \frac{12 \times 1 \times 10^{-6}}{2 \times 10^{-2} \times 12 \times 10^3} = 0.05 \times 10^{-6} \text{ farad.}$$

Operation at a pulse duration of 2-μsec was considered satisfactory, even though it resulted in a 4 per cent drop in pulse voltage at the magnetron

Fig. 5·1.—Photograph of the original Model 3 hard-tube pulser.

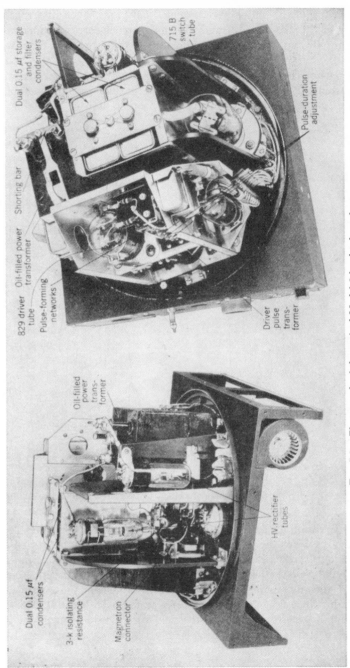

FIG. 5·2.—Photograph of the revised Model 3 hard-tube pulser.

input, because these pulses were intended only for beacon interrogation. The current drop in the 2J21 and 2J22 magnetrons corresponding to this change in pulse voltage was approximately 10 to 15 per cent for a 1-μsec pulse.

When using the TR tubes and receivers first developed for microwave-radar systems, it was considered necessary that the trailing edge of the voltage pulse applied to the magnetron drop to zero in $\frac{1}{2}$ μsec or less.

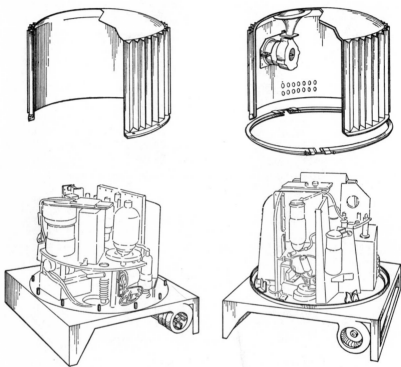

Fig. 5·3.—Sketch showing the two types of airtight housing used with the Model 3 hard-tube pulser.

In order to accomplish this voltage drop when using a resistance as the recharging path for the storage condenser, this resistance had to be only three or four times the static resistance of the magnetron. Since the resulting pulse-power loss in the recharging resistance was appreciable, the need for high efficiency made this arrangement impractical. A 10-mh inductance was chosen for the recharging path because it brought the trailing edge of the pulse down quickly and wasted less power since the pulse current in this shunt path is only 1.2 amp at the end of a 1-μsec pulse.

In the original design the isolating element in series with the high-voltage power supply was a 5-mh inductance. Oscillations in the voltage of the storage condenser occurred during the charging interval, as indicated in the curves of Figs. 2·39 and 2·40. The amplitude of these oscillations was sufficient to induce voltages in other parts of the circuit,

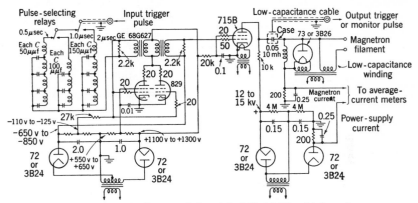

FIG. 5·4.—Schematic diagram of the original Model 3 hard-tube pulser.

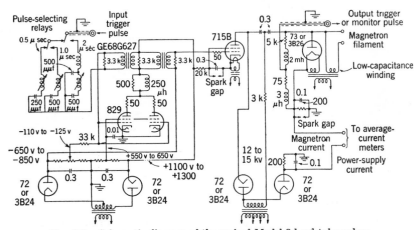

FIG. 5·5.—Schematic diagram of the revised Model 3 hard-tube pulser.

causing false signals to appear on the indicator of the radar system. It was therefore necessary to introduce a 500-ohm resistor in series with the 5-mh charging inductance in order to eliminate these oscillations. The result of the addition is shown in Fig. 2·40. Since it proved difficult to find a satisfactory 500-ohm resistor that was not too bulky, the 5-mh inductance was soon replaced by a 10,000-ohm resistor. The shape of the trailing edges obtained with the 10-mh recharging path and the

10,000-ohm isolating resistor for the three pulse durations is shown in the oscilloscope traces reproduced in Fig. 2·25. The traces reproduced in Fig. 2·19 indicate the corresponding behavior when the 10-mh inductance was replaced by a 10,000-ohm resistor.

As the development of radar systems and components progressed, it became evident that the importance of having a steep trailing edge on the voltage pulse had been overemphasized. Therefore, in the design of the revised version of the pulser less attention was given to this detail. Perfectly satisfactory operation of the radar system could be obtained with a voltage pulse that dropped to zero in as much as 1.5 μsec.

The use of an inductance as the recharging path causes a positive backswing voltage to appear at the end of the pulse. This positive voltage is added to the power-supply voltage at the plate of the switch tube and may result in sparking, particularly when the power-supply voltage is near the safe upper limit for the tube. It is therefore necessary to introduce a shunt diode, as indicated in Chap. 2. When an inductive resistor is used as the recharging path, and the magnetron is connected directly to the output of the pulser, the shunt diode is unnecessary. (This was one of the modifications incorporated into the revised design as a result of the relaxed requirement on the time for the voltage to fall to zero.) The photographs of Fig. 2·27 show the voltage pulses obtained with an inductive resistor in parallel with the magnetron load.

It is generally desirable to have some available means of monitoring the current through the magnetron. In a hard-tube pulser, the average magnetron current is equal to the average current corresponding to the recharging of the storage condenser. This current may be measured simply by connecting an ammeter in series with the recharging path as indicated in the Figs. 5·4 and 5·5. This meter must be bypassed by a capacitance sufficiently large to prevent the meter from being damaged by the pulse current that flows while the switch tube is conducting. The precautions necessary for such average-current measurements are discussed in detail in Appendix A. A resistor is usually connected in parallel with the meter in order to provide a conducting path when the meter is disconnected. This resistance must be large enough so that it introduces a negligible error in the ammeter reading, but not so large that it appreciably increases the condenser-charging time constant. (In the Model 3 pulser this resistance was about 200 ohms.) When a shunt diode is used in the pulser, the average-current meter must be connected in such a way that it measures the sum of the currents in the diode and the recharging path.

When the design of the Model 3 pulser was begun, no really satisfactory switch tube was available. The 304TH, which had been used in previous designs, required so much cathode-heating power that it could not be considered for a small airtight unit. The development of the 715B provided a tube that was capable of withstanding the high voltage and had sufficient cathode emission for the required plate current. Since this tube has an oxide cathode, much skepticism was expressed concerning its suitability for an application where a plate voltage of as much as 15 kv and a pulse-plate current of almost 15 amp were needed. Extensive life tests, however, showed that factory tests could be devised that would eliminate the relatively few tubes that could not meet the pulser requirements.

The 715B tube is a tetrode and, as indicated in Chap. 3, its pulse characteristics make it very suitable as a pulser switch tube. The bias voltage that is necessary to keep the tube nonconducting during the interpulse interval is about −500 volts, although occasional tubes require as much as −750 volts. The Model 3 pulser was designed with a bias voltage of at least −650 volts in order to insure a negligible plate current during the interpulse interval for the majority of 715B tubes. The bias voltage and the screen-grid voltage of +1250 volts are both obtained from the power supply in the driver circuit. Since a high resistance is connected in series with the screen grid as a protection against excessive screen grid current, it is necessary to bypass the screen grid to the cathode with a reasonably large capacitance. This capacitance was 0.06 μf in the original model, but was increased to 0.3 μf in the revised pulser. The increase in size of the bypass capacitance improved the pulse shape for marginal tubes, since it decreased the drop in screen voltage during the pulse.

With a screen-grid voltage of 1250 volts and a positive grid drive of 200 to 250 volts, a pulse current of 12 amp can be obtained in the magnetron for a tube drop of about 1.5 kv in the 715B. The plate current at the start of the pulse consists of the load current and the current through the 10,000-ohm isolating resistor. At the end of the pulse, the current that has been built up in the 10-mh shunt inductance is an additional contribution to the plate current. As stated previously, this additional plate current is about 1.2 amp for a 1-μsec pulse. Thus, the plate current should increase from 12 amp to 13.2 amp during the pulse if the magnetron current remains constant. The drop in the voltage on the storage condenser, however, causes the load current to decrease by an amount which may actually be more than the increase in current occurring in the 10-mh inductance, and as a result the net plate current may be less at the end than at the beginning of the pulse.

A plot of the components of the cathode current in a 715B switch tube used in one of these pulsers is shown in Fig. 5·6. The pulse current in the magnetron load, the current in the 10-mh inductance, the screen-grid current, and the total cathode current were measured by means of a synchroscope and calibrated noninductive resistors. The block labeled "$I_{g_1} + I_{10K \text{ resistor}} + \text{errors}$" was not measured, but its magnitude agrees well with the expected value. With a power-supply voltage of 12 kv and a magnetron-pulse voltage of 10·5 kv, the current in the isolating resistor is about 1 amp, which leaves a value of about 0.5 to 0.9 amp for the control-grid current. This value agrees with the pulse characteristics for the 715B shown in Fig. 3·7. The drop in voltage on the 0.05-μf

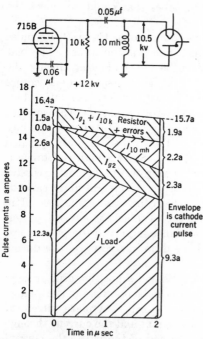

FIG. 5·6.—Components of 715B cathode-current pulse with magnetron load.

storage condenser for a 2-μsec pulse should be about 480 volts. The observed drop in magnetron current was 3 amp, corresponding to a dynamic resistance of 160 ohms, a value that is also in agreement with the known characteristics of the 725A magnetron used for these measurements. From this plot it may be seen that the total cathode current actually decreases slightly during the pulse. The slight decrease in the screen-grid current is due to a drop in screen-grid voltage during the pulse caused by a bypass condenser of insufficient capacitance (0.06 μf).

Because of the high frequency of the primary power source, 400 to 2400 cycles/sec for the airborne radar systems, it was possible to consider using a voltage-doubler rectifier for the high-voltage supply. The size of the power transformer and the voltage on the filter condensers for this design were less than those for an equivalent half-wave or full-wave rectifier. The over-all specifications for the systems using the Model 3 pulser called for reasonably good regulation of the voltage from the alternators. Therefore, because the inherent voltage regulation of the voltage-doubler power supply was poor, it was necessary to specify that the same duty ratio be used for each of the three pulse durations. The high-voltage power supply in this pulser consisted of two 0.15-μf 8-kv condensers in a single can, and two RKR72 rectifier tubes. (Later the 3B24 became available and replaced the RKR72.) The high voltage could be changed by means of an 8-ohm variable resistor connected in series with the primary of the high-voltage transformer. In order to cover a wider range of voltage without using a larger resistance, there were three taps on the transformer primary. The regulation of the power supply was considerably poorer with the resistance in the circuit. The curves of Fig. 5·7 indicate the regulation obtained with and without the 8-ohm resistance.

The average current taken from the high-voltage power supply during the operation of a pulser serves as a convenient means of monitoring the circuit behavior. A power-supply current that is higher than the value corresponding to the average current in the magnetron indicates the breakdown of insulation somewhere in the high-voltage part of the circuit. In this way, it is often possible to detect the start of breakdown of the insulation in the filter and storage condensers. The

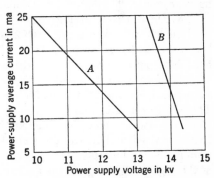

Fig. 5·7.—Regulation obtained with the voltage-doubler power supply used in a light-weight medium-power airborne pulser. Curve *A* is for 8 ohms in series and *B* is for no resistance in series with the primary of the power transformer.

average current is measured in the ground connection to the power supply in the same manner used to measure the magnetron average current. In this pulser, the average power-supply current was about 5 ma higher than the average magnetron current, in the range 8 ma to 12 ma, when a 0.001 duty ratio was used.

One of the major circuit modifications made in the design of the revised Model 3 pulser was a change in the high-voltage power supply. At the beginning of the description of the pulser output circuit, it is stated that a 2 per cent drop in pulse voltage was considered allowable for a 1-μsec pulse. One of the factors involved in this consideration was the physical size of the storage condenser. If it had been possible to use a capacitance larger than 0.05 μf in the available space, a drop in voltage smaller than 2 per cent would have been desirable. A smaller drop in voltage during the pulse was obtained by combining the condensers of the voltage-doubler rectifier with the storage condenser, as shown in Fig. 5·5. The same condensers serve both purposes, and the effective storage capacitance was therefore 0.15 μf. Thus, the drop in voltage is one third of that obtained with the 0.05-μf condenser of the original design.

The power-supply arrangement of the revised pulser had one disadvantage, namely, that the effective filtering action was not as good as that obtained with the original arrangement. This disadvantage was alleviated, however, by the fact that the minimum frequency of the primary power supply had been raised from 400 cps to 800 cps by the time this revision was considered. With the 800 cps a-c supply, a small amount (two or three per cent) of amplitude jitter was observable on the magnetron current pulse. This small amplitude jitter was not found to have any observable effect on the magnetron operation.

The Driver Circuit.—The regenerative driver designed for this pulser used an 829 tube and a GE 68G627 pulse transformer. The circuit for this driver is discussed in Sec. 4·2 and is shown in detail in Figs. 5·4 and 5·5. The power supply for the driver consisted of two half-wave rectifiers, one for the positive and one for the negative voltages required. The same positive voltage was used for the 829 plate and the 715B screen grid. The 829 screen grid and bias voltages were obtained from taps on the bleeder resistance connected across the two parts of the power supply. In the revised design, the filter condensers in the driver power supply were made considerably smaller than those in the original, again because of the higher frequency of the a-c input.

The pulse-forming networks used in the early driver units consisted of several inductance and capacitance sections. As stated in Sec. 4·2, the impedance of these networks is not critical, so it was possible to use standard sizes of condensers and then adjust the inductances to produce the desired pulse duration. The general procedure in designing such a network is to make an approximate calculation of the values of L_N and C_N from the two relationships $\tau = 2\sqrt{L_N C_N}$ and $Z_N = \sqrt{L_N/C_N}$ with $Z_N \approx 1000$ ohms. The actual value of L_N is then determined empirically using the nearest standard condenser size. Once the constants for the networks are found, it is somewhat of a problem to control the production methods so as to have pulse durations that lie within a ± 10 per cent tolerance about the nominal value. This problem arises from the fact that the actual pulse duration depends on many factors, such as the network itself, the pulse transformer, the stray inductances and capacitances in the driver circuit, the tube characteristics (to some extent), and also the load presented to the driver by the grid circuit of the switch tube. The final procedure adopted by the pulser manufacturers was to test each completed network for proper pulse duration, rather than to depend on inductance and capacitance measurements.

Experience with the regenerative-driver circuit indicated that a satisfactory pulse shape could be obtained with pulse-forming networks that were reduced to single inductances and condensers, at least for a pulse-duration of 1 μsec or less. Accordingly, the networks used in the revised design were built in this manner, as shown in Fig. 5·5. It thus became feasible to make the single inductance variable, and thereby to have an available means for varying the pulse duration. In the units manufactured by the Stromberg-Carlson Company the inductance was varied by means of a copper slug that could be moved toward or away from the end of the coil. This copper slug provided an adjustment of about ±10 per cent in the pulse duration. In units manufactured by the Philco Corporation, the variation was obtained by means of a ferro-magnetic slug that could be moved along the axis of the coil. A variation of about ±20 per cent was made available by this arrangement. The variable inductance proved to be a great convenience because it allowed the pulse duration to be adjusted after the completion of the whole driver unit.

Protective Measures.—Because of the strict limitation on the size of the Model 3 pulser, it was decided that a minimum of time-delay and overload-protection devices would be incorporated. Consequently, the control circuit was made as simple as possible. Two relays were provided to be actuated by the available 24 v d-c. The first controlled the a-c input to all except the high-voltage transformer. By energizing the second relay, the high-voltage power supply was turned on. The only control over the delay time required after turning on the filaments and before turning on the high voltage was a sign warning the operator to wait three minutes. Instead of a relay for overload protection, two fuses were provided, a 10-amp fuse in the main a-c line to the pulser, and a 5-amp fuse in series with the high-voltage power transformer.

In the original unit, a bleeder resistance was provided across the high-voltage power supply. When the input circuit to the power transformer was opened, this bleeder reduced the voltage on the filter condenser rapidly enough to give reasonable protection against electric shock. The bleeder resistance could not be used with the revised pulser, however, and it was therefore necessary to provide a shorting device. This device was a mechanically operated shorting bar that short-circuited the power supply when the airtight housing was removed.

Heat Dissipation.—Since the unit was required to be airtight, it was necessary to circulate the air within the housing in order to obtain as much heat transfer as possible to the walls. This circulation was accomplished by means of a small blower with a 24-v d-c motor. The outside of the housing was corrugated to increase the surface area exposed to the external air. The power input to the original pulser was about 450 watts for an output of 144 watts. Thus, about 300 watts were dissipated within the airtight container. The temperature rise within the unit under these conditions was about 55°C. With an external fan blowing air against the outside of the housing at the rate of 60 ft³/min, this temperature rise was reduced to about 40°C. The heat dissipation in the revised pulser was reduced slightly from the above figure and, with improved heat transfer to the walls of the housing, the internal temperature rise was about 40°C without an external fan. In the revised design, better heat transfer to the outside air was obtained by the use of a double-walled housing.   The internal blower forced the heated air to pass between the walls of the inner and outer housing wall, as shown in the sketch in Fig. 5·3.   Because of the high temperature at which the components of this pulser must operate, special attention was given to the choice of the condensers.   The Sprague Vitamin Q condensers proved satisfactory up to 105°C, and were therefore used in both the original and revised Model 3 pulsers.

5.2. The Model 9 Pulser—A 1-Mw Hard-tube Pulser.—The need for a high-power pulser to be used in the testing of magnetrons became urgent early in 1941.   The research and development that was started at this time led to the design of a hard-tube pulser that could deliver a pulse power of 1 Mw (25 kv at 40 amp) to a magnetron.   The original design of this unit was called the Model 4 pulser, but after some modifications were introduced, particularly in the driver circuit, the pulser became known as the Model 9.   In addition to its use in determining the performance characteristics of magnetrons, this pulser was used in some ground-based radar systems.   One of these systems in particular was widely used as a mobile radar unit in both defensive and offensive operations during the war.   The Model 9 pulser was used in this radar application because its operational characteristics satisfied the requirements for precision ranging and automatic following.   The operational use of this radar system demanded that a very high degree of reliability be maintained over long periods of time under conditions of almost continuous operation.   Because of the somewhat unsatisfactory life of the available switch tubes and magnetrons with the full 1-Mw pulse power, the pulser was operated at a pulse-power output of about 800 kw.

The Model 9 pulser was designed to meet the following specifications:
Output pulse power: 1000 kw (25 kv at 40 amp).
Maximum duty ratio: 0.002.
Pulse duration: 0.25 to 2.0 μsec (remote control of pulse selection).
Size and weight: As small as possible compatible with good engineering design.
Input voltage: 115 volts, 60 cycles/sec, single phase (the units for the mobile radar system were built for three-phase supply).

The specified voltage and current output for this hard-tube pulser required that the high-voltage power supply be designed for about 30 kv and 100 ma.   Because of this high voltage and average current, it was impractical to design the pulser and the power supply as a single unit.   Consequently, the pulser was built in one cabinet and the power supply in another, necessarily making the total weight larger than it would be for a single unit.   The completed pulser occupies a cabinet 26 by 34 by 55 in. and weighs about 800 lb.   The power-supply cabinet is approximately the same size but weighs about 1200 lb.   The photographs reproduced in Fig. 5·8 indicate the disposition of the components in the pulser cabinet.   The schematic diagram for the Model 9 pulser with control circuits omitted is shown in Fig. 5·9.

The Output Circuit.—For the measurements necessary in determining the performance characteristics of a magnetron, it is desirable to have the shape of the output pulse from the pulser as rectangular as possible. It was therefore decided that the top of the voltage pulse should be flat to better than the 2 per cent figure allowed in the Model 3 pulser design. The choice of the actual energy-storage capacitance to be used was influenced by the available high-voltage condensers.   Since a value of 0.125 μf was chosen, the drop in pulse voltage for a 1-μsec pulse is about 1.3 per cent at the full output power from the pulser (25 kv at 40 amp). This value of the storage capacitance was considered sufficient for the majority of the applications, and for many of these, the drop in voltage was not greater than 1 per cent because the actual pulse current used was less than the maximum value of 40 amp.

As in the case of the Model 3 pulser, the trailing edge of the voltage pulse was required to drop to zero in less than 0.5 μsec.   With a magnetron load, the rate of fall of the pulse voltage depends on the amount of energy stored in stray capacitance during the pulse, and on the nature of the recharging path for the storage condenser.   The stray capacitance and voltage were larger for the Model 9 pulser than for lower-power pulsers, and consequently, if a resistance were to be used as the recharging path, its value would have to be so small that a large amount of pulse power would be wasted.   It was therefore decided to use a 5-mh inductance in place of the resistance, this value being adequate even for the 0.5- and 0.25-μsec pulses.

The isolating element in series with the high-voltage power supply is a 10,000-ohm resistance.   Thus, a pulse current of about 2.5 amp flows through this resistance at maximum pulse voltage output from the pulser. The power lost during the pulse interval in this resistance at the maximum duty ratio of 0.002 is, therefore,

$$P = I_c^2 R_c \tau (\text{PRF}) = (2.5)^2 \times 10^4 \times 0.002 = 125 \text{ watts.}$$

If the maximum duty ratio of 0.002 corresponds to operation at a pulse duration of 1 μsec and a PRF of 2000 pps, the interpulse interval is 5×10^{-4} sec.   If it is assumed that the 10,000-ohm resistor constitutes the entire recharging path for the storage condenser, the power dissipated during the interpulse interval may be calculated as outlined in Sec. 2·4. Thus, in this case, the time constant is

$$RC = 10^4 \times 0.125 \times 10^{-6} = 1.25 \times 10^{-3} \text{ sec.}$$

and the interpulse interval is equal to $0.4RC$. The rms charging current is then 1.006 times the average current. For operation at full pulse power and 0.002 duty ratio, the average recharging current is 80 ma, so $(I_c)_{rms} = 80.5$ ma, and the power lost in the charging resistor is $(0.08)^2 \times 10^4 \approx 64$ watts. The isolating resistance must therefore be capable of dissipating about 200 watts. Because of the high voltage

Fig. 5·8.—Photographs of

across this resistance, the pulser was designed with four 2500-ohm units in series.

In order to eliminate the backswing voltage inherent in the use of the inductance recharging path, it was necessary to incorporate a shunt diode into the pulser design. This diode had to be capable of passing a pulse current of several amperes, and of withstanding an inverse voltage of 25 kv. The choice of tube for this function was somewhat limited, and it proved to be more economical of space and cathode power to use two 8020 diodes in parallel, rather than a single large tube. It was necessary to use more than one 8020 tube because the plate dissipation was greater than that allowed for a single tube.

The average magnetron current is measured by a meter connected in series with the recharging path for the storage condenser.   In the Model 9 pulser, a current-sensitive relay is connected in series with this meter. The contacts of this relay are connected in series with the primary winding

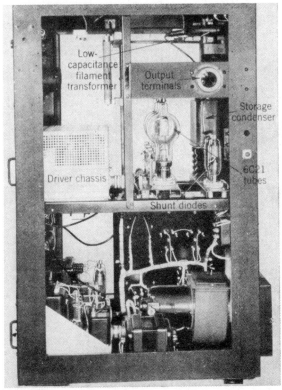

the Model 9 1-Mw pulser.

of the transformer used to heat the magnetron cathode.   By adjusting a resistance in parallel with the coil of this relay, it is possible to have the magnetron-cathode heater current shut off when the average magnetron current reaches a certain minimum value.   This feature was added to this pulser because the back-bombardment heating of the magnetron cathode became large enough at high average power to keep the cathode hot without any current in the heater.   This automatic reduction of the cathode-heating power minimized the danger of overheating the cathode, and the consequent shortening of the life of the magnetron.

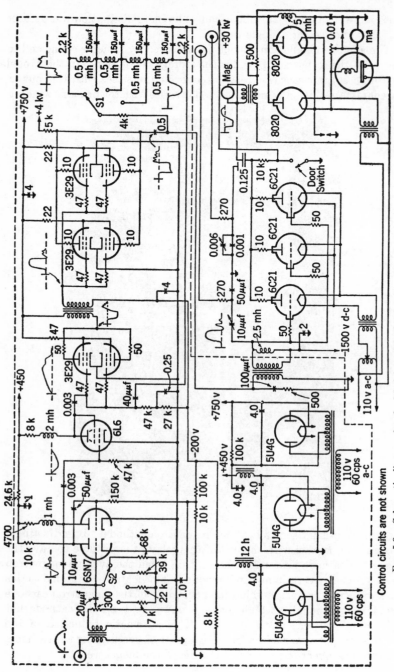

FIG. 5·9.—Schematic diagram for the Model 9 1-Mw hard-tube pulser.   Control circuits are not shown.

Control circuits are not shown

A survey of available tubes that could be used as the switch in the Model 9 pulser indicated that the Eimac 1000 UHF triode, later called the 6C21, was the best choice. The pulse characteristics for this tube, shown in Fig. 3·10, indicate that three tubes in parallel are required to obtain a pulse current of 40 amp in the pulser load. It proved to be more economical of cathode-heating power and grid-drive power to use several of these tubes in parallel, instead of a single large tube that could withstand the plate voltage of 30 kv and carry the required pulse current. Although the 1000 UHF was rated for a considerably lower plate voltage, laboratory tests proved that the tube could be operated at 30 kv under the conditions of pulse operation.

The pulse currents in the 10,000-ohm isolating resistance and in the 5-mh recharging inductance must be added to the load pulse current when determining the total plate current for the switch tubes. For a 40-amp load current in the Model 9 pulser, the total plate current is 45 to 50 amp. The curves of Fig. 3·10 indicate that this plate current can be obtained with three 6C21 tubes in parallel if the positive grid drive is 1000 to 1500 volts and the tube drop is 4 to 5 kv. Under these conditions the pulse-grid current becomes about 1.5 to 2.5 amp for each tube. In order to keep the 6C21 tube from conducting during the interpulse interval, the grid must be biased at least 1200 volts negative when the plate voltage is 30 kv. The pulser was designed with a grid bias of 1500 volts to insure a negligible plate current during the interpulse interval for any tube. The grid-driving power necessary for the switch-tube operation in this pulser is therefore about 20 kw. This value is not unreasonably large for a 1-Mw pulser.

The Driver Circuit.—The driver circuit used for the Model 9 pulser has been described in Sec. 4·3. A block diagram and a simplified schematic of this driver are shown in Figs. 4·9 and 4·10. The 3E29 tube was chosen for the final pulse amplifier in this driver because the grid swing of 2.5 to 3 kv required for the 6C21 tubes could not be obtained from an 829 tube. As stated in Chap. 3, the 829 tube has a plate-voltage rating for pulse operation of 2 kv, whereas the 3E29 was designed for a plate voltage of 5 kv. Although the grid current of 5 to 8 amp in the three 6C21 tubes could be obtained with a single 3E29 tube, the driver was designed with two of these tubes in parallel in order to provide a greater factor of safety. A plate voltage of 4 kv and a screen-grid voltage of 720 volts was used for these final amplifier tubes in the driver.

Since the voltage output available from the 6L6 buffer amplifier following the multivibrator was not sufficient, an intermediate amplifier tube was necessary. An 829 could serve this purpose, but in order to reduce the number of tube types, another 3E29 was used instead, which operated with the plate voltage and the screen-grid voltage obtained from a 750-volt power supply.

As stated in Sec. 4·3, the pulse duration obtained from this driver is changed by varying the length of the delay line in the feedback (tail-biting) circuit. This variation is accomplished by means of a series of taps on the delay line which can be selected by a switch. This switch is mechanically linked with another switch that changes the constants in the multivibrator in order to keep the pulse duration for the multivibrator about 25 to 40 per cent larger than that desired at the output of the driver.

The driver for the Model 9 pulser was constructed in a unit physically separable from the rest of the pulser. This arrangement provides an easy means of servicing the driver and making any desired modifications. All the d-c voltages necessary for the driver circuit, with the exception of the 4-kv supply for the 3E29 plates, are obtained from power supplies contained in the driver unit.

Modifications to Obtain Continuously Variable Pulse Duration over the Range 0.5 μsec to 5 μsec.—A slight modification of the driver circuit made it possible to vary the pulse duration continuously over the range 0.5 to 5 μsec. This variation was accomplished by removing the delay line entirely and introducing a variable resistance in place of the switch and the series of fixed resistances in the grid circuit of the normally "on" half of the 6SN7 multivibrator tube. Since the pulse duration is approximately an exponential function of this grid resistance, a tapered potentiometer was designed to allow the pulse duration to vary with the position of the adjustment control in a reasonably linear manner. The modified multivibrator is shown in Fig. 5·10. The circuit elements indicated in heavy lines are those that were changed from the original arrangement shown in Fig. 5·9 in order to obtain satisfactory operation over the 0.5-to 5.0-μsec range in pulse duration. The only other change in the driver circuit necessary for this purpose was the addition of an inductive resistor

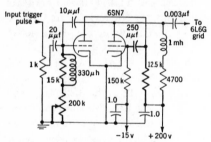

Fig. 5·10.—Modified multivibrator circuit for driver in Model 9 pulser to provide pulse durations continuously variable over the range 0.5 to 5 μsec.

with a resistance of 1000 ohms and an inductance of 160 μh across the secondary of the pulse transformer following the first 3E29 tube. This element was necessary to make the driver output pulse fall more rapidly; it was not needed in the original circuit, because the feedback pulse through the delay line provided a sufficiently fast rate of fall for the driver pulse.

Besides these changes in the driver circuit, two other modifications were made in the Model 9 pulser for the extension to 5-μsec operation.

The 0.125-μf storage capacitance was replaced by a 0.3-μf capacitance. With the larger capacitance, the drop in voltage during a 5-μsec pulse is about two per cent at the full power output of 25 kv and 40 amp. The other change in the output circuit consisted of replacing the 5-mh induct-

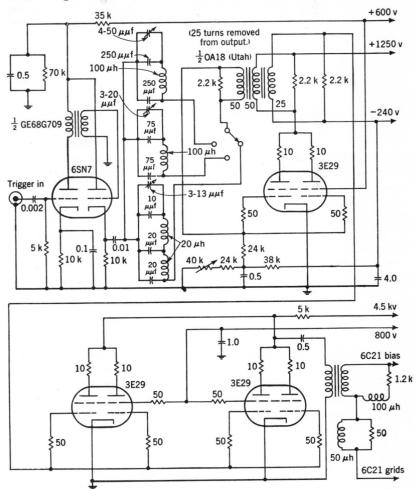

Fig. 5·11.—Regenerative driver for 0.1- to 0.5-μsec operation of the Model 9 pulser.

ance in the storage-condenser recharging path by a 2.5-mh inductance and 4000-ohm resistance in series. With this inductance-resistance combination, the trailing edge of the voltage pulse is brought down quickly, and the pulse current in these elements is considerably less than that in the 5-mh inductance for long-pulse operation.

Modification to Obtain Pulser Operation over the Range 0.1 *μsec to* 0.5 *μsec.*—A regenerative-driver circuit similar to that described in Sec. 4·2 was also designed to be used with the Model 9 pulser for pulse durations from 0.1 to 0.5 μsec. The schematic circuit is shown in Fig. 5·11. This driver was constructed to be physically and electrically interchangeable with the variable-pulse-duration driver, thus providing a pulser that can be operated over the range in pulse duration from 0.1 to 5 μsec. For the operation, from 0.25 to 0.5 μsec, the 4000-ohm resistance in the storage-condenser recharging path is short-circuited in order to make the voltage pulse fall quickly, and for 0.1-μsec operation only 1 mh of the 2.5-mh inductance is used. When a long tail on the voltage pulse is not objectionable, the output circuit of the pulser can be used in the same manner as for the longer pulse operation.

Protective Measures.—Because of the high voltage necessary for this 1-Mw hard-tube pulser, great care is taken to protect the operator from accidental shock. Interlocks are provided on all doors, and all the power supplies have bleeder resistances to discharge the filter condensers. An automatic shorting bar is actuated so as to discharge the storage condenser when the cabinet doors are opened. Overload relays and fuses are incorporated to protect components against abnormal increases in voltage and current in critical parts of the circuit.

Since several kilowatts of power are dissipated inside the pulser cabinet, it is necessary to provide protection against overheating of components. A large blower is therefore installed to draw air through a filter from outside the cabinet and circulate it inside the cabinet.

5·3. A High-power Short-pulse Hard-tube Pulser.—This pulser was designed and constructed for the purpose of determining the behavior of magnetrons and the operation of radar systems under conditions of high pulse power and very short pulse duration. For these tests it was specified that the pulser be capable of delivering pulse power of 1 Mw or more to a magnetron at various pulse durations in the range from 0.03 μsec to 0.15 μsec. The pulse shape was to be as rectangular as possible in order that a reasonable evaluation could be made of the magnetron and radar-system performance in terms of the pulse duration. It was further required that the pulse-power input to the magnetron be adjustable from small to large values without any appreciable change in the pulse shape or the pulse duration. The combination of these requirements dictated that the pulser be of the hard-tube type.

The schematic diagram for the pulser circuit designed to meet the above requirements is shown in Fig. 5·12. Photographs of the unit constructed for the laboratory tests are reproduced in Fig. 5·13.

The Output Circuit.—Because of the limitation imposed by available components, particularly the switch tube, the pulser was designed for a maximum voltage-pulse amplitude of about 30 kv, and a pulse current of about 35 amp.   Since it was desired that the short pulses be nearly rectangular, the output circuit had to be designed for a very high rate of rise of voltage.   The inductance and the shunt capacitance in the pulser circuit therefore had to be kept as small as possible.   In order to minimize the inductance introduced by the circuit connections, the components were mounted as close together as their physical size would permit, allowing for the spacing necessary to prevent high-voltage flash-over.   The importance of keeping the stray capacitance small is evident when

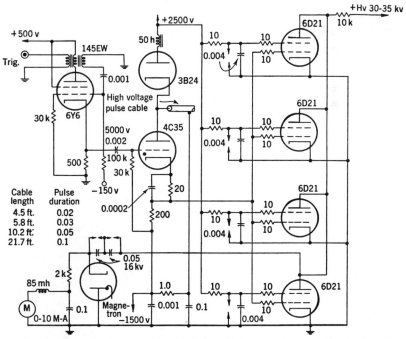

Fig. 5·12.—Schematic diagram of the circuit for a high-power short-pulse hard-tube pulser.

the charging current, $C_s \, dv_l/dt$, for this capacitance is considered.   For example, if the capacitance across the output terminals of the pulser is 20 $\mu\mu$f and the voltage pulse at the load is to rise to 30 kv in 0.01 μsec, the condenser-charging current is 60 amp.   Since this current must flow through the switch tube, the maximum plate current needed to obtain a large value of dv/dt may be considerably greater than that needed to deliver the required pulse power to the load.   The magnetron may have a capacitance of 10 to 15 $\mu\mu$f, between cathode and anode, so it is obvious that the additional capacitance introduced by the pulser circuit must be small.

Fig. 5·13.—Photographs of a hard-tube pulser constructed for laboratory tests at very short pulse duration and high pulse power.

The storage capacitance used for this pulser consisted of two 0.05-μf 15-kv condensers connected in series.   The effective capacitance of 0.025 μf was ample for the short pulse durations, since the drop in voltage is only 140 volts for a 0.1-μsec 35-amp pulse.   These condensers were arranged so as to keep the connections short and the stray capacitance to ground low, as may be observed in the photographs of Fig. 5·13.

One of the most serious problems encountered in the design of this pulser was the choice of a satisfactory switch tube.   The requirements of high pulse voltage and high pulse current could not be met by a single tube of any available type.   It was necessary to choose the 6D21 tetrode from the standpoint of the high plate voltage needed, and to use four of these tubes in parallel in order to obtain the plate current required for the maximum pulse-power operation.   The curves of Fig. 3·10 indicate that four 6D21 tubes are capable of a total plate current of 70 to 80 amp, which is sufficient to allow the voltage pulse to rise at the rate of 3000 kv/μsec for a stray capacitance of about 20 $\mu\mu$f.

In order to minimize the inductance in the pulse circuit, the plate terminals of the four 6D21 tubes were interconnected by means of a thick brass plate.   This brass plate served also as the mechanical support for one end of the storage condenser in order to provide a short connection and to keep the capacitance to ground small.   The other terminal of the storage condenser was attached to the magnetron-cathode terminal as can be seen in Fig. 5·13.   The inductance of the ground connection to the cathodes of the four 6D21 tubes was also kept small by mounting the sockets on a heavy brass plate that served as the common ground terminal for the pulser circuit.

The low value of stray capacitance across the pulser output aided the quick return of the pulse voltage to zero at the end of the pulse.   In order to make the voltage fall to zero in a few hundredths of a microsecond, however, it was still necessary to use a relatively low resistance for the storage-condenser recharging path.   A value of 2000 ohms was used, although this value was only about twice the normal load resistance. The use of an inductance for the recharging path was not considered, because it would then be necessary to add a shunt diode to eliminate the backswing voltage, and the addition of such a diode to the circuit would of necessity increase the stray capacitance.   It was considered more important to keep this capacitance small than to decrease the pulse power lost in the shunt path by the use of an inductance.

The Driver Circuit.—Because of the relatively large pulse power required to drive the grid of four 6D21 tubes, it was decided to use a pulse-forming network driver of the type discussed in Sec. 4·3.   This driver was a line-type pulser using inductance charging of the pulse-forming network.   A hold-off diode was used in the network-charging circuit in order to provide some flexibility in the range of pulse recurrence frequencies that could be used.   The circuit was so arranged that the screen-grid voltage for the 6D21 tubes was obtained from the power supply used to charge the network.

The pulse-forming network in this driver consisted of a short length of 50-ohm high-voltage pulse cable.   The pulse duration could then be easily changed by varying the length of the cable.   The lengths actually used for various pulse durations were obtained experimentally, and are indicated in the diagram of Fig. 5·12.   The approximate length to be used for a particular pulse duration can be calculated since it is known that the velocity of propagation for a voltage wave in this cable is about 450 ft/μsec and that the wave must traverse the length of cable twice during the pulse.   The coil of cable used for the pulse-forming network may be seen in the photograph of Fig. 5·13.

In order to obtain a fast rate of rise for the pulse applied to the grids of the 6D21 tubes, it was necessary to keep the connection between the driver and the grid terminals as short as possible.   The 4C35 switch tube of the driver was therefore mounted upside down beneath the plate supporting the four tubes.   Since the cathode of the 4C35 must rise and fall in potential along with the 6D21 grids, a low-capacitance transformer was used to supply the cathode-heating power.

Operation.—This pulser was operated at pulse durations as short as 0.02 μsec and at a pulse power of 950 kw with a magnetron load.   The magnetron pulse current was not observed in the usual way (see Appendix A), in which a resistor is introduced between the magnetron anode and ground, because for these short pulses the added capacitance and inductance introduced by such a resistor was sufficient to cause distortion of the pulse shape.   The pulse current was determined from the measured average magnetron current, the pulse recurrence frequency, and the pulse duration.   The pulse duration was measured for the r-f envelope pulse, and the oscilloscope sweep speed calibrated by measuring the frequency difference between the first minima on either side of the center frequency of the r-f spectrum.   This calibration was done with a 0.1-μsec pulse whose frequency difference of 20Mc/sec could be measured with reasonable precision.

Photographs of the oscilloscope traces for some voltage and r-f pulses obtained with this pulser are reproduced in Fig. 5·14.   The time delay between the start of the voltage pulse and the start of the r-f pulse is characteristic of magnetrons, and its magnitude depends on a large number of factors (cf. Chap. 9 of Vol. 6).   The relatively slow rate of rise for the r-f envelope pulse is due in part to the detector and the oscilloscope circuit used to obtain the trace.   The fraction of the observed time required for the r-f pulse to build up that was due to the circuit and the fraction that was inherent in the magnetron output were not determined in these cases. Other experiments[1] have indicated that the time for this buildup may be about 0.01 μsec.

One of the interesting results obtained with this pulser is the fact that a magnetron can operate satisfactorily with considerably higher pulse-power input as the pulse duration is decreased. With a 725A magnetron, for example, the operation was satisfactory, that is, there was no sparking, with a pulse-power input of 900 kw at a pulse duration of 0.03 μsec. The r-f power output under these conditions was 195 kw. In contrast, the magnetron could not be operated above 15 kv and 15 amp without sparking when the pulse duration was about 2 μsec.

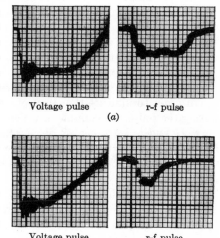

Voltage pulse   r-f pulse
(a)

Voltage pulse   r-f pulse
(b)

FIG. 5·14.—Photographs of oscilloscope traces for voltage and r-f pulses obtained with a high-power short-pulse hard-tube pulser. (a) 0.1 μsec pulses, (b) 0.03 μsec pulses.

5·4. The Application of Pulse-shaping Networks to the Hard-tube Pulser.—Throughout the preceding discussions of the design of hard-tube pulsers, the effect of the value of the storage-condenser capacitance on the change in pulse voltage and pulse current during a pulse is emphasized. It is shown in Chap. 2 that, if the time constant for the discharging circuit of the storage condenser is large compared with the pulse duration, the drop in pulse voltage during the pulse is given approximately by the relation $\Delta V_l = I_{l}\tau/C_w$. If the pulse voltage changes, the pulse current also changes, but, as indicated in Chap. 2, the above relation is a sufficiently good approximation when ΔV_l is only a small percentage of the pulse voltage.

When the load on a hard-tube pulser is a pure resistance,

$$\frac{\Delta I}{I_{max}} = \frac{\Delta V}{V_{max}},$$

where I_{max} and V_{max} are the maximum load current and voltage at the beginning of the pulse. With a magnetron or biased-diode load the dynamic resistance is generally only a small fraction of the static resistance, and $\Delta I/I_{max} > \Delta V/V_{max}$, the inequality becoming larger as the

[1] F. F. Rieke and R. C. Fletcher, "Mode Selection in Magnetrons," RL Report No. 809 Sept. 28, 1945.

dynamic resistance becomes smaller. In some cases the magnitude of the current change may be so large that the operation of the magnetron oscillator is unsatisfactory. For given values of I_l and τ the magnitude of ΔV can be decreased by increasing C_w, but the resulting increase in condenser size becomes a serious problem when the size and weight of the completed pulser are important. The purpose of the present discussion is to point out a method for reducing the change in load current during the pulse without increasing the storage capacitance. The method consists of adding a network in series with the discharging circuit of the storage condenser. The network may be simply a resistance and an inductance in parallel, or it may be a more complex combination of resistance, inductance, and capacitance.

In order to indicate the effect of such a network on the load current during the pulse, an example in which the network consists of an inductance, L, and a resistance, R, in parallel is discussed in detail. The following discussion deals only with the load current associated with the top of the pulse, so the output circuit of the pulser may be simplified by neglecting the stray capacitance and inductance inherent in any design. The circuit is further simplified by considering an ideal switch with its

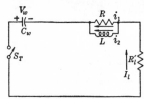

FIG. 5·15.—Simplified output circuit of a hard-tube pulser with an LR-network to minimize the change in load current during the pulse.

effective resistance combined in the load resistance. The analysis is made for the circuit shown in Fig. 5·15 with a pure-resistance load. The initial voltage on the storage condenser is V_w, and the current in L is assumed to be zero before the switch S_T is closed in order to start the pulse. The resistance R_l' includes any resistance in series with the pulse circuit exclusive of that introduced by the network. Thus R_l' represents the effective resistance $(R_l + r_p)$ for a resistance load R_l and a switch tube of resistance r_p. Using Kirchoff's laws, the Laplace-transform equations for this circuit are

$$Ri_1(p) + R_l'I_l(p) + \frac{I_l(p)}{C_w p} = \frac{V_w}{p}, \tag{1}$$

$$Ri_1(p) + Lpi_2(p) = 0, \tag{2}$$

and

$$i_1(p) + i_2(p) = I_l(p). \tag{3}$$

An equation for $I_l(p)$ is obtained by combining Eqs. (1), (2), and (3), with the result

$$I_l(p) = \frac{\dfrac{V_w}{(R + R_l')}\left(p + \dfrac{R}{L}\right)}{p^2 + \dfrac{RR_l'C_w + L}{(R + R_l')LC_w}\,p + \dfrac{R}{(R + R_l')LC_w}}. \tag{4}$$

Let

$$2a = \frac{RR'_l C_w + L}{(R + R'_l)LC_w} \tag{5}$$

and

$$b = \frac{R}{(R + R'_l)LC_w}. \tag{6}$$

Then Eq. (4) may be written

$$I_l(p) = \frac{\dfrac{V_w}{(R + R'_l)}\left(p + \dfrac{R}{L}\right)}{(p + a)^2 + \omega^2}, \tag{7}$$

where $\omega^2 = b - a^2$. $\tag{8}$

The inverse Laplace transformation of Eq. (7) gives

$$I_l(t) = \frac{V_w}{(R + R'_l)}\, e^{-at}\left[\cos \omega t + \frac{(R - La)}{L\omega} \sin \omega t\right]. \tag{9}$$

If $b < a^2$, let $k^2 = -\omega^2 = a^2 - b$. Then

$$I_l(t) = \frac{V_w}{(R + R'_l)}\, e^{-at}\left[\cosh kt + \frac{(R - La)}{Lk} \sinh kt\right]. \tag{10}$$

If $b = a^2$,

$$I_l(t) = \frac{V_w}{(R + R'_l)}\, e^{-at}\left[1 + \frac{(R - La)}{L} t\right]. \tag{11}$$

These three equations give the load current as a function of time for any combination of the circuit parameters. Since in most pulser designs the time interval involved is very small, the point of interest is whether or not a condition can be found for the circuit parameters such that $I(t)$ is a slowly varying function near $t = 0$. This condition can be determined by differentiating Eqs. (9), (10), and (11) with respect to time and equating the derivative to zero. Thus from Eq. (9)

$$\frac{dI_l}{dt} = \frac{V_w}{(R + R'_l)}\, e^{-at}\left[-\omega \sin \omega t + \frac{(R - La)}{L} \cos \omega t - a \cos \omega t \right.$$
$$\left. - \frac{a(R - La)}{L\omega} \sin \omega t\right]. \tag{12}$$

Equating this derivative to zero for $t = 0$ gives the condition

$$R = 2La. \tag{13}$$

With the value of a from Eq. (5), Eq. (13) becomes

$$L = R^2 C_w. \tag{14}$$

The identical condition is obtained by carrying out the same procedure with Eqs. (10) and (11). If the relation of Eq. (14) is used, Eqs. (9), (10), and (11) become

$$I_l(t) = \frac{V_w}{(R + R_l')} e^{-\frac{t}{2RC_w}} \left(\cos \omega t + \frac{1}{2RC_w\omega} \sin \omega t \right), \tag{15}$$

$$I_l(t) = \frac{V_w}{(R + R_l')} e^{-\frac{t}{2RC_w}} \left(\cosh kt + \frac{1}{2RC_w k} \sinh kt \right), \tag{16}$$

and

$$I_l(t) = \frac{V_w}{(R + R_l')} e^{-\frac{t}{2RC_w}} \left(1 + \frac{t}{2RC_w} \right). \tag{17}$$

Thus, when the condition of Eq. (14) is satisfied by the components of the *LR*-network, the plot of load current as a function of time has a zero slope at $t = 0$. The equation for the load current without the *LR*-network in the pulser output circuit is

$$I_l(t) = \frac{V_w}{R_l'} e^{-\frac{t}{R_l'C_w}}. \tag{18}$$

Since the plot of current versus time from this equation has a slope not equal to zero at $t = 0$, the decrease in load current obtained from Eqs. (15), (16), and (17) should be less for small values of t than that from Eq. (18).

A numerical example shows more specifically the effect of the *LR*-network on the change of load current during the pulse. Assume the following values for the circuit parameters for Fig. 5·15:

$$V_w = 12.5 \text{ kv.}$$
$$R_l' = 1000 \text{ ohms.}$$
$$C_w = 0.05 \ \mu\text{f.}$$
$$R = 50 \text{ ohms.}$$
$$L = R^2C_w = 125 \ \mu\text{h.}$$
$$\tau = 1 \ \mu\text{sec.}$$

If $L = R^2C_w$ is substituted in Eqs. (5) and (6), Eq. (8) becomes

$$\omega^2 = b - a^2 = \frac{3R - R_l'}{4R^2C_w^2(R + R_l')}. \tag{19}$$

In the present example, $3R < R_l'$, so

$$k^2 = a^2 - b = \frac{R_l' - 3R}{4R^2C_w^2(R + R_l')}, \tag{20}$$

and the current is given by Eq. (16). The change in current during

1 μsec is therefore

$$\Delta I_l = \frac{12.5 \times 10^3}{1050} [1 - e^{-0.2} (\cosh 0.18 + 1.1 \sinh 0.18)]$$
$$= 11.9 \times 0.005 = 0.06 \text{ amp.}$$

Without the LR-network, the change in load current obtained from Eq. (18) is

$$\Delta I_l = \frac{12.5 \times 10^3}{1000} [1 - e^{-0.02}]$$
$$= 12.5 \times 0.02 = 0.25 \text{ amp.}$$

Using the approximate calculation $\Delta V_l = \dfrac{I_l}{C_w} \tau$, the change in pulse voltage is

$$\Delta V_l = \frac{12.5}{0.05} = 250 \text{ volts,}$$

and

$$\Delta I_l = \tfrac{250}{1000} = 0.25 \text{ amp.}$$

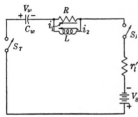

Thus the droop in the current pulse is decreased by a factor of four when the LR-network is inserted.

If the load is a biased diode or a magnetron, the output circuit of the pulser appears as shown in Fig. 5·16. The analysis for this circuit is identical to that for the circuit of Fig. 5·15, r_l' replacing R_l' and $V_w - V_s$

Fig. 5·16.—Simplified output circuit of a hard-tube pulser with a biased-diode load and an LR-network to minimize the change in load current during the pulse.

appearing in place of V_w. The resistance r_l' represents the sum of the dynamic resistance of the biased diode and the effective switch-tube resistance, that is, $(r_l + r_p)$. As another numerical example indicating the effect of the LR-network, consider the following values for the circuit parameters:

$$V_w = 12.5 \text{ kv.}$$
$$V_s = 10 \text{ kv.}$$
$$C_w = 0.05 \ \mu\text{f.}$$
$$r_l' = 200 \text{ ohms.}$$
$$R = 50 \text{ ohms.}$$
$$L = R^2 C_w = 125 \ \mu\text{h.}$$
$$\tau = 1 \ \mu\text{sec.}$$

Since $r_l' > 3R$, Eq. (16) again applies, and the change in load current during 1 μsec is

$$\Delta I_l = \tfrac{2500}{250} [1 - e^{-0.2} (\cosh 0.089 + 2.2 \sinh 0.089)]$$
$$= 10 \times 0.015 = 0.15 \text{ amp.}$$

Without the LR-network, the change in current according to Eq. (18) is

$$\Delta I_l = \tfrac{2500}{200}(1 - e^{-0.1}) = 12.5 \times 0.095 = 1.19 \text{ amp.}$$

Using the approximate calculations for ΔV,

$$\Delta V_l = \frac{12.5}{0.05} = 250 \text{ volts}$$

and

$$\Delta I_l = \tfrac{250}{200} = 1.25 \text{ amp,}$$

which agrees reasonably well with the value of 1.19 amp calculated by the exact relation of Eq. (18).

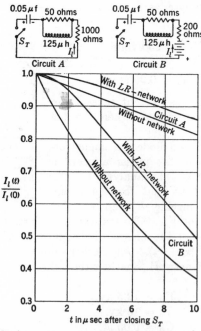

Fig. 5·17.—Change in load current as a function of time with and without an LR-network in series with the output circuit of a hard-tube pulser.

In order to keep the load current constant within 0.15 amp by increasing the capacitance of the storage condenser, this capacitance has to be about 0.4 μf. It is therefore evident that a significant advantage results from the use of the LR-network in series with the discharging circuit of the storage condenser. If the allowable drop in the load current is larger than the values obtained in the above examples, the use of an LR-network makes it possible to have a smaller capacitance for the storage condenser.

The general effect of the addition of the network on the load current is indicated by the curves of Fig. 5·17.   One set of curves is given for a 900-ohm resistance load, and another set for a biased-diode load with a 100-ohm dynamic resistance, the switch-tube resistance being 100 ohms for each set.   These curves show that a marked improvement in the slope of the top of the current pulse can be obtained even for relatively long pulse durations.   The curves also indicate that the use of an *LR*-network is more important in the operation of the pulser with a low-resistance load.

The examples given above indicate that there is also a disadvantage associated with the use of the *LR*-network.   The presence of the resistance *R* in series with the load results in a lower pulse current for a given condenser voltage V_w.   For the resistance load, the maximum value of the pulse current is 12.5 amp without the network and 11.9 amp with the network.   For the biased-diode load, the corresponding current values are 12.5 amp and 10 amp.   Thus, the pulse power delivered to the biased-diode load having a dynamic resistance of 100 ohms is 110 kw with the *LR*-network, and 141 kw without it.   In order to obtain the same pulse power in the load in both cases, it is necessary to increase the condenser voltage from 12.5 kv to 13.1 kv when the network is used.   The actual power loss in the resistance of the *LR*-network is small (about 5 kw in the example given here), but the requirement of a higher condenser voltage is sometimes an inconvenience.   In the design of a hard-tube pulser, it is therefore necessary to weigh the reduction in pulse power or the increase in condenser voltage against the drop in load current during the pulse or an increase in the capacitance of the storage condenser.

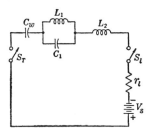

Fig. 5·18.—Output circuit of a hard-tube pulser with a network of passive elements to maintain approximately constant load current during the pulse.

Another method by which the pulse current can be kept approximately constant for pulse durations of about a microsecond is indicated in the diagram of Fig. 5·18.   This arrangement was first suggested to members of the pulser group at the Radiation Laboratory by Mr. A. A. Varela of the Naval Research Laboratory, Anacostia, D.C.

This arrangement has an advantage over the LR-network in that the network consists of passive elements.   There is, however, a loss in pulse voltage, which makes it necessary to charge the condenser C_w to a higher voltage than is required without the network for a given pulse voltage at the load.   Another possible disadvantage of this arrangement is the need for three circuit elements, including a condenser with a relatively high voltage rating.

PART II

THE LINE-TYPE PULSER

The general characteristics of line-type pulsers are given in Sec. 1·4, and a comparison of some features of the two principal types of pulsers are made in Sec. 1·5. The next six chapters of this volume present a detailed discussion of the line-type pulser. Before going into the analysis of the components and circuit behavior, it is well to summarize the general philosophy from which the line-type pulser has been developed.

Fundamentally, the pulser consists of a reservoir of electrical energy that is allowed to discharge completely into a load at predetermined times to form the pulses, and that is connected to a source in such a way that the same amount of energy is stored in it during each interpulse interval. Obviously, there are many types of energy reservoirs that are unsatisfactory because the rate of discharge of their energy into the load does not produce the desired pulse shape. Chapter 6, dealing with pulse-forming networks, sets forth the analysis by which combinations of inductances and capacitances are determined to approximate a specific output pulse shape, and gives the results obtained by various methods of analysis for the pulse shapes most commonly used in pulsers for microwave radar. The pulse-forming networks have been derived by considering circuits that do not include losses, or stray capacitances and inductances, and for which the load resistance is equal to the network impedance. The effects on the output from the pulser of nonlinear loads, of impedance mismatch between load and network, of losses and of stray capacitances in the circuit are considered in Chap. 7.

Chapter 8 gives a discussion of the types of switches most commonly used with line-type pulsers, and of the auxiliary circuits that they require. The different methods of restoring the energy to the pulse-forming network between pulses are considered in detail in Chap. 9, and the over-all performance of the pulser as it is affected by the various components and by variations in load impedance is discussed in Chap. 10. Finally, Chap. 11 gives a few examples of pulsers in use at present, and also indicates the possibilities of some variations in the usual pulser circuit.

It is worth noting again that the fundamental circuits of line-type pulsers are always very simple. There can be many variations, depending on the required polarity of the output pulse and the power supply available. Possibly their greatest advantage, next to their inherent simplicity, stems from the fact that only sufficient energy for one pulse is stored at any one time; by comparison, the energy stored in the reservoir of the hard-tube pulser is nearly always twenty to fifty times that required by the load for a single pulse.   The possibility of damage to the load or to the pulser is thus naturally greater with a hard-tube than with a line-type pulser.

The circuit simplicity results in less flexibility than can be obtained from hard-tube pulsers.   The latter type can usually be altered with little effort to satisfy new requirements of pulse duration and recurrence frequency.   In the present state of development, a line-type pulser requires a new pulse-forming network if the pulse duration is to be changed and, in the case of a-c charging of the network, it is also inflexible as to recurrence frequency.

CHAPTER 6

THE PULSE-FORMING NETWORK

BY H. J. WHITE, P. R. GILLETTE, AND J. V. LEBACQZ[1]

The pulse-forming network serves the dual purpose of storing exactly the amount of energy required for a single pulse and of discharging this energy into the load in the form of a pulse of specified shape. The required energy may be stored either in capacitances or in inductances, or in combinations of these circuit elements. Networks in which the energy is stored in an electrostatic field are referred to as voltage-fed networks; networks in which the energy is stored in a magnetic field are referred to as current-fed networks. Networks of the voltage-fed type are used almost universally in practice because only with this type can the usual gaseous-discharge switches, such as spark gaps and thyratrons, be used. The current-fed networks have certain important advantages, but thus far no suitable switch is available that permits high-power operation. Therefore, the discussion of networks is confined largely to the consideration of the voltage-fed type.

6·1. The Formation and Shaping of Pulses. Determination of Pulse-forming Networks for Generating Pulses of Arbitrary Shape.— A general mathematical procedure exists for the determination of pulse-forming networks to generate pulses of arbitrary shape, and the outlines of the theory are given for the case of voltage-fed networks. If it is assumed that all the energy is stored in one condenser, the pulse-generating circuit takes the form of Fig. 6·1. The required current pulse $i(t)$ flowing in the circuit may be arbitrary in shape but practical considerations limit it to finite single-valued functions having a finite number of discontinuities and a finite number of maxima and minima. In

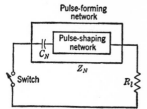

FIG. 6·1.—Basic circuit for generating pulses of arbitrary shape (voltage-fed network).

analyzing this problem the Laplace-transform method is used. The transform for the current may be found from the definition of the Laplace transform, and is

$$i(p) = \int_0^\infty i(t)e^{-pt}\,dt. \tag{1}$$

[1] Section 6.5 by P. R. Gillette, Sec. 6.6 by J. V. Lebacqz, the remainder of Chap. 6 by H. J. White.

The Laplace-transform equation for the circuit of Fig. 6·1 is

$$\left(R_l + Z_N + \frac{1}{C_N p}\right) i(p) = \frac{Q_N}{C_N p} = \frac{V_N}{p}, \tag{2}$$

where R_l is the load resistance, Z_N is the network impedance, C_N is the network storage capacitance, and Q_N is the initial charge on the network. The amplitude of $i(p)$ is determined by V_N, the initial voltage on C_N. For the present, V_N may be considered as a known constant, and Eq. (2) may be solved explicitly for the unknown impedance of the network, giving

$$Z_N = \frac{V_N}{p i(p)} - R_l - \frac{1}{C_N p}. \tag{3}$$

As a simple illustration, suppose that the current pulse is specified as being rectangular with amplitude I_l and duration τ, and that the load is a pure resistance of value R_l. Then $i(p)$ is found from Eq. (1) to be

$$i(p) = \frac{I_l}{p}(1 - e^{-p\tau}).$$

Substituting in Eq. (3), there is obtained

$$Z_N = \frac{p V_N}{p I_l (1 - e^{-p\tau})} - R_l - \frac{1}{C_N p},$$

or rearranging,

$$Z_N + \frac{1}{C_N p} = R_l \left[\frac{\left(\dfrac{V_N}{I_l R_l}\right) - 1 + e^{-p\tau}}{1 - e^{-p\tau}} \right].$$

If the numerator and denominator are multiplied by $e^{p\tau/2}$,

$$Z_N + \frac{1}{C_N p} = R_l \left[\frac{\left(\dfrac{V_N}{I_l R_l} - 1\right) e^{\frac{p\tau}{2}} + e^{\frac{-p\tau}{2}}}{e^{\frac{p\tau}{2}} - e^{-\frac{p\tau}{2}}} \right]$$

$$= R_l \left[\coth \frac{p\tau}{2} + \frac{\left(\dfrac{V_N}{I_l R_l} - 2\right) e^{\frac{p\tau}{2}}}{e^{\frac{p\tau}{2}} - e^{-\frac{p\tau}{2}}} \right].$$

Choosing $V_N = 2 I_l R_l$, there is obtained

$$Z_N + \frac{1}{C_N p} = R_l \coth \frac{p\tau}{2} \tag{4}$$

The right-hand member of Eq. (4) is recognized as the impedance function for an open-circuited lossless transmission line of characteristic impedance $Z_0 = R_l$, and transmission time $\delta = \tau/2$. Hence, in this case, either the pulse-shaping circuit plus the capacitance C_N must be an electrical equivalent for the transmission line, or the transmission line itself may be considered as one form of the network that generates the required rectangular pulse.

Unfortunately, in all but the simplest cases it proves very difficult to recognize an actual physical network from the form of Z_N given by Eq. (3), and there is no straightforward method for changing the expression into a form which is so recognizable. The difficulty is increased by the fact that Z_N generally contains dissipative as well as reactive elements. Hence, actual designs are usually based on more specialized and indirect approaches to the problem, the most important of which are discussed below.

Pulses Generated by a Lossless Transmission Line.—Since the microwave oscillators for which most pulsers have been designed require the application of an essentially rectangular pulse, the lossless open-ended transmission line considered in the foregoing example may be taken as a starting point in the discussion. The nature of the transient produced by

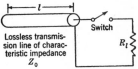

FIG. 6·2.—Schematic circuit diagram for producing an ideal rectangular pulse from a transmission line.

the discharge of such a transmission line into a resistance load (see Fig. 6·2), may be studied in more detail by further application of the Laplace transform or operational method of analysis.

The a-c impedance, Z, of the transmission line, is given by elementary transmission line theory as

$$Z = Z_0 \coth j\omega\delta.$$

The Laplace-transform impedance is found by substituting p for $j\omega$, where p is the transform parameter. Then

$$Z(p) = Z_0 \coth p\delta, \tag{5}$$

where δ is the one-way transmission time of the line, and Z_0 is its characteristic impedance. The current transform is then

$$
\begin{aligned}
i(p) &= \frac{V_0}{p(R_l + Z_0 \coth p\delta)} \\
&= \frac{V_0}{p(Z_0 + R_l)} \cdot \frac{1 - e^{-2p\delta}}{1 + \dfrac{Z_0 - R_l}{Z_0 + R_l} e^{-2p\delta}}
\end{aligned}
$$

$$= \frac{V_0(1 - e^{-2p\delta})}{p(Z_0 + R_l)}\left[1 - \frac{Z_0 - R_l}{Z_0 + R_l} e^{-2p\delta} + \left(\frac{Z_0 - R_l}{Z_0 + R_l}\right)^2 e^{-4p\delta} - \cdots\right], \tag{6}$$

where V_0 is the initial voltage on the transmission line. The inverse transform gives the current as

$$i(t) = \frac{V_0}{Z_0 + R_l} \left\{ 1 - U(t - 2\delta) - \frac{Z_0 - R_l}{Z_0 + R_l} \left[U(t - 2\delta) - U(t - 4\delta) \right] \right.$$
$$\left. + \left(\frac{Z_0 - R_l}{Z_0 + R_l} \right)^2 \left[U(t - 4\delta) - U(t - 6\delta) \right] - \cdots \right\}, \quad (7)$$

where

$$U(\Delta t) = 1 \quad \text{for } \Delta t > 0$$
$$U(\Delta t) = 0 \quad \text{for } \Delta t < 0$$
$$\Delta t = (t - n\delta), \quad n = 2, 4, 6, \cdots .$$

If $R_l = Z_0$, that is, if the line is matched to the load, the current consists of a single rectangular pulse of amplitude $I_l = V_0/2Z_0$ and duration $\tau = 2\delta$. Current and voltage pulses for $R_l = Z_0$, $R_l = 2Z_0$, and $R_l = \frac{1}{2}Z_0$ are shown in Fig. 6·3.

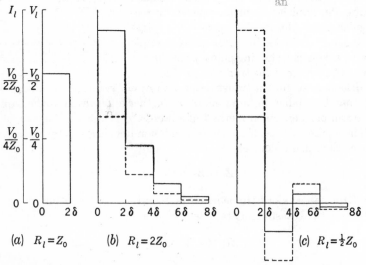

Fig. 6·3.—Current and voltage pulses for a lossless transmission line discharging into a resistance load. The solid and broken lines represent the voltage and current pulses, respectively.

The effect of mismatching the load is to introduce a series of steps into the transient discharge. These steps are all of the same sign when $R_l > Z_0$, and alternate in sign when $R_l < Z_0$. An elementary explanation of the steps can be made in terms of reflections caused at the terminals of the line by mismatching the load resistance. These reflections traverse the line to the open end in time δ, are completely reflected there, and travel back to the load end in a total time 2δ, where they appear as positive or negative steps depending upon the mismatch ratio. The reflections continue in this way, with constantly diminishing amplitude, until all the energy initially stored in the line is dissipated in the load resistor. Both the design and operation of line-type pulsers are affected by these reflections.

A transmission line having a one-way transmission time of δ generates a pulse of duration 2δ; assuming a pulse of 1-μsec duration and a signal velocity on the line of 500 ft/μsec (a representative value), a line of length $l = 500 \times 1/2 = 250$ ft is required. It is obvious that a high-voltage line or cable of this length would be impractical because of its large size and weight, and hence, that a substitute in the form of a line-simulating network is necessary for any practical equipment. Pulse-forming networks have other advantages in that the pulse shape may be altered by varying the values of the network parameters and the number of elements.

6·2. Networks Derived from a Transmission Line.—The development of pulse-forming networks that simulate a transmission line is a mathematical problem in network synthesis. As may be anticipated, no network having a finite number of elements can exactly simulate a transmission line which in reality has distributed rather than lumped parameters. As the number of elements for a given network type is increased, the degree of simulation will improve. It may happen, however, that the network pulse is a good approximation to the rectangular pulse during only a portion of the pulse interval. For example, the network pulse may exhibit overshoots and excessive oscillations, especially near the beginning and end of the pulse. These possibilities must be kept in mind, and the properties of networks derived by formal mathematical methods must be investigated with care to determine how closely the networks approximate transmission lines.

Network Derived by Rayleigh's Principle.—From the mathematical point of view, physical problems involving distributed parameters give rise to partial differential equations, whereas lumped-parameter problems give rise only to ordinary differential equations. Inasmuch as the partial differential equation for a physical problem may usually be derived by taking the limit of a set of ordinary differential equations as the number of equations in the set approaches infinity,[1] it is clear that a finite number can at best give only an approximate answer to the distributed-parameter problem, but that the degree of approximation improves as the number of equations, and therefore the number of physical elements, is increased. This line of reasoning also appears plausible on purely physical grounds.

---

[1] Usually referred to as Rayleigh's principle. See, for example, A. G. Webster, *Partial Differential Equations of Mathematical Physics*, 2nd ed., Stechert, New York, 1933, pp. 93–97.

Application of Rayleigh's principle to the transmission line yields the two-terminal line-simulating network shown in Fig. 6·4.

The properties of the line-simulating network of Fig. 6·4 may conveniently be investigated by finding its impedance function. For present purposes the operator function is used rather than the a-c impedance function. These two alternative forms are equivalent, but the operator form is particularly useful in calculating the transient response.

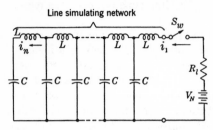

Line simulating network

FIG. 6·4.—Two-terminal line-simulating network derived by Rayleigh's principle.

The impedance function may be found by writing down the set of n transform equations for the network and noting that these are difference equations, each equation except the first and last being of the form

$$-\frac{i_{r-1}(p)}{Cp} + \left(Lp + \frac{2}{Cp}\right) i_r(p) - \frac{i_{r+1}(p)}{Cp} = 0, \tag{8}$$

where r is the rth mesh. The general solution of this difference equation is

$$i_r(p) = Ae^{r\theta} + Be^{-r\theta} \tag{9}$$

where $\cosh \theta = 1 + (LC/2)p^2$, and A and B are arbitrary constants to be determined by substitution in the first and last mesh equations. Consider first the case for which the resistance R_l, in series with the battery V_N, is put equal to zero. The circuit is then composed of purely reactive elements, and the currents that flow upon closing the switch persist— that is, the currents continue indefinitely and represent a steady-state rather than a transient condition. Transients can arise only if dissipative elements are present. Solving for the arbitrary constants A and B and reducing to hyperbolic functions, the following expression is obtained for the current transform $i_1(p)$:

$$i_1(p) = CV_N \frac{\sinh n\theta}{\sinh (n+1)\theta - \sinh n\theta}.$$

The corresponding input-impedance transform for the network is then

$$Z(p,n) = \frac{V_N}{pi_1(p)} = \frac{1}{Cp}\left[\frac{\sinh (n+1)\theta}{\sinh (n\theta)} - 1\right]. \tag{10}$$

It may be of interest to find the limiting form of $Z(p,n)$ as n approaches infinity in such a way that the total inductance and capacitance of the network remain constant.

$$\lim_{n \to \infty} Z(p,n) = \lim_{n \to \infty} \frac{1}{Cp} \left[\frac{\sinh (n + 1)\theta}{\sinh (n\theta)} - 1 \right]$$

$$= \lim_{n \to \infty} \frac{1}{Cp} [\cosh \theta + \coth n\theta \sinh \theta - 1]$$

But

$$\cosh \theta = 1 + \frac{LC}{2} p^2 = 1 + \frac{L_N C_N}{2n^2} p^2,$$

$$\sinh \theta = \sqrt{\cosh^2 \theta - 1} = \frac{\sqrt{L_N C_N}}{n} p \sqrt{1 + \frac{L_N C_N}{4n^2} p^2},$$

$$n\theta = 2n \sinh^{-1} \frac{\sqrt{L_N C_N}}{2n} p,$$

which gives

$$\lim_{n \to \infty} Z(p,n) = \lim_{n \to \infty} \frac{n}{C_N p} \left[\frac{L_N C_N}{2n^2} p^2 + \frac{\sqrt{L_N C_N}}{n} p \sqrt{1 + \frac{L_N C_N p^2}{4n^2}} \right.$$

$$\left. \coth \left(2n \sinh^{-1} \frac{\sqrt{L_N C_N}}{2n} p \right) \right] = \sqrt{\frac{L_N}{C_N}} \cdot \coth p \sqrt{L_N C_N}$$

$$= Z_N \coth p\delta, \tag{11}$$

which is the exact form for the impedance function for a transmission line given in Eq. (5). Thus, the network impedance function reduces in the limit to the transmission-line impedance function, in accord with Rayleigh's principle.

The pulse shape generated by the line-simulating network of Fig. 6·4 on matched resistance load, $R_l = \sqrt{L_N/C_N} = \sqrt{L/C}$, may be found by calculating the charging-current pulse when the voltage V_N is applied to the circuit of Fig. 6·4. If the voltage transform is divided by the sum of the load resistance and the network impedance [Eq. (10)],

$$i_1(p) = \cfrac{\cfrac{V_N}{p}}{\sqrt{\cfrac{L}{C}} + \cfrac{1}{Cp} \left[\cfrac{\sinh (n + 1)\theta}{\sinh n\theta} - 1 \right]}$$

$$= \cfrac{C V_N}{p \sqrt{LC} + \left[\cfrac{\sinh (n + 1)\theta}{\sinh n\theta} - 1 \right]};$$

but from the value of θ in Eq. (9)

$$p = \frac{2}{\sqrt{LC}} \sinh \frac{\theta}{2},$$

hence

$$i_1(p) = C V_N \frac{\sinh n\theta}{\sinh (n + 1)\theta + \left(2 \sinh \frac{\theta}{2} - 1 \right) \sinh n\theta}, \tag{12}$$

Equation (12) is valid for any number of sections n. The simplest case occurs when $n = 1$, that is, when the network is reduced to a single mesh. In this case

$$i_1(p) = CV_N \frac{\sinh \theta}{\sinh 2\theta + \left(2 \sinh \dfrac{\theta}{2} - 1\right) \sinh \theta}$$

$$= \frac{CV_N}{2 \cosh \theta + 2 \sinh \dfrac{\theta}{2} - 1}$$

$$= \frac{CV_N}{2 + LCp^2 + \sqrt{LC}\, p - 1}$$

$$= \frac{V_N}{L} \cdot \frac{1}{p^2 + \dfrac{1}{\sqrt{LC}} p + \dfrac{1}{LC}},$$

which is recognized as the current transform for a one-mesh RLC-circuit with $R = \sqrt{L/C}$.

By the method used in deriving Eq. (11), the limit of $i_1(p)$ as n approaches infinity in such a way that the total distributed capacitance C_N and the total distributed inductance L_N remain fixed is shown to be

$$\lim_{n \to \infty} i_1(p) = \frac{V_N}{2 \sqrt{\dfrac{L_N}{C_N}}\, p} (1 - e^{-2\sqrt{L_N C_N}\, p}). \tag{13}$$

This is the Laplace transform for a rectangular current pulse of amplitude

$$\frac{V_N}{2 \sqrt{L_N/C_N}}$$

and of duration $2 \sqrt{L_N C_N}$, and is the result to be expected according to Rayleigh's principle.

In order to check the theory, both calculated and experimental pulse shapes were obtained for a five-section uniform-line network on matched resistance load, that is, when $R_l = Z_N$. The calculated pulse shape was found by using Eq. (12) with $n = 5$. In carrying out the solution, it is necessary to convert from the hyperbolic to the algebraic form corresponding to Eq. (12). Since the denominator is of the 10th degree ($= 2n$), the roots are tedious to find. The resulting pulse shape is plotted in Fig. 6·5a, using dimensionless ratios for the coordinates. The corresponding experimental pulse shape, shown in Fig. 6·5b, was obtained by using an experimental network for which the actual values of all the parameters were within 1 per cent of the theoretical values. The correspondence between the calculated and experimental pulse shapes is very close, the only significant difference being in the initial overshoot for which the calculated value is about twice the observed value. This difference occurs probably because the hydrogen-thyratron switch used in the experimental pulse-generator circuit does not close instantaneously, and also because there are, in any physical system, unavoidable losses and distributed capacitances and inductances.

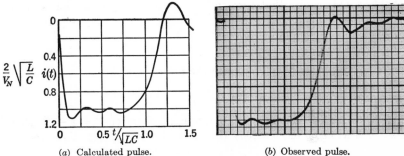

(a) Calculated pulse.   (b) Observed pulse.

Fɪɢ. 6·5.—Pulse shapes produced by a five-section uniform-line network on matched resistance load.

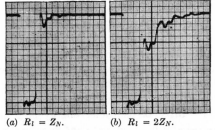

(a) $R_l = Z_N$.   (b) $R_l = 2Z_N$.

Fɪɢ. 6·6.—Voltage pulse shapes obtained with the network of Fig. 6·5 as seen with a slow sweep speed.

The oscillograms in Fig. 6·6 were taken with the same network; Fig. 6·6a is identical with Fig. 6·5b except that a slower sweep speed was used in order to show the complete pulse tail. The effect of mismatch with $R_l = 2Z_N$ is shown in Fig. 6·6b, in which the series of steps as shown in Fig. 6·3b is evident, although not very well defined. It may be concluded that the five-section uniform-line network is a poor equivalent for a transmission line. A larger number of sections would give better line-simulation, but this approach is not a very promising one.

Relation to Steady-state Theory.—The network of Fig. 6·4 comprises a low-pass filter for alternating sine-wave currents. The correspondence between its transient d-c pulse properties and steady-state sine-wave properties is of considerable interest. For steady-state sine-wave currents, the solution of the network is of the same form as Eq. (9), that is, for the rth mesh

$$i_r(t) = Ae^{r\theta} + Be^{-r\theta}, \tag{14}$$

where θ is now defined by the expression

$$\cosh \theta = 1 - \frac{LC\omega^2}{2}. \tag{15}$$

Equation (14) shows that $i_r(t)$ will be attenuated only if θ has a negative real component, that is, if

$$\theta = \alpha + j\beta \qquad \text{and} \qquad \alpha < 0$$

Then, as $\cosh \theta$ can be expressed in the form

$$\cosh \theta = \cosh \alpha \cos \beta - j \sinh \alpha \sin \beta,$$

it is clear that, for $\alpha = 0$, $\cosh \alpha = 1$, $\sinh \alpha = 0$ and $\cos \beta = 1 - LC\omega^2/2$. Inasmuch as $\cos \beta$ must satisfy the inequality $|\cos \beta| \leq 1$, there results

$$\left| 1 - \frac{LC\omega^2}{2} \right| \leq 1,$$

or

$$0 \leq \frac{LC\omega^2}{2} \leq +2. \tag{16}$$

Thus all frequencies, $0 \leq f \leq 1/\pi \sqrt{LC}$, are passed without attenuation, whereas all higher frequencies are increasingly attenuated.

The Fourier series for a succession of identical and uniformly spaced rectangular pulses contains discrete frequencies extending throughout the band to infinity. Most of the pulse energy is accounted for, however, in the frequency band between zero and several times $1/\tau$. A very conservative estimate for the significant upper frequency limit might be taken as $10/\tau$. Thus, it is reasonable to set the cutoff point for the low-pass filter that will transmit such rectangular pulses without appreciable distortion as

$$f_c = \frac{1}{\pi \sqrt{LC}} = \frac{10}{\tau},$$

or

$$\sqrt{LC} = \frac{\tau}{10\pi}. \tag{17}$$

The quantity $\sqrt{LC}$ represents the delay time per section of the low-pass filter; therefore, an n-section filter structure, when used as a pulse-generating network, should produce a pulse of duration

$$\tau = 2n \sqrt{LC}. \tag{18}$$

The factor 2 arises from the fact that the pulse wave traverses the filter twice and is reflected back to the load from the open end once. If Eqs. (17) and (18) are solved for n, the number of sections, a value of $n = 5\pi \approx 16$ is obtained. Less conservative estimates for the frequency-transmission band required might yield, for example, $n = 5$ or 10.

Networks Derived by Rational-fraction Expansions of Transmission-line Impedance and Admittance Functions.—Two other networks that simulate a transmission line may be derived by the process of expanding the transmission-line impedance and admittance functions in an infinite series of rational fractions, and then identifying the terms of the series thus obtained with network elements. As given earlier in Eq. (5), the operational form of the impedance function for a lossless open-ended transmission line of characteristic impedance Z_0 and one-way transmission time δ is

$$Z(p) = Z_0 \coth p\delta.$$

The rational-fraction expansion for $Z(p)$ is[1]

$$Z(p) = \frac{Z_0}{\delta p} + \sum_{n=1}^{\infty} \frac{\dfrac{2Z_0\delta}{\pi^2 n^2} p}{\dfrac{\delta^2}{\pi^2 n^2} p^2 + 1}. \tag{19}$$

The term $Z_0/\delta p$ is the operational impedance of a capacitance of value $C_N = \delta/Z_0$. The remaining terms represent the operational impedance of a series of parallel combinations of capacitance and inductance. For such a combination the impedance operator is

$$Z_n = \frac{L_n p}{1 + L_n C_n p^2}.$$

By comparison of coefficients,

$$L_n = \frac{2Z_0\delta}{\pi^2 n^2} = \frac{2L_N}{\pi^2 n^2}, \quad (20a)$$

$$C_n = \frac{\delta}{2Z_0} = \frac{C_N}{2}. \quad (20b)$$

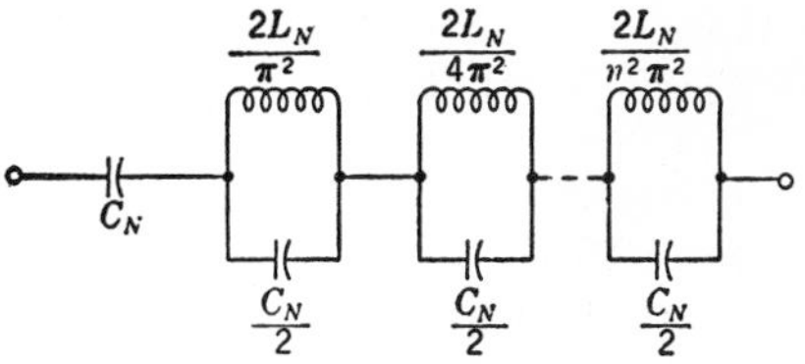

FIG. 6·7.—Two-terminal network to simulate an open-ended transmission line, obtained by rational-fraction expansion of the impedance function.

The resulting network is shown in Fig. 6·7.

The second line-simulating network is found by making a similar expansion of the admittance function

$$Y(p) = \frac{1}{Z(p)} = \frac{1}{Z_0} \tanh p\delta, \tag{21}$$

[1] E. T. Whittaker and G. N. Watson, *Modern Analysis*, American ed., Macmillan, New York, 1943, pp. 134–136.

that is,

$$Y(p) = \sum_{n=1}^{\infty} \frac{\dfrac{8\delta}{\pi^2 Z_0} \cdot \dfrac{p}{(2n-1)^2}}{\dfrac{4\delta^2 p^2}{\pi^2 (2n-1)^2} + 1}, \tag{22}$$

Each term can be identified with a series inductance-capacitance circuit for which

$$Y_n = \frac{C_n p}{L_n C_n p^2 + 1}.$$

A comparison of the coefficients shows the values of C_n and L_n to be

$$C_n = \frac{8}{(2n-1)^2 \pi^2} \cdot \frac{\delta}{Z_0} = \frac{8 C_N}{(2n-1)^2 \pi^2} \tag{23a}$$

and

$$L_n = \frac{Z_0 \delta}{2} = \frac{L_N}{2}, \tag{23b}$$

and the resulting network is shown in Fig. 6·8.

The networks of Figs. 6·7 and 6·8 are approximately equivalent for a finite number of sections, but become exactly equivalent as n approaches infinity, that is, for an infinite number of sections. The total capacitance for the network of Fig. 6.8 is

$$C_N = \sum_{n=1}^{\infty} C_n = \frac{8 C_N}{\pi^2} \sum_{n=1}^{\infty} \frac{1}{(2n-1)^2} = \frac{8 C_N}{\pi^2} \cdot \frac{\pi^2}{8},$$

which is equal to the series capacitance in the network of Fig. 6·7, and is also the sum required by energy considerations when the network and transmission line are charged to the same constant potential.

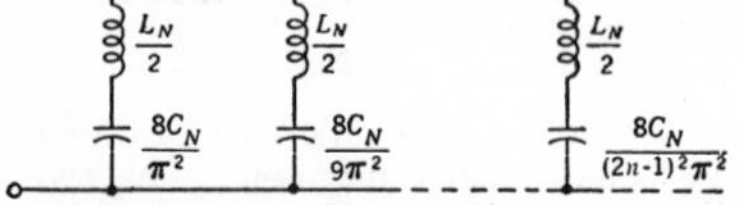

It is difficult and tedious to obtain solutions for the current-pulse shapes to be expected on resistance load when using more than two or three sections for the networks of Fig. 6·7 or Fig. 6·8. However, certain conclusions can be drawn from other considerations. For the network of Fig. 6·7 with a finite number of sections, it is clear that the current at the first instant (on matched resistance load) is double the matched value.

Fig. 6·8.—Two-terminal network to simulate an open-ended transmission line, obtained by rational-fraction expansion of the admittance function.

The nature of the pulse to be expected for the network of Fig. 6·8 with a finite number of sections can be investigated by calculating the input current when a unit step voltage from a generator of zero internal impedance is applied to the network. This is a particularly simple calculation as each network section acts as an isolated unit, and the total current is simply the sum of the currents for the individual sections. The current for the rth section is

$$i_r(t) = \sqrt{\frac{C_r}{L_r}} \sin \frac{t}{\sqrt{L_r C_r}} = \frac{4}{(2r-1)\pi} \sqrt{\frac{C_N}{L_N}} \sin \frac{(2r-1)\pi}{2} \cdot \frac{t}{\sqrt{L_N C_N}}.$$

and the total current is then

$$i(t) = \frac{4}{\pi} \sqrt{\frac{C_N}{L_N}} \sum_{r=1}^{n} \frac{1}{(2r-1)} \sin \frac{(2r-1)\pi}{2} \cdot \frac{t}{\sqrt{L_N C_N}}. \qquad (24)$$

Equation (24) with $n \to \infty$ is the Fourier-series expansion for a rectangular wave of amplitude $\sqrt{C_N/L_N}$ and period $4\sqrt{L_N C_N}$, that is, the waveform that would be obtained for the original transmission line.

The degree to which the Fourier series, Eq. (24), converges toward a rectangular wave determines the extent to which the network simulates a transmission line. The convergence of a Fourier series is uniform in any region for which the original function is continuous (and has a limited total fluctuation), but is nonuniform in any region containing a point of ordinary discontinuity. In the present instance, the only points at which trouble might be expected are the points of discontinuity which occur at $t = 0$ and at integer multiples of $t = 2\sqrt{L_N C_N}$. Hence, the convergence of the series should be investigated near these points. Denote the sum of the series (24) by $S_n(t)$. Then, it can be shown that, at time t slightly greater than zero,

$$\lim_{n \to \infty} S_n(0^+) = \frac{1}{2} \int_0^{\pi} \frac{\sin \theta}{\theta} \, d\theta = 0.926.$$

Hence the maximum instantaneous current is given by

$$i(0^+) = \frac{4(0.926)}{\pi} \sqrt{\frac{C_N}{L_N}} = 1.179 \sqrt{\frac{C_N}{L_N}}. \qquad (25)$$

Thus, the current rises initially to a value about 18 per cent above the value that would be obtained for an actual transmission line, and at this point the network fails in its simulation of the transmission line. A similar effect occurs for $t = 2\sqrt{L_N C_N} \pm \epsilon$, where ϵ approaches zero. An overshoot of the same type occurs when using a finite number of network sections. (This overshoot effect of the Fourier series near a point of ordinary discontinuity is known as the Gibbs phenomenon.)

It is clear then that the networks of Figs. 6·7 and 6·8 fail to give a rectangular wave in that substantial overshoots occur near the beginning and end of the wave, even though the number of network sections is increased without limit.

The response of the networks of Figs. 6·7 and 6·8 in a pulse-generating circuit is similar, in a general way, to their performance in the rectangular wave-generating circuit just discussed, except that a single pulse is produced instead of a continuing rectangular wave. When using a large number of sections of Fig. 6·8 and any number of sections of Fig. 6·7, this single pulse exhibits the same overshoot phenomenon near its beginning, and the amplitude of the overshoot is not reduced by increasing the number of network sections. The pulse shapes produced on resistance load by the networks of Figs. 6·7 and 6·8 are only approximately the same for a finite number of sections, but become identical as n approaches infinity (for an infinite number of sections).

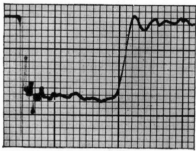

FIG. 6·9.—Voltage pulse shape obtained with the network of Fig. 6·7.

The pulse shape produced by the network of Fig. 6·7 with a finite number of sections has a high initial spike because the network has no series inductance, consisting merely of a series of anti-resonant sections and a series condenser. This spike is illustrated in the experimental pulse shape of Fig. 6·9 obtained with a six-section network; the pulse shape is a poor simulation of a rectangular pulse. The high initial current is clearly in evidence, and is followed by a series of damped oscillations. The initial current does not reach twice the matched value as theoretically expected because of the distributed capacitance of the load and the initial voltage drop in the hydrogen-thyratron switch used in the experimental pulser. In contrast, it may be noted that the network of Fig. 6·8, which consists of resonant sections in parallel, does have inductance in series with all the condensers. The initial current must therefore be zero, and there is not likely to be a high current spike as long as the number of sections is not very large. This premise is corroborated by the shape

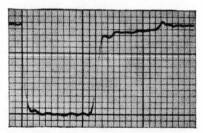

FIG. 6·10.—Voltage pulse shape for the six-section network of Fig. 6·8.

of the experimental pulse of Fig. 6·10, taken for a six-section network.

Figure 6·11a shows the same pulse photographed with a slower sweep speed; Fig. 6·11b shows the effect of mismatching the load resistance R_l.

In this case, $R_l = 2Z_N$, or twice the characteristic impedance of the network. The steps on the pulse tail are well defined, and four of them are clearly visible. A comparison of this pulse with the corresponding ideal pulse that would be produced by a lossless transmission line, as shown in Fig. 6·3b, reveals a very close similarity. Therefore, for a line-simulating network of the admittance type, it may be concluded that the generated

pulse shape on resistance load is good for a finite, but not very large, number of sections. It has been shown that a very large number of sections produces overshoots on the pulse. The six-section network appears to have an insufficient number of sections to produce the optimum pulse shape, as is indicated in Fig. 6·10 by the fact that the initial peak is somewhat lower than the average top of the pulse. An increase in the

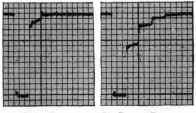

(a) $R_l = Z_N$.   (b) $R_l = 2Z_N$.

Fig. 6·11.—Voltage pulse shapes obtained with network of Fig. 6·8 as seen with a slow sweep speed.

number of sections would be expected to bring the first peak up to the average top of the pulse and, for a large enough number of sections, above that average. It is, therefore, to be expected that some intermediate number of sections produces the optimum pulse shape.

6·3. Guillemin's Theory and the Voltage-fed Network.—The results of the preceding section show that networks designed to simulate a lossless transmission line have limitations of a fundamental nature. In the generated pulse these limitations are evidenced by overshoots near the beginning of the pulse and excessive oscillations during the main part of the pulse as evidenced by Fig. 6·9. Guillemin correctly diagnosed these difficulties as being due to the attempt to generate a discontinuous pulse by means of a lumped-parameter network. In other words, the ideal rectangular pulse generated by a lossless transmission line has an infinite rate of rise and fall, and cannot be produced by a lumped-parameter network.

Guillemin[1] then argued that, inasmuch as it is impossible to generate such an ideal rectangular pulse by means of a lumped-parameter network, the theoretical pulse that is chosen should intentionally have finite rise and fall times. Mathematically, this condition means that the discontinuity in the pulse shape is eliminated, and that the Fourier series for the generated wave has the necessary property of uniform convergence throughout the whole region. The property of uniform convergence insures that overshoots and oscillations in the pulse can be reduced to

---

[1] E. A. Guillemin, "A Historical Account of the Development of a Design Procedure for Pulse-forming Networks," RL Report No. 43, Oct. 16, 1944.

any desired degree by using a sufficient number of sections. The introduction of an arbitrary pulse shape leads to a new difficulty, however, in
that the impedance function necessary to produce the given pulse shape
is unknown.

The logical way to determine the impedance function would be to
use the basic circuit of the line-type pulser and work backward from the

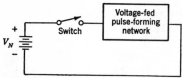

specified pulse shape to the impedance
function necessary to produce it. This
procedure proves too difficult, however, and instead, the steady-state
problem for the circuit of Fig. 6·12 is
solved. The alternating-current wave
shape produced by this circuit is specified to be similar to the pulse shape
desired. It is then assumed that the

Fig. 6·12.—Circuit for producing a
specified steady-state alternating-current wave similar to the desired single-
pulse shape.

network determined on this basis will, when used in the basic line-type
pulser, produce a pulse shape reasonably close to the desired form. This
assumption has proved surprisingly valid in practice.

There is a wide choice of reasonable pulse shapes possible. Two of
those originally discussed by Guillemin are shown in Fig. 6·13a and b.

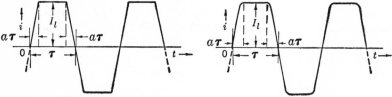

(a) Trapezoidal alternating-current wave.   (b) Alternating-current wave with flat top
and parabolic rise and fall.

Fig. 6·13.

The rising portion of the wave in Fig. 6·13b is formed by an inverted
parabola and joins smoothly to the flat top of the wave; the falling
portion is similar but reversed. The equation for the parabolic rise is

$$\frac{i(t)}{I_l} = 2\,\frac{t}{a\tau} - \frac{t^2}{a^2\tau^2}. \tag{26}$$

The Fourier series for these waves may be found by the ordinary
method as follows:

Case 1. *Trapezoidal wave.* As $i(t)$ is an odd function, the series
contains only sine terms, and there is no constant term. Then

$$i(t) = I_l \sum_{\nu=1}^{\infty} b_\nu \sin \frac{\nu\pi t}{\tau}, \tag{27}$$

where

$$b_\nu = \frac{2}{\tau} \int_0^\tau \frac{i(t)}{I_l} \sin \frac{\nu\pi t}{\tau} \, dt, \tag{28}$$

and $i(t)$ is defined by the equations

$$\frac{i(t)}{I_l} = \begin{cases} \dfrac{t}{a\tau}, & 0 \leqq t \leqq a\tau, \\ 1, & a\tau \leqq t \leqq \tau - a\tau, \\ \dfrac{\tau - t}{a\tau}, & \tau - a\tau \leqq t \leqq \tau. \end{cases} \tag{29}$$

The indicated integrations for b_ν yield

$$b_\nu = \frac{4}{\nu\pi} \cdot \frac{\sin \nu\pi a}{\nu\pi a}, \quad \text{where } \nu = 1, 3, 5, \cdots. \tag{30}$$

Case 2. *Wave with flat top and parabolic rise and fall.* Again $i(t)$ is an odd function, so that only sine terms occur in the Fourier series. Again,

$$i(t) = I_l \sum_{\nu=1}^\infty b_\nu \sin \frac{\nu\pi t}{\tau},$$

where

$$b_\nu = \frac{2}{\tau} \int_0^\tau \frac{i(t)}{I_l} \sin \frac{\nu\pi t}{\tau} \, dt,$$

and $i(t)$ is defined by

$$\frac{i(t)}{I_l} = \begin{cases} \left(2\dfrac{t}{a\tau} - \dfrac{t^2}{a^2\tau^2} \right), & 0 \leqq t \leqq a\tau, \\ 1, & a\tau \leqq t \leqq \tau - a\tau, \\ \left[1 - \left(\dfrac{t - \tau + a\tau}{a\tau} \right)^2 \right], & \tau - a\tau \leqq t \leqq \tau. \end{cases} \tag{31}$$

From these equations, b_ν is found to be

$$b_\nu = \frac{4}{\nu\pi} \left(\frac{\sin \dfrac{\nu\pi a}{2}}{\dfrac{\nu\pi a}{2}} \right)^2, \quad \text{where } \nu = 1, 3, 5, \cdots. \tag{32}$$

It is of interest to note that the order of convergence of the several waveforms considered is

Rectangular wave.............................like $\dfrac{1}{\nu}$

Trapezoidal wave.............................like $\dfrac{1}{\nu^2}$

Wave with flat top and parabolic rise and fall......like $\dfrac{1}{\nu^3}$

These results could have been predicted from the general theory of the Fourier series. Likewise, it can be predicted that the Fourier series for a wave that has continuous derivatives up to order n, but a discontinuous nth derivative, will converge like $1/\nu^{n+1}$.

Determination of Parameters of the Admittance Network Required to Generate a Specified Steady-state Waveform.—Each term of the Fourier series, Eq. (27), consists of a sine wave of amplitude b_ν and frequency $\nu/2\tau$. Such a current is produced by the circuit of Fig. 6·14.

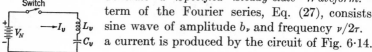

FIG. 6·14.—Circuit generating a sinusoidal steady-state current.

$$i_\nu = V_N \sqrt{\frac{C_\nu}{L_\nu}} \sin \frac{t}{\sqrt{L_\nu C_\nu}}, \qquad \nu = 1, 3, 5, \cdots. \quad (33)$$

The value of L_ν and C_ν may be determined by comparison with the coefficients of the Fourier series, Eq. (27), which gives

$$L_\nu = \frac{Z_N \tau}{\nu \pi b_\nu}, \qquad (34)$$

$$C_\nu = \frac{\tau b_\nu}{\nu \pi Z_N},$$

where $Z_N = V_N/I_l$, and may be called the characteristic impedance of the network.

The resultant network required to produce the given wave shape consists of a number of such resonant LC-sections in parallel, as shown in Fig. 6·15. The values of b_ν, L_ν, and C_ν for the several waves studied are given in Table 6·1.

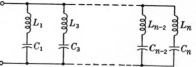

FIG. 6·15.—Form of voltage-fed network derived by Fourier-series analysis of a specified-alternating-current waveform.

Networks of the parallel admittance type derived above are often inconvenient for practical use. The inductances have appreciable

TABLE 6·1.—VALUES OF b_ν, L_ν, AND C_ν FOR NETWORK OF FIG. 6·15

Waveform	b_ν	L_ν	C_ν
Rectangular	$\dfrac{4}{\nu\pi}$	$\dfrac{Z_N\tau}{4}$	$\dfrac{4}{\nu^2\pi^2}\cdot\dfrac{\tau}{Z_N}$
Trapezoidal	$\dfrac{4}{\nu\pi}\left(\dfrac{\sin \nu\pi a}{\nu a}\right)$	$\dfrac{Z_N\tau}{4\left(\dfrac{\sin \nu\pi a}{\nu\pi a}\right)}$	$\dfrac{4}{\nu^2\pi^2}\dfrac{\tau}{Z_N}\dfrac{\sin \nu\pi a}{\nu\pi a}$
Flat top and parabolic rise and fall	$\dfrac{4}{\nu\pi}\left(\dfrac{\sin \frac{1}{2}\nu\pi a}{\frac{1}{2}\nu\pi a}\right)^2$	$\dfrac{Z_N\tau}{4\left(\dfrac{\sin \frac{1}{2}\nu\pi a}{\frac{1}{2}\nu\pi a}\right)^2}$	$\dfrac{4}{\nu^2\pi^2}\dfrac{\tau}{Z_N}\left(\dfrac{\sin \frac{1}{2}\nu\pi a}{\frac{1}{2}\nu\pi a}\right)^2$

distributed capacitance, which in effect shunts them and therefore tends to spoil the pulse shape, whereas the condensers have a wide range of values which makes manufacture difficult and expensive. Therefore, it is desirable to devise equivalent networks that have different ranges of values for capacitance and inductance.

Theoretically, it is possible to determine a large number of equivalent networks. The methods for carrying out the determinations are all based on mathematical operations on the impedance function of the network.[1] From the mathematical point of view, the impedance function completely characterizes the network, and all networks that have the same impedance function are equivalent. The determination of equivalent networks is therefore primarily a mathematical problem.

Equivalent Network Derived by Foster's Reactance Theorem.—The admittance function for the network of Fig. 6·15 may be written by inspection, and is

$$Y(p) = \sum_{\nu=1,3,\ldots}^{n} \frac{C_\nu p}{L_\nu C_\nu p^2 + 1}. \tag{35}$$

The right-hand member of Eq. (35) can be converted into the quotient of two polynomials the denominator of which is the product of all the denominators in the sum. Then, by inverting the quotient thus found, the impedance or reactance function, $Z(p)$, is determined, that is,

$$Z(p) = \frac{1}{Y(p)} = \frac{\displaystyle\prod_{\nu=1,3,\ldots}^{n}(L_\nu C_\nu p^2 + 1)}{\displaystyle\sum_{\nu=1,3,\ldots}^{n} C_\nu p \prod_{\substack{\gamma=1,3,\ldots \\ \gamma=\nu \text{ is omitted}}}^{n} (L_\gamma C_\gamma p^2 + 1)}. \tag{36}$$

The numerator is of degree $2n$ and the denominator of degree $2n-1$; consequently, $Z(p)$ has a pole at infinity as well as at zero. The zeros of $Z(p)$ are the poles of $Y(p)$, as must be true from circuit theory. The poles of $Z(p)$ must be found by carrying out the indicated operations and finding the roots of the resulting polynomial. As usual, the labor in finding these roots may be heavy.

The function $Z(p)$ may then be expanded in partial fractions about its poles, and an expression of the following form is obtained:

$$Z(p) = \frac{A_0}{p} + \sum_{\nu=2,4,\ldots}^{2n-2} \frac{A_\nu p}{B_\nu p^2 + 1} + A_{2n} p. \tag{37}$$

---

[1] For a detailed discussion of equivalent networks, see E. A. Guillemin, *Communication Networks*, Vol. II, Wiley, New York, 1935, pp. 184–221.

Equation (37) represents the impedance function for the network of Fig. 6·16. By inspection,

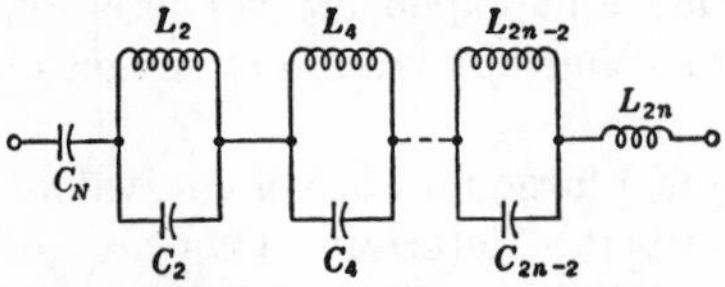

$$C_N = \frac{1}{A_0}, \qquad L_{2n} = A_{2n}, \qquad (38)$$

and it can be shown that the remaining elements are given by

$$L_\nu = A_\nu, \qquad C_\nu = \frac{B_\nu}{A_\nu}. \qquad (39)$$

Fig. 6·16.—Form of network equivalent to that of Fig. 6·15 derived by Foster's reactance theorem.

The values for C_N and L_{2n} are found from Eq. (35) by noting that

$$C_N = \lim_{p\to 0} \frac{1}{p} Y(p) = \sum_{\nu=1,3,\ldots}^{n} C_\nu, \qquad (40a)$$

and that

$$\frac{1}{L_{2n}} = \lim_{p\to\infty} p Y(p) = \sum_{\nu=1,3,\ldots}^{n} \frac{1}{L_\nu}. \qquad (40b)$$

Thus, C_N is equal to the sum of the C_ν's shown in Fig. 6·15, and L_{2n} is equal to the inductance of all the L_ν's in parallel.

Equivalent Networks Derived by Cauer's Extension of Foster's Theorem. Two additional forms of physically realizable networks may be found by making continued-fraction expansions of the reactance or admittance functions and identifying the coefficients thus obtained with network elements. The continued-fraction expansion represents a ladder network, as can easily be seen by forming the impedance

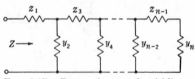

Fig. 6·17.—Form of network yielding a continued-fraction impedance function.

function, Eq. (41), for the ladder network of Fig. 6·17 by the method commonly used in finding a-c impedances:

$$Z = z_1 + \cfrac{1}{y_2 + \cfrac{1}{z_3 + \cfrac{1}{y_4 + \cdot}}}$$

$$\cdots + \cfrac{1}{z_{n-1} + \cfrac{1}{y_n}}. \qquad (41)$$

An equation of the form of Eq. (41) may be formed from Eq. (36) by dividing the denominator of Eq. (36) into its numerator, which gives z_1, inverting the remaining fraction and dividing again, which gives y_2, and continuing this process.   The first division to find z_1 gives by inspection

$$z_1 = L'_1 p, \qquad \text{where} \frac{1}{L'_1} = \sum_{\nu = 1,3,\ldots}^{n} \frac{1}{L_\nu},$$

and is equal to the series inductance of the Foster network of Fig. 6·16. When the network involves more than a very few sections, this process can, from a practical point of view, be carried through only with numerical coefficients.   It can be shown, however, that the network of Fig. 6·16 always yields a network of the form of Fig. 6·18.

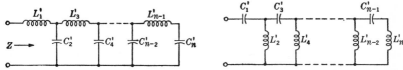

FIG. 6·18.—Form of network equivalent to that of Fig. 6·16, derived by continued-fraction expansion of the impedance function.

FIG. 6·19.—Form of network equivalent to that of Fig. 6·15 derived by continued-fraction expansion of the admittance function.

A network of the admittance type, shown in Fig. 6·15, can also be transformed into a ladder network by an exactly similar process, starting, however, with the admittance function Eq. (35) rather than with the reactance function.   The form of the network thus obtained is similar to that of Fig. 6·18, except that the inductances and capacitances are interchanged, as is shown in Fig. 6·19.   The values of C'_1 and L'_n can be determined by simple means, for it is clear from Eq. (34) that

$$C'_1 = \lim_{p \to 0} \frac{1}{p} Y(p) = \sum_{\nu = 1,3,\ldots}^{n} C_\nu, \tag{42}$$

that is, C'_1 is the sum of all the capacitances C'_ν of Fig. 6·15.   Likewise, from Eq. (34),

$$\frac{1}{L'_n} = \lim_{p \to \infty} pY(p) = \sum_{\nu = 1,3,\ldots}^{n} \frac{1}{L_\nu}. \tag{43}$$

Summarizing the discussion on equivalent pulse-forming networks, it may be said that three additional canonical forms of networks that are equivalent to the admittance network of Fig. 6·15 can be found by mathematical operations on the admittance and impedance functions.

Many more equivalent networks can be found by combining these mathematical operations in various ways, but most of these additional networks are of only limited interest. The form or forms of networks to be used in practice are determined by such practical considerations as ease of manufacture and specific pulser requirements.

Networks of Equal Capacitance per Section.—The most important pulse-forming network obtained by combining the canonical network

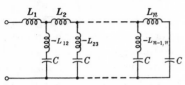

FIG. 6·20.—Pulse-forming network having equal capacitances.

forms is the type shown in Fig. 6·20, which has equal capacitances. From the standpoint of mass production in manufacture, it is highly desirable to have all capacitances of equal value. This is particularly true for high-voltage networks because the condensers for these constitute by far the most difficult and expensive item to manufacture. The network of Fig. 6·18 has capacitance values that are not very far from equal, and is therefore chosen as the starting point in deriving the network of Fig. 6·20. The network derived under the condition that the capacitances be equal may be expected to have inductances in the shunt legs to compensate for the altered values of the capacitances. If the actual capacitance in a given shunt leg is increased in transforming from the network of Fig. 6·18 to that of Fig. 6·20, the compensating inductance may be expected to be negative, and vice versa. The detailed procedure for the derivation of the equal-capacitance network is described below.

The capacitances of Fig. 6·20 are all known, each being equal to C_N/n where C_N is the total energy-storage capacitance, whereas the inductances are all unknown. The admittance and impedance functions for the network are the known functions specified by Eqs. (35) and (36). In the unknown network of Fig. 6·20 it is noted that, if an impedance L_1p is subtracted from the impedance function $Z(p)$ so that

$$Z_1(p) = Z(p) - L_1p, \qquad (44)$$

a zero of $Z_1(p)$ appears—that is, the series combination of L_{12} and C corresponds to a zero of $Z_1(p)$ or to a pole of $Y_1(p) = 1/Z_1(p)$. The admittance of the series combination of L_{12} and C is $\dfrac{Cp}{L_{12}Cp^2 + 1}$. Hence, the poles of $Y_1(p)$ corresponding to the L_{12} and C resonant section must be given by

$$p = \pm \sqrt{\frac{1}{-L_{12}C}} = \pm p_1,$$

and $Y_1(p)$ can be expressed in the form

$$Y_1(p) = \frac{a_1}{p - p_1} + \frac{a_2}{p + p_1} + Y_2(p), \qquad (45)$$

where $Y_2(p)$ is a remainder admittance function regular at $\pm p_1$.

The constants a_1 and a_2 can be found by algebra, for

$$a_1 = \lim_{p \to p_1} (p - p_1) Y_1(p) = \lim_{p \to p_1} \left[\frac{p - p_1}{Z(p) - L_1 p} \right]$$

$$= \frac{1}{\dfrac{d}{dp} [Z(p) - L_1 p]_{p = p_1}} = \frac{1}{Z'(p_1) - L_1}.$$

Likewise,

$$a_2 = \frac{1}{Z'(-p_1) - L_1}.$$

Since $Z'(p)$ is a function of p^2, as may be seen by differentiating Eq. (37), $a_1 = a_2 = a$.   Thus $Y_1(p)$ can be expressed as

$$Y_1(p) = \frac{2ap}{p^2 - p_1^2} + Y_2(p). \qquad (46)$$

The first term of the right-hand member of Eq. (46) must be the admittance of L_{12} and C in series, so

$$\frac{Cp}{L_{12}Cp^2 + 1} = \frac{\dfrac{1}{L_{12}} \cdot p}{p^2 + \dfrac{1}{L_{12}C}} = \frac{2ap}{p^2 - p_1^2}. \qquad (47)$$

The identity (47) gives the following two equations for determining the two unknowns p_1 and L_{12}:

$$L_{12} = \frac{1}{2a} = \frac{Z'(p_1) - L_1}{2}, \qquad (48a)$$

and

$$\frac{1}{L_{12}C} = -p_1^2, \qquad (48b)$$

where p_1^2 is a root of $Z(p) - L_1 p = 0$; thus, $L_1 = Z(p_1)/p_1$.   From Eq. (36) it is evident that the roots of $Z(p) - L_1 p = 0$ are all of the form p_j^2, and that there are n such roots.   The root p_1^2 is found by eliminating L_{12} between Eqs. (48a) and (48b), and is given by

$$\frac{1}{C} = \frac{-p_1^2}{2} \left[Z'(p_1) - \frac{Z(p_1)}{p_1} \right]. \qquad (49)$$

Since the value of C is known and only p_1 is unknown, Eq. (49) determines p_1.

Then

$$L_1 = \frac{Z(p_1)}{p_1}, \tag{50a}$$

$$L_{12} = \frac{1}{-Cp_1^2} = \frac{1}{2}[Z'(p_1) - L_1]. \tag{50b}$$

It is clear that L_{12} is negative for all cases for which p_1^2 is positive, and vice versa. In order to examine further the sign of the root p_1^2, suppose that $Z_1(p)$ is expressed as the ratio of two polynomials—which is always possible—that is,

$$Z_1(p) = \frac{N(p^2)}{D(p)}.$$

The coefficient of the leading term of $N(p^2)$ then contains the factor $(L_1' - L_1)$, where L_1' is the first inductance in the network of Fig. 6·18. All the other factors for all the coefficients of the polynomial $N(p^2)$ are positive because they are comprised of combinations of the inductances and capacitances of the network. By Descartes' rule of signs, $N(p^2) = 0$ can have no positive roots unless the coefficients of its terms have at least one change of sign when considered as a sequence. This change of sign can occur only if $(L_1' - L_1) < 0$, that is, if $L_1 > L_1'$, in which case there is a single positive root. Hence, if $p_1^2 > 0$, it follows that $L_1 > L_1'$, for which condition L_{12} is negative.

The nature of the root p_1^2 may also be seen by expressing Eq. (49) in a somewhat different form. For this purpose it is noted that

$$Z'(p) - \frac{Z(p)}{p} = p\frac{d}{dp}\left[\frac{Z(p)}{p}\right].$$

If the form of $Z(p)$ given by Eq. (37) is used,

$$\frac{Z(p)}{p} = \frac{A_0}{p^2} + \sum_{\nu=2,4,\ldots}^{2n-2} \frac{A_\nu}{B_\nu p^2 + 1} + A_{2n}$$

and

$$p_1\frac{d}{dp}\left[\frac{Z(p)}{p}\right]_{p=p_1} = \frac{-2A_0}{p_1^2} - 2\sum_{\nu=2,4,\ldots}^{2n-2} \frac{A_\nu B_\nu p_1^2}{(B_\nu p_1^2 + 1)^2}.$$

Using this result, Eq. (49) becomes

$$\frac{1}{C} = A_0 + \sum_{\nu=2,4,\ldots}^{2n-2} \frac{A_\nu B_\nu p_1^4}{(B_\nu p_1^2 + 1)^2}, \tag{51}$$

or, as $A_0 = 1/C_N$ and $1/C = n/C_N$,

$$\frac{n-1}{C_N} = \sum_{\nu=2,4}^{2n-2} \frac{A_\nu B_\nu p_1^4}{(B_\nu p_1^2 + 1)^2}. \tag{52}$$

The range of variation possible for C may be found by letting p_1^2 vary between zero and infinity. The limits are

$$\frac{1}{C} = A_0 = \frac{1}{C_N}, \qquad \text{when } p_1^2 = 0,$$

$$\frac{1}{C} \to A_0 + \sum_{\nu=2,4,\ldots}^{2n-2} \frac{A_\nu}{B_\nu} = \frac{1}{C_N} + \frac{1}{C_2} + \frac{1}{C_4} + \cdots + \frac{1}{C_{2n-2}},$$

$$\text{when } p_1^2 \to \infty.$$

The C_ν's are for the network of Fig. 6·16. Inasmuch as the series inductance L_{2n} of the network of Fig. 6·16 is equal to L_1' of Fig. 6·18, it is clear that the first capacitance C_2' of the latter network must be given by

$$\frac{1}{C_2'} = \frac{1}{C_N} + \frac{1}{C_2} + \frac{1}{C_4} + \cdots + \frac{1}{C_{2n-2}}.$$

Thus C must satisfy the inequalities

$$\frac{1}{C_N} < \frac{1}{C} < \frac{1}{C_2'},$$

or

$$C_2' < C < C_N. \tag{53}$$

In particular, it is noted that

$$C_2' < C = \frac{C_N}{n}$$

is a condition to be satisfied if p_1^2 is to be a positive root of $N(p^2) = 0$.

The foregoing procedure serves to determine L_{12} and L_1, and reduces the degree of $Z_1(p)$ by 2. The whole process may then be repeated on the remainder function $Z_2(p) = 1/Y_2(p)$, where $Y_2(p)$ is defined by Eq. (46), and L_2 and L_{23} are thereby determined. A new remainder function $Z_3(p) = 1/Y_3(p)$ is left, and the whole process can be repeated again and again until all of the roots are exhausted.

Since negative inductance can be realized physically by the use of

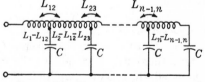

Fig. 6·21.—Equal-capacitance mutual-inductance network equivalent to that of Fig. 6·20.

mutual inductance, the network of Fig. 6·20, in which the inductances L_{12}, L_{23}, $\cdots$ $L_{(n-1)n}$ are negative, may be realized by a mutual-inductance network of the form shown in Fig. 6·21. The latter network, however, is a very practical form because all the inductances, including the mutual inductances, may be provided by winding coils on a single tubular form, and the condensers may then be tapped in at the proper points.

Design Parameters for Guillemin Networks.—As has been seen, there are only a few canonical types of network that simulate rectangular waves. In contrast, Guillemin's networks have a pulse-shape parameter (a in the formulas) which is, in effect, the fractional rise and fall time of the generated pulse. This parameter may be chosen arbitrarily to have any value between zero and one-half. The value zero corresponds to the rectangular pulse and the value one-half corresponds to a triangular pulse. The number of network sections required to simulate the pulse shape corresponding to any given value of a is more or less in inverse proportion to a, that is, a one-section network is satisfactory for $a = \frac{1}{2}$, whereas a very large number of network sections are required to give a rectangular pulse shape, corresponding to a small value of a.

In addition to the parameter a, there is another factor in Guillemin networks which may be varied, namely, the shape of the rising and falling sections of the pulse. The treatment herein has been limited to pulse shapes having linear and parabolic rising and falling sections. A great many more types are possible, but it does not appear profitable to consider them here. Pulse shapes having rapid rates of rise can be satisfactorily generated by networks that simulate trapezoidal pulses having small values of a; pulse shapes having slower rates of rise are satisfactorily produced by networks that simulate parabolic-rise pulses having somewhat larger values of a.

The first Guillemin networks were designed on the basis of a trapezoidal pulse shape having a rise time of approximately 8 per cent. Both five- and seven-section networks were built, but the improvement of the seven-section over the five-section network was very slight. No more than five sections are therefore necessary to generate a pulse having an 8 per cent rise-time parameter. Elimination of the fifth section was found to have an appreciable, although small, deteriorating effect on the pulse.

The number of network sections necessary to give good pulse shape can be estimated with fair accuracy by observing the relative magnitudes of the Fourier-series coefficients for the corresponding steady-state alternating-current wave. In the case of the five-section network just discussed, the relative amplitude of the fifth to the first Fourier coefficient is 0.04 and that of the sixth to the first is 0.02. In this case, the elimination of all harmonic components having amplitudes relative to the fundamental of 2 per cent or less has an inappreciable effect on the pulse shape, whereas the effect of eliminating the 4 per cent harmonic is appreciable although still small.

The basic network derived by the Guillemin design procedure is shown in Fig. 6·15, and consists of a series of resonant LC-elements connected in parallel. Design parameters for the first five sections of a network of this type, as well as the corresponding Fourier-series coefficients, are given in Table 6·2 for pulses having both linear and parabolic rise and fall, and for a range of values of the rise-time parameter a.

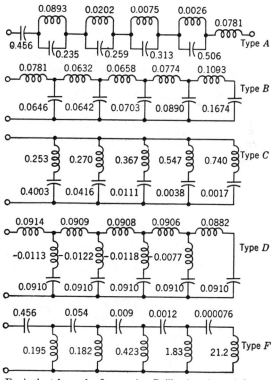

FIG. 6·22.—Equivalent forms for five-section Guillemin voltage-fed network. Multiply the values of the inductances by $Z_N\tau$ and the values of the capacitances by τ/Z_N. The inductances are in henrys and the capacitances in farads if pulse duration τ is expressed in seconds and network impedance Z_N in ohms.

It may be noted that a few negative values of inductance and capacitance are listed for a trapezoidal pulse with $a = 0.20$. These negative values are, of course, not realizable in a physical network.

Equivalent networks can be derived from the values listed in Table 6·2 by the mathematical procedures outlined above. A set of equivalent networks for the five-section network producing a trapezoidal pulse with a rise time of about 8 per cent is shown in Fig. 6·22.

Examples of one-, two-, and three-section networks, all for pulses

TABLE 6·2.—VALUES OF INDUCTANCES AND CAPACITANCES FOR FIVE-SECTION PULSE-FORMING NETWORK OF FIG. 6·15

Waveform	a	Fourier coefficients					Inductance					Capacitance				
		b_1	b_3	b_5	b_7	b_9	L_1	L_3	L_5	L_7	L_9	C_1	C_3	C_5	C_7	C_9
Rectangular	0	1.2732	0.4244	0.2547	0.1819	0.1415	0.2500	0.2500	0.2500	0.2500	0.2500	0.4053	0.04503	0.01621	0.00827	0.00500
Trapezoidal	0.05	1.2679	0.4089	0.2293	0.1474	0.0988	0.2510	0.2595	0.2777	0.3578	0.3578	0.4036	0.04318	0.01459	0.00670	0.00349
Trapezoidal	0.08	1.2601	0.3854	0.1927	0.1015	0.0482	0.2526	0.2753	0.3303	0.4478	0.7340	0.4011	0.04089	0.01227	0.00462	0.00170
Trapezoidal	0.10	1.2524	0.3643	0.1621	0.0669	0.0155	0.2542	0.2912	0.3927	0.6796	2.2875	0.3987	0.03865	0.01032	0.00304	0.00055
Trapezoidal	0.20	1.1911	0.2141	0	−0.0393	−0.0147	0.2672	0.4455	∞	−1.1561	−2.4052	0.3791	0.02272	0	0.00179	−0.00052
Parabolic rise	0.05	1.2699	0.4166	0.2418	0.1640	0.1194	0.2507	0.2547	0.2632	0.2773	0.2961	0.4042	0.04420	0.01539	0.00745	0.00422
Parabolic rise	0.10	1.2627	0.3939	0.2064	0.1194	0.0691	0.2521	0.2694	0.3084	0.3808	0.5122	0.4019	0.04179	0.01314	0.00543	0.00244
Parabolic rise	0.20	1.2319	0.3127	0.1032	0.0246	0.0017	0.2584	0.3393	0.6168	1.8472	20.94	0.3921	0.03318	0.00657	0.00112	0.00006
Parabolic rise	0.25	1.2092	0.2610	0.0564	0.00353	0.0017	0.2632	0.4065	1.1292	12.887	21.37	0.3849	0.32769	0.00359	0.00016	0.00006
Parabolic rise	0.33	1.1609	0.1720	0.00930	0.00338	0.0064	0.2742	0.6168	6.8493	13.44	5.5556	0.3695	0.01825	0.00059	0.00015	0.00023
Parabolic rise	0.40	1.1142	0.1080	0	0.0085	0.0015	0.2857	0.9821	∞	5.346	23.15	0.3547	0.01146	0	0.00039	0.00005
Parabolic rise	0.50	1.0319	0.0382	0.00825	0.00300	0.0014	0.3085	2.7747	7.7160	15.15	25.00	0.3285	0.00406	0.00053	0.00014	0.00005

Multiply the inductances by Z_{NT} and the capacitances by τ/Z_N. The inductances are given in henrys and the capacitances in farads if the pulse duration is expressed in seconds and the network impedance is in ohms. a is fractional rise time of wave, see Figs 6·13a and b.

$$i(t) = \frac{V_N}{Z_N} \sum_{\nu=1,3,\ldots}^{\infty} b_\nu \sin \frac{\nu \pi t}{\tau}.$$

with parabolic rise and for various values of the rise-time factor *a*, are shown in Fig. 6·23. The two- and three-section examples are of the type known as type A and consist of one or more antiresonant sections in series with an inductance and a storage condenser. Calculated pulse shapes produced on a matched resistance load by these three networks are shown

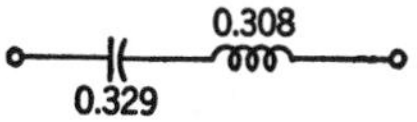

(a) One-section, *a* = 0.50. 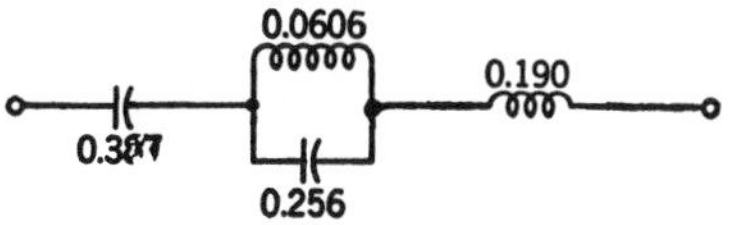   (b) Two-section, *a* = 0.33.

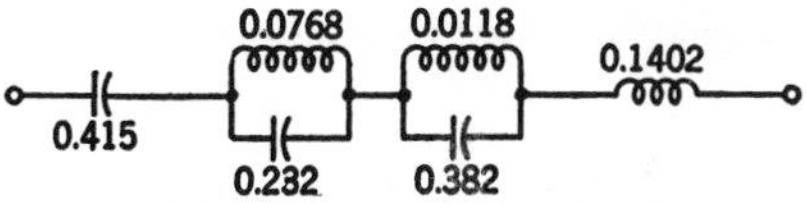

(c) Three-section, *a* = 0.25.

Fig. 6·23.—Theoretical parameters of one-, two-, and three-section type-*A* voltage-fed networks for parabolic rise. Multiply the inductances by $Z_{N}\tau$ and the capacitances by τ/Z_N. The inductances are in henrys and the capacitances in farads if pulse duration τ is expressed in seconds and network impedance Z_N in ohms.

in Figs. 6·24, 6·25*a*, and 6·26*a* respectively. The calculated pulse shape for the five-section network of Fig. 6·22 is shown in Fig. 6·27.

Considerable improvement in the pulse shapes from networks of more than one section can be produced by slight departures from the theoretical values of the parameters. Figure 6·25*b* shows the improvement over Fig. 6·25*a* resulting from a 15 per cent increase in the series inductance, and Fig. 6·25*c* shows the further improvement resulting from a 5 per cent increase in the capacitance of the storage condenser. Figure 6·26*b* shows the improvement over Fig. 6·26*a* resulting from similar increases in inductance and capacitance in the three-section network. The fact that these improvements can be made is perhaps an indication that the correspondence between the steady-

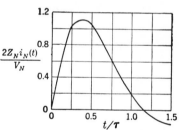

Fig. 6·24.—Calculated pulse shape for the one-section network of Fig. 6·23*a*.

state waveform and the transient pulse, which was assumed to be exact, is in reality only approximate.

Design Parameters for Equal-capacitance Networks.—The physically realizable form of the equal-capacitance network in Fig. 6·22 is shown in Fig. 6·28. The values of inductance given in Fig. 6·28 are obtained from those given for the type *D* network in Fig. 6·22 by making the algebraic sum of the inductances around corresponding meshes the same in the two cases. As has been stated, all the inductances and the mutual induct-

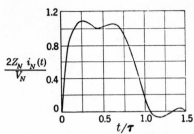

(a) Theoretical parameters.

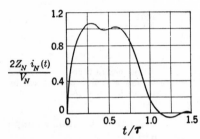

(b) L_4 increased 16 per cent from theoretical value.

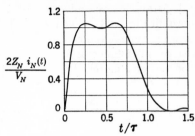

(c) L_4 increased 16 per cent, C_N increased
5 per cent from theoretical value.

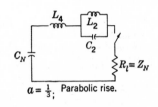

$a = \frac{1}{3}$; Parabolic rise.

Fig. 6·25.—Calculated pulse shapes for the two-section network of Fig. 6·23b.

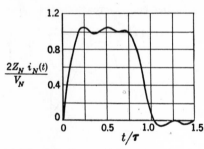

(a) Theoretical parameters.

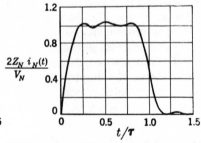

(b) L_6 increased 21 per cent, C_N increased 4
per cent from theoretical value.

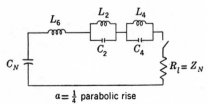

$a = \frac{1}{4}$ parabolic rise

Fig. 6·26.—Calculated pulse shapes for the three-section network of Fig. 6·23c.

ances may be obtained by winding coils on a single tubular form, and by adjusting the spacing between successive coils; however, care must be taken to insure that mutual-inductance effects between alternate coils are negligible.

The networks derived from the theoretical type D network by replacing the negative inductances in series with each condenser by mutual inductances between adjacent coils are normally referred to as type E networks. Experimental work done in early 1942 by J. R. Perkins proved the validity of the assumptions made in designing networks with inductances as given in Fig. 6·28.

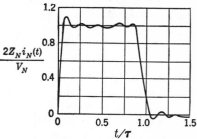

FIG. 6·27.—Calculated pulse shape for the five-section network of Fig. 6·22.

Further simplifications can be made, however, by noting that the values of the inductances of the three center sections and of the mutual inductances from section to section are very nearly equal. It has been found in practice that they can be made equal without affecting the pulse shape appreciably.

One way of reducing a type E network to this latter physical form

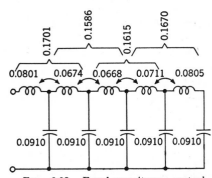

FIG. 6·28.—Equal-capacitance mutual-inductance network equivalent to the equal-capacitance network in Fig. 6·22. The inductances are in henrys and the capacitances in farads if the pulse duration is expressed in seconds and network impedance in ohms.

consists in winding a continuous solenoid in such a way that its total inductance $L_N = \tau Z_N/2$. The total network capacitance, $C_N = \tau/2Z_N$, is divided equally between the sections, and each condenser is connected to a tap on the solenoid. The taps are located to obtain equal inductance for all sections except the ends, which should have 20 to 30 per cent more self-inductance, and the ratio of length to diameter of the coil is chosen by a method involving the use of Nagaoka's function to give a mutual inductance which is 15 per cent of the self-inductance of each center section. The relative values of inductance and capacitance obtained by this method show good agreement with those given in Fig. 6·28, and networks of five or more sections built in this manner give excellent results. The same pulse shapes can be obtained, however, by the use of coils judiciously designed and located, as long as the sum of their self- and mutual inductances agrees closely with the values of Fig. 6·28.

If networks of less than five sections are to be designed, it is usually found that it is no longer possible to obtain satisfactory pulse shapes by using the same inductance per section.   If the values corresponding to a type *D* network are known, the necessary values of self- and mutual inductances can again be computed, and the coils wound and spaced the right distance to duplicate these values.   Or, charts can be obtained experimentally to determine the percentage inductance for each section and the total mutual inductance required to give a pulse shape that has certain characteristics of time of rise and ripple.   The number of sections in the network varies with the time of rise required for the particular application: practical experience indicates that it is not always desirable to obtain a very fast rise (see, for instance, discussion on magnetron mode-changing in Chap. 10 of this volume and in Chap. 8 of Vol. 6); and, in general, a shorter time of rise results in a ripple of higher amplitude on the top of the pulse.   Practical considerations involving the size of the condensers and the inductances, as well as the effect of other pulser components, make it generally undesirable to use a large number of sections for very short pulses.   Experience gained with type *E* networks shows that optimum over-all results are usually obtained for the following number of sections: 1 to 3 for pulse durations of less than 0.5 μsec, 2 to 5 for pulse durations from 0.5 to 2.5 μsec, and 3 to 8 for pulse durations from 2.5 to 5.0 μsec.

To recapitulate, the Guillemin theory provides a means of designing pulse-forming networks that duplicate accurately the pulse shapes normally required on a resistance load.   It is then possible to compute the actual pulse shape produced by the theoretical network and, by judicious changes in some of the parameters, to approximate even more closely the desired pulse shape.

The theoretical design procedure is likely to be lengthy, especially for networks of more than two sections.   In practice, therefore, it was found easier to derive experimentally any variations from the Guillemin design for a given pulse shape and number of sections, rather than to work through the detailed theory for each variation.   The experimental procedure is necessary in any case to compensate for unavoidable simplifications in the theory.   Stray capacitances and inductances, the effect of different qualities of dielectrics, the nonlinear and reactive characteristic of the load, and losses in the network cannot be accounted for easily in any kind of theoretical computation.

For instance, the pulse photographs of Fig. 6·29 show the modifications in pulse shape that can be obtained by altering some of the parameters of the network of Fig. 6·30.   The first photograph shows the

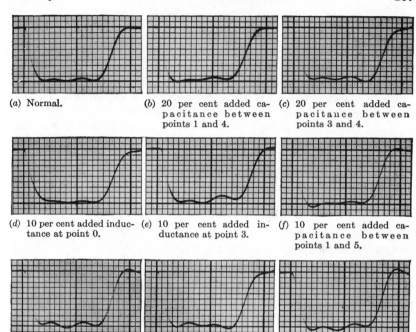

(a) Normal.

(b) 20 per cent added capacitance between points 1 and 4.

(c) 20 per cent added capacitance between points 3 and 4.

(d) 10 per cent added inductance at point 0.

(e) 10 per cent added inductance at point 3.

(f) 10 per cent added capacitance between points 1 and 5.

(g) 10 per cent added capacitance between points 2 and 5.

(h) 10 per cent added capacitance between points 3 and 5.

(i) 10 per cent added capacitance between points 1 and 5, 2 and 5, and 3 and 5.

FIG. 6·29.—Effect of variations in the values of L and C on the pulse shape obtained with a type E network. The numbered circuit points correspond to those shown in Fig. 6·30.

desired pulse shape after the parameters of the network had been adjusted experimentally. The next four indicate the effect of changing the value of some of the parameters, and the last four show the effect of stray capacitance from various points of the coil to ground. The changes in pulse shape obtained for small variations in parameters indicate the ease with which it is possible to meet specific requirements, but they also show the necessity of holding the values of elements to close tolerances and of minimizing the stray capacitances.

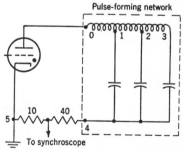

FIG. 6·30.—Circuit diagram for Fig. 6·29.

6·4. Current-fed Networks.—Current-fed networks are distinguished from voltage-fed networks in that the energy is stored in inductances instead of in capacitances. A current-fed network is therefore recharged by building up a current in an inductance that is an integral part of the network. Upon discharge, a portion of the built-up current appears in the load in the form of a pulse whose shape may be controlled by varying the network construction. The whole theory of current-fed networks is entirely analogous to that of voltage-fed networks, except that the current rather than the voltage plays the primary role.

As in the case of voltage-fed networks, it is instructive to consider first those current-fed networks that produce ideal rectangular voltage pulses on resistance load. The voltage across the resistance load for an ideal rectangular pulse is defined by the function $v(t)$,

$$v(t) = \begin{cases} V_l, & \text{for } 0 < t < \tau, \\ 0, & \text{for } t > \tau. \end{cases}$$

The corresponding Laplace transform, $v(p)$, is

$$v(p) = \frac{V_l}{p}(1 - e^{-p\tau}). \tag{54}$$

In solving this problem, it is simpler to consider the inverse case—that is,

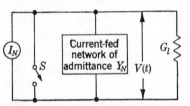

the case for which the pulse is produced by charging the network in parallel with the load resistance from a constant-current source. Since the pulse produced by discharging the network is identical with the charging pulse, the two cases are equivalent as far as determining the form of the network is concerned.

The charging pulse is generated by opening the switch S in the circuit shown in Fig. 6·31. The Laplace-transform equation for the circuit written on a current-node basis is

$$(Y_N + G_l)\,v(p) = \frac{I_N}{p}, \tag{55}$$

where Y_N is the network admittance, G_l is the load conductance, and I_N is the initial current from a constant current source. Solving for Y_N,

$$Y_N = \frac{I_N}{p\,v(p)} - G_l = \frac{I_N}{V_l(1 - e^{-p\tau})} - G_l$$

$$= G_l\,\frac{\dfrac{I_N}{G_l V_l} - 1 + e^{-p\tau}}{1 - e^{-p\tau}}. \tag{56}$$

If the numerator and denominator are multiplied by $e^{p\tau/2}$ and the terms rearranged to introduce the coth function, there results

$$Y_N = G_l \left[\coth \frac{p\tau}{2} + \frac{\left(\dfrac{I_N}{G_l V_l} - 2 \right) e^{\frac{p\tau}{2}}}{e^{\frac{p\tau}{2}} - e^{-\frac{p\tau}{2}}} \right]. \tag{57}$$

The constant I_N has been treated as known, but is in fact arbitrary. Choosing

$$I_N = 2G_l V_l,$$

the expression for Y_N reduces to

$$Y_N = G_l \coth \frac{p\tau}{2}. \tag{58}$$

By substituting Eq. (58) in Eq. (55) and solving for $v(p)$, the unknown quantity, it may be seen that $I_N = 2G_l V_l$ is the correct choice for I_N. The expression $G_l \coth p\tau/2$ is recognized as the input admittance of a lossless transmission line of characteristic impedance $Z_0 = 1/G_l$ and of electrical length $\tau/2$ when the far end of the line is short-circuited. The required current-fed network must, therefore, be either a transmission line of this type, or an electrical equivalent of such a line.

The functioning of the short-circuited transmission line in producing the desired rectangular pulse may readily be understood in terms of the elementary theory of wave propagation on such a line. At the instant at which the switch is opened, the current I_0 from the constant-current source divides equally between the line and the resistance load if the resistances of the two are equal. A rectangular voltage wave of amplitude $\frac{1}{2}I_0 Z_0$ travels down the line, is totally reflected with reversal of sign at the short-circuited end, and travels back to the input end in a total elapsed time of $2\delta = \tau$. When the reflected wave reaches the input end, the voltage there drops immediately to zero and remains zero thereafter because the line is properly matched by the resistance $R_l = Z_0$, and there is no reflection at the input end. However, the line is fully charged with magnetic energy because a constant current of value I_0 is flowing through it. The voltage pulse generated at the load during the charging period clearly has an amplitude of $\frac{1}{2}I_0 R_l$ and duration 2δ.

If the circuit between the constant-current source and the transmission line is then broken, an exactly similar voltage pulse is generated by the resulting discharge of the magnetic energy stored on the line. The total energy stored on the line is $\frac{1}{2}L_0 I_0^2$, where L_0 is the total distributed inductance of the line. This energy must be equal to that dissipated in the load, or

$$\frac{1}{2} L_0 I_0^2 = G_l V_l^2 \tau = \frac{I_0^2 \tau}{4G_l},$$

which reduces to the relation

$$L_0 = \frac{\tau}{2G_l} = \frac{R_l\tau}{2}.$$ (59)

The analogy between the transmission line used as a voltage-fed current-pulse-generating source and as a current-fed voltage-pulse-generating source is very close.   The far end of the line is open-circuited when it is used as a voltage-fed network and short-circuited when it is used as a current-fed network.   In the first case, the line is charged to a voltage V_0, which produces a current pulse on matched load of amplitude $V_0/2R_l$; in the second case, the l ne is charged to a current I_0, which produces. a voltage pulse on matched load of amplitude

$$\frac{I_0}{2G_l} = \frac{I_0R_l}{2}.$$

Current-fed Networks Derived from a Transmission Line.—Current-fed networks may be derived from the short-circuited transmission line by methods exactly analogous to those used in Sec. 6·3 in deriving voltage-fed networks from the open-circuited transmission line.   A summary of the networks thus derived is included, but the details of the derivations are omitted as they are considered sufficiently obvious.

Current-fed Network Simulating a Uniform Line Derived by Rayleigh's Principle.—This network, shown in Fig. 6·32, is identical in form to the voltage-fed network of Fig. 6·15 except that the far end is short-circuited instead of open-circuited.

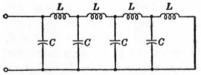

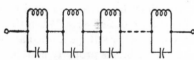

FIG. 6·32.—Current-fed pulse-forming network of the uniform-line type.

FIG. 6·33.—Current-fed network derived by rational-fraction expansion of the transmission-line admittance function.

Current-fed Networks Derived by Rational-fraction Expansions of the Admittance and Impedance Functions of a Short-circuited Transmission-line.—These are analogous to the similar networks derived by rational-fraction expansions of the impedance and admittance functions for the open-circuited transmission line.   The network derived by expanding the admittance function

$$Y = Y_0 \coth \frac{p\tau}{2}$$

is shown in Fig. 6·33.

Similarly, the network derived by the rational-fraction expansion of the impedance function

$$Z = Z_0 \tanh \frac{p\tau}{2}$$

is illustrated by Fig. 6·34.

Current-fed Networks of the Guillemin Type.—The theory of the Guillemin current-fed network is similar to that of the voltage-fed network, except that the roles of the voltage and current are interchanged. Instead of generating a specified steady-state alternating current by applying a constant-voltage source to the unknown voltage-fed network,

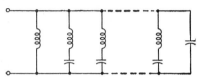

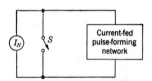

FIG. 6·34.—Current-fed network derived by rational-fraction expansion of the transmission-line impedance function.

FIG. 6·35.—Circuit for generating a specified alternating-voltage wave similar to the desired single-pulse shape.

a specified steady-state alternating voltage is generated by applying a constant-current source to the unknown current-fed network. Compare the circuit of Fig. 6·12 with that of Fig. 6·35. The alternating-voltage wave in this case is started by opening the switch rather than by closing it as in the case of the voltage-fed network.

A Fourier-series expansion is made for the specified alternating-voltage wave shape and the coefficients of the resulting series are identified with the network of Fig. 6·36.

The voltage across the νth anti-resonant section is given by

$$v_\nu = I_N \sqrt{\frac{L_\nu}{C_\nu}} \sin \frac{t}{\sqrt{L_\nu C_\nu}}. \quad (60)$$

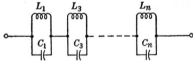

FIG. 6·36.—Form of current-fed network derived by Fourier-series analysis of a specified alternating-voltage waveform.

A comparison of Eq. (60) with Eq. (33), which is the corresponding expression for the voltage-fed network, shows that the two are identical in form with the exception that I_N appears in Eq. (60) instead of V_N and that L_ν and C_ν are interchanged. All of the results derived for the voltage-fed network may be immediately applied to the current-fed network by making the changes stated in the previous sentence.

In particular, the values of L_ν and C_ν are given by the equations

$$L_\nu = \frac{\tau b_\nu}{\nu \pi Y_N} = \frac{Z_N \tau b_\nu}{\nu \pi} \qquad (61)$$

and

$$C_\nu = \frac{\tau Y_N}{\nu \pi b_\nu} = \frac{\tau}{\nu \pi b_\nu Z_N}. \tag{62}$$

The parameter values given in Tables 6·1 and 6·2 for the voltage-fed network of Fig. 6·15 apply directly to the current-fed network of Fig. 6·36, provided that the L_ν's and C_ν's are interchanged and the induct-

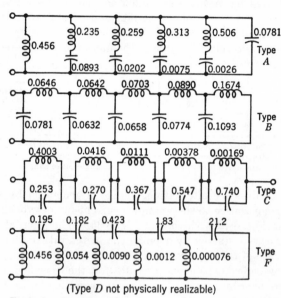

(Type *D* not physically realizable)

Fig. 6·37.—Equivalent forms for five-section Guillemin current-fed networks. Multiply the inductances by $Z_N\tau$ and the capacitances by τ/Z_N. Inductances are given in henrys and capacitances in farads if the pulse duration τ is in seconds and the network impedance Z_N is in ohms.

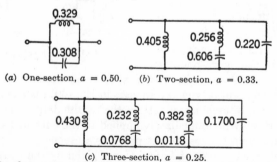

(a) One-section, $a = 0.50$.   (b) Two-section, $a = 0.33$.

(c) Three-section, $a = 0.25$.

Fig. 6·38.—One-, two-, and three-section type *A* current-fed networks. Multiply the inductances by $Z_N\tau$ and the capacitances by τ/Z_N. Inductances are given in henrys and capacitances in farads if the pulse duration τ is in seconds and the network impedance Z_N is in ohms.

ances are written in terms of $\tau/Y_N = Z_N\tau$ and the capacitances in terms of $Y_N\tau = \tau/Z_N$. As an example, reference to Table 6·1 row 1 gives the following values for the corresponding current-fed network

$$L_\nu = \frac{4Z_N\tau}{\nu^2\pi^2}, \qquad C_\nu = \frac{\tau}{4Z_N}.$$

Likewise the voltage-fed networks shown in Figs. 6·22 and 6·23 can be transformed to current-fed networks by following an identical procedure. The current-fed networks thus derived are shown in Figs. 6·37 and 6·38. The five-section networks are correspondingly designated in Figs. 6·22 and 6·37. The type D current-fed network is not realizable in physical form because some of the capacitances are negative. It is therefore omitted from Fig. 6·37.

6·5. Materials and Construction.[1] *Coils.*—The losses in the coils of a network can be determined by calorimetric measurement during operation, provided that the coils can be thermally insulated from the condenser elements. An alternate method is to calculate the frequency

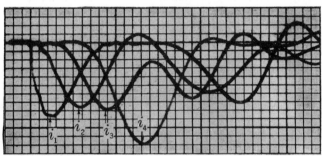

FIG. 6·39.—Condenser-discharge currents in the four-section type-E network shown in Fig. 6·40.

distribution of the currents in the various coils, and to determine the Q of the coils at those frequencies either by calculation or by measurement. The Q of a coil may often be calculated approximately with the use of one of various empirical formulas which are given in handbooks. It is usually much easier, however, to measure the Q of a sample on an r-f bridge. The frequency distributions may be calculated from Table 6·2.

The calculation of losses in the coils and in the condensers of a type E network during discharge may be simplified by the use of a single effective frequency instead of the band of frequencies given by Table 6·2. The discharge currents in the condensers of a four-section type E network are shown in the oscillogram of Fig. 6·39 as obtained with the circuit of Fig. 6·40.

[1] By P. R. Gillette.

The following approximate method of calculating this effective frequency leads to values of losses that are accurate enough for all practical purposes, although the frequency itself may be inaccurate.   The actual currents shown in Fig. 6·39 may be represented approximately by por-

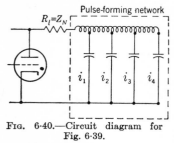

Pulse-forming network

FIG. 6·40.—Circuit diagram for Fig. 6·39.

tions of sine waves as shown in Fig. 6·41a. The current in the end condenser is assumed to consist of two overlapping waves of the same form as those for the other condensers.   These waves may be added to give the coil currents, as indicated in Fig. 6·41.   The frequency of the sine waves, in terms of the number of sections and the pulse duration, is given approximately by the expression $f = n/2\tau$.   The effective frequency for the rise and fall of current is given to a similar degree of accuracy—that is, to within a factor of two—by the same expression.

The discharge currents in the coils may each be broken up into a rising, a flat, and a falling portion, and the losses calculated separately for each portion.   The power dissipated in a coil during the rise and fall may be calculated on the assumptions (1) that the current is a sine wave of period equal to four times the rise time and of peak amplitude equal to the pulse amplitude, and (2) that the effective resistance is the a-c resistance corresponding to the frequency of this sine wave.   The power dissipated during the flat portion of the pulse may be calculated on the assumption that the current is a direct current of magnitude equal to the pulse amplitude.   The power dissipated during the charging period may be calculated on the assumption that the current is a sine wave of frequency equal to half the pulse recurrence frequency.   The total average power dissipated in the coil is the sum of the

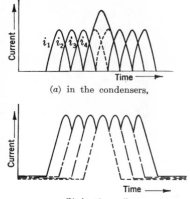

(a) in the condensers,

(b) in the coils.

FIG. 6·41.—Simplified representations of currents in the elements of a pulse-forming network.

values of losses computed as above.

In this way the correct wire size, the respective merits of solid, stranded, and litz wire, and coil shapes (single-layer, bank-wound, etc), may be determined.   The power loss is usually a far more important consideration than is current density in the choice of wire size.   Losses in coil forms may be reduced by the use of materials having low dielectric loss and by the use of hollow rather than solid forms.   Increasing the Q of coils by increasing their size may cause difficulties unless care is taken to keep the self- and mutual inductances constant.

In addition to the generation of heat, the effect of losses in the coils is primarily to attenuate the high frequencies.   A pulse with a smoother top and a slower rate of rise is thus produced with coils of higher losses.

Condensers.—A network that satisfies all electrical requirements can be constructed of separate coils and standard mica condensers of suitable current and voltage ratings.   A bulky network results, however, because of the problem of insulating the separate components, and also because the current ratings of standard condensers are based on continuous operation rather than on duty ratios of about 0.1 per cent.   The expedient of overrating smaller conventional condensers is dangerous because they are designed with interdependent voltage and current ratings.   It has therefore been found necessary to develop new techniques in design and construction.   All components are put in one container, with common means of insulation.   The condensers are designed to withstand the high voltages, but have a smaller current-carrying capacity than is ordinarily associated with such voltages.

Losses in the condenser elements can be calculated and measured by methods analogous to those suggested for coils.   The losses may be measured calorimetrically, or the effective frequencies may be calculated by one of the two methods outlined in the discussion of coil losses, and the effective dissipation factor of the completed condenser either measured or calculated for those frequencies.   The effective dissipation factor includes the losses in the dielectric, the foil, and the impregnant.   Under most conditions, the effective current through the condenser foils is well within the current-carrying capacity of the thinnest commercial foils. For high duty ratios and short pulse durations, where the skin depth is less than the foil thickness, the foil resistance may become a limitation.

Dielectrics such as mica, oil-impregnated paper (hereafter referred to as "paper"), and a relatively new material known as diaplex have been used successfully.   Diaplex is an organic-inorganic material that was developed as a substitute for mica, and has been used in a number of special applications for which the requirements are especially stringent. Paper, the material used most commonly in high-voltage condensers, has found by far the widest application in network manufacture.   Mica and paper condenser elements are almost always oil-filled; diaplex units are usually oil-filled, but it is also possible to use a plastic material as a bonding medium.

In general, best results are obtained when the losses in a network are evenly divided between the inductive and capacitive reactances.   If this rule is followed, it is generally possible to use paper dielectric for the condensers. In this case, the temperature-limiting constituent of the condensers is the paper dielectric, and that of the coils is the enamel or other organic insulation. If mica or diaplex dielectrics are used in the condensers, and the coils are wound with glass-insulated wire, the phenolic insulating members, impregnating oil, and solder become the temperature-limiting constituents. Mica or diaplex is therefore used as the dielectric in high-temperature units, and special high-temperature types of phenolics, oils, and solders are employed in the construction of the networks.

A "hot-spot" temperature, the maximum stable operating temperature of the materials, is generally taken as a maximum both for condensers and coils. In paper condensers, the amount (thickness) of paper dielectric is determined by the hot-spot temperature, which is usually 125°C. If the thickness of dielectric has been chosen with regard to this temperature, the occurrence of corona in the paper may easily be avoided by conventional methods. The same consideration applies to diaplex at low and medium voltages. However, corona will appear at the higher voltages if a liquid impregnant is used, apparently because strong electric fields drive the oil out from between the layers of dielectric material.

For mica condensers, the losses increase at a much greater rate than the applied voltage, partly because of corona in the voids of the mica itself. Hence, measurements made when the input power is low are not adequate to determine the maximum power that can be applied without exceeding the safe temperature for the other components. Mica is unique among dielectrics in that corona of moderate intensity does not produce chemical degradation of the dielectric, which would induce further losses. In this respect, paper is by far the worst of the three types of dielectric under discussion. Dielectric losses may also increase faster than the applied voltage with materials other than mica. Hence, empirical life-testing of the network is an important part of the design procedure.

Some of the electrical characteristics of mica, diaplex, and oil-impregnated paper condensers are listed in Table 6·3.

TABLE 6·3.—ELECTRICAL CHARACTERISTICS

	Mica	Diaplex	Paper
Dielectric constant (25°C, 1 kc/sec)	6.7	4.8	3.8
Dissipation factor (25°C, 1 kc/sec, %)	0.15	0.35	0.2

The variation with frequency and temperature of the capacitance and dissipation factor of condensers constructed with the three different types of dielectric is illustrated by the curves in Figs. 6·42 and 6·43.

Whereas the dielectric constant of mica and diaplex is nearly independent of frequency, that of paper decreases as the frequency is increased, particularly at low temperatures.   Therefore, the energy stored in paper condensers of a pulse-forming network cannot be entirely removed in high frequency components of the pulse shape.   Thus, at low temperatures, short pulses of 0.5 μsec or less have a duration shorter than that which is predicted from low-frequency measurements.

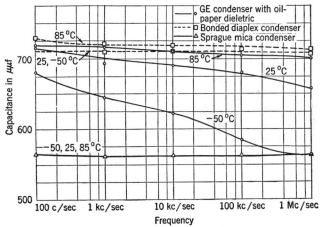

FIG. 6·42.—Variation of capacitance with frequency and temperature.

The dissipation factor of paper becomes very great at high frequencies, indicating that, as the time delay per section is decreased, the proportion of losses in a paper network increases rapidly.   In a mica or diaplex network this effect is not nearly so pronounced.   The increase in dissipation with frequency also causes the pulse from a paper network to be more rounded than that from a similar mica or diaplex network. The curve showing dissipation factor as a function of temperature leads to the interesting conclusion, borne out in practice, that the losses in a paper network are a minimum at 75°C.

To summarize, both mica and diaplex may be used to advantage in small light-weight high-temperature units.   Paper, because of its lower maximum operating temperature, gives, in general, a more bulky network.   It may be used in the storage condensers of type A networks, but the antiresonant sections usually require higher Q's than may be achieved with paper.   Finally, the rapid decrease in dielectric constant at low temperatures discourages the use of paper in units required to operate at extremely low temperatures.   Since paper is the least expensive of the three dielectrics discussed, it is generally chosen for applications in which only a normal range of ambient temperature is encountered.

After the type of dielectric to be used in a given network is chosen, the required volume must be determined. This volume depends not only upon the amount of energy to be dissipated, but also upon the maximum hot-spot temperature that the dielectric can withstand in normal operation, the efficiency of heat transfer from the dielectric to

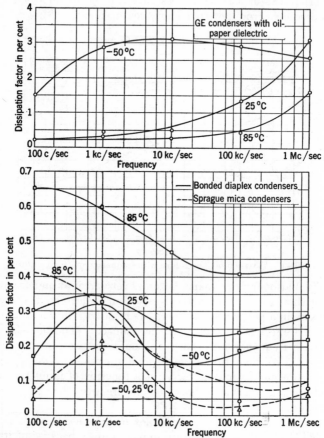

FIG. 6·43.—Variation of dissipation factor with frequency and temperature.

the case, the efficiency of heat transfer from the case to the surroundings, and the maximum temperature of the surroundings. The efficiency of heat transfer from case to surroundings may be improved by mounting the case so that there is a large area of contact between it and a heavy metal plate, by the proper use of fins, and by forced air circulation. The efficiency of heat transfer from the dielectric and coil to the case may be improved by spacing the elements in the case in such a way as to achieve the freest possible convection of oil, and hence the maximum convective cooling action.   Improvement in any of these factors reduces the required volume of the dielectric.

FIG. 6·44.—Typical type-*E* networks.

Examples.—The four network designs listed in Table 6·4 are typical examples of networks used in pulsers for radar systems.   The networks are shown in Fig. 6·44, and the pulse shapes produced on the appropriate resistance loads are shown in Fig. 6·45.

TABLE 6·4.—TYPICAL TYPE E NETWORKS

No.	Peak charging voltage, kv	Pulse duration, μsec	PRF, pps	Impedance, ohms	Nominal pulse power, kw	No. of sections	Dimensions*			Wt.	Application	Mfg.
							w., in.	l., in.	ht., in.			
1	3.5	0.84 / 2.24	840 / 420	50	25	3 / 3 + 5	1¼	3¾	2¾	12 oz	Airborne	GE
2	8	0.25 / 0.50 / 2.60 / 5.20	1600 / 800 / 400 / 200	50	200	2 / 2 / 4 / 4 + 4	2	10⅜	5⅝	5 lb 9 oz	Airborne	Sprague
3	8	1.0	1000	50	200	5	3¾	4½	5¼	4 lb 9 oz	Ground-based	Sprague
4	17	2.0	300	25	2000	2	4¼	13½	9½	24 lb 11 oz	Ground-based	GE

* Not including insulators.

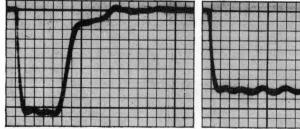

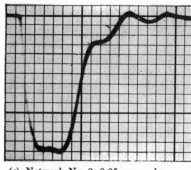

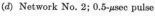

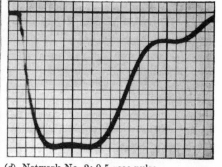

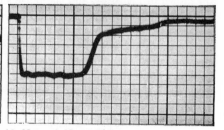

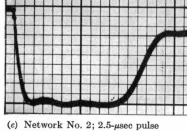

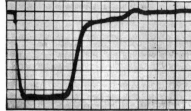

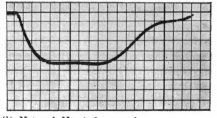

(a) Network No. 1; 0.84-μsec pulse   (b) Network No. 1; 2.24-μsec pulse

(c) Network No. 2; 0.25-μsec pulse   (d) Network No. 2; 0.5-μsec pulse

(e) Network No. 2; 2.5-μsec pulse   (f) Network No. 2; 5-μsec pulse

(g) Network No. 3; 1-μsec pulse   (h) Network No. 4; 2-μsec pulse

FIG. 6·45.—Pulse shapes on resistance load from the networks listed in Table 6·4.

The construction of network No. 3 may be considered as typical of that employed in the majority of type *E* networks.   It is housed in a terne-plate can with metalized glass bushings.   The can is of sufficient resiliency to take care of differential expansion.   The five condenser sections are designed to distribute the voltage effectively by four series sections and to minimize the inductance arising from the lead connections.   The gradient is approximately 210 volts per mil.   The condenser sections are held between bakelite end plates by means of metal bands.   The total capacitance of the network is adjusted so that it will be within ± 5 per cent of the rated value after impregnation.

The inductance consists of two close-wound coils wound on a ½-in. bakelite form.   The input inductance is wound with 32 turns of No. 22 enameled wire and is mounted separately from the main coil, which consists of 26, 26, 26, and 31 turns of the same size wire.   Although the input inductance must be separated from the other inductances because of the choice of can size and shape, it is possible to obtain a satisfactory wave shape on resistance load.   The coils are mounted in a bakelite frame that can be attached to the end plates of the condenser bank before the assembly is placed in the can.

6·6. Test Procedures.[1]—The electrical tests to which networks are subjected include a voltage-breakdown test, an insulation-resistance test, and a dissipation factor test; tests involving the determination of pulse duration, rate of rise, general pulse shape and impedance; and, finally, determinations of the temperature rise (which is a measure of efficiency) and life of the unit under normal operating conditions.   Only those tests designed specifically for networks are described in this section.

For temperature-rise and life tests, the network is operated under normal rated conditions in a pulser of a type similar to that in which it is to be used.   Tests are conducted at both the maximum and minimum ratings for continuous operating temperatures, as well as at normal room temperature.

The impedance of a network may be measured in several ways Probably the most obvious method is to discharge the network into a pure-resistance load through a bidirectional switch, and to adjust the resistance until no reflection is obtained after the pulse.   The resistance of the network is then equal to the load resistance.   The main drawback of this method is that it introduces an unknown quantity, the switch resistance.   This difficulty can be avoided to a certain extent by the use of a long cable whose impedance has previously been determined by other methods, but the possible difference in its impedance under pulse and r-f conditions makes this expedient of doubtful value.   In addition, the voltage of the first step is related to the voltage of the main pulse by

[1] By J. V. Lebacqz.

$$\frac{V_1}{V_l} = \frac{R_l - Z_N}{R_l + Z_N},$$

which can be rewritten

$$Z_N = \frac{1 - \dfrac{V_1}{V_l}}{1 + \dfrac{V_1}{V_l}} R_l.$$

In practice, the voltage V_1 has to be 1 to 2 per cent of V_l in order to give a noticeable deflection on the CRT screen and, under these conditions, the maximum accuracy for measuring Z_N is only 2 to 4 per cent. Actually, the error is greater because of the change in switch resistance during conduction after the pulse and the variation in pulse shape introduced by network attenuation and phase shift. For the same reasons, it has not proved satisfactory to measure impedance of actual networks by intentionally using a load that gives a large mismatch, and computing the impedance from the above formula as a function of the ratio of step voltages. Other methods used for cables (r-f bridge measurements of open-circuit and short-circuit impedances) are usually not applicable to pulse-forming networks because of distortions introduced by the lumped constants, and because only two terminals are available in the majority of cases. Pulsed bridge circuits were tried, and proved to be the most satisfactory means of measuring network impedance.

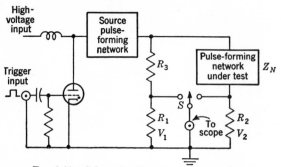

FIG. 6·46.—Schematic diagram of pulsed bridge.

The circuit finally adopted at the Radiation Laboratory is given in Fig. 6·46. As can readily be seen, the circuit is essentially a conventional bridge in which the external voltage is supplied by a pulse-forming network. Although with this system the switch resistance has no effect on the value obtained for impedance, great care must be exercised to eliminate stray capacitances and small additional inductances. This circuit has been used in either of two ways: as a matching method, or as a computation method. In the matching method, the switch S is a commutator and R_1 is made equal to R_2. The resistance R_3 is then varied until the traces of the voltage across R_1 and R_2 appear superimposed on the CRT screen through the action of the switch S, as indicated in Fig. 6·47a. The value of Z_N is then equal to R_3.

In the computation method, all the resistors are fixed, and the value of Z_N is easily obtained by measurement of the voltages V_1 and V_2 because

$$Z_N = \frac{V_1}{V_2}\frac{R_2}{R_1}(R_3 + R_1) - R_2.$$

The matching method is more convenient for the routine checking of networks. Difficulties are apt to arise, however, because of the inductance unavoidably introduced in building a variable resistance capable of

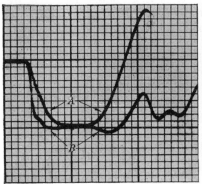 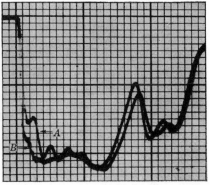

(a) Oscillogram showing balance of impedance in pulsed bridge. Trace A is obtained from the network arm of the bridge and trace B from the resistance arm.

(b) Oscillogram showing effect of noninductive resistor in pulsed bridge. Trace A is obtained with an inductive resistance and trace B with a noninductive resistance.

Fig. 6·47.

withstanding the power and voltage requirements. In the setup that has been used at the Radiation Laboratory, the resistor consists of noninductive elements connected through three selector switches to enable variations in steps of 10, 1, and 0.1 ohms. The additional connections necessitated by this system result in the appearance of oscillations on the top of the pulse, as indicated by Fig. 6·47b. This figure shows the wave shape through the resistance arm of the bridge only; the smoother trace corresponds to use of a noninductive resistance for R_3, the other one to the use of a variable resistance for R_3. The two resistors were equal to within 0.1 ohm.

The choice of the best possible pulse-forming network for the source still remains to be discussed. Experience has indicated that the value obtained for the impedance of the network under test depends slightly on the characteristics of the source. It is necessary to keep the resistances R_1 and R_2 small in order to produce the desired amount of deflection on the scope if the measurement is to be made at a power level comparable to that for which the network is designed. Thus, if the two networks have very nearly the same impedance, the source network is working into a load impedance that is considerably smaller than its own impedance. It has also been observed that this amount of mismatch has an effect on the oscillations on the top of the pulse. Figure 6·47a indicates that the response of a network and of a resistance to the leading edge of the pulse is not the same. In view of this fact, it is probably desirable to use for a source network one that has an impedance approximately equal to that of the load and whose other characteristics correspond, as nearly as possible, to those of the network under test. In order to meet these conditions, however, a large number of special source networks are required. In practice, either a network of the same series, or one of approximately the same pulse duration and impedance as the one under test, is used.

The values of impedance obtained by pulsed-bridge methods can be duplicated easily with a circuit of the same type. Any discrepancies in the results that are obtained by the two methods (these discrepancies have been as high as 5 per cent) are caused chiefly by the inductance of the adjustable resistor that is used in the matching method.

CHAPTER 7

THE DISCHARGING CIRCUIT OF THE LINE-TYPE PULSER

By J. V. Lebacqz

7·1. General Properties of the Discharging Circuit.—The basic characteristics of the discharging circuit are determined entirely by the elements making up that circuit: the pulse-forming network, the switch tube, and the load. A pulse cable and a pulse transformer are often added between the pulser and the load although they are not essential to the operation of the equipment. The pulse cable is usually added only for convenience in engineering, and for greater flexibility in the physical location of the pulser and the load. The pulse transformer, on the other hand, can often be considered a necessary component of the pulser because it reduces the maximum network voltage that is necessary, and thus eases the problems of switching. As a result, the design problems are simplified, and a saving in weight and an increase in reliability are generally effected. The introduction of a pulse cable and a pulse transformer also affects the general characteristics of the discharging circuit.

The general properties of the discharging circuit can conveniently be arrived at by considering the simple circuit of Fig. 7·1.

As has been seen in Chap. 6, a charged loss-less transmission line produces a rectangular pulse of energy if it is connected through an ideal switch to a pure resistance equal in magnitude to the characteristic impedance of the line. In practice, however, the pulse-forming networks do not duplicate exactly the pulse shape obtained from a loss-less transmission line.

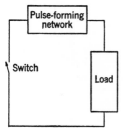

Fig. 7·1.—Simple schematic diagram of the discharging circuit for a line-type pulser.

The switch in a line-type pulser is not required to open the circuit at the end of the pulse because the current ceases to flow when all the energy stored in the pulse-forming network is dissipated. This important property of the circuit makes it possible to take advantage of the high current-carrying capacity and low voltage drop that are characteristic of gaseous-discharge switches. The mechanism of the switch operation has an important effect on the operation of the circuit, as is discussed later.

The loads to which pulsers must supply power are not, in general, pure resistances. For most radar applications, the oscillator tube can be considered as a biased diode, as is already shown in Chap. 2 (Fig. 2·11). Random variations in the values of either the bias voltage or the dynamic resistance may occur from pulse to pulse or during a single pulse, and their effect on pulser performance must be considered.

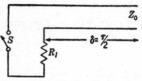

FIG. 7·2.—Ideal discharging circuit for a line-type pulser.

Some of the characteristics of the circuit can be determined by considering the discharge of a lossless transmission line of impedance Z_0 through a resistance R_l. Consider the circuit of Fig. 7·2, in which the switch can be closed instantly, and is assumed to have zero resistance when closed. If the line is charged to a potential V_0, the current in the load after closing the switch is given by

$$i_l(t) = \frac{V_0}{Z_0 + R_l}\left\{1 - U(t - 2\delta) - \frac{Z_0 - R_l}{Z_0 + R_l}[U(t - 2\delta) - U(t - 4\delta)]\right.$$
$$\left. + \left(\frac{Z_0 - R_l}{Z_0 + R_l}\right)^2[U(t - 4\delta) - U(t - 6\delta)] - \cdots\right\}, \quad (6.7)$$

where

$$U(\Delta t) = 1 \quad \text{for } \Delta t > 0,$$
$$U(\Delta t) = 0 \quad \text{for } \Delta t < 0,$$
$$\Delta t = (t - n\delta), \quad n = 2, 4, 6, \cdots.$$

In general, only the energy transferred to the load during the first time interval 2δ is of practical value, and in that case,

$$I_l = V_0\frac{1}{R_l + Z_0} \quad (1)$$

and

$$V_l = V_0\frac{R_l}{R_l + Z_0} \quad (2)$$

The pulse power in the load is

$$P_l = V_lI_l = \frac{V_0^2}{(R_l + Z_0)^2}R_l, \quad (3)$$

and the energy dissipated in the load is

$$W_l = P_l\tau = \frac{V_0^2}{(R_l + Z_0)^2}R_l\tau, \quad (4)$$

where $\tau = 2\delta$ is the duration of the pulse at the load. As can immediately be seen from the foregoing equations, the pulse power and the energy dissipated in the load per pulse are a function of the load resistance. The value of load resistance for maximum power transfer can be obtained by differentiation of Eq. (3);

$$\frac{dP_l}{dR_l} = \frac{V_0^2}{(R_l + Z_0)^2} - \frac{2V_0^2 R_l}{(R_l + Z_0)^3} \equiv 0,$$

and the maximum power transfer is obtained when

$$R_l = Z_0. \tag{5}$$

With this condition,

$$I_l = \frac{V_0}{2Z_0}, \tag{6}$$

$$V_l = \frac{V_0}{2}, \tag{7}$$

$$P_l = \frac{V_0^2}{4Z_0} \tag{8}$$

and

$$W_l = \frac{V_0^2}{4Z_0}\tau. \tag{9}$$

The value of load resistance for maximum pulse power given by Eq. (5) could have been anticipated from physical considerations; Eqs. (1) to (4) apply only for the first interval 2δ. If the load impedance equals the line impedance there are no reflections, and all the energy stored in the line is dissipated in the load during the interval 2δ. Any mismatch causes part of the energy to be dissipated in the load after the time 2δ, and thus results in a decrease in power during the main pulse.

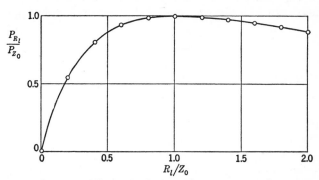

FIG. 7·3.—Effect of load mismatch on power transfer.

Fortunately, exact matching of the load to the transmission-line impedance is not particularly critical from the standpoint of power transfer, as long as the mismatch does not exceed 20 to 30 per cent, as can be shown by taking the ratio of the power into any load resistance R_l to the power into a matched load Z_0. This ratio is

$$\frac{P_{R_l}}{P_{Z_0}} = \frac{\frac{V_0^2}{(R_l + Z_0)^2} R_l}{\frac{V_0^2}{4Z_0}} = 4 \frac{R_l}{Z_0} \frac{1}{\left(1 + \frac{R_l}{Z_0}\right)^2}. \tag{10}$$

The values obtained for Eq. (10) are plotted in Fig. 7·3, showing the flatness of the curve near the maximum. As an example, the values of R_l/Z_0 for which 3 per cent of the energy stored in the transmission line is dissipated after the time 2δ, equal to the pulse duration τ, are found as follows:

$$\frac{1 - 0.03}{1} = 0.97 = 4 \frac{\frac{R_l}{Z_0}}{\left(1 + \frac{R_l}{Z_0}\right)^2},$$

$$\left(\frac{R_l}{Z_0}\right)_1 = 1.42,$$

$$\left(\frac{R_l}{Z_0}\right)_2 = 0.70.$$

Thus, from power considerations alone, the matching of the load to the line impedance has very little effect on the discharging circuit, since only 3 per cent or less of the energy stored in the transmission line is not dissipated in the load if the load impedance varies from 70 to 142 per cent of the transmission-line impedance.

The energy dissipated in the load under matched conditions is equal to the energy stored in the transmission-line capacitance before the pulse, or

$$\frac{V_0^2 \cdot \tau}{4Z_0} = \frac{1}{2} C_0 V_0^2,$$

which gives the fundamental relation

$$\tau = 2C_0 Z_0. \tag{11}$$

The pulser design is affected by the pulse-power and energy-per-pulse requirements in several ways. Equation (8) shows that the pulse output is proportional to the square of the voltage on the transmission line or network, and inversely proportional to the line or network impedance. Figure 7·4 gives the maximum pulse power P_{Z_0} that can be expected from an ideal pulser for various line impedances and voltages.

If nearly matched conditions are to be realized, it can be seen that the voltage necessary to supply a high pulse power to a high-impedance load becomes prohibitively high. For example, for a pulse-power requirement of 1 Mw into an 800-ohm load, the theoretical transmission-line voltage is 60 kv. The practical figure is higher because the losses in the discharging circuit have been neglected. A slightly lower network voltage can be used if the line and the load are intentionally mismatched

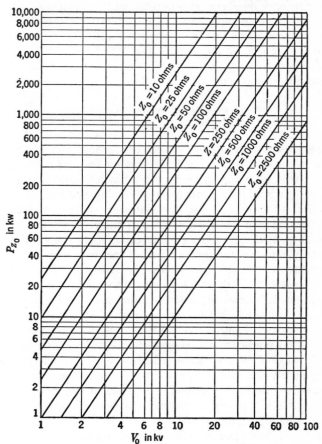

FIG. 7·4.—Maximum pulse power output vs. transmission-line voltage at various impedance levels.

because the power transfer is not seriously affected. In practice, up to about 40 per cent mismatch can be tolerated ($R_l/Z_0 = 1.4$), and under this condition, the line impedance is approximately 600 ohms with an 800-ohm load, and the voltage is 50 kv instead of 60 kv.

Handling voltages of this order of magnitude presents serious engineering problems. The most important problem is that of securing a suitable switch. Gaseous-discharge switches are not readily suited to the very high voltages required in the high-impedance circuit. Neither would these circuits use the high current-carrying capacity of these switches to the best advantage. On the other hand, vacuum tubes have a high effective resistance, and the losses that occur when these are used as switches in high-impedance line-type pulsers result in low efficiency.

The small storage capacitance that results from the use of a high-impedance transmission line or network leads to other difficulties. This capacitance is given by $C_0 = \tau/2Z_0$ [Eq. (11)] and, for a given pulse duration, decreases proportionally to the increase in line impedance. Assuming, for example, an 0.8-μsec pulse and an 800-ohm transmission line,

$$C_0 = \frac{0.8 \times 10^{-6}}{2 \times 0.8 \times 10^3} = 500 \ \mu\mu\text{f}.$$

The small transmission-line or network capacitance may prove a serious handicap in the design of the charging circuit because a charging diode with peak inverse voltage greater than 30 kv is required to prevent the size of the charging inductance from becoming prohibitive. Also, the construction of the network itself presents very serious problems because the network inductances increase proportionately with the impedance, and the effect of distributed capacitance on wave shape becomes proportionately greater as the total active network capacitance is decreased.

In spite of these difficulties, several line-type pulsers were designed in the early days of the Radiation Laboratory to operate directly into high-impedance loads. However, a much more satisfactory solution to the problem was achieved by the development of an impedance-matching pulse transformer. These pulse transformers can be used over the wide range of output power (from 500 watts to 20 Mw) required from pulsers and over a range of pulse duration from less than 0.1 to more than 5 μsec without seriously affecting the shape of the output pulse. The impedance ratio of a pulse transformer is essentially equal to the square of the turns ratio. For a 1-Mw pulser supplying an 0.8-μsec pulse to an 800-ohm load, and using a 4/1 pulse transformer, the load $R_{l2} = 800$ ohms that is across the secondary appears across the primary as

$$R_{l1} = \tfrac{800}{16} = 50 \text{ ohms}.$$

The maximum line or network voltage is now about 15 kv and its capacitance

$$C_0 = \frac{0.8 \times 10^{-6}}{100} = 8000 \ \mu\mu\text{f}.$$

The disadvantages of a pulser coupled directly to a high-impedance load have now disappeared. Another advantage in the use of pulse transformers is the possibility of introducing a physical separation between the

pulser and its load.   In many radar applications, it has been found necessary to separate the oscillator from the pulser itself—in some cases,
because of the physical motion of the oscillator.   Under these conditions,
a pulse cable links the pulser to the load.   Theoretically, pulse cables
can be made in almost any impedance range, but practical considerations
limit their impedance to less than 100 ohms.   In the United States, the
50-ohm impedance level for pulse cable was standardized, and, for convenience in matching cable to pulser when necessary, the great majority
of line-type pulsers were designed to use 50-ohm pulse-forming networks.
In special applications requiring an exceptionally high-power output,
however, networks of 25 and even 12.5 ohms were used.   In Great
Britain, on the other hand, the network impedance was centered around
80 ohms—again for convenience in cable matching.

Since the loads used in microwave radar usually have input characteristics similar to those of a biased diode, the
performance of the pulser circuit with this
load must be considered in some detail.   The
method of approach, however, can be extended
to pulser circuits with loads of any type
imaginable.

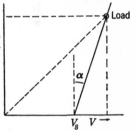

The current-voltage characteristic of a biased-diode load can be represented by Fig. 7·5.
For any point along the load characteristic,

$$R_l = \frac{V_l}{I_l} = \frac{V_s + I_l \tan \alpha}{I_l} = \frac{V_s + I_l r_l}{I_l},$$

FIG. 7·5.—Voltage-current
characteristics of a biased-
diode load.

where r_l is the dynamic resistance of the diode.   Under these conditions
the general expression (see Eq. (1)) for the current in the load becomes

$$I_l = \frac{V_0}{R_l + Z_0} = \frac{V_0}{\dfrac{V_s + I_l r_l}{I_l} + Z_0} = \frac{V_0 I_l}{V_s + I_l(r_l + Z_0)},$$

or

$$I_l = \frac{V_0 - V_s}{r_l + Z_0} = \frac{V_0}{Z_0} \frac{1 - \dfrac{V_s}{V_0}}{1 + \dfrac{r_l}{Z_0}}, \tag{12a}$$

so

$$R_l = r_l + V_s \frac{r_l + Z_0}{V_0 - V_s}, \tag{12b}$$

and

$$V_l = I_l R_l = \frac{V_0 - V_s}{r_l + Z_0}\left(r_l + V_s \frac{r_l + Z_0}{V_0 - V_s}\right) = V_0 \frac{r_l}{Z_0} \frac{1 + \dfrac{Z_0}{r_l}\dfrac{V_s}{V_0}}{1 + \dfrac{r_l}{Z_0}}. \tag{13}$$

In this case, the conditions for optimum power transfer between the transmission line and the load depend on the bias voltage as well as on the initial voltage on the line. Substituting $R_l = Z_0$ in Eq. (12b),

$$(Z_0 - r_l)(V_0 - V_s) = V_s(r_l + Z_0),$$

which may be simplified to

$$Z_0 = r_l \frac{V_0}{V_0 - 2V_s}, \tag{14}$$

or

$$V_0 = \frac{2V_s}{1 - \dfrac{r_l}{Z_0}}. \tag{15}$$

Equation (15) expresses the voltage to which the transmission line must be charged in order that the load operate at the only point corresponding to matched conditions, or to maximum power transfer.

Then, for matched conditions,

$$I_l = \frac{V_0}{Z_0} \frac{1 - \dfrac{1 - \dfrac{r_l}{Z_0}}{2}}{1 + \dfrac{r_l}{Z_0}} = \frac{V_0}{2Z_0}, \tag{16}$$

$$V_l = V_0 - I_l Z_0 = \frac{V_0}{2}, \tag{17}$$

and

$$P_l = \frac{V_0^2}{4Z_0}. \tag{18}$$

It is seen that the expressions for current, voltage, and pulse power are identical with Eqs. (6), (7), and (8) obtained for a pure-resistance load.

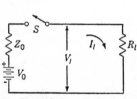

Fig. 7·6.—Simplified equivalent circuit for a line-type pulser with a resistance load.

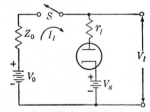

Fig. 7·7.—Simplified equivalent circuit for a line-type pulser with a biased-diode load.

Expressions identical to those for the current and the voltage in the line-type pulser can be obtained from the consideration of a simple series circuit containing a battery of constant voltage V_0 and internal resistance Z_0, a switch closed for the time τ, and a load resistance R_l (see Fig. 7·6).

For this circuit

$$I_l = \frac{V_0}{Z_0 + R_l}$$

and

$$V_l = V_0 \frac{R_l}{Z_0 + R_l}.$$

[See Eqs. (1) and (2).]   For a biased-diode load (Fig. 7·7) of dynamic resistance r_l,

$$I_l = \frac{V_0 - V_s}{Z_0 + r_l}$$

and

$$V_l = V_s + r_l \frac{V_0 - V_s}{Z_0 + r_l} = \frac{V_0 r_l + V_s Z_0}{Z_0 + r_l}.$$

[See Eqs. (12) and (13).]

Since the circuits of Figs. 7·6 and 7·7 give the same results as those obtained by the transmission-line theory, they can be considered adequate equivalent circuits for a further discussion of the currents and voltages in line-type pulsers.   On the other hand, this circuit is not satisfactory for determining energy relations because Z_0 is not physically a dissipative element.   The value of Z_0 is determined from a fundamental considera- tion of the charging of an infinite transmission line, across which a battery voltage is suddenly applied, and is then defined as the ratio of voltage to current in the line.   If the line is assumed to be lossless, the impedance, $Z_0 = \sqrt{L_0/C_0}$, has the dimensions of a pure resistance, but does not dis- sipate energy.   It can easily be seen that the circuits of Figs. 7·6 and 7·7 are identical with those of the hard-tube pulser discussed in Chap. 2. The principal difference lies in the ratio of Z_0 to R_l or r_l.   For most practical applications of line-type pulsers, Z_0 is very nearly equal to R_l, or to $r_l \dfrac{V_0}{V_0 - 2V_s}$, whereas, in general, a hard-tube pulser is operated with a load whose impedance is high compared with the pulser internal impedance (effectively the resistance of the switch tube, which is dis- sipative).   This difference is very important in the consideration of pulser regulation, efficiency, and the effect of other circuit parameters on pulse shape.

7·2. Pulser Characteristics.—A typical discharging circuit for a line- type pulser can be represented by the diagram of Fig. 7·8.   The ideal rectangular pulse that was considered in the preceding section is usually

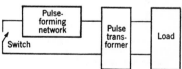

FIG. 7·8.—Block diagram of the dis- charging circuit of a line-type pulser.

unobtainable in practice because of the characteristics of the various com- ponents used in the circuit.   Some of the effects on pulser behavior and on pulse shape introduced by the characteristics of the separate components are discussed in this and in the following sections. A brief résumé of the characteristics that affect the behavior of the discharging circuit is given here to facilitate reference.

The Pulse-forming Network.—As explained in Chap. 6, the pulse-forming networks used in practice can only produce an approximately rectangular output-pulse on a pure-resistance load. In order to simplify the mathematical analysis, it is assumed in this chapter that the pulse shape generated by the network is either rectangular or trapezoidal. It should be noted, however, that most practical networks also produce

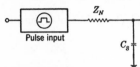

Fig. 7·9.—Electrical equivalent of a pulse-forming network for the study of pulse shapes.

amplitude oscillations during the "flat" portion of the pulse—that is, between the end of the rise and the beginning of the fall. In general, these oscillations are small and are neglected. In addition, actual networks always have stray capacitances to ground that must be taken into account when particularly fast rates of rise or fall are desired.

For simplicity in analysis, the stray capacitances to ground are lumped and connected at the capacitance input terminal of the network. The pulse-forming network can then be represented as in Fig. 7·9, in which the subscripts 0 for a lossless transmission line have been replaced by N.

The Switch.—Three types of switches have been used extensively in pulser operations: rotary spark gaps, fixed triggered gaps, and thyratrons.

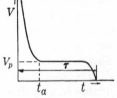

Fig. 7·10.—Typical switch drop as function of time.

In general, the electrical characteristics of these three types are the same during the main pulse or conducting period. Fixed gaps and thyratrons both show a rapid decrease in tube drop from time $t = 0$ (when the tube begins to conduct), and the tube drop stays very nearly constant for the remainder of the pulse. A typical curve of tube drop during a pulse is shown in Fig. 7·10. The time t_a required for the voltage to decrease to a steady-state value, V_p varies with the particular switch considered and is usually about 0.3 μsec for triggered gaps, and 0.1 μsec for thyratrons. For a given tube the steady value of the tube drop is very nearly independent of the current, as shown by Fig. 7·11. The average values

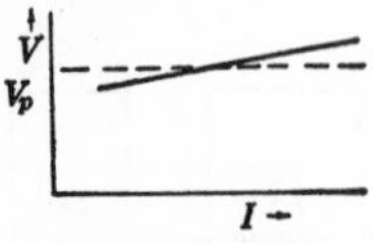

Fig. 7·11.—Typical switch drop as function of current.

for V_p under actual operating conditions are approximately 120 to 150 volts per gap for typical fixed spark gaps, and 70 to 110 volts for typical hydrogen thyratrons.

The data taken with rotary spark gaps points to approximately the same results as were obtained with fixed gaps or thyratrons. Rotary gaps, like thyratrons, have been used successfully at pulse durations of the order of magnitude of 0.1 μsec, indicating a very fast decrease in voltage drop across the gap after the initiation of conduction. Although the time jitter of the rotary gap does not directly affect the discharging circuit, it may affect the final charging voltage of the network. Under unfavorable conditions, the resulting change in power output from pulse to pulse may be several per cent.

The principal difference that is introduced in the behavior of the circuit by the switches occurs immediately after the pulse. Rotary gaps and triggered fixed gaps are essentially bidirectional devices, but the thyratron is unidirectional, and therefore holds off any negative voltage appearing at the plate as a result of impedance mismatch. This fact has a definite effect on the shaping of the tail of the pulse, causing post-pulse conduction for bidirectional switches and a higher voltage back-swing for the thyratron switch. Different principles of circuit-element protection must also be applied because of differences in the switches.

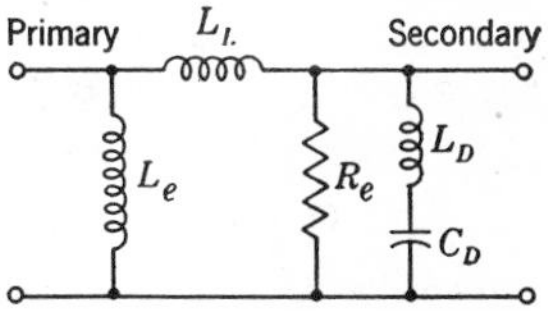

The Pulse Transformer.—An equivalent circuit adequate for the discussion of the effect of pulse transformers is derived in Sec. 12·1, and is given in Fig. 7·12 for reference. To make the analysis easier, however, further simplifications are usually introduced, and

FIG. 7·12.—Equivalent circuit for a pulse transformer.

those circuit elements that have little effect on the particular portion of the pulse under consideration are neglected.

For simplicity, it is assumed in the following discussions that any pulse transformer introduced in the circuit having a voltage stepup ratio of n is replaced by a 1/1 transformer, and equivalent circuits for line-type pulsers are all referred to the secondary of the pulse transformer. Under these conditions, the actual primary voltages are multiplied by n, the actual primary currents are divided by n, and the actual impedances are multiplied by n^2, that is,

$$R_{sec} = n^2 R_{pri},$$
$$L_{sec} = n^2 L_{pri},$$
$$C_{sec} = \frac{1}{n^2} C_{pri}.$$

The assumption that the losses in the pulse transformer are negligible is sufficiently accurate for discussions of pulse shapes, and is warranted by the simplifications it introduces in the mathematics. When the losses have to be taken into account, it can be assumed that the voltage transformation is conserved, that is, the ratio of primary to secondary voltage is equal to the ratio of the number of turns in the pulse transformer. The losses then appear as shunt losses and affect the ratio of currents and impedances as follows:

$$V_{sec} = nV_{pri},$$

$$I_{sec} = \frac{1}{n\eta_t} I_{pri},$$

$$Z_{sec} = n^2\eta_t Z_{pri},$$

where η_t is the efficiency of the pulse transformer.

The Load.—As previously stated, the load most widely used in radar applications of pulse generators has the characteristics of a biased diode. In addition, a certain amount of capacitance is usually present in parallel with the load, and its effect on the leading and trailing edges of the pulse must be considered. Although the scope of this chapter does not permit a specific study of all the possible types of pulser loads that can be used, an important special application of the circuit has been found in the triggering of series gaps. In this case, the pulse shape is relatively unimportant, and the load is essentially a pure capacitance until the breakdown of the gaps, at which time the load is short-circuited. This particular case is considered in Chap. 8.

Equivalent Circuit for a Line-type Pulser.—A complete equivalent discharging circuit for a line-type pulser, obtained from the above considerations,[1] is shown in Fig. 7·13.

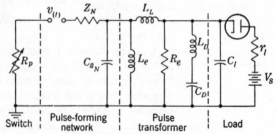

FIG. 7·13.—Equivalent discharging circuit for a line-type pulser.

For the remainder of this section, further simplifications can be made ın this circuit. First, the output-power pulse is considered to be rectangular, even though it is shown in Sec. 7·4 that a perfectly rectangular pulse is unobtainable in practice. It is therefore necessary to define the pulse duration. In general, the pulse duration of any shape pulse is considered here to be that of a rectangular pulse that has an amplitude equal to the average amplitude (see Appendix B) of the top of the pulse under

---

[1] The series resistance R_p includes the equivalent switch resistance and the series losses in the network and pulse transformer.

consideration, and that delivers the same amount of energy to the load as does the pulse under consideration. Then the equation

$$\tau = \frac{\int_0^{T_r} v_l i_l \, dt}{V_l I_l}$$

gives the equivalent pulse duration, where V_l and I_l are the amplitudes of the voltage and current pulse averaged over the top of the pulse, and v_l and i_l are the instantaneous values of voltage and current.

The general circuit that is of interest in this discussion includes the losses of the components that make up the circuit. With the above definition of pulse duration, however, it is not necessary to refer to the actual pulse shape in order to determine the power and energy relationships; instead, the equivalent rectangular pulse is considered. The equivalent circuit of Fig. 7·13 can thus be further simplified by the following assumptions:

1. The series inductances are neglected, since no voltage can appear across them during the "top" of a rectangular load-current pulse.
2. The time constant of Z_N and C_D is considered to be so small compared with the pulse duration that the charging time of C_D, and therefore C_D itself, can be neglected.
3. The voltage drop across Z_N and the series resistances produced by current flowing through L_e is considered to be negligible, since the output current pulse is assumed to remain rectangular in shape, and thus L_e can also be neglected.

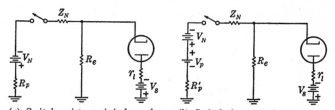

(a) Switch resistance is independent of current.   (b) Switch drop is independent of current.

FIG. 7·14.—Equivalent circuits for the study of power transfer.

4. The series losses produced by the switch, network, and pulse transformer can, in general, be lumped into one resistance R_p, as indicated in Fig. 7·14a. This assumption is equivalent to saying that the switch has a constant resistance that is independent of the current. In cases where the switch drop is not very small (less than 10 per cent) compared with the network voltage, it is preferable to assume that the switch has a constant voltage drop V_p,

as indicated in Fig. 7·14b. In this case, the value of the series resistance is represented by R_p'.

Pulse Power, Power Transfer, and Load Line.—If the case of a resistance load, for which $V_s = 0$ and $r_l = R_l$, is considered first, the current in R_l corresponding to Fig. 7·14a is given by

$$V_N = I_l \left(1 + \frac{R_l}{R_e}\right)(Z_N + R_p) + I_l R_l,$$

or

$$I_l = \frac{V_N R_e}{(R_e + R_l)(Z_N + R_p) + R_e R_l},$$

which can be written

$$I_l = \frac{V_N}{Z_N \left(1 + \dfrac{R_p}{Z_N}\right) + R_l \left(1 + \dfrac{Z_N + R_p}{R_e}\right)}. \tag{19}$$

Introducing the coefficients

$$\alpha = 1 + \frac{Z_N + R_p}{R_e}$$

and

$$\beta = 1 + \frac{R_p}{Z_N},$$

Eq. (19) becomes

$$I_l = \frac{V_N}{Z_N \beta + R_l \alpha}. \tag{20}$$

A comparison of this expression with Eq. (1),

$$I_l = \frac{V_0}{Z_0 + R_l}, \tag{1}$$

indicates that the load current is reduced by the losses in the circuit, since V_0 and Z_0 are equivalent to V_N and Z_N respectively (the subscript zero refers to lossless transmission lines and the subscript N to actual networks). For this reason, the coefficients α and β are referred to as "loss coefficients," α representing the shunt losses, and β the series losses.

From Eq. (20), the load voltage is given by

$$V_l = \frac{V_N R_l}{Z_N \beta + R_l \alpha} \tag{21}$$

and the pulse power by

$$P_l = \frac{V_N^2 R_l}{(Z_N \beta + R_l \alpha)^2}. \tag{22}$$

The relation between R_l and Z_N for maximum power transfer into the load for a given network voltage can again be found by differentiating Eq. (22), and equating the result to zero; thus

$$\frac{dP_l}{dR_l} = \frac{V_N^2}{(Z_N\beta + R_l\alpha)^2} - \frac{V_N^2 R_l 2\alpha}{(Z_N\beta + R_l\alpha)^3} = 0,$$

or

$$Z_N\beta + R_l\alpha - 2R_l\alpha = 0$$
$$R_l = Z_N \frac{\beta}{\alpha}. \tag{23}$$

Equation (23) shows that, when losses are taken into account, the maximum power transfer to the load is obtained for a value of load resistance that is different from the characteristic impedance of the network. If only series losses exist ($R_e = \infty$), maximum power transfer is obtained for a load resistance that is equal to the network impedance plus the resistance corresponding to the series losses, that is, $R_l = Z_N + R_p$. If only shunt losses exist ($R_p = 0$), the value of load resistance for maximum power transfer must be equal to the equivalent resistance of the network impedance and shunt-loss resistance in parallel, that is,

$$R_l = \frac{Z_N R_e}{Z_N + R_e}.$$

In general, the series and parallel losses are of the same order of magnitude ($\alpha \approx \beta$). Therefore, it is usually sufficient to make Z_N equal to R_l, and the departure from optimum power transfer is not great because of the flatness of the power-transfer curve (Fig. 7·3). When the conditions for maximum power transfer are realized for a resistance load, the expressions for load voltage, current, and power are

$$V_l = \frac{V_N}{2\alpha}, \tag{24}$$

$$I_l = \frac{V_N}{2Z_N\beta}, \tag{25}$$

and

$$(P_l)_{max} = \frac{V_N^2}{4Z_N\alpha\beta}. \tag{26}$$

The load current, voltage, and power are easily obtained by the same methods from Fig. 7·14b if V_N is replaced by $V_N - V_p$, R_p by R_p', α by α' and β by β', giving

$$I_l = \frac{V_N - V_p}{Z_N\beta' + R_l\alpha'}, \tag{27}$$

$$V_l = \frac{(V_N - V_p)R_l}{Z_N\beta' + R_l\alpha'}, \tag{28}$$

and

$$P_l = \frac{(V_N - V_p)^2 R_l}{(Z_N \beta' + R_l \alpha')^2},\tag{29}$$

The maximum power that can be delivered by the circuit is

$$(P_l)_{\max} = \frac{(V_N - V_p)^2}{4 Z_N \alpha' \beta'}.\tag{30}$$

The principal reason for a representation of this type in the study of the obtainable pulse power is to emphasize the effect of tube drop in the design of low-power pulsers. As long as the tube drop is only a few per cent of the network voltage either presentation is adequate. However, the rapid increase in losses, and the corresponding decrease in available power as the switch drop increases, are more evident from Eq. (30) than from Eq. (26). For instance, if V_p is about 10 per cent of V_N, the losses in the switch amount to nearly 20 per cent of the load power.

In Fig. 7·4 a series of curves for $P_{Z_0} = V_0^2/(4 Z_0)$ are plotted. The same curves can, of course, be used to represent Eq. (26) if the coordinates are made to represent $[\alpha\beta\, P_l)_{\max}]$ and V_N instead of P_{Z_0} and V_0, or Eq. (30) if the coordinates are changed to $[\alpha'\beta'(P_l)_{\max}]$ and $(V_N - V_p)$ respectively.

If the load is considered in the more general terms of a biased diode of instantaneous static impedance

$$R_l = \frac{V_s + I_l r_l}{I_l},$$

the expression for load current [Eq. (20)] becomes

$$I_l = \frac{V_N}{Z_N \beta + \left(\dfrac{V_s + I_l r_l}{I_l}\right)\alpha}.$$

This equation can be rewritten as

$$I_l = \frac{V_N - V_s \alpha}{Z_N \beta + r_l \alpha},\tag{31}$$

which is of the same form as Eq. (12).

With the value of I_l from Eq. (31), the voltage across the load,

$$V_l = I_l r_l + V_s,$$

becomes

$$V_l = \frac{V_N r_l + V_s Z_N \beta}{Z_N \beta + r_l \alpha},\tag{32}$$

and the pulse power is

$$P_l = V_l I_l = \frac{(V_N r_l + V_s Z_N \beta)(V_N - V_s \alpha)}{(Z_N \beta + r_l \alpha)^2}.\tag{33}$$

Maximizing the power as a function of r_l, it is found that the network voltage giving maximum power transfer to the load is

$$V_N = 2V_s \frac{\alpha}{1 - \dfrac{r_l}{Z_N} \cdot \dfrac{\alpha}{\beta}}. \tag{34}$$

A comparison of Eqs. (15) and (34) shows that when the losses in the circuit are considered, the voltage on the network for maximum load power is greater than that obtained when the losses are neglected, by a factor approximately equal to α. The same expression may be obtained by maximizing the power as a function of V_s, or by introducing the expression for static impedance of the biased diode into Eq. (23) and using Eq. (31). It is therefore evident that there is only one operating point for a nonlinear load where maximum power is obtained and, accordingly, that there is only one definite value of network voltage that leads to operation at that point. It is fortunate that the circuit performance is not greatly affected by slight deviations from the conditions giving maximum power transfer.

To demonstrate this point, Eq. (33) may be rewritten to express the pulse power as

$$P_l = \frac{V_N^2}{4Z_N} \frac{4\left(\dfrac{r_l}{Z_N} + \dfrac{V_s}{V_N}\beta\right)\left(1 - \dfrac{V_s}{V_N}\alpha\right)}{\left(\beta + \dfrac{r_l}{Z_N}\alpha\right)^2}.$$

By introducing Eq. (34) into Eq. (33), the pulse power corresponding to maximum power transfer is found to be

$$(P_l)_{\text{max}} = \frac{V_N^2}{4Z_N} \frac{1}{\alpha\beta}. \tag{35}$$

The power-transfer relation $P_l/(P_l)_{\text{max}}$ can be expressed as

$$\frac{P_l}{(P_l)_{\text{max}}} = 4\alpha\beta \frac{\left(\dfrac{r_l}{Z_N} + \dfrac{V_s}{V_N}\beta\right)\left(1 - \dfrac{V_s}{V_N}\alpha\right)}{\left(\beta + \dfrac{r_l}{Z_N}\alpha\right)^2}. \tag{36}$$

When V_s/V_N equals zero, the special case of a pure-resistance load is obtained. For any value of V_s/V_N greater than $1/\alpha$, the power output drops to zero because the expression gives a negative value for power under this condition. The curves of Figs. 7·15 and 7·16 indicate the effect of the losses in the circuit on the conditions required for optimum power transfer when the loss coefficients have the values 1.0, 1.1, and 1.2,

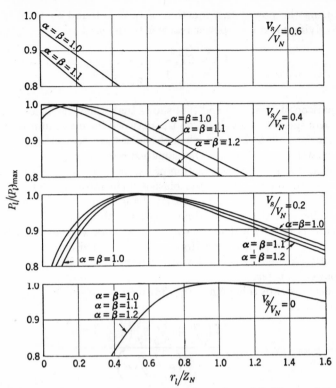

FIG. 7·15.—Power-transfer curves for various values of V_s/V_N, α and β.

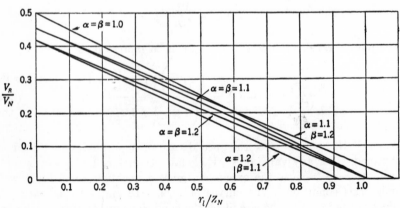

FIG. 7·16.—Relation between V_s/V_N and r_l/Z_N for maximum power transfer for various values of loss coefficients.

which cover the range ordinarily encountered in line-type pulsers.   These
curves also show that very little loss in power results from a slight mismatch, as was already determined in Sec. 7·1 (Fig. 7·4) for a resistance
load and a lossless circuit.   More important, these curves show that, in
order to achieve maximum power transfer, the dynamic resistance of the
load must decrease as the bias voltage is increased.   This phenomenon
can best be explained physically by a consideration of the load line of the
pulser, a curve that gives the relation between output current and output
voltage as the load resistance is varied, all other conditions remaining
the same.   Referring to the expressions (20) and (21), and eliminating
R_l between them, there is obtained

$$V_l = \frac{V_N}{\alpha} - I_l Z_N \frac{\beta}{\alpha} \qquad (37)$$

which is the equation for the pulser load line plotted in Fig. 7·17.   By
inspection of this equation, it can be seen that the open-circuit load voltage is V_N/α, the short-circuit load current is $V_N/(Z_N\beta)$, and that the

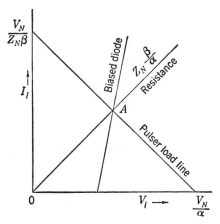

FIG. 7·17.—Diagram showing the determination of the load voltage and current by the
intersection of the load characteristic line with the pulser load line.

function is linear.   The load characteristics can be represented on the
same plot; thus a resistance load is represented by a straight line passing
through the origin, whereas a biased-diode load is represented by a
straight line intersecting the V axis in the positive region.   The intersection of the pulser load line with the load characteristic line gives the
operating point.   A load characteristic line has been drawn for

$$R_l = \left(\frac{\beta}{\alpha}\right) Z_N,$$

corresponding to optimum power transfer from the pulser to the load. Its intersection with the pulser load line at point A corresponds to a voltage $V_N/(2\alpha)$ and a current $V_N/(2Z_N\beta)$, the only point on the load line for which optimum power transfer obtains. Conversely, any load whose characteristic passes through that point enables the pulser to operate under the conditions of maximum power transfer.

Such a load could be the biased diode represented in the Fig. 7·17. It is evident from Eq. (36) that, unless negative resistance is considered, the highest value of bias voltage that permits operation at point A is $V_N/(2\alpha)$ (see Fig. 7·16). It is also apparent that the higher the bias voltage on the diode, the steeper the load characteristic must be if it is to pass through point A. This condition corresponds to a small $\Delta V/\Delta I$ or dynamic resistance, and explains why the maxima in the curves of Fig. 7·16 shift toward small values of r_l/Z_N when V_s/V_N is increased.

7·3. Pulser Regulation and Efficiency.—Pulser regulation refers to the changes in pulser output voltage, current, and power resulting from changes in operating conditions. These changes may take place either during a pulse or from pulse to pulse. The present discussion neglects the circuit inductances and stray capacitances, and is valid as long as the "transient regulation" is not considered. The results therefore apply to the cases where a change in circuit parameters has taken place between two pulses, or, if the change takes place during the pulse itself, the results are valid only after any transient effects have been damped out.

There are two types of regulation to be considered: (1) that produced by changes in the network voltage, and (2) that produced by changes in the load characteristic. In either case, transient regulation may appear. The effect on the pulser output of possible oscillations or irregularities on the top of the input voltage pulse can be analyzed only by methods similar to those of Sec. 7·4 used in studying pulse shape. If, on the other hand, the load characteristics suddenly change during a pulse, the transient behavior from one characteristic to the other depends on the values of the distributed capacitance across the load as well as on the series inductance introduced by the pulse transformer.

Neglecting transients, the circuit of Fig. 7·14 can be used for the study of regulation, leading to the expressions for load voltage, current, and power obtained in Sec. 7·2, namely,

$$V_l = \frac{V_N r_l + V_s Z_N \beta}{Z_N \beta + r_l \alpha}, \tag{32}$$

$$I_l = \frac{V_N - V_s \alpha}{Z_N \beta + r_l \alpha}, \tag{31}$$

and

$$P_l = \frac{(V_N r_l + V_s Z_N \beta)(V_N - V_s \alpha)}{(Z_N \beta + r_l \alpha)^2}, \tag{33}$$

The regulation may be obtained from these equations by differentiation.

Regulation against Variations in Network Voltage.—The voltage regulation is obtained by differentiation of Eq. (32), which gives

$$\frac{dV_l}{dV_N} = \frac{r_l}{Z_N \beta + r_l \alpha}.$$

Multiplying by dV_N, dividing by V_l, multiplying numerator and denominator of the right-hand member by V_N, and replacing the differential by a finite difference, there results

$$\left(\frac{\Delta V_l}{V_l}\right)_{V_N} = \frac{\dfrac{r_l}{Z_N \beta + r_l \alpha} V_N}{\dfrac{V_N r_l + V_s Z_N \beta}{Z_N \beta + r_l \alpha}} \frac{\Delta V_N}{V_N} = \frac{1}{1 + \dfrac{V_s}{V_N}\dfrac{Z_N}{r_l}\beta} \frac{\Delta V_N}{V_N}. \tag{38}$$

For operation at maximum power transfer,

$$\frac{V_s}{V_N} = \frac{1 - \dfrac{r_l}{Z_N}\dfrac{\alpha}{\beta}}{2\alpha}, \tag{34}$$

and the expression for voltage regulation becomes

$$\left(\frac{\Delta V_l}{V_l}\right)_{V_N} = \frac{2}{1 + \dfrac{Z_N}{r_l}\dfrac{\beta}{\alpha}} \frac{\Delta V_N}{V_N}. \tag{39}$$

The expressions for current and power regulation are obtained in the same way, with the following results:

$$\left(\frac{\Delta I_l}{I_l}\right)_{V_N} = \frac{1}{1 - \dfrac{V_s}{V_N}\alpha} \frac{\Delta V_N}{V_N}, \tag{40}$$

and

$$\left(\frac{\Delta P_l}{P_l}\right)_{V_N} = \frac{2 + \dfrac{V_s}{V_N}\left(\dfrac{Z_N}{r_l}\beta - \alpha\right)}{1 + \dfrac{V_s}{V_N}\left(\dfrac{Z_N}{r_l}\beta - \alpha\right) - \left(\dfrac{V_s}{V_N}\right)^2 \dfrac{Z_N}{r_l}\alpha\beta} \frac{\Delta V_N}{V_N}. \tag{41}$$

For the case of maximum power transfer, these equations may be simplified to

$$\left(\frac{\Delta I_l}{I_l}\right)_{V_N} = \frac{2}{1 + \dfrac{r_l}{Z_N}\dfrac{\alpha}{\beta}}\frac{\Delta V_N}{V_N}, \tag{42}$$

and

$$\left(\frac{\Delta P_l}{P_l}\right)_{V_N} = 2\frac{\Delta V_N}{V_N}. \tag{43}$$

For a resistance load, $V_s = 0$, and the expressions for regulation reduce to

$$\left(\frac{\Delta V_l}{V_l}\right)_{V_N} = \frac{\Delta V_N}{V_N}, \tag{44}$$

$$\left(\frac{\Delta I_l}{I_l}\right)_{V_N} = \frac{\Delta V_N}{V_N}, \tag{45}$$

and

$$\left(\frac{\Delta P_l}{P_l}\right)_{V_N} = 2\frac{\Delta V_N}{V_N}, \tag{46}$$

whether or not the load resistance is matched to the characteristic impedance of the network in order to obtain maximum power transfer.

An examination of expressions (38) and (40) shows that, for a biased diode, the load voltage always changes less rapidly than the network voltage, whereas the load current changes more rapidly. For instance, assuming $Z_N/r_l = 10$, $\alpha = \beta = 1$, and maximum power transfer, Eq. (39) gives

$$\left(\frac{\Delta V_l}{V_l}\right)_{V_N} = \frac{2}{11}\frac{\Delta V_N}{V_N} = 0.182\frac{\Delta V_N}{V_N},$$

and Eq. (42) gives

$$\left(\frac{\Delta I_l}{I_l}\right)_{V_N} = \frac{2}{1.1}\frac{\Delta V_N}{V_N} = 1.82\frac{\Delta V_N}{V_N}.$$

The value of V_s/V_N corresponding to the above assumptions is 0.45 (Fig. 7·16). It must be noted that the current regulation is improved (made smaller) if the ratio of V_s/V_N is decreased. For instance, for $V_s/V_N = 0.4$,

$$\left(\frac{\Delta I_l}{I_l}\right)_{V_N} = \frac{1}{0.6}\frac{\Delta V_N}{V_N} = 1.67\frac{\Delta V_N}{V_N}.$$

It is interesting to note that the output-current regulation against a change of network voltage depends only on the ratio V_s/V_N. It is also worth noting that, since the network voltage is directly proportional to the input voltage to the pulser circuit, V_N can be replaced by E_{bb} in the above expressions. This fact is important in pulser design, where tolerances on the input voltage are usually known. For all practical operating conditions of magne ron load encountered to date, V_s/V_N is in the neighborhood of 0.4 to 0.45, and hence the percentage change in magnetron current resulting from pulser regulation alone is approximately 1.75 times as great as the percentage change in input voltage.

Regulation against Variations in Load Characteristic.—Two types of regulation of the pulser output against load variation are discussed here. First, it is assumed that the bias voltage, V_s, of a biased-diode load may change either from pulse to pulse or during a pulse, but that the dynamic resistance, r_l, stays constant (this case corresponds quite closely to mode-changing in magnetrons).   The expressions obtained for this case are

$$\left(\frac{\Delta V_l}{V_l}\right)_{v_s} = \frac{\dfrac{Z_N\beta}{Z_N\beta + r_l\alpha}V_s}{\dfrac{V_N r_l + V_s Z_N\beta}{Z_N\beta + r_l\alpha}}\frac{\Delta V_s}{V_s} = \frac{1}{1 + \dfrac{V_N}{V_s}\dfrac{r_l}{Z_N}\dfrac{1}{\beta}}\frac{\Delta V_s}{V_s}, \qquad (47)$$

$$\left(\frac{\Delta I_l}{I_l}\right)_{v_s} = \frac{\dfrac{-\alpha}{Z_N\beta + r_l\alpha}V_s}{\dfrac{V_N - V_s\alpha}{Z_N\beta + r_l\alpha}}\cdot\frac{\Delta V_s}{V_s} = \frac{1}{1 - \dfrac{V_N}{V_s}\dfrac{1}{\alpha}}\cdot\frac{\Delta V_s}{V_s}, \qquad (48)$$

and

$$\left(\frac{\Delta P_l}{P_l}\right)_{v_s} = \frac{1 - \dfrac{r_l}{Z_N}\dfrac{\alpha}{\beta} - 2\dfrac{V_s}{V_N}\alpha}{\left(1 + \dfrac{V_N}{V_s}\dfrac{r_l}{Z_N}\dfrac{1}{\beta}\right)\left(1 - \dfrac{V_s}{V_N}\alpha\right)}\cdot\frac{\Delta V_s}{V_s}. \qquad (49)$$

For operation at the point corresponding to maximum power transfer, the expressions for regulation against load bias voltage become

$$\left(\frac{\Delta V_l}{V_l}\right)_{v_s} = \frac{1 - \dfrac{r_l}{Z_N}\dfrac{\alpha}{\beta}}{1 + \dfrac{r_l}{Z_N}\dfrac{\alpha}{\beta}}\cdot\frac{\Delta V_s}{V_s},$$

$$\left(\frac{\Delta I_l}{I_l}\right)_{v_s} = -\frac{1 - \dfrac{r_l}{Z_N}\dfrac{\alpha}{\beta}}{1 + \dfrac{r_l}{Z_N}\dfrac{\alpha}{\beta}}\cdot\frac{\Delta V_s}{V_s},$$

and

$$\left(\frac{\Delta P_l}{P_l}\right)_{v_s} = 0.$$

It is obvious that the power regulation at the point of matched condition is perfect—that is, a small change in load bias voltage around that point produces no change in power output from the pulser—since the tangents to the power-transfer curves (Fig. 7·15a) are parallel to the V_s/V_N axis at the points of maximum power transfer (matched conditions). For the same reason, the values of voltage and current regulation must be equal, but of opposite sign. For $Z_N/r_l = 10$ and $\alpha = \beta = 1$,

$$\left(\frac{\Delta V_l}{V_l}\right)_{V_s} = \frac{0.9}{1.1}\frac{\Delta V_s}{V_s} = 0.82\frac{\Delta V_s}{V_s}.$$

The second case to be considered is that in which the bias voltage, V_s, stays constant, but the dynamic resistance varies. Of special interest is the condition $V_s = 0$, giving the regulation as a function of load variation for a pure-resistance load as

$$\left(\frac{\Delta V_l}{V_l}\right)_{R_l} = \frac{1}{1 + \dfrac{R_l\alpha}{Z_N\beta}} \cdot \frac{\Delta R_l}{R_l}, \qquad (50)$$

$$\left(\frac{\Delta I_l}{I_l}\right)_{R_l} = \frac{-\dfrac{R_l\alpha}{Z_N\beta}}{1 + \dfrac{R_l\alpha}{Z_N\beta}} \cdot \frac{\Delta R_l}{R_l}, \qquad (51)$$

and

$$\left(\frac{\Delta P_l}{P_l}\right)_{R_l} = \frac{1 - \dfrac{R_l\alpha}{Z_N\beta}}{1 + \dfrac{R_l\alpha}{Z_N\beta}}\frac{\Delta R_l}{R_l}. \qquad (52)$$

For operation at maximum power transfer,

$$\left(\frac{\Delta V_l}{V_l}\right)_{R_l} = \frac{1}{2}\frac{\Delta R_l}{R_l},$$

$$\left(\frac{\Delta I_l}{I_l}\right)_{R_l} = -\frac{1}{2}\frac{\Delta R_l}{R_l},$$

and

$$\left(\frac{\Delta P_l}{P_l}\right)_{R_l} = 0.$$

It must be noted again that the above expressions apply only to small variations in the value of the load resistance. If the load variation is very large, as in the case of an accidental short circuit at the load, it is better to refer to the load line of the pulser under consideration.

A special case of regulation from pulse to pulse, corresponding to the pulser using a unidirectional switch, is considered later (see Sec. 10·2). As has already been pointed out, the network energy is conserved under these conditions if R_l/Z_N is less than one, and the network voltage after the next charging cycle is higher than normal. Since a discussion of this phenomenon involves the over-all pulser circuit it is beyond the scope of this section, which is concerned primarily with the characteristics of the discharging circuit.

Efficiency.—The over-all efficiency of a line-type pulser can be obtained only by a consideration of the different parts of its circuit. Losses occur in the discharging as well as in the charging circuit. If η_d and η_c are the efficiencies of the discharging and charging circuits respectively, the total efficiency η_p of the pulser circuit is $\eta_p = \eta_d \times \eta_c$. This efficiency, however, does not take into consideration all the power that has to be supplied to the pulser. For d-c charging, a rectifier circuit having an efficiency η_b usually has to be introduced. For a-c charging, the frequency of existing power supplies is such that a special motor-alternator or frequency converter is usually needed, which is also considered to have an efficiency η_b. Finally, there are overhead losses, some of which are associated with the switch and some with the auxiliary circuits and equipment. The hydrogen-thyratron switch requires filament power and sometimes a trigger amplifier, the series-gap switch requires a trigger generator, and the rotary-gap switch requires a driving motor (whose power loss may already be included in η_b). The auxiliary circuits and equipment include line-switching relays, control circuits, cooling fans, etc. If the power required for the overhead is designated as P_L, the over-all efficiency is given by

$$\eta_0 = \frac{(P_l)_{av}}{\dfrac{(P_l)_{av}}{\eta_b\eta_p} + P_L} = \frac{\eta_b\eta_p}{1 + \dfrac{P_L\eta_b\eta_p}{(P_l)_{av}}}. \tag{53}$$

The following discussion is concerned principally with the efficiency of the discharging circuit, with an occasional reference to the over-all pulser efficiency. The over-all efficiency for a few special applications is considered in Chap. 11.

The discharging-circuit efficiency is the ratio of the energy transferred to the load to the energy taken from the pulse-forming network per pulse. This definition of discharging efficiency is considered because, under some conditions of load mismatch, some of the energy may be conserved on the network when a unidirectional switch is used, as is evident from consideration of an idealized circuit (Fig. 7·2). The energy dissipated in the load is given by

$$W_l = \frac{V_N^2}{(R_l + Z_N)^2} R_l \tau_l,$$

and the voltage left on the network after the main pulse is

$$V_{N-1} = V_N \frac{R_l - Z_N}{R_l + Z_N}.$$

If $R_l > Z_N$, V_{N-1} is of the same polarity as V_N, and the network discharges completely even through a unidirectional switch. If $R_l < Z_N$, an amount of energy $\frac{1}{2}C_N V_{N-1}^2$ is left on the network because a unidirectional switch does not permit the network voltages of polarity opposite to that of V_N to discharge. Under the latter condition, the amount of energy taken from the network is

$$W_N = \frac{1}{2}C_N(V_N^2 - V_{N-1}^2) = \frac{1}{2}C_N V_N^2\left[1 - \frac{(R_l - Z_N)^2}{(R_l + Z_N)^2}\right]$$
$$= \frac{1}{2}C_N V_N^2 \frac{4R_l Z_N}{(R_l + Z_N)^2}.$$

As was shown in Sec. 7·1,

$$\tau_N = 2C_N Z_N,$$

and the energy taken from the network is

$$W_N = \frac{V_N^2 R_l}{(R_l + Z_N)^2}\tau_N,$$

which is exactly equal to that transferred to the load, provided that τ_l and τ_N are equal. This condition is obviously attained in a circuit containing only pure-resistance components, such as that of Fig. 7·2.

It may be concluded from the above considerations that it is desirable to use unidirectional switches and permit the load to be mismatched. Other disadvantages, however, result from changes in load impedance (see Sec. 10·2), and usually make it desirable to drain off most of the energy left on the network after the pulse. Accordingly, in the remainder of this discussion this energy is considered to be lost, that is, the network is considered to be completely discharged after each pulse.

In Sec. 7·2 it has been shown that the maximum pulse power in the load is given by

$$(P_l)_{\text{max}} = \frac{V_N^2}{4Z_N}\frac{1}{\alpha\beta}. \tag{26}$$

Then, if τ_l is the duration of the power pulse at the load, the maximum energy per pulse is given by

$$(W_l)_{\text{max}} = \frac{V_N^2}{4Z_N}\frac{\tau_l}{\alpha\beta}, \tag{54}$$

and the energy stored in the network is

$$W_N = \frac{1}{2}C_N V_N^2 = \frac{V_N^2}{4Z_N}\tau_N, \tag{55}$$

where τ_l and τ_N are the equivalent pulse durations at the load and at the network. It must be noted that these pulse durations are not necessarily equal. Since the pulse power considered above is the average of any oscillations that may be present at the top of the pulse, the effect of the inductances and capacitances is small and has been neglected. The only factor that may be significant is the voltage drop across $Z_N\beta$ caused by the current flowing through L_e and C_D. Actually, the time constants are such that the effect of C_D can, in general, be neglected except for the first 0.1 μsec. In order to avoid introducing the pulse duration into the expressions for pulse power, and because the pulse shape was considered rectangular, the effect of L_e has been neglected until now.

Actually, the effect of the shunt inductance cannot be neglected in discussions of efficiency. For simplicity, however, an approximate expression may be used. It is assumed, as before, that the voltage across the load remains constant for the duration of the pulse, instead of drooping because of the additional voltage drop across the network impedance that results from the current flowing through L_e. Under these conditions, the current through L_e at any time is given by

$$i_{L_e} = \frac{V_l}{L_e} t,$$

where t is the time elapsed from the beginning of the pulse, and the energy stored in the inductance at the end of a pulse of duration τ_l is

$$\frac{1}{2} L_e i_{L_e}^2 = \frac{V_l^2}{2L_e} \tau_l^2.$$

The assumption of constant voltage V_l introduces a value for the losses in the inductance L_e that is in excess of the actual value. On the other hand, any energy stored in the series inductance, L_L, of the circuit at the end of the pulse is neglected because the value of this inductance is small compared with L_e. For this reason, an assumption leading to the higher value for the losses in the shunt inductance seems to be reasonable.

The losses in the total shunt capacitance across the load $C_s = C_D + C_l$ appear only when the load is a biased diode, and can be written as $\frac{1}{2}C_s V_s^2$.

If the inductances and capacitances are neglected, the energy output under the conditions for optimum power transfer is

$$(W_l)_{\max} = \frac{V_N^2 \tau_N}{4Z_N \alpha\beta}.$$

Actually, this energy output is decreased by the losses in L_e and C_s to

$$(W_l)_{\text{eff}} = \frac{V_N^2 \tau_N}{4Z_N \alpha\beta} - \frac{V_l^2}{2L_e} \tau_l^2 - \frac{1}{2} C_s V_s^2. \tag{56}$$

For optimum power transfer

$$V_l = \frac{V_N}{2\alpha}$$

from Eq. (24),

$$V_s = \frac{V_N}{2\alpha}\left(1 - \frac{r_l}{Z_N}\frac{\alpha}{\beta}\right)$$

from Eq. (34), and

$$(W_l)_{\text{eff}} = \frac{V_N^2}{4Z_N\alpha\beta}\left[\tau_N - \frac{\beta}{\alpha}\frac{Z_N}{2L_e}\tau_l^2 - \frac{\beta}{\alpha}\frac{C_sZ_N}{2}\left(1 - \frac{r_l}{Z_N}\frac{\alpha}{\beta}\right)^2\right].$$

Since $Z_N = \tau_N/2C_N$, the discharging circuit efficiency can be expressed as

$$\eta_d = \frac{(W_l)_{\text{eff}}}{W_N} = \frac{1}{\alpha\beta}\left[1 - \frac{\beta}{\alpha}\frac{Z_N}{2L_e}\frac{\tau_l^2}{\tau_N} - \frac{\beta\gamma}{4\alpha}\left(1 - \frac{r_l}{Z_N}\frac{\alpha}{\beta}\right)^2\right], \qquad (57a)$$

where $\gamma = C_s/C_N$. In general, τ_l is nearly equal to τ_N; therefore only a very small error in introduced by rewriting

$$\eta_d = \frac{1}{\alpha\beta}\left[1 - \frac{\beta}{\alpha}\frac{Z_N}{2L_e}\tau_N - \frac{\beta\gamma}{4\alpha}\left(1 - \frac{r_l}{Z_N}\frac{\alpha}{\beta}\right)^2\right]. \qquad (57b)$$

The equation for efficiency for unmatched conditions is not given because it cannot readily be expressed in terms of the pulser parameters; however, it can usually be determined with sufficient accuracy by multiplying the efficiency for optimum power transfer by the actual power transfer.

An examination of Eq. (57b) shows that the efficiency of the discharging circuit decreases when the pulse duration is increased, and when γ (the ratio of distributed to network capacitance) is increased. If the distributed capacitance is constant, γ varies inversely with pulse duration; consequently, the third term of the expression causes a decrease in efficiency when the pulse duration is decreased. Since the effects of the last two terms of Eq. (57a) are in opposition to each other, the curve showing efficiency as a function of pulse duration for a given set of pulser parameters may be expected to have a maximum. The expression for the particular pulse duration that corresponds to maximum efficiency is easily obtained by the differentiation of Eq. (57b), and is

$$\tau_N = \sqrt{L_eC_s}\left(1 - \frac{r_l}{Z_N}\frac{\alpha}{\beta}\right). \qquad (58)$$

Assuming the usual ratio of 0.1 for r_l/Z_N and values for L_e and C_s that are found in typical pulse transformers and loads, the pulse durations corresponding to maximum efficiency are found to be about 0.5 to 3 μsec.

Actually, the efficiency for very short pulses decreases much more rapidly than is indicated by Eq. (57) because of the nonlinear characteristic of the switch drop as a function of time.   As explained in Chap. 8, a great part of the power loss in the switch occurs during the first 0.3 μsec, and sometimes during an even shorter time.   As a result, the coefficient β should actually be a function of time; however, the values obtained by expression (57) are sufficiently correct for most practical purposes.   For very short pulses, the efficiency obtained from Eq. (57) is usually too high unless a value of β that holds for these short pulses can be used.

The efficiency can also be expressed as the ratio of the average power transmitted to the load to the average power supplied by the pulse-forming network.   Since

$$(P_l)_{av} = W_l \times f_r$$

and

$$(P_N)_{av} = W_N \times f_r,$$

the expression is the same as that obtained above.   The efficiency of the charging circuit is discussed in Chap. 9.   For d-c charging, it is given as

$$\eta_c = \frac{1 + e^{-\frac{\pi}{2Q}}}{2}$$

and, for a-c charging, as

$$\eta_c \approx 1 - \frac{n\pi}{3Q}$$

Hence, the over-all circuit efficiency η_p can be obtained from the relation $\eta_p = \eta_c \times \eta_d$.

The pulser power output is usually measured by two methods.   The average power input into a magnetron may be represented by

$$(P_l)_{av} = V_l \times (I_l)_{av}, \tag{59}$$

or by

$$(P_l)_{av} = V_l \times I_l \times \tau_l \times f_r. \tag{60}$$

If Eq. (59) is used, the average magnetron current is measured directly by an appropriately protected d-c milliammeter (see Appendix A).   For Eq. (60), a current-viewing resistor is used to present the current pulse on the screen of the cathode-ray tube of a synchroscope.   The average amplitude of the top of the pulse I_l, as well as the pulse duration τ_l (at $\frac{1}{2}I_l$), is either measured directly with the synchroscope, or the area $\int_0^{\tau_l} i_l \, dt$ is integrated graphically from photographs of the oscilloscope trace.   In general, readings of individual points by the two methods agree to within a few per cent; most of the difference can be attributed to experimental errors and, for a large number of readings, these errors cancel each other.   In some cases, however, a systematic difference in the readings is introduced, either by a small amount of post-pulse conduction, or by capacitance currents that may be recorded by the average-current meter, but are neglected in interpreting the oscilloscope trace.   A systematic difference greater than two per cent, however, usually indicates some fundamental difficulty with the calibration of either the sweep speed, the recurrence frequency, or the average-current meter.   All three calibrations are apt to be troublesome, those of the sweep speed and the recurrence frequency because they may vary slightly from time to time, that of the average-current meter because of the change in calibration produced by the shunt resistance that is usually introduced for protection in the metering circuit.

It must be pointed out that, at best, Eqs. (59) and (60) are approximate.   They are rigorous only for a biased-diode load having a dynamic impedance equal to zero because they are obtained by assuming that the load voltage stays constant during the current pulse.   In general, the results obtained from these equations are sufficiently precise as long as the top of the voltage pulse is flat and the duration of the top of the current pulse is long compared with the sum of the times of rise and fall of the current.   Because of these restrictions, the method is not usually very precise for short pulses (less than 0.5 μsec), for which the time of fall of the current is often of the same order of magnitude as the duration of the top of the pulse.

Obviously, the average-current meter cannot be used to measure average-power output for a resistance load, since the network-charging current flows through the meter and cancels the reading of the discharging circuit.   Under these conditions, the average power may be computed from oscillographic observation, or measured by a calorimeter.

The power input to the circuit can be measured by the standard procedure, a d-c voltmeter and an ammeter giving the output from the power supply when d-c charging is used, and a wattmeter giving the input to the resonant transformer for a-c charging.

The average network power can be obtained by measuring the peak forward network voltage V_N, that is,

$$(P_N)_{\text{av}} = \tfrac{1}{2} C_N V_N^2 f_r.$$

If a unidirectional switch is used without shunt diodes to "bleed off" the inverse voltage left on the network by load mismatch,

$$(P_N)_{\text{av}} = \tfrac{1}{2} C_N (V_N^2 - V_{N-1}^2) f_r.$$

The correction can usually be neglected because a value $V_{N-1}/V_N = 0.2$, which corresponds to a mismatch larger than usually tolerated, introduces an error in P_N of only 4 per cent.   In practice, it is difficult to obtain an accuracy greater than 2 per cent in measuring V_N, which corresponds to a 4 per cent inaccuracy in the value of $(P_N)_{av}$.

Because of the inherent inaccuracy in the measurement of $(P_N)_{av}$, it is generally not advisable to give as much weight to the measured values for the efficiencies of the discharging and charging circuits as is given to measurements of over-all circuit efficiency.

Values of over-all circuit efficiency for line-type pulsers may range from less than 60 per cent to about 80 per cent depending on the power level, on the type of switch, and on the load.

7·4. The Discharging Circuit and Pulse Shape.—A basic equivalent circuit that can be used to study the behavior of line-type pulsers during the discharge of the pulse-forming network has been obtained in Sec. 7·2 (Fig. 7·13) by considering the characteristics of the various components of the circuit. This same circuit can also be used for an analysis of the output-pulse shape. Some further simplifications are necessary, however, if the equations are to be kept workable. Examination of the circuit indicates that those elements that have a large influence on the shaping of some parts of the pulse can readily be neglected in the study of other parts of the pulse without introducing appreciable errors. The number of meshes, and hence the degree of the differential equations, is thereby reduced. Thus, the discussion on pulse shape is divided into three parts concerning the leading edge, the top, and the trailing edge of the pulse.

The Leading Edge of the Pulse.—The time variation of the switch drop during the ionization period undoubtedly affects the rise of the voltage across the load. Except in a few special cases, however, the complications introduced in the equations by a nonlinear parameter are not warranted by the change in the results. A few examples are treated later to show the order of magnitude of the effect of variation in switch resistance, but for the remainder of the discussion the series losses are represented by a resistance R_p, assumed to be constant, and the series resistance $Z_N + R_p$ is replaced by Z_1.

The effect of capacitance C_{sN} (of the order of magnitude of 20 $\mu\mu f$) can be neglected because the time constant of this capacitance and its series resistance Z_1 (about 1000 ohms) is approximately 0.02 μsec. Hence, C_{sN} is almost entirely charged in about 0.08 μsec, and the effect of charging this capacitance can be neglected except when very short rise times or very short pulses are considered. Since the pulse-transformer shunt inductance, L_e, is always much larger than the other inductances in the circuit, the pulse current flowing through it during the first few tenths of a microsecond is very small, and can be neglected for practical purposes. The load distributed capacitance C_l is, in general, much smaller than the pulse-transformer distributed capacitance C_D. The two can be lumped together if the charging inductance L_D is neglected. Actually, neglecting

C_l introduces some difference only at the very beginning of the pulse, as explained later, whereas neglecting L_D leads to unsatisfactory conditions at the transition between the rise and the top of the pulse; hence, C_l is neglected here. The pulse-transformer shunt losses, represented by R_e, are usually so small (that is, R_e is so large) that they have little effect on the voltage buildup across the load. For this reason they are neglected, and, until the output voltage exceeds the bias of the diode load, the circuit of a line-type pulser may be simplified as shown in Fig. 7·18. Assuming that the initial current through the inductances and the initial charge on the condenser are zero, the differential equation for this circuit is

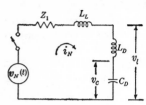

Fig. 7·18.—Simplified equivalent circuit of a line-type pulser for the analysis of the leading edge of the pulse.

$$(L_L + L_D)\frac{di_N}{dt} + Z_1 i_N + \frac{1}{C_D}\int i_N\,dt = v_N(t).$$

The Laplace-transform equation is then

$$(L_L + L_D)p i_N(p) + Z_1 i_N(p) + \frac{i_N(p)}{C_D p} = v_N(p).$$

Solving for $i_N(p)$,

$$i_N(p) = \frac{C_D p v_N(p)}{C_D(L_L + L_D)p^2 + Z_1 C_D p + 1} \tag{61}$$

and the Laplace-transform equation for v_l is obtained from the relation

$$v_l(p) = L_D p i_N(p) + \frac{i_N(p)}{C_D p},$$

and is given by

$$v_l(p) = \frac{(L_D C_D p^2 + 1)v_N(p)}{C_D(L_L + L_D)p^2 + Z_1 C_D p + 1}. \tag{62}$$

For any specific form of applied voltage $v_N(t)$, the Laplace transform $v_l(p)$ defines a time function $v_l(t)$ that expresses the voltage applied to the load. As long as $v_l(t) < V_s$, the circuit of Fig. 7·18 is applicable. A time t_1 can be found at which $v_l(t) = V_s$, and the values of current $i_N(t_1)$ through the inductances and voltage $v_C(t_1)$ across the condenser at that time can be determined. The value of v_C is obtained by the Laplace-transform equation

$$v_C(p) = \frac{i_N(p)}{C_D p}.$$

At time $t = t_1$,

$$V_{C_1} = \frac{1}{C_D}\int_0^{t_1} i_N\,dt.$$

This is the initial condition that applies to the study of the top of the pulse, during which time the load is taking power from the pulser.

The Top of the Pulse.—The simplifications of the equivalent circuit of a line-type pulser applying to this part of the discussion are essentially the same as those used for the rising portion of the pulse.   The capacitance C_{sN} can be neglected, and R_e is, in general, so large compared with R_l (static impedance of the load) that it may be omitted also.   The pulse transformer shunt inductance L_e should be included in this part of the discussion.   The simplification of the equations, however, makes it advisable to consider the effect of L_e independently.   If it is assumed that the voltage across L_e is very nearly constant during the pulse, the current through it is given by

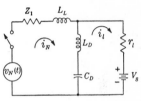

$$i_{L_e} = \frac{V_l}{L_e} t.$$

In general, this current does not exceed 10 per cent of the load current, so its effect is usually to introduce only a slight additional voltage drop across Z_1, with a resulting droop in the voltage and current pulses.   Since this

Fig. 7·19.—Simplified equivalent circuit of a line-type pulser for the analysis of the top of the pulse.

droop is neglected in the following discussion, the circuit for analyzing the top of the pulse reduces to that of Fig. 7·19.

The differential equations are, for $t_1 \leqq t \leqq t_2$,

$$Z_1 i_N + L_L \frac{di_N}{dt} + L_D \frac{d}{dt}(i_N - i_l) + \frac{1}{C_D}\int (i_N - i_l)\, dt = v_N(t),$$

and

$$L_D \frac{d}{dt}(i_l - i_N) + \frac{1}{C_D}\int (i_l - i_N)\, dt + r_l i_l = -V_s$$

with the initial conditions

$$i_N = i_N(t_1) = I_{L_1}$$

and

$$v_C = v_C(t_1) = V_{C_1}.$$

The Laplace-transform equations can be written

$$(C_D p Z_1 + C_D L_L p^2 + C_D L_D p^2 + 1)i_N(p) - (C_D L_D p^2 + 1)i_l(p)$$
$$= C_D[p v_N(p) - V_{C_1} + p I_{L_1}(L_L + L_D)],$$
$$(C_D L_D p^2 + 1)i_N(p) - (C_D L_D p^2 + 1 + r_l C_D p)i_l(p) = C_D(V_s - V_{C_1} + L_D p I_{L_1}).$$

By usual methods, the expressions for the current transforms are found to be

$$i_l(p) = \frac{N_l(p)}{\Delta} \tag{63}$$

and

$$i_N(p) = \frac{N_L(p)}{\Delta},\tag{64}$$

and the voltage transform v_l is

$$v_l(p) = \frac{V_s}{p} + r_l\dot{i}_l(p) = \frac{V_s\Delta + pr_lN_l(p)}{p\Delta} = \frac{N(p)}{\Delta},\tag{65}$$

where

$$\frac{\Delta}{C_D} = p\left\{C_DL_LL_Dp^3 + C_D[r_l(L_L + L_D) + L_DZ_1]p^2 \right.$$
$$\left. + (L_L + C_Dr_lZ_1)p + (Z_1 + r_l)\right\}.$$

$$\frac{N_l(p)}{C_D} = L_DC_Dv_N(p)p^3 - [C_DV_s(L_L + L_D) + L_DC_DZ_1I_{L_1} - L_LC_DV_{c_1}]p^2$$
$$+ [L_LI_{L_1} + C_DZ_1(V_{c_1} - V_s) + v_N(p)]p - V_s,$$

$$\frac{N_L(p)}{C_D} = L_DC_D[v_N(p) + L_LI_{L_1}]p^3$$
$$+ \{r_lC_D[v_N(p) + I_{L_1}(L_L + L_D)] - V_sC_DL_D\}p^2$$
$$+ [v_N(p) + L_LI_{L_1} - r_lC_DV_{c_1}]p - V_s,$$

$$\frac{N(p)}{C_D} = C_DL_D[V_sL_L + rv_N(p)]p^3$$
$$+ [r_lC_D(L_LV_{c_1} - L_DZ_1I_{L_1}) + V_sC_DL_DZ_1]p^2$$
$$+ \{L_L(V_s + r_lI_{L_1}) + r_l[v_N(p) + C_DZ_1V_{c_1}]\}p + V_sZ_1.$$

Again, for any particular time function $v_N(t)$, the Laplace transforms for load voltage and load current lead to time functions that can be computed. The complexity of the solution is such, however, that little can be said about the effect of individual parameters. Examples are treated later, and more detailed discussions of a few special cases are given. This circuit can be used to obtain a reasonable approximation of the pulse shape until a time t_2. This time is defined as that for which the static resistance R_l of the load equals the shunt resistance R_e of the pulse transformer.

The Trailing Edge of the Pulse.—The trailing edge is the part of the pulse that is applied to the load following the main pulse of energy delivered by the pulse-forming network. The shape is determined principally by the energy stored in stray capacitances and inductances in the circuit if it is assumed that maximum power transfer to the load is obtained, as is discussed in Sec. 7·3. Accordingly, it is assumed that $v_N(t) = 0$ after $t = t_2$ as defined above. At this time, the energy that has been stored in the shunt inductance of the pulse transformer cannot be neglected. Since this inductance was not considered in the previous calculations, it is necessary to estimate the current flowing through it at the time t_2.   This current is given with sufficient precision by

$$i_{L_e}(t_2) = \frac{V_l}{L_e}(t_2 - t_1) = I_{L_2}.$$

At the time corresponding to zero current in the load, the currents in the transformer leakage and charging inductances (L_L and L_D) cause energy to be stored in these elements.   This energy can be neglected, however, by comparison with that stored in the shunt inductance. Energy stored in the distributed capacitance C_D must, of course, be considered.   The discharging circuit may then be reduced to a parallel $R_eL_eC_D$-combination.

At this point, however, the assumption that the pulse-forming network may be replaced by a source of internal impedance Z_N no longer holds because, on this assumption and with $v_N(t) = 0$, Z_N is in parallel with the discharging circuit, causing a very fast dissipation of the energy stored in that circuit.   Since a pulse-forming network is not a dissipative element, but rather is capable of storing electrical energy, the above assumption is obviously false.

Practical networks are made up of series-parallel combinations of capacitances and inductances.   In order to reduce the number of loops to a minimum, it is assumed that the network can be replaced by a simple series LC-circuit, with the conditions that

$$Z_N = \sqrt{\frac{L_N}{C_N}}$$

and

$$\tau = 2C_N Z_N,$$

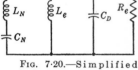

Fig. 7·20.—Simplified equivalent circuit of a line-type pulser for the analysis of the trailing edge of the pulse.

leading to the equivalent circuit of Fig. 7·20. If the pulse-transformer leakage inductance is not negligible compared with the network inductance L_N, it can be added in series with L_N.   The same equivalent circuit is still applicable if L_N is replaced by $(L_N + L_L)$ in the equations.

The initial conditions for this circuit are determined as follows.   The voltage on C_D and the current through L_e are obtained from the analysis of the top of the pulse.   Since it is assumed that the energy stored in the network has been entirely dissipated in the load before the time t_2, the voltage across the network capacitance C_N can be assumed equal to zero at the time t_2.   However, the voltage across the network is not zero, but is given by $V_C(t_2) = V_{C_2}$, and causes a rate of change of current through the network inductance given by

$$\frac{di_N}{dt} = \frac{V_{c_2}}{L_N}.$$

The current through the network is considered to be equal to the current I_{N2} that was flowing through the source at the time t_2, and can be obtained from the analysis of the top of the pulse. This value satisfies Kirchhoff's law of currents in the present circuit, but implies a small amount of energy left in the network inductance; however, this energy is usually very small compared with the energy stored in the pulse-transformer shunt inductance. The equations for the circuit of Fig. 7·20 can then be written

$$L_N \frac{di_N}{dt} + L_e \frac{d}{dt} (i_N - i_L) + \frac{1}{C_N} \int i_N \, dt = 0,$$

$$L_e \frac{d}{dt} (i_L - i_N) + \frac{1}{C_D} \int (i_L - i_l) \, dt = 0,$$

$$\frac{1}{C_D} \int (i_l - i_L) \, dt + i_l R_e = 0,$$

giving the following Laplace-transform equations:

$$L_N i_N(p)p + L_e[i_N(p) - i_L(p)]p + \frac{i_N(p)}{C_N p} = L_N I_{N2} + L_e I_{L2}.$$

$$L_e[i_L(p) - i_N(p)]p + \frac{i_L(p) - i_l(p)}{C_D p} = -L_e I_{L2} - \frac{V_{c_2}}{p}.$$

$$\frac{i_l(p) - i_L(p)}{C_D p} + i_l(p) R_e = \frac{V_{c_2}}{p}.$$

From these, an expression for the Laplace transform of the current i_l can be obtained, which, multiplied by R_e, gives

$$v_l(p) = R_e i_l(p) = R_e \frac{N_l'(p)}{\Delta'},$$

where

$$N_l'(p) = L_e[L_N C_D C_N V_{c_2} p^3 + L_N C_N (I_{N2} - I_{L2}) p^2 + C_D V_{c_2} p - I_{L2}],$$

and

$$\Delta' = L_N L_e R_e C_N C_D p^4 + L_N L_e C_N p^3$$
$$+ R_e (L_e C_D + L_e C_N + L_N C_N) p^2 + L_e p + R_e.$$

For most practical values of the coefficients at least two of the roots of the denominator Δ' are complex, and result in a damped oscillation of high frequency ($1/f$ is of the order of magnitude of τ). This oscillation is superimposed on a low-frequency damped oscillation that corresponds to the voltage backswing on the network after the pulse. This voltage backswing can be estimated fairly accurately by obtaining the Laplace transform $i_N(p)$, from which the network-condenser voltage is obtained as

$$v_N(p) = -\frac{i_N(p)}{C_N p}.$$

This backswing has a polarity opposite to that of the original source voltage, and, if a unidirectional switch is used, is approximately equal to the inverse voltage left on an actual network.

7·5. Computed and Actual Pulse Shapes.—In order to keep the treatment as general as possible, the previous discussion makes no reference to the time function that can be used, and pertains to a biased-diode load, which was chosen because of the flexibility that results from varying either its bias or its resistance.

If the load is highly capacitive, it is possible to use the same procedure by replacing the distributed capacitance C_D by the load-plus-transformer capacitance. If the load is a pure resistance, $V_s = 0$, and the first step is eliminated. It is conceivable that a pulser may be used to initiate an arc of negative-resistance characteristic; it should then be possible to use a negative value for r_l to fit the arc voltage-current characteristic over the appropriate range, and again the general solution holds.

The pulsers most widely used by the Radiation Laboratory had magnetron loads, and therefore the following examples consider the case of a magnetron such as the 4J52 operated from a typical pulser. Assuming that the characteristics of this magnetron are $V_s = 13$ kv, and $r_l = 100$ ohms, and its operating current is 15 amp, the corresponding static load resistance is about 1000 ohms. In discussing examples of this type, it is convenient to refer all quantities in the pulser discharging circuit, including the pulse-transformer parameters, to the secondary of the pulse transformer. The sum of pulse-forming-network impedance and estimated series losses is thus assumed to be $Z_1 = 1200$ ohms, which necessitates a network voltage equal to

$$V_N = \frac{V_s + (r_l I_l)(R_l + Z_1)}{R_l} = \frac{(13,000 + 100 \times 15)2200}{1000} \approx 32,000 \text{ volts.}$$

The characteristics of the pulse transformer are: $L_L = 90$ μh, $L_D = 22$ μh, $C_D = 60$ μμf, $L_e = 50$ mh, and $R_e = 20,000$ ohms. For the first example, the function $v_N(t)$ is assumed to be a trapezoidal pulse with a time of rise equal to zero, a flat top of 2.5 μsec, and a time of fall of 0.25 μsec. The second example considers a similar pulse shape with a time of rise equal to 0.25 μsec, a flat top of 2.5 μsec, and a time of fall of 0.5 μsec.

The time function of the applied voltage for the rising edge of the pulse is

$$v_N(t) = V_N,$$

which gives the Laplace-transform equation

$$v_N(p) = \frac{V_N}{p}.$$

Introducing the voltage transform in Eqs. (61) and (62), the following time functions are obtained:

$$\frac{i_N(t)}{V_N} = \frac{e^{-\alpha t} \sin \omega t}{(L_L + L_D)\omega},$$

$$\frac{v_l(t)}{V_N} = 1 - e^{-\alpha t}\left(\frac{L_L}{L_L + L_D} \cos \omega t + \frac{\alpha}{\omega} \frac{2L_D + L_L}{L_L + L_D} \sin \omega t\right),$$

where

$$\alpha = \frac{Z_1}{2(L_L + L_D)}$$

and

$$\omega = \sqrt{\frac{1}{C_D(L_L + L_D)} - \alpha^2}.$$

The voltage time function is plotted in Fig. 7·21. It may be noted that the voltage time function does not start from zero voltage, as is obviously never the case in practice. The two assumptions responsible for this

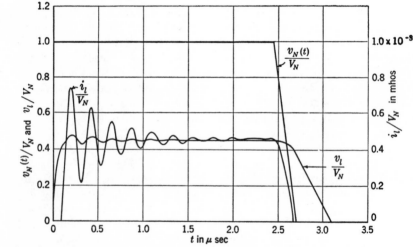

Fig. 7·21.—Computed load-current and voltage pulses for a line-type pulser (trapezoidal applied pulse, instantaneous rise).

apparent discrepancy are (1) that the rise of applied voltage is instantaneous, which is not possible in practice, and (2) that the capacitance across the load has been added to the pulse-transformer distributed capacitance. Hence, at the first instant, the total applied voltage appears across the series inductance of the circuit, and, since part of that inductance is directly across the load, a fraction of the voltage equal to $L_D/(L_L + L_D)$ must appear across the load.

This analysis is carried on until, by successive approximations, a time t_1 is found such that

$$\frac{v_l(t_1)}{V_N} = \frac{V_s}{V_N}.$$

The current through the circuit and the voltage across the condenser C_D at that time are then computed. For the particular values of parameters chosen above, $t_1 = 0.087 \ \mu\text{sec}$, $I_{L_1}/V_N = 416 \times 10^{-6}$ mhos, and

$$\frac{V_{C_1}}{V_N} = 0.383.$$

The general form of the time function for the top of the pulse is too complex to permit a useful analysis of the effect of individual parameters, even with an applied voltage of the simple form assumed here. For the particular values chosen for the parameters, the load voltage is of the form

$$\frac{v_l(t)_{t_1 \leq t \leq t_2}}{V_N} = A_v + B_v e^{bt} + C_v e^{ct} \sin(\omega_1 t + \theta),$$

in which the first term has the value

$$A_v = \frac{\dfrac{V_s}{V_N} Z_1 + r_l}{Z_1 + r_l} = 0.452,$$

which is the steady-state value of the voltage arrived at from other considerations in Sec. 7·2.

The term $B_v e^{bt}$ is an exponential with a very rapid decay, corresponding to the increase from starting to operating voltage. Again, for this example, $B_v = -0.0048$, and $b = -14.5$ for t expressed in microseconds. The last term corresponds to the oscillations on the top of the pulse, for which $C_v = -0.416$, $c = -2.24$ for t expressed in microseconds, $\omega_1 = 27.35$, and $\theta = 1.431$. The time function for the current is of the same form as that for the voltage; the coefficients are given by

$$A_i = \frac{1 - \dfrac{V_s}{V_N}}{r_l + Z_1},$$

$$B_i = \frac{B_v}{r_l},$$

and

$$C_i = \frac{C_v}{r_l},$$

and the exponents, frequency, and phase angle are the same.

A plot of the load-voltage time function obtained with the above assumptions is given in Fig. 7·21. The amplitude of oscillations is much greater than that observed in practice because of the shock excitation of the pulse-transformer circuit. This excitation is introduced partly by the discontinuous function chosen for the applied voltage, and partly by the assumption that the switch voltage drops instantaneously to its operating value.

When the applied voltage begins to decrease at $t = 2.5$ μsec, its time function is given by

$$v_N(t) = V_N\left(1 - \frac{t'}{a}\right),$$

with $t' = 0$ at $t = 2.5$ μsec, where t' is expressed in microseconds and $a = 0.25$ μsec. The Laplace transform for the voltage

$$\left(\frac{V_N}{p} - \frac{V_N}{ap^2}\right),$$

introduced in Eqs. (63) and (65) leads to a time function containing terms of the same form as those for $v_N(t) = V_N$, plus a term that is directly proportional to the time. For the particular example chosen, the oscillatory term is negligible, and the expressions for the load voltage and current can be written

$$\frac{v_l(t)}{V_N} = 0.475 - 0.308t - 0.023e^{-14.52t}$$

and

$$10^6 \frac{i_l(t)}{V_N} = 687 - 3077t - 230e^{-14.52t} \text{ mhos.}$$

The expression for $v_l(t)$ is used until $t = t_2$, t_2 having been defined as the time for which

$$\frac{v_l}{i_l} = R_e.$$

The load static impedance at any instant is given by

$$\frac{v_l}{i_l} = \frac{V_s + i_l r_l}{i_l} = \frac{r_l}{1 - \dfrac{V_s}{v_l}}.$$

Equating this value to R_e, the load voltage is determined as a function of load parameters, that is

$$V_l(t_2) = V_s \frac{R_e}{R_e - r_l}.$$

The time t_2 at which this voltage is reached can now be obtained from the time function for v_l. In the present example, it is 2.71 μsec. This value is used in turn to determine the initial currents to be introduced in the circuit from which the trailing edge of the pulse is computed.

The amplitude of oscillations on the top of the current pulse is determined to a large extent by the energy stored in the charging inductance of the pulse transformer, and their frequency is determined almost entirely by the distributed capacitance and charging inductance of the pulse transformer.

Since the applied voltage $v_N(t)$ is considered equal to zero for $t > t_2$, the initial conditions for the trailing edge of the pulse can readily be found as follows:

$$\frac{I_{L_2}}{V_N} = \frac{v_l}{V_N L_e}(t_2 - t_1) = \frac{0.452}{50 \times 10^{-3}} \times 2.62 \times 10^{-6} \approx 24 \times 10^{-6} \text{ mhos,}$$

$$\frac{V_{c_2}}{V_{NL}} = 0.408,$$

and

$$\frac{I_{N2}}{V_N} \approx 28 \times 10^{-6} \text{ mhos.}$$

The values for L_N and C_N are found to be

$$C_N = \frac{2.5 \times 10^{-6}}{2400} \approx 1000 \times 10^{-12} \text{ farads,}$$

and

$$L_N = Z_N^2 C_N \approx 1.4 \times 10^{-3} \text{ henrys.}$$

If these values are introduced in the Laplace-transform equation for this circuit (Eq. (65)), the time function for the voltage across R_e is found to be

$$\frac{v_l(t)_{t>t_2}}{V_N} = -0.178e^{-0.0225t} \sin (0.134t - 0.132)$$

$$-0.386e^{-0.394t} \sin (3.52t - 1.49).$$

As can be seen from Fig. 7·22, the load voltage during the tail of the pulse consists essentially of two damped sine waves, one of relatively high amplitude, frequency, and damping that corresponds approximately to the $L_N C_D$-circuit, and one of lower amplitude, frequency, and damping that corresponds very nearly to the $L_e C_N$-circuit.

The voltage buildup on the network capacitance C_N is given by the expression

$$\frac{v_N(t)_{t>t_2}}{V_N} = -0.182e^{-0.0225t} \sin (0.134t - 0.121)$$

$$+0.022e^{-0.394t} \sin (3.52t + 1.434),$$

and is also plotted on Fig. 7·22. If the switch is unidirectional, the network voltage V_N reaches a maximum negative value, at which time the discharging circuit is disconnected from the network, and only the charging circuit needs to be considered.

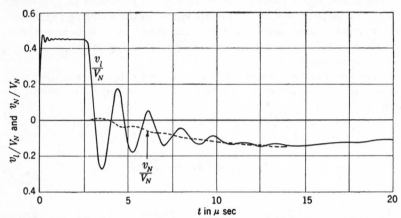

Fig. 7·22.—Computed voltage pulse on the load and backswing voltage on the load and on the pulse-forming network (trapezoidal applied pulse, instantaneous rise).

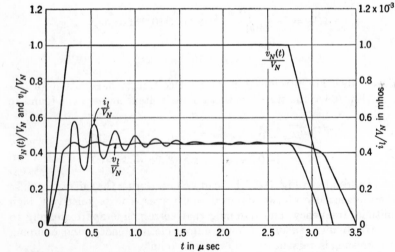

Fig. 7·23.—Computed load-current and load-voltage pulses for a line-type pulser (trapezoidal applied voltage, finite time of rise).

One assumption that is implicit in the above discussion is that the charging circuit has no effect on the shape or on the trailing edge of the pulse. This assumption is correct only if the charging inductance is very large compared with the shunt inductance of the pulse transformer. The effect may become appreciable if the ratio $\sqrt{L_c/L_e}$ is less than 10.

Figure 7·23 shows the voltage and current pulse shapes obtained for the same circuit conditions as those applying to the preceding discussion, but with an applied pulse shape that has a finite time of rise. The detailed analysis is not repeated, but it is worthy of note that the amplitude of the oscillations on the top of the pulse is reduced by a factor of at least two by the decrease in the shock excitation in the circuit, as is to be expected. In actual practice, the amplitude should be reduced even more because, as explained later, the switch-resistance characteristics in a line-type pulser tend to decrease the rate of rise of the pulse on the load even though a unit step function of voltage is applied to the circuit.

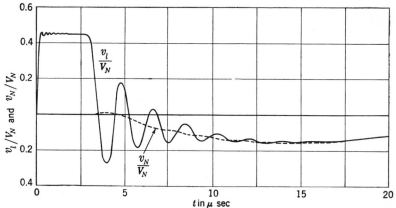

Fig. 7·24.—Computed voltage pulse on the load and backswing voltage on the load and on the pulse-forming network (trapezoidal applied voltage, finite time of rise).

The similarity between Fig. 7·24 and Fig. 7·22, showing the load voltage during and immediately after the pulse, and the voltage on the network capacitance, is quite obvious. The principal difference between the two cases is a phase shift of the post-pulse oscillations corresponding approximately to the time of build-up of the front edge of the pulse.

The series of oscillograms shown in Fig. 7·25 have been obtained with a circuit simulating a line-type pulser in order to indicate the effects of distributed capacitance and pulse-tranformer inductances on the top of the pulse. It may be noted that the damping of the oscillations is faster than that predicted by theory as a result of the losses in the simulating circuit, which were neglected when making computations. It is highly probable, however, that the losses in the actual circuit are even higher than those obtained by the use of air-core inductances and mica condensers. The frequency of the oscillations on the top of the pulse is seen to depend on the value of the charging inductance L_d and on the distributed capacitance, but not on the leakage inductance. The ampli-

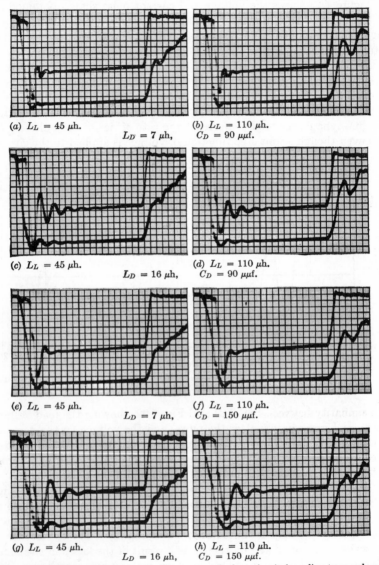

(a) $L_L = 45$ μh.

(b) $L_L = 110$ μh.

$L_D = 7$ μh, $C_D = 90$ μμf.

(c) $L_L = 45$ μh.

(d) $L_L = 110$ μh.

$L_D = 16$ μh, $C_D = 90$ μμf.

(e) $L_L = 45$ μh.

(f) $L_L = 110$ μh.

$L_D = 7$ μh, $C_D = 150$ μμf.

(g) $L_L = 45$ μh.

(h) $L_L = 110$ μh.

$L_D = 16$ μh, $C_D = 150$ μμf.

Fig. 7·25.—Observed output pulses from an equivalent circuit for a line-type pulser.

tude of the first oscillation is, to a certain extent, determined by the leakage inductance and the distributed capacitance, but it is evident that the principal factor contributing to that amplitude is the charging inductance.

A comparison of these photographs with those shown in Fig. 7·30 indicates that the amplitude of the oscillations obtained in an actual pulser circuit and with a magnetron load is less than that to be expected from theoretical considerations. The circuit constants used for the above computations and photographs are very nearly equal to those obtaining for Fig. 7·30. The simplifying assumptions, such as the lumping of capacitances and inductances to obtain a workable circuit, account for this difference.

Effect of the Switch Resistance.—During the foregoing discussion the switch resistance is assumed constant in order to simplify the equations, although it is a function of time for the start of the pulse. A very simple example is treated here to show the effect of the switch resistance on the front edge of the voltage pulse on a resistance load. Figure 7·26 repre-

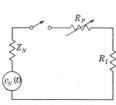

FIG. 7·26.—Equivalent discharging circuit for study of the effect of switch resistance.

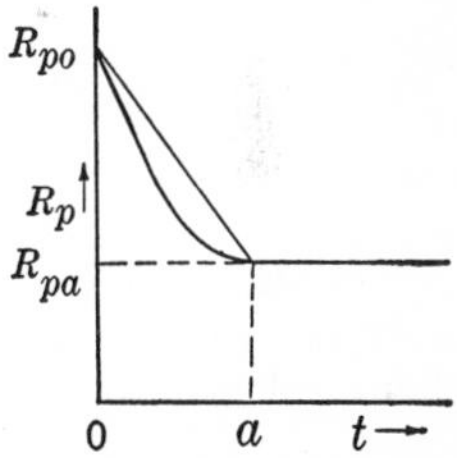

FIG. 7·27.—Assumed switch-resistance characteristics.

sents the discharging circuit and Fig. 7·27 gives the assumed switch-resistance characteristics.

Two assumptions are made concerning the variation of switch resistance as a function of time (discussed in Chap. 8):

1. That the resistance decreases linearly from a value R_{p0} at the beginning of the pulse to a value R_{pa} at a time $t = a$, and is equal to R_{pa} for the remainder of the pulse.
2. That the decrease in resistance from the same value R_{p0} to the value R_{pa} at $t = a$ is parabolic.

This latter method avoids any discontinuity if the vertex of the parabola is at point A and if its axis is parallel to the resistance axis. For a linear drop in resistance, the switch resistance from the time $t = 0$ to the time $t = a$ is expressed as

$$r_p = R_{p0} + \frac{R_{pa} - R_{p0}}{a} t = R_{pa} + (R_{p0} - R_{pa})\left(1 - \frac{t}{a}\right),$$

and the voltage across the load resistance R_l is then given by

$$v_l(t) = \frac{v_N(t)R_l}{Z_N + R_l + r_p} \qquad \text{for } 0 < t < a,$$

or

$$\frac{v_l(t)}{v_N(t)} = \frac{R_l}{Z_N + R_l + R_{pa} + (R_{p0} - R_{pa})\left(1 - \frac{t}{a}\right)}.$$

Assuming that $v_N(t) = 0$ for $t < 0$, that $v_N(t) = V_N$ for $t > 0$, and that $Z_N = R_l$, $R_{p0} = 2R_l$, $R_{pa} = 0.05\,R_l$, and $a = 0.25\,\mu sec$, the time function of the load voltage may be simplified to

$$\frac{v_l(t)}{V_N} = \frac{1}{4 - 7.8t}$$

for $0 < t < a$, where t is expressed in microseconds. For $t > a$,

$$\frac{v_l(t)}{V_N} = \frac{R_l}{Z_N + R_l + R_{pa}} = \frac{1}{2.05}$$

for the values chosen.

Assuming a parabolic decrease in resistance, the expression for resistance becomes

$$r_p = (R_{p0} - R_{pa})\left(1 - \frac{t}{a}\right)^2 + R_{pa} \qquad \text{for } (0 < t < a),$$

and the load voltage becomes

$$\frac{v_l(t)}{V_N} = \frac{R_l}{Z_N + R_l + R_{pa} + (R_{p0} - R_{pa})\left(1 - \frac{t}{a}\right)^2}.$$

Again, for $t > a$,

$$\frac{v_l(t)}{V_N} = \frac{R_l}{Z_N + R_l + R_{pa}}.$$

With the values of constants assumed for a linearly varying resistance, the expression for the voltage across the load resistance becomes

$$\frac{v_l(t)}{V_N} = \frac{1}{4 - 15.6t + 31.2t^2}.$$

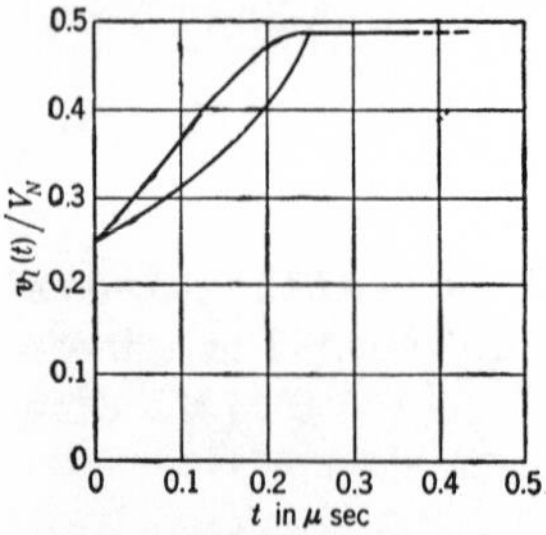

Fig. 7·28.—Computed effect of a variable switch resistance on the front edge of the voltage pulse for a resistance load and a rectangular applied pulse.

The effect of a variable switch resistance is shown in Fig. 7·28. This effect is seen to be essentially the same as that obtained from a time function $v_N(t)$, with a time of rise longer than the actual one, and a constant switch resistance R_{pa}. Hence, the method of approach described earlier in this section can be used with reasonable accuracy, if the proper assumptions are made concerning the time of rise of the applied voltage $v_N(t)$.

Effect of Pulse Cable between Pulser and Load.—If a pulse cable is inserted between the pulser and the pulse transformer, its effect on the pulse shape does not lend itself to easy mathematical treatment for the loads encountered in practice.   In general, it can be said that, if the load is a biased diode, the shapes of the top of the current pulse and the trailing edge of the voltage pulse are affected by changes in the length of a cable between pulser and load.   Oscillograms of 0.2-μsec voltage and current pulses obtained with a 4J52-magnetron load using 6 and 50

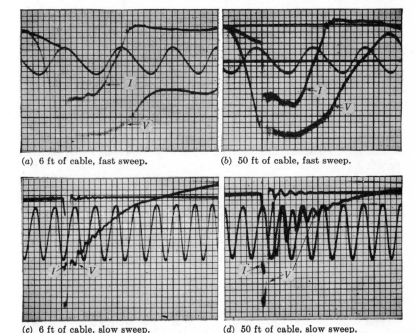

(a) 6 ft of cable, fast sweep.   (b) 50 ft of cable, fast sweep.

(c) 6 ft of cable, slow sweep.   (d) 50 ft of cable, slow sweep.

Fig. 7·29.—Oscillograms showing the effect of cable length on the pulse shapes for a 0.2-μsec current pulse.

ft of cable are shown in Fig. 7·29.   Slow and fast sweeps were used to show both the top of the current pulse and the trailing edge of the voltage pulse; sweep calibrations of 5 and 1 Mc/sec respectively are also shown. Two facts are immediately obvious: (1) in this particular case, the current amplitude tends to decrease as a function of time if a short cable is used, and to increase if a long cable is used, and (2) high-amplitude oscillations are present on the trailing edge of the voltage pulse when the long cable is used.

Not enough information is available at present to evaluate exactly the causes for the changes introduced in the pulse shape by the cable; the problem involves, in addition to the cable characteristics, the variety of parameters considered previously in this section.   These characteristics include impedance, attenuation, and phase shift, which may vary as a function of frequency.   Thus, individual cases lead to entirely different results.

Another example is shown in Fig. 7·30, where voltage and current pulse shapes on a 4J52 magnetron are shown for a 2.4-μsec pulse.   In this case, additional oscillations appear in the current pulse when a long cable is used.   After the first 0.7 μsec, these oscillations take the shape of

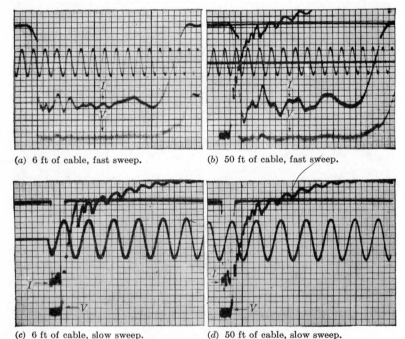

(a) 6 ft of cable, fast sweep.   (b) 50 ft of cable, fast sweep.

(c) 6 ft of cable, slow sweep.   (d) 50 ft of cable, slow sweep.

Fig. 7·30.—Oscillograms showing the effect of cable length on the pulse shapes for a 2.4-μsec current pulse.

a distorted damped rectangular wave superimposed on the current pulse. Graphical subtraction of the two current pulses leads to the conclusion that this distortion is the result of a highly damped sine-wave oscillation superimposed on a slightly damped rectangular wave.   The half period of this distorted rectangular wave is slightly longer than the two-way transit time in the cable; the difference can almost entirely be accounted for by the time delay in the pulse transformer.   The amplitude of oscillations on the trailing edge of the voltage pulse is essentially the same for both long and short cables; the period, however, is slightly increased by the addition of a long cable.

CHAPTER 8

SWITCHES FOR LINE-TYPE PULSERS

By J. V. Lebacqz, H. J. White, J. R. Dillinger, A. S. Jerrems, and
K. J. Germeshausen

Some of the requirements for switches that can be used to initiate the
discharge of the pulse-forming network have already been mentioned in
Chap. 1. Briefly, these requirements may be summarized as follows:

1. The switch should be nonconducting during the charging period.
2. The switch should be capable of closing very rapidly at predetermined times.
3. The switch resistance should be as small as possible during the
   discharge of the network.
4. The switch is not required to interrupt the pulse current, since the
   current drops to zero or nearly to zero at the end of the pulse.
5. The switch should regain its nonconducting state rapidly after
   the end of the pulse.

The requirements of low resistance and rapid closing of the switch
suggest that either spark gaps or gaseous-discharge tubes should be used
as switches in line-type pulsers. The problem of closing the switch or
initiating the discharge at predetermined times has been a serious one
because, for some applications, an accuracy of about 0.02 μsec is desired.
Both thyratrons and triggered spark gaps have been developed to meet
this exacting requirement successfully. Rapid deionization of the gas
after the discharge is essential if high recurrence frequencies are required.
Since the nature and pressure of the gas, the electrode geometry, the total
ionization produced by the pulse current, and the type of charging circuit used all affect the deionization time, some compromise may have
to be reached between the pulse power and the maximum recurrence
frequency, independent of the safe allowable average power. In spark
gaps electrode erosion occurs, changing the gap geometry and the breakdown characteristics. Attention must also be given to the residual gases
produced by the spark under certain conditions.

Since rotary spark gaps had been used successfully in radio code transmitters, they were suggested for use in radar pulsers, and proved very
satisfactory. They presented three main disadvantages, however: (1)

they are not well suited for high recurrence frequencies, (2) they have an inherent uncertainty in the time of firing, which may be as high as 50 μsec, and (3) they cannot readily be adapted to applications requiring airtight enclosures.   As a result, developmental work was started on both fixed spark gaps and thyratrons.   The early investigations covered such possibilities as veatrons (vacuum arc devices) and ignitrons,[1] fixed two- and three-electrode gaps operating in air with a forced circulation of the air in order to aid deionization,[2] and mechanical switches operating in a vacuum.[3]   The "trigatron,"[4] an enclosed three-electrode gap was found to be satisfactory for lowpower applications in which long life was not required.   Some work was done on an enclosed three-electrode gap for applications requiring high power and long life.[5]   Of all these devices, an enclosed fixed gap having two electrodes and operated in series with one or two similar gaps showed the greatest promise of early satisfactory development, and the effort was therefore concentrated on these so-called "series gaps."[6]

A series-gap switch is preferable to the rotary spark gap for the following reasons: (1) the time fluctuations in the initiation of the discharge are smaller (1 to 2 μsec for one type of series gap, 0.02 μsec for another type), (2) it can easily be operated at more than one pulse recurrence frequency in a given installation, (3) it can be operated at recurrence frequencies that are higher than those conveniently obtained with a rotary gap, and (4) each fixed spark gap is completely enclosed.

Early work on existing mercury thyratrons[7] indicated the desirability of developing a switch that would eliminate the variation of characteristics as a function of ambient temperature, and that would use a gas that would not damage the cathode when passing the high peak currents required.   After much experimentation, the hydrogen thyratron was developed at the Radiation Laboratory, and proved to be the most satis-

[1] C. M. Slack, "Report on Pulser Tube Development," NDRC 14-105, Westinghouse Electric Corporation, May 15, 1942.

[2] L. Tonks (General Electric Company), "Fixed Spark Gaps and Associated Circuits," *Spark Gap Colloquium*, RL Report No. 50-1, Sept. 28, 1942.

R. G. Fluharty, "Life Test Report on Triggered Spark Gaps Developed by L. Tonks at the G. E. Company," RL Internal Report 51-Apr. 7, 1943.

[3] J. V. Lebacqz, H. O. Anger, and T. W. Jarmie, "Mechanical Vacuum Switches, Transmission Line and RC Pulsing Circuits," NDRC 14-156, U. of Calif., June 1, 1943.

[4] J. D. Craggs, M. E. Haine, and J. M. Meek, "The Development of Triggered Gaps with Particular Reference to Sealed Gaps," Metropolitan-Vickers Electric Co., Ltd., Report No. C-311, September 1942.

[5] C. M. Slack, and E. G. F. Arnott, "Report on Enclosed Pressure Gaps," NDRC 14-150, Westinghouse Electric Corporation, Dec. 31, 1942.

[6] F. S. Goucher, J. R. Haynes, W. A. Depp, and E. J. Ryder, "Spark Gap Switches for Radar," *Bell System Technical Journal*, Oct. 1946.

[7] A. W. Hull (General Electric Company), "Mercury Vapor Thyratron," *Modulator Colloquium*, RL Report No. 50-2, June 9, 1943, pp. 118–120.

factory switch throughout the power range which it covers. With this switch, the time fluctuation can easily be kept to 0.02 μsec or less, and the auxiliary circuits required for the trigger pulse are very simple compared with those necessary to supply a high-voltage trigger pulse to the series-gap switch.

The characteristics, uses, and special requirements of rotary spark gaps, enclosed fixed spark gaps, and hydrogen thyratrons in pulser circuits are considered in this chapter.

THE ROTARY SPARK GAP

By J. V. Lebacqz and H. J. White

A very brief discussion of the sparking mechanism at or near atmospheric pressure may be helpful in understanding the limitations and advantages of the different kinds of rotary spark gaps. A spark may be defined, for the purpose of the present discussion, as the transient, unstable breakdown of a gas between electrodes whereby the gas is suddenly changed from a good insulator to a relatively good conductor. It results from the formation of a highly ionized path between two electrodes, and, within the limits of voltages considered here, the final voltage-current characteristics of the spark usually depend more on the external circuit than on the gap dimensions.

A spark is initiated between two electrodes by raising the voltage to, or above, the static-breakdown voltage. The static-breakdown voltage is the minimum voltage that, if applied to a given gap for a long enough time, eventually causes it to break down. The concept of time is introduced here because the breakdown is initiated by the ionization of the gas molecules by free electrons accelerated in a strong electric field. Under favorable conditions, the process is cumulative and breakdown results; however, the time lag, or the time elapsed between the application of the static-breakdown voltage and the initiation of the discharge, may be as long as several minutes. If a voltage higher than the static-breakdown voltage is applied, or if a large number of electrons are made available in the gap, the chances of obtaining conditions favorable to ionization increase and the statistical time lag decreases. In general, if the voltage applied to the gap is two to three times the static-breakdown voltage, and if some initial ionization is provided, the time lag of the gap can be reduced to 10^{-9} to 10^{-7} seconds.

Once the ionization process has been initiated, some time still elapses before the breakdown takes on the character of a spark. This time is referred to as the "breakdown time" of the gap and depends on its geometry and on the pressure and nature of the gas, as well as on the shape of the applied voltage wave. Observations indicate that the breakdown time is usually very small—of the order of magnitude of 10^{-8} sec—although it increases for very nonuniform fields, and for low gas pressures.

Since the breakdown of a gap can be controlled accurately by adequate overvoltage, the problem becomes that of obtaining the necessary overvoltage. This overvoltage can be obtained either by applying a high transient voltage to one of the electrodes if the gap geometry is fixed, or by varying the gap spacing as a function of time, as in the rotary spark gap.

8·1. Electrical Considerations in the Design of Rotary Spark Gaps.—Rotary spark gaps consist of a set of moving electrodes rotating in front of one or more fixed electrodes. The minimum spacing is adjusted so that the corresponding static-breakdown voltage is smaller than the voltage required on the network, and the motion of the electrodes is synchronized in such a way that the maximum network voltage is obtained a short time before the minimum spacing is reached. Although the final design of successful rotary gaps has been achieved primarily by trial and error, there are some fundamental factors to be kept in mind, and some experimental data that can be used as a guide. These factors are the gap geometry, the nature of the gas and electrode materials, and the number of electrodes.

Gap Geometry.—Nearly all the successful rotary spark gaps used in pulsers were designed with cylindrical electrodes. It is necessary to minimize the changes in gap geometry which are unavoidable in spark gap operation, if the operating point is to remain reasonably constant during life. The gaps were therefore built either with parallel electrodes having sufficient overlap to increase the effective area which the spark may strike, or the electrodes are in two planes normal to the axis of rotation. The moving electrodes are radial and the fixed electrode makes an angle of 20° to 40° with the raidus, so that the gap geometry is essentially unaltered as the electrode wears away slowly from its tip.

Simple considerations of the voltage gradient between two moving cylindrical electrodes with parallel axes may be used to bring out some of the limitations of a gap of this type. Consider two electrodes (Fig. 8·1) of equal diameter d, and having a minimum spacing a. For any distance s between the axis of the moving electrode and its position corresponding to minimum spacing, the breakdown distance between the two electrodes is given by

$$D = \sqrt{s^2 + (d + a)^2} - d.$$

For a rotary gap, the angular velocity of the moving electrode is constant. Then, if t_0 denotes the time at which $D = a$, the distance s can be expressed as a function of angular velocity ω and radius r of the circumference of the center of the electrode. Then $s = \omega r(t_0 - t)$. This equation is correct only to the same approximation that $\omega(t_0 - t) \approx \sin \omega(t_0 - t)$; for usual rotary-gap practice, the angle over which the spark may take place is always so small that the error introduced is negligible. Hence, the average voltage gradient between electrodes can be expressed as

$$E = \frac{V_N}{D} = \frac{V_N}{\sqrt{s^2 + (d + a)^2} - d} = \frac{V_N}{\sqrt{\omega^2 r^2 (t_0 - t)^2 + (d + a)^2} - d},$$

where V_N is the network voltage. For reasons explained later, resonant charging is nearly always used for rotary-gap pulsers. In this case, the network voltage is so nearly constant near the discharge point that it may be assumed constant without introducing appreciable error. An exact discussion of the sparking phenomena requires a knowledge of the maximum electric field between electrodes for every position of the moving electrode. In the following discussion it is assumed that the voltage gradient E is uniform between the electrodes. It is also assumed that a spark may occur at any time after the electric field exceeds 30 kv/cm, and occurs instantaneously if the electric field reaches a value of 70 kv/cm. These assumptions are obviously far from correct, and are not intended to give a quantitative solution to the problem of gap design. If made consistently for various conditions, however, they do lead to results that are in accord with experience, and are therefore sufficiently accurate to indicate the expected trends of the phenomena. For instance, it is shown later that the experimental average gradient before static breakdown for a given gap varies as a function of spacing, and is higher than 30 kv/cm

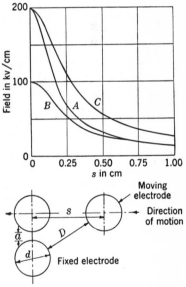

Fig. 8·1.—Average field between rotary-gap electrodes. Curve A is for $V_N = 10$ kv, $a = 0.05$ cm, curve B is for $V_N = 10$ kv, $a = 0.10$ cm, and curve C is for $V_N = 20$ kv, $a = 0.10$ cm.

at the smaller spacings. The introduction of this variation in the minimum average gradient in the discussion at this point would result in many additional complications without altering the conclusions.

For any given values of applied voltage, electrode dimensions and minimum spacing, and velocity of the moving electrode, a time $t = t_1$ can be found at which the voltage gradient reaches 30 kv/cm. Similarly, a time $t = t_2$ may be defined as the time at which $E = 70$ kv/cm. The spark then occurs between t_1 and t_2. Thus, $(t_2 - t_1)$ corresponds to the maximum time jitter that may be expected because of uncertainty in the initiation of the gap discharge.   As an example, consider the hypothetical gap of Fig. 8·1, and assume that the electrodes are 0.25 cm in diameter. The average gradient has been plotted as a function of s for several values of V_N and a.   Then, with the assumptions made above, a spark may take place at any point between $s = 0.25$ and $s = 0.5$ cm for curve A; between $s = 0.18$ and $s = 0.43$ cm for curve B; and between $s = 0.41$ and $s = 0.85$ cm for curve C.   To express these results as a function of time, some electrode velocity must be assumed.   Taking $r = 10$ cm and a rotor speed of 60 revolutions per second, the linear velocity of the moving electrode is

$$\omega r = 2\pi \times 60 \times 10 = 3750 \text{ cm/sec}$$

Then, the maximum time jitter can be estimated as 0.25/3750 sec or 65 μsec for curves A and B, and about 115 μsec for curve C.

These values are larger than those normally found in practice (1) because of the crudeness of the assumptions concerning field distribution and breakdown voltages, (2) because the time lag at minimum breakdown voltage has been considered equal to zero, and (3) because the possibility of the formation of corona has been neglected.   Actually, for the gap geometry considered, the minimum value of the average static gradient at breakdown is probably nearer 40 than 30 kv/cm.   If this value is chosen, and if the gap is assumed to break down with a time lag smaller than 1 μsec when the voltage is equal to 150 per cent of the minimum breakdown voltage, 60 kv/cm in this case, the values obtained for inherent time jitter in the gap are 30 μsec for curves A and B and about 50 μsec for curve C.   Nevertheless, the results can be used either to compare the behavior of gaps having different geometries, that is, where the ratio of the minimum spacing to the electrode diameter varies, or to compare the operation of gaps with similar geometries at different voltages.

The time jitter to be expected is inversely proportional to the relative speed of the electrodes.   Thus, in order to decrease the inherent time jitter caused by the statistical nature of the sparking process, it is theoretically sufficient to increase the steepness of the curve showing the variation of field with spacings or time within the range of voltage gradients that is most apt to produce a spark.   One method of achieving the desired result is to increase the speed of the moving electrode.   A judicious choice of electrode diameter and spacing for a given operating voltage is also necessary.   For instance, referring to Fig. 8·1 and the previous discussion, it is seen that the time jitter of the gap with a minimum spacing of 0.10 cm for an applied voltage of 20 kv is almost twice its value for an applied voltage of 10 kv.

If the moving-electrode velocity is held constant, the inherent time jitter of a gap that has an electrode diameter and minimum spacing that are twice those of the gap considered in the previous example and that operates at 20 kv is still much greater than that of the gap operating at 10 kv. Since the mechanical design imposes a limit on the maximum electrode velocity, it is advantageous, in some cases, to use two gaps in series if the total voltage becomes very great. This method has been used in some rotary gaps designed at the Radiation Laboratory.

If the voltage across a rotary gap is increased gradually, the gap begins to break down erratically when the field corresponding to the minimum spacing reaches the critical gradient at which the spark may occur with a long time lag. If the voltage is further increased, the gap begins to break down on every pulse, and usually reaches a point of optimum operation. If the voltage is increased still further, the length of the gap at which the spark jumps increases, as well as the time jitter.

Another very important consideration in gap design is that of deionization. As pointed out previously, the gap is not required to interrupt the main pulse current. The network, however, starts to recharge immediately after the pulse, and care must be taken that its voltage does not exceed the breakdown voltage of the gap at any time before the end of the desired interpulse interval. Since the air in the vicinity of the electrodes is highly ionized by the passage of the spark current, it is safe to assume that there is very little time lag before breakdown, even for the minimum voltage gradient. If losses are neglected and the network is assumed to discharge completely, the voltage across the gap may be expressed as

$$v_N = \frac{V_N}{2}(1 - \cos \omega_0 t)$$

for d-c resonant charging, and the average field is

$$E = \frac{v_N}{D},$$

where D is defined as before. As an example, consider the gap of Fig. 8·1 curve A with $V_N = 10$ kv, and assume that the spark has taken place when $E = 40$ kv/cm. If the pulse recurrence frequency is 600 pps,

$$v_N = 5(1 - \cos 600 \,\pi t),$$

and the electrode velocity is 3750 cm/sec. Thus, the voltage gradient across the gap can readily be plotted as in Fig. 8·2 for various positions of the moving electrode. For the particular values of parameters chosen, there is no danger of the gap restriking and establishing a short-circuiting arc across the power supply. If the same gap were used at $V_N = 20$ kv, however, the network discharge might take place at $s = 0.7$ cm. Then, the voltage built up on the network at the time of minimum spacing between the electrodes would be about 610 volts, corresponding to an average gradient greater than 12 kv/cm. Because of the nonuniformity of the field, which can be caused by rough electrodes resulting from long

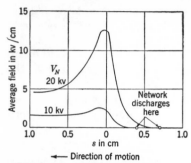

operation, the gap may be expected to restrike under these conditions. The average voltage gradient as a function of pin spacing has been plotted for this case in Fig. 8·2.

In conclusion, some practical results are given. Experience has shown that high-power gaps work satisfactorily with an average gradient between 60 and 70 kv/cm corresponding to minimum spacing (Fig. 8·1), and that low-power gaps may be built and operated with minimum spacings that would correspond to average gradients of between 200 and 300

FIG. 8·2.—Average field between electrodes during the beginning of a charging cycle for $d = 0.25$ cm, $a = 0.05$ cm, $f_r = 600$ pps, $\omega r = 3750$ cm/sec, where d, a and s are shown in Fig. 8·1.

kv/cm if the gap did not break down before that point were reached. These figures are only indicative of the range that has been used, and each case has to be considered separately, depending on the required recurrence frequency, the time jitter, the type of charging circuit, and the type of load.

Gas and Electrode Material.—According to the most widely accepted theories, gap breakdown takes place exclusively in the gas and is independent of the material used for electrodes, except inasmuch as it may contribute to the initial ionization of the gas, either by radioactivity or by photoelectricity. Thus, the choice of electrode material is determined by other considerations, such as the necessity of obtaining a long trouble-free operating life. Since high temperatures are developed in high-current sparks, refractory material should be used for the electrodes, and consequently tungsten was chosen for the initial tests on rotary spark gaps. Because of the satisfactory operation of these gaps, tungsten electrodes were used in nearly all the rotary gaps designed at the Radiation Laboratory. The original gaps were designed to operate in air at atmospheric pressure, where a breakdown field of 30 to 50 kv/cm, depending on the spacing, is applied. Tests on sealed rotary gaps, as well as on fixed spark gaps, indicated that the presence of oxygen was necessary to obtain a satisfactory life from the tungsten electrodes. The exact reason is not known, but it is believed that the formation of a layer of tungsten oxide provides a protective covering for the gap sparking surfaces that greatly reduces the electrode wear. Ventilated rotary gaps using tungsten electrodes have been used in the great majority of radar applications, although they cannot be used in airborne radar sets because of the change in breakdown voltage with pressure. Sealed rotary gaps have been used in one airborne radar set, for which the life requirements are much less severe than for ground-based or shipborne sets.

A number of life tests on rotary gaps have been made both at the Radiation Laboratory and at the Bell Telephone Laboratories. The results are all in reasonable agreement, and show that the rate of cathode wear is much larger than that of anode wear. Since the electrode wear appears to be approximately proportional to the total charge passed by the gap, a logical unit for rate of wear is the loss of mass per unit charge. In practice, a convenient unit for rate of wear is milligrams per ampere-hour. Experimental data obtained both at the Bell Telephone Laboratories and the Radiation Laboratory show that, for pulse currents from 40 to 170 amp, the rate of cathode wear in air varies between about 2 and 6 mg/amp-hour, 3 or 4 mg/amp-hour being the median value. In nitrogen or gas mixtures that do not contain oxygen, the rate of wear is 10 to 20 times greater. The order of magnitude of the rate of anode wear in air is only $\frac{1}{5}$ that of the cathode.

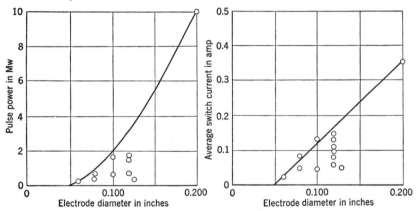

FIG. 8·3.—Diameter of the moving electrode for satisfactory gap operation and life.

Figures 8·3 and 8·4 show the relationship between pulse power and average current and the diameters of the moving and fixed electrodes, obtained from gap designs that have given satisfactory operating life. In these gaps, the fixed electrode is the anode and, as there are always several moving electrodes, the wear is divided between them. The values indicated by the curves can be regarded as the maximum safe operating power and current for any given electrode diameter, as determined from present experience, that allows a satisfactory gap life.

Number of Electrodes.—The number of fixed and rotary electrodes, N_f and N_r, is related to the angular velocity, ω, of the rotor (in revolutions per second) and the required pulse recurrence frequency, f_r, by the relation

$$f_r = N_f N_r \omega.$$

This relation applies only if the respective positions of fixed and rotating electrodes are such that the minimum spacing between electrodes is never reached simultaneously by more than one fixed and one rotating electrode. If, for instance, there are six rotor and six stator electrodes all spaced 60 mechanical degrees apart, the total number of sparks per revolution is six, the same number that would be obtained for one, two, or three stator electrodes equally spaced. If, on the other hand, there are five rotor and three stator electrodes equally spaced, the number of sparks per revolution is 15, and $f_r = 15\omega$.

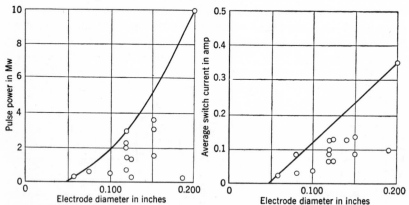

Fig. 8·4.—Diameter of the fixed electrode for satisfactory gap operation and life.

In general, because of the mechanical difficulties involved, only one fixed electrode is used, except for special applications such as the Marx circuit (see Sec. 11·8) or the half-wave a-c charging circuit (see Sec. 11·6). In these cases, it is necessary to obtain two or more sparks simultaneously, and the number of fixed electrodes must therefore be at least equal to the total number of discharge paths desired. It should also be pointed out that the formula gives the average recurrence frequency for one complete cycle, and does not specify the actual value of the recurrence period. In general, it is desired to make all the interpulse intervals equal, so the angle between rotating electrodes is constant and equal to $2\pi/N_r$ for the usual case of one fixed electrode. The radius of the circle of rotating electrodes is determined by considerations of electrode velocity necessary to minimize the time jitter and to prevent the restriking of the spark between electrodes during the charging period. It has been found that satisfactory operation can generally be maintained if the distance in inches between consecutive electrodes is greater than one tenth the maximum network voltage expressed in kv. A factor of between one sixth and one eighth is commonly used to provide a desirable factor of safety.

Finally, the length and overlap of the electrodes should be considered. Although no general rules can be given, a few facts can be used as a guide. The overlap should be large enough to allow a reasonable sparking area in order to prevent the gap geometry from being changed very rapidly by the wearing away of the electrodes; on the other hand, it has been found that the time jitter increases if the overlap becomes excessive. The total length of the electrodes protruding from the rotor or the stator bushing must be sufficient to produce as little field distortion as practicable at the ends of the cylindrical electrodes. The values which have been used in the rotary gaps designed at the Radiation Laboratory are given in Table 8·1, and can be used as a guide in the design of gaps of similar specifications.

From considerations of electrode wear, the rotating electrodes are usually made the cathode of the gap. With the pulser circuits most commonly used, it is therefore sufficient to ground the rotor to complete the pulser discharging circuit. Possibly the simplest way of accomplishing this grounding is to use a solid metal rotor and let the bearings carry the current; however, because of the local sparking and electrolysis action which takes place, the life of the bearings is considerably reduced if current is allowed to pass through them. Consequently, all rotors should be built with an insulating disk between the shaft and the sparking electrodes. The pulse current can then be collected either by brushes, which are satisfactory for low voltages and low power, or by a sparking segment that is located very near the rotor.

8·2. Considerations of Mechanical Design.—The speed of rotation, the rotor diameter, the minimum electrode spacing, the number of electrodes, and their size and shape can be determined by considerations of electrical design. There still remains to be determined the rotor size, the motor power, the gap housing, and methods of mounting the electrodes. Actually, both mechanical and electrical design have to be carried out simultaneously, at least up to a certain point. For example, the rotor speed may have to be determined by the motor speeds available, and the number of electrodes adjusted to obtain the required recurrence frequency.

Size of Rotor.—The rotor disk must run true on the motor shaft, must be free from wobble, and must have a thickness sufficient to insure rigidity and to permit machining. Nickel-plated brass is commonly used as the rotor material, and the thickness varies from $\frac{1}{4}$ to $\frac{3}{8}$ in. The holes for mounting the tungsten pins used as electrodes are either bored or ground and tapered to insure an accurate fit. In order to obtain smooth satisfactory operation of a rotary gap, it is important to maintain the positions of the rotary electrodes within the specified maximum tolerances. A precision index head must be used for this purpose.

The importance of machining tolerances can readily be understood from the following discussion. Let

$$L = \frac{2\pi r}{N_r}$$

be the average peripheral spacing between rotary electrodes, and assume that $N_f = 1$. If one of the rotary electrodes is displaced by an amount ΔL along the circumference from the position it should occupy, so that the distance to adjacent pins is $(L \pm \Delta L)$ respectively, the corresponding interpulse intervals are given by

$$T_r - \Delta T_r = \frac{T_r}{L}(L - \Delta L)$$

and

$$T_r + \Delta T_r = \frac{T_r}{L}(L + \Delta L),$$

if the effects of time lag in breakdown discussed in Sec. 8·1 are neglected. It is thus seen that, for a displacement ΔL in one electrode, the expected time jitter produced by mechanical inaccuracy is given by

$$\Delta T_r = \pm T_r \frac{\Delta L}{L}.$$

If a tolerance of l is imposed on the peripheral location of the electrodes, the minimum and maximum spacings between consecutive electrodes may vary from $(L - 2l)$ to $(L + 2l)$ and the maximum time jitter that may be expected from this cause alone is

$$\Delta T_r = +T_r \frac{2l}{L}.$$

Errors in the radial position of the electrodes have a similar effect, as can readily be understood from Fig. 8·1. If, for $V_N = 10$ kv, the minimum distance a is increased from 0.05 to 0.1 cm (about 0.02 to 0.04 in., or a radial displacement of 0.02 in.), and the breakdown of the gap is assumed to take place without time lag for an average field of 40 kv/cm, the distance s at which breakdown takes place is decreased from 0.40 to 0.33 cm. Hence, the effect on time jitter is the same as if the spacing between consecutive rotary electrodes varied by 0.07 cm. This particular case must be considered as an exception, in that the radial tolerance in position leads, in general, to less time jitter than an equal peripheral tolerance, and not to more as indicated by this example.

The tolerances at the sparking point, which is usually near the tip of the electrode and not at the rotor disk, are the values to be controlled. Experience at the Radiation Laboratory indicates that, for most satisfactory operation, these tolerances should not exceed 0.005 in. for peripheral and 0.003 in. for radial alignment at that point.   Assuming that the electrodes are 1 in. long and perfectly spaced on the rotor, they have to be aligned with a deviation of less than 10 min of arc in order to satisfy the tolerance requirements.

The results of tests on a 7-pin rotary gap with an outside diameter of 5.5 in. and rotating at 3450 rpm indicate the effect of machining inaccuracy on time jitter.   The average peripheral spacing was about 2 in., and the measured radial tolerance was ± 0.002 in.   For a maximum measured variation in peripheral spacing of 0.036 in., the maximum theoretical time jitter from this cause alone would be 45 μsec, and the observed time jitter was approximately 50 μsec.   When the variation in peripheral spacing was reduced to 0.010 in., the observed time jitter was reduced to approximately 25 μsec; a value of 13 μsec would be expected from the error in spacing alone.   The figures for observed time jitter were obtained under conditions of network voltage corresponding to a minimum jitter.

Motor and Housing.—In all practical gaps designed at the Radiation Laboratory, the rotor is mounted directly on the shaft of the driving motor; hence, the speed of the motor is easily determined.   As has been mentioned previously, a compromise usually has to be reached between the number of electrodes and the speed of rotation.   One of the factors limiting this speed is the life of the bearings: very fast motors normally tend to develop play in the bearings, which adds to the tolerances of the gap and may render it inoperative in a very short time.

Once the motor speed is determined, its power can be obtained by considerations of rotor inertia, which determines the required starting torque, and its windage and friction losses, which determine the running torque.   Because of the required rigidity, the shaft and bearings have to be chosen as large as is practicable for the motor size required.   In Table 8·1 the pertinent motor data for a large number of rotary gaps are listed, which can be used as a guide in design.   All rotary gaps have been enclosed in a metal housing.   The main purpose of the housing is to allow for self-ventilation of the gap and to prevent the corrosive vapors formed by the spark from escaping into the cabinet containing the pulser components.   The nitric acid, which can be formed by combination of these vapors and water vapor in the air, must not be allowed to condense on any vital part of the pulser.   By enclosing the gap in a housing it is also possible to reduce noise, to protect against accidental electrode breakage, and to reduce the windage losses with a corresponding saving in motor size.

Housings have been made of pressed steel, cast iron, or cast aluminum. The cast housings are usually preferred for the higher powers, and are used almost exclusively for gaps in a-c charging pulsers. In this case, the housing is required to perform the additional function of phasing the gap breakdown with the applied-voltage wave shape. This phasing is usually accomplished by rotating with respect to the frame of the motor the part of the housing that carries the high-voltage fixed electrode. Any number of screw and gear arrangements can be used to achieve this purpose, and the housing has to be machined in order to permit some rotation, the amount of which depends on the number of rotary electrodes. In some cases, the phasing adjustment is motor-driven in order to permit remote control.

The self-ventilation of the rotor and pins is usually sufficient to provide an air circulation of 1 or 2 ft^3/min, which is adequate for the cooling of the gap and removal of the corrosive vapors. The air inlet and the exhaust port leading to the outside air through pipes are usually equipped with sound absorbing mufflers or silencers, and also with Davy screens if explosive gases or vapors are likely to accumulate in the neighborhood of the gap.

Types of Rotary Gaps.—Of all the possible gap configurations, several have been used extensively and have proved the most satisfactory. In all of these gaps, the electrodes were tungsten rods, so the types of gaps are classified by their geometry.

Figure 8·5a shows a perspective view of the parallel-pin rotary gap with sparking sector. A gap of this type was used extensively for a pulse-power range of 500 to 3000 kw. The clearance between the rim of the rotor disk and the sparking sector is usually from 0.010 to 0.050 in., corresponding to a static-breakdown voltage between 1 and 5 kv, approximately. Hence, little time delay occurs once the gap between the pins has broken down, and most of the network voltage appears between the pins until this gap is broken down, since capacitance between them is very much smaller than that between the rim and ground. An important advantage of the parallel-pin gap is that its operation is relatively independent of the exact amount of electrode overlap, which in turn means that close end-play tolerances are not required of the motor driving shaft.

Figure 8·5b shows a variation of the preceding design called the parallel-pin double gap. In this case, the rotor must be insulated for the full network voltage, and not just for the breakdown voltage of the sparking sector. The rotary pins extend on either side of the insulating rotor, and spark to two fixed pins. A gap of this type is especially useful

when using a Marx-circuit pulser (see Sec. 11·8) because, by using as
many pairs of fixed pins as there are stages in the Marx circuit, the need
for more than one rotor is avoided.   It is well suited for use in high-
voltage circuits.

The radial-pin gap is commonly used for handling high powers.   The
fixed pin normally wears away rapidly, but it can be set at an angle as

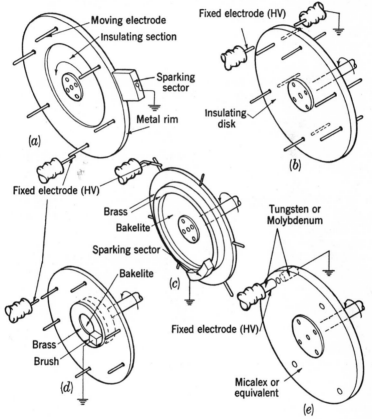

FIG. 8·5.—Types of rotary gaps.   (*a*) Parallel-pin gap with a sparking sector.   (*b*)
Parallel-pin gap, double gap with an insulating rotor.   (*c*) Radial-pin gap with a sparking
sector.   (*d*) Opposing-pin gap with a grounding brush.   (*e*) Gap with holes in insulating
disk.

indicated in Fig. 8·5c in order to maintain very nearly constant gap
geometry despite the erosion.   For powers in excess of 3 Mw, the minimum gap spacing can be made greater than 0.05 in.   As a result, the
motor end play need not be kept to unusually small values; however, it is
clear that, at small minimum spacings, the shaft end play must be very
accurately controlled.   A gap of this type has been successfully used in a

10-Mw a-c charging pulser in which the gap current exceeds 1000 amp. It was conservatively estimated that the fixed electrode would not need replacement in less than 1000 hours.

Figure 8·5d shows the opposing-pin gap, which was used in early experimental sets. This gap was unsuitable for long service because of the rapid change in geometry with erosion. Except for very low powers, the grounding brush has also been abandoned because of the rapid deterioration of the brush and slip-ring surface.

Many other types of gaps have been tried, including the "paddle wheel," adopted directly from the old radio transmitters. Two others

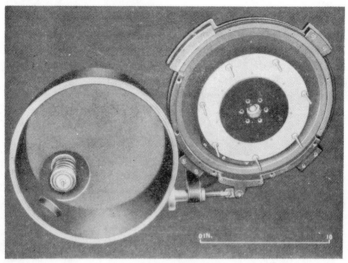

Fig. 8·6.—Photograph of a parallel-pin rotary gap.

deserve brief mention. Attempts at improvement of the types of gaps described above were made by introducing one or more corona points, in order to supply a larger initial ionization. In practice, it was found that the corona point improved the gap performance only over a very narrow range of voltages near the lowest operating point of the gap, and was ineffective or even had an adverse effect at higher voltages. As a result, the corona points were not used, except in a few gaps designed to operate below 6 kv.

A gap in which both electrodes are stationary, and where breakdown is obtained by varying the dielectric constant and dielectric strength of the gap space, has also been built and operated satisfactorily. This variation was accomplished in one case by the method sketched in Fig. 8·5e, which shows a micalex disk rotating between two fixed massive electrodes. A series of holes drilled in the micalex causes the gap characteristics to change as the holes pass between the electrodes, in such a way that a spark takes place at that time.   The life of a gap of this type is limited by the eventual deterioration of the insulating disk, which is eaten away by the sparks.   Since this gap has no particular advantage over those of Fig. 8·5a, b, or c, it has not been used in radar pulsers. Photographs of rotary gaps of the parallel-pin and radial-pin types are shown in Figs. 8·6 and 8·7 respectively.

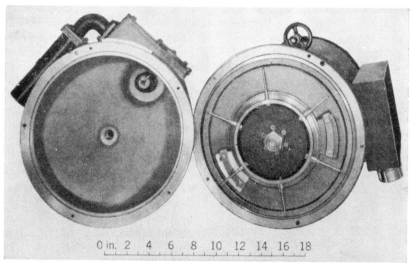

FIG. 8·7.—Photograph of a radial-pin rotary gap.

8·3. Rotary-gap Performance.—Little experimental data has been obtained for rotary gaps, and it is accordingly difficult to present a scientifically satisfying explanation of gap performance.   Probably this dearth of extensive investigation had two causes: (1) the gaps that were built worked satisfactorily, even though their operation was not completely understood, and (2) the time jitter inherent in the gaps makes their study difficult and unrewarding.   Nevertheless, the results presented in this section are believed to be, on the whole, representative of rotary-gap performance.

Gap Efficiency.—Considering the general characteristics of a spark, the gap efficiency may be expected to be high, and general experience has indicated that such is the case.   Measurements carried out by the Bell Telephone Laboratories for one gap corroborate this conclusion.   The test was made by calorimetric methods on a gap operating at 7 kv, 70 amp, and discharging a 50-ohm network into a 50-ohm load; the pulse duration was 0.75 μsec and the recurrence frequency 1600 pps.   Under these conditions, the average power input to the load was about 300 watts, and the power loss about 12 watts, resulting in a gap efficiency of approximately 96 per cent.   The gap efficiency may be expected to be higher at larger currents and longer pulse durations.   The driving power of the gap, of course, is not included in the efficiency figure quoted above, and must be considered in order to obtain the over-all pulser efficiency.

Time and Amplitude Fluctuation of the Pulses.—As has been pointed out before, the minimum spacing between electrodes is normally adjusted so that the gap is overvolted by a factor of 2 to 10 at the point of closest approach.   As a result, the spark always takes place before the closest

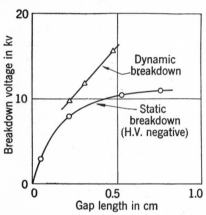

FIG. 8·8.—Breakdown characteristics of the rotary gap used in a 1-Mw pulser.

approach is realized, and the uncertainty in the time of breakdown produces time jitter.   In order to reduce time jitter to a minimum, as explained in Sec. 8·1, it is desirable to have the steepest part of the average field-spacing characteristic (Fig. 8·1) occur at those fields at which breakdown is most likely to occur, or at about 40 kv/cm. (see Fig. 8·8).   If sufficient ionization is available, usually as a result of preceding sparks, the time jitter of the gap can be held to less then 10 μsec.   This figure depends on the relative velocity of the electrodes, and decreases as the velocity increases; it does not take into account the time jitter produced by mechanical inaccuracies, as discussed in Sec. 8·2.

Amplitude jitter, or fluctuation, of pulses produced by a rotary-gap pulser proved, in general, to be of secondary importance as long as a-c or d-c resonant charging was used.   The reason is obvious from a consideration of the shape of the charging wave near the discharge point. For d-c resonant charging, the network voltage, neglecting losses, is given by

$$v_N = E_{bb}(1 - \cos \omega_r t),$$

so that, for $t = T_r$,

$$V_N = 2E_{bb}$$

and, for $t = T_r - \Delta T_r$,

$$v_N = 2E_{bb} \cos (\omega_r \Delta T_r).$$

If $\Delta T_r = 0.05T_r$,

$$v_N = 2E_{bb} \cos \frac{\pi}{20} = 1.975E_{bb}.$$

If $\Delta T_r = 0.02 T_r$,

$$v_N = 2E_{bb} \cos \frac{\pi}{100} \approx 2E_{bb}\left(1 - \frac{\pi^2}{20000}\right) \approx 2E_{bb}(1 - 0.0005).$$

In other words, a time jitter equal to 5 per cent of the recurrence period results in an amplitude variation in network voltage of about 1.2 per cent. The resultant variation in pulse power is less than 2.5 per cent. For a 2 per cent time jitter, the pulse-power variation is only 0.1 per cent. Since the time jitter is nearly always less than 2 per cent of the recurrence period, the pulse-amplitude jitter can usually be neglected.

The performance of the rotary gap for a-c resonant charging is somewhat different from that for d-c resonant charging. A complete theoretical analysis of the difference has not been made. However, a partial analysis indicates that, with d-c resonant charging, the operation of the rotary gap tends to be slightly unstable. If the gap breaks down prematurely on one spark, there is a residual current left in the charging reactor which causes the subsequent voltage wave to rise to a slightly higher peak value at a somewhat earlier time. The next succeeding spark thus tends to occur still earlier. This effect may be cumulative over several cycles, and the spark thus tends to fluctuate in a statistical way about some mean time interval determined by the electrode spacing.

With a-c resonant charging, on the other hand, the rotary-gap operation appears to be stable. In this case, if the gap breaks down prematurely, the subsequent voltage wave rises to a slightly higher peak, but at a somewhat later time. Thus the gap voltage at a time T_r after a premature spark is not appreciably affected. There is therefore no tendency for the gap to break down still earlier, as in the case of d-c resonant charging, but rather there is a tendency to prevent the gap from breaking down prematurely. Thus slight variations in the breakdown time are not magnified by the charging circuit, and the operation tends to be stable with respect to such variations. It should be pointed out, however, that a rotary-spark-gap pulser using a-c charging requires a careful selection of the effective charging inductance and careful adjustment of the gap phasing before the best stability can be obtained.

If d-c linear charging is used, the amplitude fluctuation in the network voltage is almost directly proportional to the time jitter, and the percentage variation in pulse power is twice the ratio of the time jitter to the recurrence period. There is, in addition, some danger of the gap restriking at the beginning of the charging period because of the rapid increase in the voltage across the electrodes, which are still approaching each other. As a result, the rotary spark gap is unsuitable for use with pulsers having d-c linear charging.

Breakdown Voltages and Fields of Rotary Gaps.—The average field at

TABLE 8·1.—DESIGN DATA

Type of charging	D-c resonant charging					D-c charging		
Electrical ratings Voltage range, kv	7–16	5–>9	12–22	12–22	5–>9	8–13	12–25	12–24
Peak current, amp	160	>90	220	220	>90	130	250	480
Normal operating voltage, kv	12	8	≈18	≈18	8	13	25	20
Normal operating current, amp	120	80	180	180	80	130	250	400
Normal average current, ma	45	100	130	130	70	70	92	140
Pulse recurrence frequency, pps	410	825	800	800	750; 375	580	410	350
Pulse duration, μsec	0.9	1.5	0.9	0.9	$1\frac{1}{8}$; $2\frac{1}{4}$	0.9	0.9	1.0
Pulse power, kw	600	360	1500	1500	300	700	3000	4000
Pins No. of fixed pins	1	1	2	2	2;1	1	1	1
No. of rotary pins.........	7	14	10	14	4	10	7	6
Dia. of fixed pins, in.	0.100	0.188	0.125	0.150	0.125	0.120	0.150	0.150
Dia. of rotary pins, in.	0.100	0.125	0.100	0.100	0.125	0.120	0.120	0.120
Dia. of rotary-point circle, in.	4.5	9	10	14	6	7	7.5	9.6
Pin length, in.	$\frac{7}{8}$	$\frac{11}{16}$, $\frac{13}{16}$	$1\frac{1}{8}$	$1\frac{1}{8}$	$\frac{5}{8}$	$1\frac{1}{8}$	$1\frac{15}{16}$	$1\frac{15}{16}$
Minimum spacing, in	0.015	0.028	0.020	0.020	0.010	0.015	$\frac{1}{8}$	$\frac{1}{8}$
Overlap, in.	$\frac{1}{4}$	$\frac{5}{16}$	$\frac{1}{2}$	$\frac{1}{2}$	$\frac{1}{4}$	$\frac{1}{2}$	$\frac{3}{16}$	$\frac{1}{4}$
Motor Type	ind.	ind.	d-c	d-c	ind.	ind.	ind.	ind.
Driving power, H.P.	$\frac{1}{15}$	$\frac{1}{20}$	$\frac{1}{4}$	$\frac{1}{4}$	$\frac{1}{25}$	$\frac{1}{20}$	4*	5*
Motor speed, rpm	3500	3535	4800	3400	5600	3450	3450	3500

* Drives the main pulse generator as well as the rotary gap.   ind. = induction motor

for Rotary Spark Gaps

A-c resonant charging							Half-cycle, a-c resonant charging	A-c diode charging	Blum-lein
12–24	15–27	12–20	7–12	7–12	12–25	8–12	12–25		15–27
240	1170	200	120	120	250	120	250		1000
20	24	18	11	11	25	12	22	8.5	26
200	1000	180	110	110	250	120	220	65	1000
130	350	100	80	40	90	45	130	30	350
650	350	630	800	400	400	400	120	420	350
1.0	1.0	0.9	0.9	0.9	0.9	0.9	5.0	1.0	1.0
2000	10,000	1600	600	600	3000	600	2300	200	10,000
1	1	1	1	1	1	1	4	1	1
11	6	11	14	7	7	6	4	7	6
0.120	0.2	0.120	0.080	0.080	0.120	0.100	3–0.080 1–0.120	0.060	0.2
0.120	0.2	0.120	0.080	0.080	0.120	0.080	0.120	0.060	0.2
9.6	$12\frac{1}{4}$	9.6	5.5	5.5	7.5	4	9.6	4	$12\frac{1}{4}$
$1\frac{15}{16}$	$1\frac{15}{16}$	$1\frac{15}{16}$	$1\frac{1}{8}$	$1\frac{1}{8}$	$1\frac{15}{16}$	1	$1\frac{15}{16}$	$\frac{7}{8}$	$1\frac{15}{16}$
$\frac{1}{8}$	$\frac{1}{8}$	$\frac{1}{8}$	$\frac{1}{32}$	$\frac{1}{32}$	$\frac{1}{8}$	$\frac{1}{16}$	$\frac{1}{32}$	0.015	$\frac{1}{8}$
$\frac{1}{4}$	1	$\frac{1}{4}$	$\frac{1}{4}$	$\frac{1}{4}$	$\frac{3}{16}$	$\frac{1}{4}$	$\frac{1}{4}$	$\frac{9}{16}$	1
ind.	ind.	ind.	M-G	M-G	M-G	2-cycle gas engine	syn.	M-G	ind.
4*	12*	4*				5*	$\frac{1}{4}$		12*
3500	3500	3400	3450	3450	3450	4000	1800	3600	3500

syn. = synchronous motor   M-G = motor-generator

breakdown of a rotary gap can be measured with good accuracy by measuring the spark length with a cathetometer and the voltage with a divider.   The static characteristic corresponds to measurements obtained when the gap is stationary, and the dynamic characteristic is the breakdown voltage measured while the gap is rotating.   Figure 8·8 gives the observed breakdown voltage and computed average fields for the rotary gap used in a 1-Mw pulser, the electrode diameter of which is 0.120 in. The average field at breakdown is observed to be considerably higher for the rotating than for the stationary gap, particularly at the longer spacings.   This fact is presumably due to the presence of corona in the static case.   When the electrodes are moving relative to one another, the corona does not have time to form in the rapidly diminishing gap spacing before breakdown occurs.

Considering a spacing of 0.3 cm, the average voltage gradient before dynamic breakdown is about 40 kv/cm, and the static average gradient is 30 kv/cm.   The gradient at the electrodes can be calculated by the relation[1]

$$g_{max} = \frac{V}{2r \sqrt{\dfrac{(S/2r) - 1}{(S/2r) + 1}} \times \ln \left[\dfrac{S}{2r} + \sqrt{\left(\dfrac{S}{2r}\right)^2 - 1} \right]}$$

from which the maximum gradient for dynamic breakdown is found to be 52 kv/cm, and that for static breakdown to be about 40 kv/cm.   Since the electron multiplication varies exponentially with the Townsend coefficient α and the distance, and since α increases very rapidly in the high fields corresponding to the dynamic breakdown, the electron current builds up very rapidly once the breakdown has started.   The time for this buildup is estimated at 0.01 μsec from other data.

In general, the ratio of the maximum to the minimum operating voltages for satisfactory operation of rotary gaps is about two.   The minimum voltage is limited by the failure of the gap to break down consistently at the minimum electrode spacing, and the maximum voltage is usually determined by the restriking of the spark as explained in Sec. 8·1.   Table 8·1 gives the pertinent data referring to most rotary gaps designed and built either for service in radar systems or for laboratory testing of pulser components or magnetrons.

ENCLOSED FIXED SPARK GAPS

By J. R. Dillinger

When two or three fixed two-electrode gaps are connected in series, the breakdown of the entire switch can be accomplished rapidly by the

---

[1] F. W. Peek Jr, *Dielectric Phenomena in High-voltage Engineering*, 3rd ed., McGraw-Hill, New York, 1929, p. 25.

successive breakdown of the individual gaps. This breakdown is obtained by applying a very high trigger voltage to one or both junction points. Since enclosed fixed spark gaps of this type have been used more frequently in this country than those of any other type, most of the following discussion is concerned with them. The trigatron and a three-electrode gap of one other type, in which breakdown is obtained by suddenly distorting the electric field between the main electrodes by applying a high voltage to a trigger electrode, are discussed briefly in Sec. 8·10.

Two series-gap designs have been evolved. One has a cylindrical-rod anode surrounded by a hollow cylindrical cathode,[1] and the other has a rod anode mounted above a mercury cathode,[2] (the mercury is immobilized by a metallic sponge, and the mercury surface is continuously renewed through capillary action.) The basic features of the cylindrical-electrode gap and of the metallic-sponge mercury-cathode gap are given in Sec. 8·8 and 8·9 respectively. The cylindrical-electrode gap is the result of early efforts[3] to find a switch that would operate at lower voltages and have a smaller time jitter than the rotary gap, and that, in addition, would be completely enclosed. Later work showed that a gap of this type could be used over a wide range of operating conditions. The metallic-sponge mercury-cathode gap is not limited by cathode erosion and therefore operates satisfactorily at higher powers and longer pulse durations. The time jitter in gaps of this type has been reduced to 0.02 μsec.

As a result of work done at the Bell Telephone Laboratories, the Westinghouse Electric Corporation, and the Radiation Laboratory, series gaps have been developed that have an operating-voltage range such that the maximum operating voltage is slightly greater than twice the minimum operating voltage. These gaps operate successfully at voltages up to 30 kv, pulse currents up to 900 amp, and pulse durations from 0.25 to 5 μsec. At the longer pulse durations, the maximum allowable pulse current is smaller. The maximum voltage at which a given switch operates is smaller for the higher recurrence frequencies, and the time jitter increases as the recurrence frequency is increased. Increased dissipation and electrode wear make the operation of these gaps

---

[1] F. S. Goucher, S. B. Ingram, J. R. Haynes, and W. A. Depp, "Glass Enclosed Triggered Spark Gaps for Use in High Power Pulse Modulators," BTL Report MM-43-110-3, Feb. 26, 1943.

F. S. Goucher (Bell Telephone Laboratories), "Development of Enclosed Triggered Gaps," *Modulator Colloquium*, RL Report No. 50-2, June 9, 1943, pp. 1–15.

[2] J. R. Haynes, "Some Experiments with Mercury Cathode Series Spark Gap Tubes," BTL Report MM-45-110-20, Mar. 3, 1945.

[3] S. B. Ingram (Bell Telephone Laboratories), "Application of Fixed Spark Gap Tubes," *Modulator Colloquium*, RL Report No. 50-2, June 9, 1943, pp. 16–24.

at recurrence frequencies above 1000 pps impractical for very high power output.

8·4. General Operating Characteristics of Series Gaps.—Two or three gaps connected in series, as shown in Fig. 8·9, constitute the switch in a line-type pulser. It is therefore necessary to consider the characteristics of a set of two or three gaps in series as well as those of a single gap.

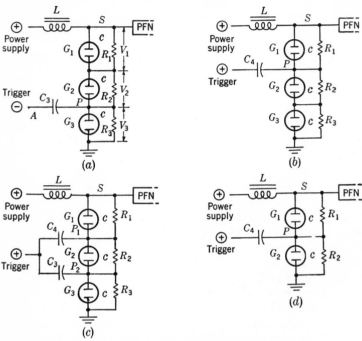

Fig. 8·9.—Four commonly used series-gap circuits.

Static- and Dynamic-breakdown Voltages of a Single Gap.—The static-breakdown voltage of a gap is defined as the voltage at which the gap sparks when the d-c voltage across it is slowly increased. This voltage can be used as an indication of the general hold-off characteristics of a single gap, but its value is not very reproducible, particularly after the gaps have been operated for a few hours. However, it is more nearly reproducible for mercury-cathode gaps than for aluminum-cathode gaps because the surface-discharge characteristics are more nearly constant for a liquid cathode.

The dynamic-breakdown voltage is defined as the voltage at which the gap breaks down for given conditions of residual ionization. Immediately after a pulse of current passes through a single gap, many ions are left in the gap. These ions recombine rapidly, but some residual ionization still remains $1/f_r$ seconds after the pulse, where f_r is the pulse recurrence frequency. The dynamic-breakdown voltage therefore varies with the conditions of residual ionization, and thus with the recurrence frequency, the pulse duration, and the pulse current.

Definitions of V_{max}, V_{min}, *and* V_{start}.—These three quantities are the characteristic breakdown voltages of the switch as contrasted with those of a single gap. In the following discussion, it is assumed that a voltage of the form

$$v_N(t) = \frac{V_N}{2} (1 - \cos \pi f_r t)$$

is applied to point S in the circuits shown in Fig. 8·9, where $v_N(t)$ is the voltage at any time t, and V_N is the maximum value of this resonant-charging transient. For charging waves of other forms, the definitions of the characteristic breakdown voltages are the same, but the actual values may be different. For example, V_{max} is slightly higher for linear charging than for resonant charging. It is also assumed in this discussion that a trigger pulse of the proper shape, and of amplitude sufficient to render the gaps conducting at intervals of $1/f_r$ when $v_N(1/f_r) = V_N$, is applied to the points P.

If the maximum value, V_N, of the d-c resonant-charging transient applied to a given gap switch is slowly increased, a value is reached at which the switch breaks down before the trigger pulse is applied. This premature breakdown is called a "pre-fire." When a pre-fire occurs, the trigger loses control, and continuous conduction may set in, making it impossible to regain control. The maximum value of V_N at which the rate of pre-firing is still negligible, for a given switch and operating conditions, is defined as V_{max}. If the voltage-dividing resistors, the trigger-coupling condensers, and the recurrence frequency are such that the voltage is divided equally across the gaps at all times, V_{max} has the highest value that is theoretically possible, and is then called V_S. Since equal division of voltage is not obtained in practice, the observed value of V_{max} is always less than V_S. This observed value is referred to as V_M, and can be determined by observing the charging waves on an oscilloscope as the voltage is increased to a value just below that which is sufficient to cause pre-firing. The value of V_S can be determined from curves showing the variation in the ratio V_M/V_S with circuit conditions and recurrence frequency.

Ideally, for a given switch and operating conditions, V_S is equal to the number of gaps in the switch multiplied by the dynamic-breakdown voltage of a single gap. Since this voltage fluctuates during the life of the gap in a random manner, it is extremely difficult to relate V_S to any breakdown-voltage measurement for a single gap. This fluctuation is very noticeable for aluminum-cathode gaps operated at powers so high that their anodes become rough. In practice, the dynamic-breakdown voltage of a single gap is defined as V_S divided by the number of gaps.

As the residual ionization is increased beyond some minimum value, V_S decreases. The variation of V_S with recurrence frequency and pulse duration is shown in the curves of Fig. 8·10. In order to obtain the data

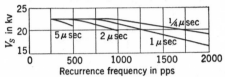

FIG. 8·10.—V_S as a function of recurrence frequency.

for these curves, three WX3226 gaps filled to a total pressure of 110 cm of mercury with a mixture of 80 per cent hydrogen and 20 per cent argon were operated as the switch in a pulser having a 50-ohm network and a 50-ohm resistance load. The variations in pulse current corresponding to changes in switch voltage, of magnitude represented by these curves, have a negligible effect on the value of V_S determined from other data taken at different pulse currents with τ and f_r constant.

If the maximum value, V_N, of the resonant-charging voltage is slowly reduced, a value is found at which the switch fails to fire (misfires) when the trigger pulse is applied. The lowest value of V_N at which the rate of misfiring is negligible is defined as V_{min}, and can be determined by observing the charging waves on an oscilloscope as the voltage is reduced until the switch is seen to miss. As the residual ionization is increased, V_{min} decreases by an amount that is small compared with the decrease in V_S.

If the power-supply voltage is increased slowly from zero, the switch voltage is equal to the power-supply voltage and is divided equally across the gaps. As the power-supply voltage is increased, a value can be found at which the switch either starts and continues to operate, or periodically starts and then stops after firing a few pulses. This power-supply voltage is defined as V_{start}.

Typical Switch Operation.—As an introduction to the problem of triggering, consider briefly the operation of three identical gaps with equal voltage-dividing resistors in the circuit (b) of Fig. 8·9. Assume that the switch voltage is zero at $t = 0$, and that the voltage V_N at the end of each charging cycle is sufficient to break down one gap within a fraction of a microsecond after being applied to it. Then, if the amplitude of the trigger pulse applied to point P is sufficient to cause the breakdown of gaps G_2 and G_3 the full switch voltage is then applied to G_1, causing G_1 to break down, and allowing the network to discharge through the switch and the load.

The process just described occurs repeatedly, and the pulser circuit delivers a pulse to the load corresponding to each trigger pulse. Assuming that the trigger circuit does not drive point P negative after the breakdown of G_2 and G_3, V_{min} should be the dynamic-breakdown voltage of a single gap. Under idealized conditions the ratio of V_S to V_{min} for three gaps in this circuit is 3/1, but, because the breakdown characteristics of gaseous-discharge devices near their upper and lower limits are statistical in nature, ratios of 2/1 to 2.5/1 are obtained. This ratio decreases during the life of cylindrical-electrode gaps operated under conditions sufficient to cause considerable anode roughening. Time jitter in the operation of this switch is caused principally by the uncertainty in the firing of gap G_1, which can not be overvolted by the trigger as can G_2 and G_3. This time jitter is small for operating voltages near V_S, but increases as V_N approaches V_{min}.

The above account of steady-state operation does not explain the starting of the gap when the pulse-generator voltages are first turned on. When the power supply is first switched on (neglecting any advantage that may result from a sudden rise in supply voltage), the network becomes charged to the no-load power-supply voltage E_{bb}, and the voltage at P becomes $\frac{2}{3}E_{bb}$. Although, under these conditions, gaps G_2 and G_3 may not be broken down by every trigger pulse, it is assumed that E_{bb} is such that they are broken down occasionally. On one of the occasions when G_2 and G_3 are broken down, E_{bb} is also assumed to be sufficient to break down G_1, and the circuit goes into steady-state operation. The minimum value of E_{bb} for which starting takes place has been defined as V_{start}, the value of which is frequently greater than the no-load power-supply voltage that corresponds to operation at V_{min}. The lowest satisfactory operating voltage of such a switch may then be limited by the starting-voltage requirements. This difficulty may be eliminated, however, by the use of a power supply with sufficiently poor regulation.

The way in which V_{min} and V_{start} depend on the trigger voltage is shown in Fig. 8·11. These data were obtained by operating the three WX3226 gaps mentioned above at a recurrence frequency of 800 pps and a pulse duration of 0.9 μsec in circuit (a) of Fig. 8·9. From Fig. 8·11 it can be seen that V_S is unaffected by the trigger voltage as expected, and

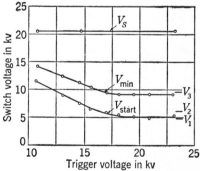

Fig. 8·11.—Operating range as a function of trigger voltage.

that both V_{min} and V_{start} increase as the trigger voltage is decreased below some minimum value. In order to determine whether satisfactory operation can be obtained over the entire range, it is necessary to consider the voltages V', V'', and V''', where V' is V_{min} divided by the resonant-charging stepup ratio (assumed to be 1.9 in this case), V'' is V' times the ratio of no-load to operating-load power-supply voltage (assumed to be 1.25), and V''' is V_{start} multiplied by 1.9. As long as V'' is greater than V_{start}, the gaps should start with the power supply adjusted for operation at V_{min}. Operation at voltages less than V''' may be objectionable because the operation at a switch voltage V''' during the starting of the gaps may produce an undesired overvolting of other components in the circuit. If V'' is less than V_{start}, the lowest switch voltage at which operation is satisfactory from the standpoint of starting is greater than V_{min}, and equal to $V_{start} \times 1.9/1.25$. If $V_{start} \times 1.9$ is greater than V_M, the switch pre-fires immediately after starting.

Range Versus Number of Gaps.—Several factors need to be considered in determining the optimum number, n_o, of gaps to use in series as the switch for a given application. The most important consideration is that of the range of operating voltage, which is defined as

$$\frac{V_S - V_{min}}{V_S + V_{min}},$$

and is expressed in per cent. The value of n_o that gives the widest possible operating range is determined from the following considerations.

Under identical operating conditions, let the dynamic-breakdown voltages of G_1 and G_2 be V_{1d} and $(n - 1)V_{1d}$ respectively. Thus, G_1 is considered to have a unit breakdown voltage, and n_o is the optimum number of gaps identical to G_1 that could be used in series as the switch. The gap G_2 may be thought of as replacing $(n - 1)$ gaps identical to G_1. These gaps are assumed to be operated in circuit (d) of Fig. 8·9, with power-supply and trigger voltages of the same polarity. If these voltages are of opposite polarity, the following discussion is still valid if G_1 and G_2 are interchanged in the circuit (d). It is assumed that any voltage applied at point S is divided so that the ratio of the voltage across G_2 to that across G_1 is exactly equal to $(n - 1)$, and that a suitable trigger pulse of sufficient amplitude is applied to point P.

In order to simplify the discussion, the following assumptions are made:

1. That the voltage V_S is n times the dynamic breakdown voltage of G_1. The problem of finding n_o thus becomes one of finding the value for n for which V_{min}/V_S is a minimum.
2. That the breakdown voltage of a single gap is independent of the manner in which the voltage is applied to the gap.

3. That the breakdown characteristics of a single gap are the same, regardless of its polarity.

There are two possible conditions for switch cutoff. Condition A occurs when G_1 fails to fire after the breakdown of G_2 because V_N is less than the dynamic-breakdown voltage of G_1. Condition B occurs when the value of n is such that the lowering of V_N changes the voltages on G_1 and G_2 so that the application of the trigger voltage, v_t, to point P breaks down G_1 before G_2, whereupon the voltage across G_2 falls to V_N, which is less than the breakdown voltage of G_2.

When the cutoff occurs according to condition A, V_{min} is given by

$$(V_{min})_A = \frac{V_S}{n} \tag{1}$$

from assumption 1.

The relationship between V_{min} and n under condition B is next derived. As the trigger voltage, v_t, rises toward the value at which breakdown occurs, the voltages across G_1 and G_2 are

$$v_1 = v_t - \frac{1}{n} V_N \tag{2}$$

and

$$v_2 = (n - 1)\left(\frac{1}{n - 1} v_t + \frac{1}{n} V_N\right). \tag{3}$$

For any particular pair of values of n and V_N, there is a trigger-voltage amplitude V_t such that

$$(n - 1)v_1 = v_2, \quad \text{for } v_t = V_t. \tag{4}$$

Substituting Eqs. (2) and (3) into Eq. (4),

$$V_t - \frac{1}{n} V_N = \frac{1}{n - 1} V_t + \frac{1}{n} V_N,$$
$$V_t = \frac{2(n - 1)}{n(n - 2)} V_N.$$

At $v_t = V_t$, the value of v_1 from Eq. (2) is

$$V_1 = \frac{2(n - 1)}{n(n - 2)} V_N - \frac{1}{n} V_N = \frac{1}{n - 2} V_N.$$

Under condition B, V_{min} for a given n is the value of V_N for which V_1 is equal to the dynamic-breakdown voltage of G_1, referred to above as V_S/n. Therefore,

$$(V_{min})_B = (n - 2)\frac{V_S}{n}. \tag{5}$$

For any value of n, V_{min} is equal to either $(V_{min})_A$ or $(V_{min})_B$, whichever is greater. Thus, from Eqs. (1) and (5), V_{min}/V_S is the greater of the two expressions

$$\frac{V_{min}}{V_S} = \frac{1}{n}$$

and

$$\frac{V_{min}}{V_S} = 1 - \frac{2}{n}.$$

Figure 8·12 is a graph showing V_{min}/V_S as a function of n. The lowest value of this ratio occurs when $n = 3$. The value of V_{min} is determined

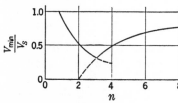

by cutoff condition A for $n \leqq 3$ and by condition B for $n \geqq 3$. The optimum number of gaps is thus $n_o = 3$.

Fig. 8·12.—Ratio of V_{min} to V_S as a function of n.

Conditions A and B are based on the assumption that sufficient trigger voltage is applied to point P. If the trigger voltage is not sufficient to break down G_2, another condition for cutoff arises. The trigger amplitude required can be determined from the data of Fig. 8·11 for a given gap design. In general, it is about twice the value of V_{min} and is therefore slightly greater than the normal operating switch voltage, assuming that the switch is usually operated at a voltage near the center of the range between V_{min} and V_M.

Two- and Three-gap Operation.—When using the cylindrical-aluminum-cathode gaps, it is generally desirable to place three gaps in series in order to obtain the maximum range, particularly at power outputs greater than 1000 kw. However, two-gap operation has proved satisfactory for some low-power applications. In using two, instead of three, gaps with equal breakdown voltages, additional requirements must be imposed on the shape of the trigger pulse in order to insure satisfactory starting. In circuit (d) of Fig. 8·9 it can be seen that the voltage at S for starting is just equal to the power-supply voltage E_{bb}. After the trigger causes G_2 to fire, the voltage E_{bb} is applied across G_1, which must break down if the gaps are to break down on the first pulse. Thus, E_{bb} must be at least as great as the breakdown voltage of one gap. After the first pulse, a voltage of about $1.9\ E_{bb}$ is applied to point S, which is sufficient to break down both gaps before the trigger is applied, since the practical ratio of V_S to V_{min} for two gaps is about 1.6.

Satisfactory starting can be assured by supplying a bidirectional trigger pulse to point P as shown in Fig. 8·13. Suppose the voltage at S is positive and equal to the power-supply voltage E_{bb}, which is assumed to be less than the breakdown voltage G_1.   Gap G_2 is then broken down on the positive part of the trigger in the region A, causing E_{bb} to be applied to G_1.   If t of Fig. 8·13 has approximately the correct value, G_2 deionizes during this time and can therefore hold off some voltage in the reverse direction.   Point P can then be driven to a negative value by region B of the trigger pulse.   The addition of the negative voltage at P to E_{bb} causes G_1 to break down, initiating the pulse.   This behavior can add to the time jitter; for an operating voltage near V_S, the switch is rendered conducting by region A of the trigger; near the middle of the range it is rendered conducting at A on some pulses and at B on others; and just above V_{min} it is rendered conducting only in region B.[1]

The choice among the three possible circuits for three-gap operation shown in Fig. 8·9 depends on several factors.   For given values for equal voltage-dividing resistors, trigger-coupling condensers, and recurrence frequency, inequalities in the voltage division across the three gaps have the least effect on the difference between V_M and V_S for circuit (a).   For three aluminum-cathode gaps, V_{min} and V_{start} are the same for (a) and (b), but are appreciably lower for (c), and for long-time operation at powers above 500 kw the change in V_M is less in circuit (c) than in the other two.   For these reasons, circuit (c) is generally preferred for the operation of aluminum-cathode gaps.   However, other considerations such as the mounting space, the polarity of the most readily available trigger voltage, and the voltage ratings of the coupling condensers may influence the final choice of circuit.

When enclosed fixed spark gaps having mercury cathodes immobilized by means of an iron sponge are used in place of those having aluminum cathodes, both the optimum number of gaps and the best method of coupling the trigger (in three-gap operation) are very different.   This difference is caused by the formation of a corona sheath about the anode, which changes the effective electrode geometry and, within limits, raises the breakdown voltage when the amplitude of the charging wave is increased.   The need for a bidirectional trigger to start the two tubes is therefore eliminated.   Test results show that the range of two of these gaps in series is satisfactory for all conditions at which they have been tested to date (see Sec. 8·9), and is greater than ± 33 per cent at powers up to 10,000 kw for more than 500 hours.   Tests also show that, if three gaps are used, circuit (a) of Fig. 8·9 is preferable to (b) or (c) from the standpoint of range alone because the breakdown characteristics of the individual tubes remain very nearly constant throughout life.   Thus, the reduction in V_M for given values of the voltage-dividing resistors,

[1] For a more complete analysis of gap operation of this type, see J. R. Haynes, "Some Characteristics of 1B22 Spark Gap Tubes," BTL Report MM-43-110-34, Oct· 27, 1943.

trigger-coupling condensers, and recurrence frequency that is occasioned by changing from circuit (*a*) to (*b*) or (*c*) is also constant throughout life. Measurements also show that V_{min} and V_{start} are the same, regardless of which of the above three-gap circuits is used, contrary to the observations made with three aluminum-cathode gaps.

8·5. Trigger Generators.[1]—Amplitude, shape, and energy are the three major characteristics of the trigger-generator output pulse that

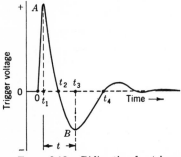

FIG. 8·13.—Bidirectional trigger pulse for satisfactory operation of a two-gap switch.

must be specified. The pulse of Fig. 8·13 is a tracing of the output of a typical condenser-discharge trigger generator. In this discussion, the amplitude of the trigger pulse is considered to be the maximum value of the first swing of the trigger in region *A*. If the operation of two aluminum-cathode gaps is to be considered, the amplitude of *B* and time *t* also have to be specified.

In operating three aluminum-cathode gaps and two or three mercury-cathode gaps, which are the arrangements of greatest interest, the shape of the trigger pulse need not be closely specified. Typical values in Fig. 8·13 are $t_1 = 1.5$, $t_2 = 9$, $t_3 = 17$, and $t_4 = 30$ μsec. For the operation of two mercury-cathode gaps with time jitter of less than 0.02 μsec, it is necessary that the rate of rise of that portion of the pulse between $t = 0$ and $t = t_1$ be at least 35 kv/μsec; 50 kv/μsec is usually taken as a design figure. Rates of rise as low as 15 kv/μsec are satisfactory for operation of three aluminum-cathode gaps: higher values do not have an appreciable effect on time jitter, because the major source of jitter in these gaps is in firing the third tube, over which the trigger has no control.

To date, it has not been necessary to specify the impedance of the trigger generator because the operation of these gaps is not critically dependent on the amount of energy dissipated in the gaps during the trigger discharge. The efficiency of the trigger circuit is usually not very important as the total power consumed by it is, in most cases, small. However, the effect of increasing the load on the trigger from that consisting of the input capacitance to the gaps in series with the coupling condensers to that of the coupling condensers alone when the gaps fire must be taken into account. This effect is of greater importance when the trigger is coupled to both intermediate points than when it is coupled to either the upper or lower point alone.

Trigger circuits for series gaps are designed to generate a voltage of

[1] By A. S. Jerrems.

amplitude as high as 35 kv to be applied to a load equal to the capacitance from point P to ground in any one of the circuits of Fig. 8·9. Since this load is about 12 to 15 $\mu\mu f$, and the trigger circuits are sensitive to loading, some consideration must be given to the viewing system used to measure this voltage.   One procedure is to use a special viewing system with very low input capacitance, and specify the voltage measured as a no-load value.   As a result, the load on the trigger is increased considerably when the output trigger lead is connected to the gaps, with a resulting decrease in trigger output.   Another procedure is to measure the load from P to ground and to use a viewing system with the same input impedance, with the result that the measured voltage is the same as that applied to point P.   This substitution method has been used in making all trigger-voltage measurements quoted in the present discussion.

The following three types of trigger circuits are discussed here:

1. The inductive kicker, in which a transient high-voltage oscillation is obtained by rapidly cutting off the current in an inductance shunted by a condenser.
2. The condenser-discharge circuit, a line-type pulser whose pulse-forming network is replaced by a condenser.
3. The saturable-core-transformer circuit.   This trigger circuit is similar to the condenser-discharge circuit, except that the transformer is saturable, and its secondary is connected in series with one or more gaps.   The secondary has a high impedance during the trigger discharge, but offers a low impedance to the main pulse because the transformer core is saturated by the pulse current.

The Inductive Kicker.—The basic circuit of an inductive kicker is shown in Fig. 8·14a.   The tube is normally cut off, and positive grid

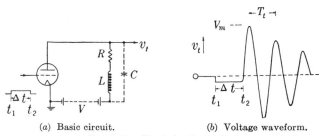

(a) Basic circuit.   (b) Voltage waveform.
Fig. 8·14.—The inductive kicker.

pulses of duration Δt are applied to it at the desired recurrence frequency. During the interval between t_1 and t_2, current builds up in the tube in a nearly linear manner.   At the end of the interval Δt, the tube is suddenly cut off, isolating the resonant circuit connected to its plate, and leaving a current flowing in L.   A transient damped oscillation of the form shown in Fig. 8·14b develops across the load and stray capacitances represented by C.   If the damping and tube drop are neglected, and if it is assumed that there is an instantaneous cutoff of tube current, the output voltage, v_t, is given by

$$v_t = I \sqrt{\frac{L}{C}} \sin \frac{t}{\sqrt{LC}},$$

where I is the current in L at t_2.   In terms of the power-supply voltage, V,

$$v_t = \frac{V(\Delta t)}{\sqrt{LC}} \sin \frac{t}{\sqrt{LC}}. \tag{6}$$

For example, the output of a circuit with $L = 0.5$ mh, $C = 20$ $\mu\mu$f, $V = 500$ volts, and $\Delta t = 1$ μsec, according to Eq. (6), is an oscillation of amplitude

$$V_m = \frac{V(\Delta t)}{\sqrt{LC}} = 5 \text{ kv}$$

and period

$$T_t = 2\pi \sqrt{LC} = 0.6 \text{ } \mu\text{sec.}$$

The approximate values of V_m calculated in this manner are invariably high, because of damping and noninstantaneous tube cutoff.   The capacitance C is made small in order to get maximum output voltage for a

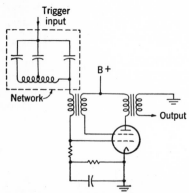

Fig. 8·15.—Simplified diagram of a line-controlled inductive-kicker circuit using screen-grid feedback with pulse-transformer output.

given peak tube current.   The inductance L is chosen for a particular circuit in order to get the desired rate of rise and amplitude of output trigger.   One such trigger circuit, with $L = 5$ mh using a 5D21 as control tube, has been found to be reliable and give values of V_m up to 16 kv on a 15 $\mu\mu$f load at 1000 pps.

The output of a circuit of the form just described is limited to the peak transient voltage that the control tube can hold off.   This limitation can be overcome by making L the primary of a stepup transformer. A circuit using an 807 tube and a stepup autotransformer, with turns ratio $n = 5$, was used successfully by the Bell Telephone Laboratories.

A disadvantage of the inductive kicker described above is the need of an additional circuit to supply the long rectangular input pulse.

A regenerative pulser using feedback from the screen-grid circuit that only requires a synchronizing trigger of indifferent shape and small amplitude has been developed. Because of the limitations on screen-grid current, the maximum available output for a given tube is less than that obtained with externally triggered circuits. Figure 8·15 is a simplified diagram of a line-controlled inductive-kicker circuit using a screen-grid feedback with a pulse-transformer output.

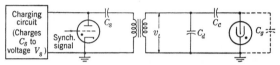

FIG. 8·16.—Typical condenser-discharge trigger circuit.

The Condenser-discharge Trigger Circuit.—The basic circuit of the condenser-discharge trigger, shown in Fig. 8·16, consists of a switch S in series with a storage capacitance C_s and a pulse transformer of stepup ratio n. The storage capacitance C_s is charged through a large resistance or inductance, and then discharged into the pulse-transformer primary when S is closed. The switch S is a thyratron fired at the desired recurrence frequency by a signal from an external synchronizer.

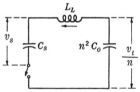

FIG. 8·17.—Equivalent circuit for the condenser-discharge trigger circuit.

The operation of the circuit of Fig. 8·16 can be analyzed with accuracy sufficient for design purposes in terms of the equivalent circuit of Fig. 8·17. If the transformer is assumed to be phase-inverting, and if the voltage v_s on the storage condenser has an initial value V_s and S closes at time $t = 0$, the output voltage is

$$v_t = \frac{nV_sC_s}{C_s + n^2C_o}\left(1 - \cos\frac{t}{\sqrt{L_LC}}\right),$$

in which

$$C_o = C_d + \left(\frac{C_cG_g}{C_c + C_g}\right)$$

and

$$C = \frac{n^2C_sC_o}{C_s + n^2C_o}$$

for the interval from time $t = 0$ to time $t_1 = \pi\sqrt{L_LC}$. The voltage and current waveforms are sketched in Fig. 8·18. The maximum value of the output pulse voltage is

$$V_t = \frac{2nV_sC_s}{C_s + n^2C_o},$$

and the voltage rises to this value in the time interval

$$\Delta t = t_1 - 0 = \pi \sqrt{L_L C}. \qquad (7)$$

For $C_s > n^2 C_o$ there is a positive charge left on C_s at the time t_1, which is then drained off through S. For $C_s = n^2 C_o$, v_s is zero at time t_1. For $C_s < n^2 C_o$ a negative charge is left on C_s, which cannot drain off if S is unidirectional. For a load consisting of a gap of capacitance C_g in series with a coupling condenser C_c, and of distributed capacitance C_d, these waveforms are distorted as a result of the firing of the gap. The effect of gap firing is, to a fair approximation, that of an abrupt change in capacitance C_o from the value above to $C_o = (C_d + C_c)$ after the gap fires.

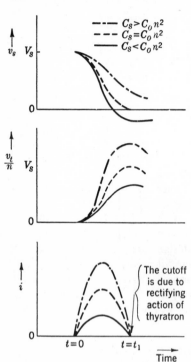

FIG. 8·18.—Voltage and current waveforms in the condenser-discharge trigger circuit.

No detailed procedure can be set down for designing condenser-discharge triggers because the best design for a particular case depends on the specifications for the trigger and on the type of charging used. For example, it may be desirable to use the lowest practical power-supply voltage for the trigger, or it may be necessary to use a power supply already set at a particular level, or limitations in the maximum condenser voltage may be imposed by trigger-switch ratings. Resonant, linear, or resistance charging may be used. In general, there are several parameters to be chosen, and it is possible, within the limits imposed by operating specifications, to maximize the efficiency. An outline of a design for a typical set of requirements is given in the following paragraphs.

A trigger is required that will take its current from the principal pulser power supply at a voltage level E_{bb} and will deliver output pulses of maximum amplitude V_t and frequency $f_r = 1/T_r$ to a total effective capacitance load C_o. It is assumed that the trigger must use a switch tube that does not hold off voltages higher than the power-supply voltage E_{bb}, and it is specified that the trigger pulse must rise to its peak value in a time interval Δt.

Because of the maximum-voltage requirement on the trigger switch, it is necessary to use resistance charging. The equivalent circuit is therefore that shown in Fig. 8·19, where S_1 is the trigger switch tube and S_2 is a hypothetical charging switch. During the interpulse interval, S_1 is open and S_2 is closed, and C_s is charged through R_c and L_L. The effect of L_L on this charging process may be neglected. When the synchronizing signal closes S_1, S_2 may be considered open, and C_s discharges through the circuit consisting of S_1, C_s, L_L, and n^2C_o in series. It is assumed that R_c is so large that it may be neglected

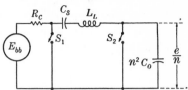

FIG. 8·19.—Equivalent circuit used in the design of a condenser-discharge trigger circuit.

during the discharging period.

Since negative voltage left on C_s at the end of a trigger pulse can only result in additional charging loss without any corresponding increase in output, it is assumed that $C_s \geqq C_o n^2$ (see Fig. 8·18), and consequently that the voltage on C_s at the beginning of each charging cycle is zero. Under this assumption, the charging and discharging equations can be written independently and combined to get the maximum-voltage-output equation

$$V_t = \frac{2C_s n E_{bb}\left(1 - e^{-\frac{1}{f_r R_c C_s}}\right)}{C_s + n^2 C_o}, \tag{8}$$

where V_t, E_{bb}, and f_r are specified, and C_o, n, and R_c are chosen such that this equation is satisfied and maximum efficiency is obtained.

Since the specifications require a particular power-supply voltage E_{bb} and power output $0.5 f_r C_o V_t^2$, the average power-supply current, I, is a reciprocal measure of the over-all efficiency of the trigger circuit. This current can be written in terms of the charging-circuit parameters, that is,

$$I = f_r E_{bb} C_s \left(1 - e^{-\frac{1}{f_r R_c C_s}}\right). \tag{9}$$

Combining Eqs. (8) and (9)

$$I = \frac{(C_s + n^2 C_o) f_r}{2n}\, V_t, \tag{10}$$

in which the variables are C_s and n. Differentiation of Eq. (10) with respect to n reveals that I has a minimum value

$$I_{\min} = f_r V_t \sqrt{C_s C_o} \tag{11}$$

at

$$n = \sqrt{\frac{C_s}{C_o}},$$

that is, for equal capacitances in the equivalent circuit.

Substituting this value for n in Eq. (8), a relation between C_s and R_c is obtained in which I is minimized with respect to n, namely,

$$R_c = -\frac{1}{C_s f_r} \frac{1}{\ln\left(1 - \frac{V_t}{E_{bb}}\sqrt{\frac{C_o}{C_s}}\right)}. \qquad (12)$$

Since $I_{\min}$ is proportional to $\sqrt{C_s}$ (see Eq. 11), it is desired to make C_s as small as possible.   The lowest value of C_s that satisfies Eq. (12) is

$$C_{so} = \frac{V_t^2}{E_{bb}^2} C_o,$$

which corresponds to $R_c = 0$.

The storage capacitance C_s must be chosen so that R_c does not dissipate appreciable power during the trigger-discharging period.   For most radar recurrent frequencies (up to about 5000 pps) it is sufficient to take

$$C_s = 3C_{so} = 3\frac{V_t^2}{E_{bb}^2} C_o. \qquad (13)$$

The charging resistance that should be used with this storage capacitance is

$$R_c = \frac{E_{bb}^2}{2.58 f_r V_t^2 C_o}$$

and the pulse-transformer ratio is

$$n = 1.7 \times \frac{V_t}{E_{bb}}.$$

Referring to Eq. (7), the value of L_L that should be used is

$$L_L = \frac{(\Delta t)^2 E_{bb}^2}{\frac{3\pi^2}{2} V_t^2 C_o}.$$

An expression for power-supply current is obtained by substituting Eq. (13) into Eq. (11), namely,

$$I = 1.732 \frac{V_t^2 C_o f_r}{E_{bb}}.$$

If the output per pulse is taken to be the energy W_o delivered to C_o when it is charged to a level V_t, the efficiency of the trigger circuit is given by

$$\eta = \frac{W_o f_r}{E_{bb} I} = \frac{0.5 C_o V_t^2 f_r (100)}{1.732 \left(\dfrac{V_t^2 C_o f_r}{E_{bb}} \right) E_{bb}} = 29 \text{ per cent.}$$

Consider a particular pulser for which the total effective trigger load C_o is approximately 30 $\mu\mu$f. Suppose that a 500-cycle/sec output trigger voltage rising to an amplitude of 16 kv in 0.5 μsec is required, and that only a 6-kv power supply is available. From the above equations, the values of the parameters are then

$$C_s = 0.0007 \ \mu\text{f}$$
$$R_c = 35 \ \text{megohms}$$
$$n \approx 5$$
$$L_L = 20 \ \mu\text{h}.$$

The current taken from the power supply is then approximately 1.1 ma.

The condenser-discharge trigger circuit is simple and flexible, and has been commonly used for triggering series spark gaps. The pulse of Fig. 8·13 is typical of this circuit. Trigger circuits have been developed using the 4C35 hydrogen thyratron as switch to give pulses with amplitudes of 35 kv on 15 $\mu\mu$f loads, and rates of rise of voltage from 15 to 200 kv/μsec. The losses in this circuit are principally in the pulse transformer, which complicates its design at voltages of about 35 kv and at recurrence frequencies of about 1200 pps.

Trigger Circuit Using a Saturable-core Transformer.—As shown in Fig. 8·20, the gap is overvolted by means of a trigger transformer whose secondary is in series with the spark gap. For most applications, the trigger transformer must be able to supply voltages of about 20 to 30

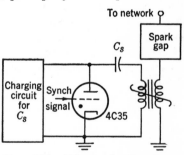

FIG. 8·20.—Trigger circuit using a saturable-core transformer.

kv, and it should have a high impedance during the rise of trigger voltage in order to avoid excessive primary current, but a low impedance during the passage of the main pulse. These requirements are met by designing the transformer so that its core becomes saturated abruptly a short time after the gap has been broken down by the trigger voltage. The effect of the saturated inductance on the principal discharging circuit is to round the leading edge of the output pulse. In order to maintain a nearly rectangular pulse shape, the saturated inductance must not be greater than 5 μh for a 25-ohm load impedance. A sufficiently high ratio of unsaturated to saturated inductance can be obtained by the use of special core materials.

This trigger circuit has not been used extensively, but laboratory tests in which it has been used to trigger a special three-electrode gap, as well as series gaps, are promising.[1]

8·6. Division of Voltage across Series Gaps.—In the foregoing discussion it has been assumed that the applied network or switch voltage is divided across the gaps that comprise the switch in the ratio of their dynamic-breakdown voltages. In general, however, such voltage division is not obtained when using practical values of voltage-dividing resistors, trigger-coupling condensers, and recurrence frequencies. Results of analyses concerning the division of voltage across series gaps in each of the four commonly used circuits shown in Fig. 8·9 for resonant charging of the network are given here.[2] It is assumed that a voltage wave of the form $v_N = \dfrac{V_N}{2}(1 - \cos \pi f_r t)$, where $0 < t < 1/f_r$, is applied at point S in each of the four circuits of Fig. 8·9. The voltages V_S and V_M have previously been defined as the theoretical and experimental values of V_{max} respectively. When using gaps with equal breakdown voltages, it is desirable to divide the applied switch voltage equally across the individual gaps in order that V_M may approach V_S.

During the network-charging cycle, the gaps G_1, G_2, and G_3 of Fig. 8·9 can be represented by the condensers c shunted by the resistors R_1, R_2, and R_3. The capacitance, c, includes the stray capacitance across each gap as well as that of the gap itself. In most circuits, c is about 10 $\mu\mu$f, 6 of which represent the capacitance of the gaps. Since the input terminals of the trigger-coupling condensers can be considered grounded during the network-charging cycle, there is effectively an unbalanced RC voltage divider in parallel with the switch.

The instantaneous values of the voltages v_1, v_2, and v_3 across G_1, G_2, and G_3 are shown in Fig. 8·21 for the circuit (a) of Fig. 8·9 with equal voltage-dividing resistors. It can be seen that the voltages across G_1 and G_2 are identical, and reach a maximum at a time t_1 smaller than the

---

[1] For additional operating characteristics, together with transformer-design information, see K. J. Germeshausen and H. R. Zeller, "Three Electrode Triggered Gap," RL Report No. 880, Oct. 11, 1945.

[2] For a more complete treatment, as well as the study of other cases, see J. R. Dillinger and F. E. Bothwell, "Division of Voltage Across Series Spark Gaps in a Line-Type Modulator," RL Report No. 682-2, Oct. 31, 1945; H. J. Sullivan, "Double-triggering and Voltage Balancing for Series Gaps," NDRC 14-493, Westinghouse-Electric Corporation, May 22, 1945.

time $1/f_r$ at which the switch voltage applied at S reaches a maximum. The voltage v_3 across G_3 lags slightly behind v_1 and v_2.

There is a maximum voltage at which satisfactory operation can be obtained with a combination of gaps having equal breakdown voltages and used with equal voltage-dividing resistors. This value is the switch voltage at $t = 1/f_r$ for which the values of v_1 and v_2 at $t = t_1$ are just less than the dynamic-breakdown voltages of G_1 and G_2. If the switch voltage is increased beyond this maximum value V_M, G_1 and G_2 will break down at $t = t_1$, causing an overvolting of G_3 and thus resulting in a pre-fire. Since V_M is equal to the sum of v_1, v_2, and v_3 at $t = 1/f_r$, each of which is less than v_1 or v_2 at $t = t_1$, and since $v_1 = v_2 = \frac{1}{3}V_S$ and $v_3 < \frac{1}{3}V_S$ at $t = t_1$, V_M must always be less than V_S. The

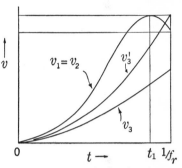

FIG. 8·21.—Sketch showing instantaneous voltages across three series gaps having equal voltage-dividing resistors and connected as in Fig. 8·9a.

ratio V_M/V_S is a figure of merit for division of voltage across the gaps and for given circuit conditions, since V_M is the value that can be realized in practice, and V_S is an ideal value obtained by assuming equal voltage division.

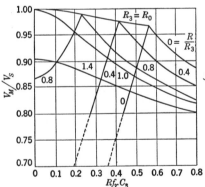

FIG. 8·22.—Ratio V_M/V_S as a function of Rf_rC_3 for the series-gap circuit of Fig. 8·9a.

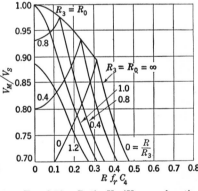

FIG. 8·23.—Ratio V_M/V_S as a function of Rf_rC_4 for the series-gap circuit of Fig. 8·9b.

Figure 8·22 shows V_M/V_S as a function of the product Rf_rC_3 for the series-gap circuit (a) of Fig. 8·9. For these curves, $R_1 = R_2 = R$, which was found to be an optimum condition, and the effect of varying the ratio R/R_3 is shown. For each value of Rf_rC_3, there is some optimum value of R_3, defined as R_0, that makes V_M a maximum. The voltage v_3 across

G_3 then varies as shown in the curve labeled v_3' in Fig. 8·21. Values of R_0 for Rf_rC_3 below about 0.57 can be found by interpolation on the curves; for Rf_rC_3 greater than 0.57, the optimum value for R_3 is infinity. For the curves of Figs. 8·22, 8·23, 8·24, and 8·25, the resistances R, R_3, and R_0 are in ohms, the capacitances c and C_3 are in farads, and the recurrence frequency f_r is in pps.

The actual solution for V_M/V_S includes both Rf_rc and Rf_rC_3 as variables, but the values of V_M/V_S are not critically dependent on Rf_rc. The curves of Fig. 8·22 are in error by less than 1 per cent for values of Rf_rc between 0 and 0.024, and by less than 2 per cent for values of Rf_rc between 0 and 0.050.

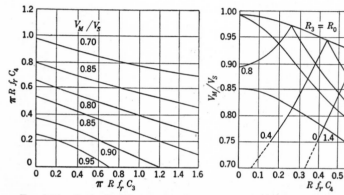

FIG. 8·24.—Ratio V_M/V_S as a function of Rf_rC_3 and Rf_rC_4 for the series-gap circuit of Fig. 8·9c.

FIG. 8·25.—Ratio V_M/V_S as a function of Rf_rC_4 for the series-gap circuit of Fig. 8·9d.

The curves of Figs. 8·22 to 8·25 are useful in choosing suitable voltage-dividing resistors and trigger-coupling condensers for series-gap circuits. From the standpoint of maximum voltage range, it is desirable to make Rf_rC_3 small. On the other hand, C_3 must be large enough to avoid serious attenuation of the trigger pulse: 20 per cent of the trigger voltage is lost if C_3 is equal to four times the capacitance from point P to ground. Also, the chosen value of R must be large enough to prevent excessive dissipation of energy in the voltage-dividing resistors.

Since the voltages across each resistor are not identical, the energy that each must dissipate is not the same, even though the resistors are of equal value. The amount of energy dissipated by each resistor depends on Rf_rC_3 and Rf_rC_4 in the same manner as the voltage distribution. In most applications, however, it is sufficient to assume equal voltage division when calculating the energy dissipated, in which case the dissipation in all resistors is $\frac{3}{8}V_N^2$ divided by the sum of the resistances.

As an example of the use of these design curves in choosing voltage-dividing resistors and trigger-coupling condensers, consider the circuit (a) of Fig. 8·9, and let it be required to operate at two recurrence frequencies $f_{r_1} = 1000$ pps and $f_{r_2} = 600$ pps. Assume that the dividing resistors are equal ($R_1 = R_2 = R_3 = R$), which is the arrangement most commonly used. If C_3 is 90 $\mu\mu$f and R is 4 megohms, $Rf_{r_1}C_3 = 0.36$ and $Rf_{r_2}C_3 = 0.22$. From Fig. 8·22 the ratio V_M/V_S is 0.905 for 1000 pps and 0.951 for 600 pps. The loss in trigger voltage across C_3 is about 14 per cent. For $R = 4$ megohms and $V_N = 20$ kv and $f_r = 1000$ pps, 5.7 watts are dissipated in each resistor R_1 and R_2 and 1.9 watts in R_3, if the uneven voltage distribution due to the charging current in condenser C_3 is considered. If the voltage is assumed to be divided equally at all times, the total wattage rating of R_1, R_2 and R_3 must equal

$$\frac{3}{8} \frac{V_N^2}{(R_1 + R_2 + R_3)},$$

or 4.2 watts each.

It can be seen from Fig. 8·22 that, at 1000 pps, V_M/V_S can be increased from 0.905 to 0.981 by making $R_3 = R_0$ instead of $R_3 = R$. However, at 600 pps, a decrease in V_M/V_S from 0.951 to about 0.835 results, which may or may not be serious depending on the variation of V_S with recurrence frequency. If this variation is assumed to be such that

$$0.835(V_S)_{600 \text{ pps}} = 0.981(V_S)_{1000 \text{ pps}},$$

and if it is desired to have the same value for V_M at both frequencies, an over-all gain in V_M/V_S is produced by setting $R_3 = R_0$.

The curves in Fig. 8·24 for circuit (c) of Fig. 8·9 are plotted differently in order to show the effects of varying both coupling capacitances, C_3 and C_4. The variables are $R_1f_rC_4$ and $R_1f_rC_3$ and lines of equal ratio V_M/V_S are plotted for $R_1 = R_2 = R_3$.

Although these curves serve as a basis for choosing the voltage-dividing resistors and trigger-coupling condensers for any given series-gap circuit, they cannot be used to determine which circuit to use for given gaps. Experience has shown that the choice of the optimum circuit depends on the type of gap being used and, in some cases, on the power level at which the gap is to be operated. From the standpoint of making V_M/V_S close to 1 for three-gap operation, the circuit (a) of Fig. 8·9 is the best, (b) the next best, and (c) the worst. However, experience has shown that, although $V_{\min}$ is not affected by variations in the division of voltage across the gaps, within limits, $V_{\min}$ for some gaps is appreciably altered, depending on where the trigger is coupled. These analyses have assumed that the dynamic-breakdown voltages of the gaps are equal and remain so throughout life. The reasons why these assumptions are not always valid are discussed in later sections.

8·7. General Considerations for Gap Design.—The three fundamental considerations in the design of enclosed gaps are (1) the choice of a suitable gas or mixture of gases, (2) the choice of suitable electrode material, and (3) the determination of a satisfactory electrode geometry. There are many other considerations, including structural details, that are not discussed here.

Choice of a Suitable Gas.—Deionization characteristics and chemical activity are of major importance in the choice of a gas. After conducting the required pulse, the gas must deionize at a sufficiently high rate in order that the gap will be able to hold off the network voltage that is applied following the pulse. In other words, the reignition voltage of the gap at any time after the pulse must be greater than the applied network or switch voltage at that time. The gas molecules should also have no metastable states in which electrons may be trapped during the discharge, and from which they would subsequently be released, causing a premature breakdown of the gap. During the required life of the tube, no constituent of the gas within the gap should be absorbed by or combine with any elements inside the tube in quantities large enough to affect the operating characteristics seriously.

In discussing the operation of rotary gaps in previous sections of this chapter, it is pointed out that the erosion of the electrodes is severe when the gaps are operated in the absence of oxygen. Because of similar experience with enclosed gaps, a gas mixture of approximately 95 per cent argon and 5 per cent oxygen was used to fill the trigatron. The oxygen maintains an oxide coating on the electrodes in the sparking area that is sufficient to limit the electrode erosion encountered during the required life of the tube. However, as the oxygen is thus used up by chemical combination, the operating characteristics of the trigatron change. The need of a satisfactory switch for pulsers of higher power than those in which the trigatron operated satisfactorily resulted in investigations[1] of enclosed gaps filled with various gas mixtures. The principal characteristic sought for in these investigations was stability of switch performance over an extended period of operation. This work included the study of gas mixtures such as argon and helium, argon and oxygen, helium and oxygen, and helium, argon, and oxygen. As a result of other work[2] there was evolved a hydrogen-argon gas mixture that was found to have good deionization characteristics and to be stable with life. At first hydrogen alone was tried, but it was found that, after a few hours operation at low pulse currents, the tube drop during the discharge was

[1] C. M. Slack and E. G. F. Arnott, "Report on Enclosed Pressure Gaps," NDRC 14-150, Westinghouse Electric Corporation, Dec. 31, 1942.

[2] F. S. Goucher, J. R. Haynes, W. A. Depp, and E. J. Ryder, "Spark Gap Switches for Radar," *Bell System Technical Journal*, October 1946.

abnormally high and fluctuated from pulse to pulse, causing undesirable amplitude jitter in the output pulse.   It was believed that this behavior did not exist during the first few hours of operation because of the presence of impurities in the hydrogen that aided the transfer from a glow to a low-voltage arc discharge.   When argon was added to the hydrogen, the tube drop was found to remain low and constant throughout the life of the tube.   Therefore, mixtures of approximately 80 per cent hydrogen and 20 per cent argon are commonly used.   The argon acts as a stable impurity in that it performs the same function throughout life, as did the impurities in the tube during the first few hours before they were "cleaned up."   The current at which this high-tube drop appeared could be reduced by increasing the percentage of argon, within limits.   This high voltage drop did not appear with tubes filled with 20 per cent argon when conducting 1-μsec 100-amp pulses, but it did appear after operating these tubes for 25 to 50 hr with 1-μsec 50-amp pulses.   Apparently, the above percentage of argon was not sufficient to effect the transfer from a glow to arc discharge at a pulse current of 50 amp without the help of the impurities present during the first few hours.   Later work showed that no argon was needed at pulse currents of about 200 amp and above.

Choice of Suitable Electrode Materials.—The choice of suitable electrode materials proved to be somewhat more difficult than the choice of a gas.   It was found that all the tested materials eroded rapidly in the hydrogen-argon gas mixture.   The rate of erosion of the electrodes in rotary gaps and in the trigatron is kept low by the presence of a tough oxide coating on the surface which is constantly replenished. Studies of the erosion of several materials and combinations of materials when operated in a hydrogen-argon gas mixture show that the rate of erosion of the cathode depends somewhat on its geometry.   Cathode erosion appears to be directly proportional to pulse current at a given pulse duration, but is not directly proportional to pulse duration at a given pulse current.   For example, at a constant pulse current, the erosion at pulse durations of 2 μsec and 5 μsec is about 2.7 and 8.3 times, respectively, that obtained at 1 μsec.

Since all cathode-erosion studies have not been made with electrodes of the same geometry, or at the same pulse duration, it is not possible to present the results in concise tabular form.   A few statements may be made, however, to indicate the scope and general results of the work. An early investigation conducted at the Bell Telephone Laboratories showed that the erosion rates of tungsten, molybdenum, and aluminum by weight were approximately the same, and much less than that of either gold or carbon.   These values agreed with those for sputtering in the abnormal hydrogen glow discharge.   A comparison made at the Radiation Laboratory of the erosion rates of vacuum-cast beryllium and aluminum under the same conditions showed that of beryllium to be 0.38 times that of aluminum by weight and 0.58 times that of aluminum by volume. The use of beryllium is objectionable because the eroded metallic vapor condenses into a fluffy material that drifts around inside the tube and causes occasional premature breakdowns of the gap. Aluminum was chosen as the cathode material in one major type of series spark gap because the material sputtered off the cathode was found to be deposited on the anode in such a way that the gap spacing stayed approximately constant under limited operating conditions. Experiments have also been made with several sintered materials containing various oxides that have low work functions. It was found that cathodes made by sintering 5 per cent barium oxide, strontium carbonate, or beryllium oxide with a mixture consisting of 95 per cent tungsten and 5 per cent nickel or copper for a binder had an erosion rate of about 0.025 times that of tungsten or molybdenum alone.[1] These materials were not used as the cathode in series gaps because of the development of the sintered iron-sponge mercury cathode, which was superior to them.

Determination of a Satisfactory Geometry.—The wartime demand for operable tubes made it necessary to design and manufacture them before an adequate study of the erosion problem could be made, and before a material could be found that solved this problem in a hydrogen-argon gas mixture. Therefore, it was necessary to determine a disposition and design of the electrodes such that cathode erosion would have a minimum effect on tube characteristics. This approach has given rise to two basic designs for enclosed fixed spark gaps. One design has concentric cylindrical electrodes, the outer one being an aluminum cathode. By providing a large cathode area, the change in the electrode spacing produced by cathode erosion can be minimized. The other design uses a mercury cathode. In order to immobilize the mercury, it is held in the interstices of a sintered honeycomb structure of iron powder, called an "iron sponge." The design is such that within the operable power range only mercury is eroded from this cathode.

8·8. The Cylindrical-electrode Aluminum–cathode Gap.—The ratio of the diameter of the outer electrode, or cathode, to that of the inner electrode, or anode, is made approximately equal to e, the base of natural logarithms. With this ratio, the highest possible breakdown voltage that does not cause the formation of corona before breakdown for a given outside diameter is obtained, and a minimum change occurs in this breakdown voltage for a slight change in the size or spacing of the electrodes.

---

[1] F. S. Goucher, J. R. Haynes, and E. J. Ryder, "High Power Series Gaps Having Sintered Iron Sponge Mercury Cathodes," NDRC 14-488, Bell Telephone Laboratories, Oct. 1, 1945.

Cathode and Anode Erosion.—If the discharge takes place at random over the large cathode area provided by this geometry, considerable erosion can be tolerated before the gap spacing is changed enough to have any appreciable effect on the breakdown characteristics of the gap. In fact, cathode erosion is not a problem in a gap of this type, except insofar as it affects the buildup of material on the anode.

These gaps are operated in a vertical position with the cathode opening downward in order to allow the material eroded from the cathode that condenses before reaching the anode to fall to the bottom of the tube. In spite of this arrangement, it has been found that a considerable fraction of the material eroded from the cathode per pulse is transferred to and deposited on the anode, which thus becomes coated with aluminum. For this reason the choice of anode material is not critical, and both iron and nickel have been used. The anode is not subjected to positive-ion bombardment during the main pulse; thus, anode erosion can take place only if there is reverse current in the circuit. In the usual designs for line-type pulsers, therefore, anode erosion does not impair the operation of a tube of this type. There are two results of the buildup of aluminum on the anode that can render the operation of the gap unsatisfactory. If the amount of material deposited on the anode per pulse is great enough to affect the voltage gradient at the anode appreciably, subsequent discharges take place to particular points on the anode, instead of being distributed over the entire surface in the sparking region. This poor distribution of the sparks causes the aluminum coating on the anode to be rough, instead of smooth. For a gap of a given design, there is a quantity of material M_1 deposited on the anode per pulse such that the anode buildup is a smooth coating for all values less than M_1. There is also some value M_2, greater than M_1, such that for all values greater than M_2 such a large fraction of subsequent discharges takes place from a few points on the anode that the material is deposited in the form of "spikes," rendering the gap inoperative in a short time. For values of anode deposit between M_1 and M_2, predominant spikes are not formed, but the deposit of aluminum on the anode is so rough that the dynamic-breakdown voltage of the gap, and hence the operating-voltage range of the switch, is decreased appreciably.

Even with a smooth anode buildup the operation of these gaps may become unsatisfactory before the end of their required lifetime. If the smooth coating is very thick, a piece may break off, particularly from the end of the anode, when it is subjected to shock and vibration. The crater thus formed on the anode causes erratic operation of the gap. In short, for satisfactory operation of a gap of given design, there is an upper limit to the amount of material that can be deposited on the anode per pulse and to the total amount of material that can be deposited on the anode during the required life of the gap.   Despite the fact that anode buildup is a very serious defect in the cylindrical-electrode aluminum-cathode gap, there are many combinations of operating conditions for which a tube of this type is satisfactory.

Some conclusions concerning the effects on cathode erosion and anode buildup of variations in recurrence frequency, pulse current, pulse duration, gas pressure, and gap spacing are stated here.   These conclusions are based on data taken for gaps having 0.200-in. and 0.330-in. spacings, similar to the WX3226 and WX3240 gaps respectively, and filled with 80 per cent hydrogen and 20 per cent argon to total pressures in the range of 68 to 175 cm of mercury.   The ratio of the cathode radius to the anode radius was maintained at approximately e for all gaps studied.[1]

The amounts of cathode erosion and anode buildup per pulse were found to be independent of the recurrence frequency in the range 200 to 1200 pps.

For a given gap spacing, pulse duration, and gas pressure, the cathode erosion and anode buildup per pulse were found to be directly proportional to pulse current in the range 100 to 400 amp.

For a given gap spacing, pulse current, and gas pressure, the cathode erosion and anode buildup per pulse increase much more rapidly than the pulse duration in the range 0.9 to 5 μsec.   As a result the maximum allowable pulse current for a given gap design decreases rapidly with increasing pulse duration.

The ratio of anode buildup to cathode erosion per pulse was found to remain constant for a given gas pressure and gap spacing, even though the pulse current varied from 100 to 400 amp, the pulse duration varied from 0.9 to 5 μsec, and the recurrence frequency varied from 200 to 1200 pps, corresponding to a variation from 25×10^{-8} to 560×10^{-8} mg in the mass of aluminum eroded from the cathode per pulse.

For a given gas pressure, pulse current, and pulse duration, an increase in gap spacing was found to decrease the amount of material eroded from the cathode per pulse, and the ratio of anode buildup to cathode erosion per pulse.   A tube with large spacing may therefore be operated satisfactorily at higher values of pulse current and longer pulse durations than a tube with smaller spacing.

For a given gap spacing, pulse current, and pulse duration, an increase in gas pressure was found to increase the cathode erosion per pulse slightly, and to increase the ratio of anode buildup to cathode erosion per pulse appreciably.   The increase in cathode erosion is perhaps due to a decrease in the size of the cathode spot with increasing gas pressure, which increases its temperature, and thus increases the amount of material evaporated from the cathode per pulse.   Because the temperature along the arc

[1] J. R. Dillinger, "General Characteristics of Aluminum-cathode Type Series Spark Gaps," RL Report No. 682-3, Nov. 21, 1945.

column is high and the gas density is therefore low, and because a higher gap-filling pressure causes a region of higher gas density to surround the arc column, it is believed that the higher pressure aids in funneling aluminum vapor from the cathode across to the anode. The higher pressure thus concentrates the distribution of aluminum vapor from the cathode spot in the direction of the anode.

Particular Designs for Enclosed Fixed Spark Gaps.—The photographs of Fig. 8·26 are of five different cylindrical-electrode aluminum-cathode gaps. Photographs (a), (b), (c), (d), and (e), in Fig. 8·27 are x-ray prints of the 1B29, 1B22, 1B31, WX3226, and WX3240 tubes respectively.

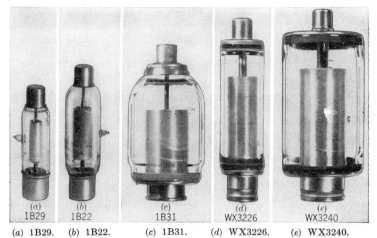

(a) 1B29.   (b) 1B22.   (c) 1B31.   (d) WX3226.   (e) WX3240.

FIG. 8·26.—Photographs of various aluminum-cathode gaps. (*Parts (a) and (b) courtesy of the Bell Telephone Laboratories.*)

The 1B29, 1B22, and 1B31 were made by the Western Electric Co. whereas the WX3226 and WX3240 were made by the Westinghouse Electric Corporation.

As the required pulse current and pulse duration increased, it became necessary to develop gaps with larger spacings in order to limit the amount of material deposited on the anode per pulse. Since the gap dissipation increases with spacing, it is desirable to keep this spacing to a minimum, compatible with the allowable rate of anode buildup. Therefore, it is undesirable to operate a gap at pulse currents and pulse durations that are appreciably lower than the design figures.

After the spacing of one of these gaps has been chosen with regard to anode buildup and dissipation, the breakdown voltage can be adjusted to the desired value by changing the gas pressure. The operation of gaps filled with 80 per cent hydrogen and 20 per cent argon has been satisfactory over a range of pressures from 50 to 250 cm of mercury.[1]

[1] E. G. F. Arnott, "Development of Series Spark Gaps," NDRC 14-327, Westinghouse Electric Corporation, Aug. 14, 1944.

The tubes that were designed to operate at voltages below 5 kv per gap were difficult to start because of insufficient background ionization. Therefore, a small amount (about 0.002 mg) of a radium salt (either radium bromide or radium chloride) was added in order to provide additional ionization, and thus to aid in starting the gaps. For voltages higher than 5 kv the gaps start readily without this salt, because of ionization produced by corona at the edges of the electrodes. Special corona points were provided in the 1B29 and 1B22, as can be seen in Fig. 8·26, in order to give further aid in starting.

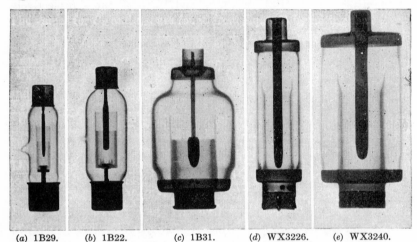

   (a) 1B29.   (b) 1B22.   (c) 1B31.   (d) WX3226.   (e) WX3240.

Fig. 8·27.—X-ray prints of various aluminum-cathode gaps. (*Parts* (*a*), (*b*), *and* (*c*) *courtesy of the Bell Telephone Laboratories.*)

Nominal ratings for each of the seven gaps developed are given in Table 8·2. The 1B34 is a WX3226 filled to a pressure of 75 cm of mercury, and the 1B41, 1B45, and 1B49 are WX3240 gaps filled to pressures of 90, 150, and 110 cm of mercury, respectively.

TABLE 8·2.—NOMINAL RATINGS FOR VARIOUS FIXED SPARK GAPS

Type	I_p, amp		τ, μsec		f_r, pps	$I_{p\text{av}}$, ma	V_{SG}, kv	$f_r \times \tau$,	$I_p \times \tau$, coulombs per pulse
1B29	30	20	0.75	0.4	2100	. . .	1.4	. . . . .	. . . .
1B22	75	50	0.75	0.4	1100	75	2.1	. . . . .	. . . .
1B34	200	75	2	0.25	2000	160	3.5	0.001	2×10^{-4}
1B31	300	30	5	0.25	1600	150	4.0	0.001	3.8
1B41	450	100	5	0.5	2000	210	5.0	0.001	7.5
1B49	450	100	5	0.5	2000	210	5.5	0.001	7.5
1B45	450	100	5	0.5	2000	210	6.5	0.001	7.5

When more than one value is given, the second value denotes the minimum allowable value of that quantity, whereas a single value or the first of two values denotes the maximum allowable value. In this table, I_p is the pulse switch current, τ is the pulse duration, f_r is the pulse recurrence frequency, I_{pav} is the average pulse switch current, and V_{SG} is the nominal operating voltage per gap, which can be relied on during at least 500 hours of operation. If two or three gaps are used in series with resonant charging, the nominal operating switch voltage is about $2V_{SG}$ and $3V_{SG}$ respectively. The usable range of operating voltage above and below V_{SG} depends on the operating conditions. It is sometimes advisable to have a nominal operating voltage above or below V_{SG} in order to operate more nearly in the center of the operating-voltage range.

Since I_p, τ, and f_r are interrelated insofar as their effect on the operation of these gaps is concerned, it is necessary to state limits on the products of these quantities taken two at a time. The product τf_r is the duty ratio, τI_p is the number of coulombs per pulse. It is evident that, in order to prevent the growth of spikes on the anodes, the pulse current must be decreased when the pulse duration is increased. A limit on the product $f_r I_p$ is included in the limit on I_{pav}, which, together with the duty ratio, limits the gap dissipation and the total amount of material deposited on the anode during life.

Change in Characteristics during Operation.—The dynamic-breakdown voltage of each gap decreases during life because of changes in the characteristics of the electrode surfaces that result from the erosion of the cathode and the buildup of material on the anode. The magnitude of this decrease depends on the rates of cathode erosion and anode buildup, which in turn depend on tube parameters and operating conditions, as discussed previously. Tests show that, for a large rate of anode buildup, the value of V_M for a set of gaps decreases during the first 100 hr of operation, and then remains very nearly constant for the remainder of a 500-hr period or longer. For a small rate of anode buildup, V_M has been observed to remain constant during operating periods more than 500 hr long. For intermediate rates of anode buildup, V_M may decrease gradually for more than 500 hr. The values of V_{min} and V_{start} are only slightly affected by these changes in electrode-surface conditions.

Figure 8·28 shows the variation of operating voltage range with time for a set of three 1B41 gaps operated in series with different trigger couplings as the switch in a 25-ohm line-type pulser at a pulse recurrence frequency of 300 pps and a pulse duration of 2 μsec. The operating switch voltage was 15.8 kv, making the pulse current approximately equal to 300 amp. The HK7-magnetron load used for the test was replaced by a resistance load for purposes of measuring the voltage range. A trigger voltage of 20 kv, measured on a 15 $\mu\mu$f load, was sufficient to obtain the maximum range from these gaps.   It is seen from Fig. 8·28 that both V_{min} and V_{start} are appreciably lower when the trigger is coupled to both intermediate points than when it is coupled to either the upper or lower point.   This test and others show that the value of V_M for new tubes with two-point triggering is lower than that for one-point triggering. After the electrodes become roughened, however, the difference becomes negligible, and, because of corona bursts in the gaps after the electrodes have become roughened, it is impossible to predict which method of triggering will give the highest V_M.   The assumption that the gaps behave as condensers, made in discussing the division of voltage across the gaps

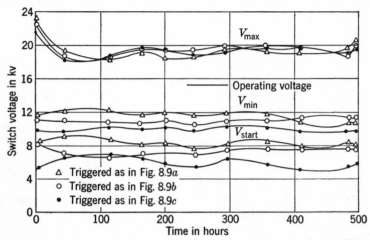

Fig. 8·28.—Operating range as a function of hours of operation for the 1B41.

for each method of triggering, does not hold after the electrodes have become roughened.   Since V_{min} and V_{start} are lower, and over a long period of time V_M is about the same whether the trigger is coupled to both points or to either the upper or lower point, it follows that two-point triggering generally gives the widest range of operation for three gaps in series.[1]

Gap Dissipation.—By connecting the vertical plates of a modified synchroscope directly across the grounded gap in the pulser switch, the voltage drop across a single gap during the discharge was determined.   The oscilloscope traces were observed with self-synchronous operation of the oscilloscope, that is, the signal voltage applied to the

[1] J. R. Dillinger, "General Characteristics of Aluminum-cathode Type Series Gaps," RL Report No. 682–3, Nov. 21, 1945; J. R. Dillinger, "Some Characteristics of the 1B41, 1B45, and 1B49 Series Spark Gaps," RL Report No. 682–4, Nov. 26, 1945; E. G. F. Arnott, "Development of Series Spark Gaps," NDRC 14-494, Westinghouse Electric Corporation, July 12, 1945.

vertical plates was also used to start the sweep. Because there is a slight time lag between the application of the voltage starting the sweep and the appearance of the trace on the oscilloscope screen, the initial portion of the voltage pulse cannot be observed. The curves in Figs. 8·29 and 8·30 were drawn from these traces, and show the voltage drop

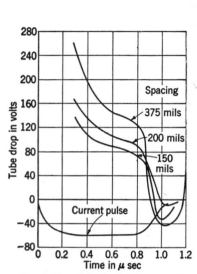

FIG. 8·29.—Voltage drop across three fixed spark gaps having different electrode spacings for a pulse duration of 0.9 μsec.

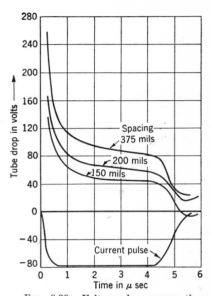

FIG. 8·30.—Voltage drop across three fixed spark gaps having different electrode spacings for a pulse duration of 4.5 μsec.

across each of three gaps having different electrode spacings for nominal pulse durations of 0.9 and 4.5 μsec, respectively. The gaps with spacings of 150, 200, and 375 mils were, respectively, the 1B22, WX3226, and a gap similar to the WX3240, but with a slightly greater spacing. The corresponding current pulse is also shown; the rounding of the leading edge of the current pulse is a result of the high tube drop during the first part of the pulse.

The tube drop was found to be independent of the gas mixture, the gas pressure, the pulse current, and the recurrence frequency within the limits of error of these measurements, and within the range over which these quantities were varied. The gas mixture was varied from 100 per cent hydrogen to 100 per cent argon, the pressure from 68 to 150 cm of mercury, the pulse current from 80 to 240 amp, and the recurrence frequency from 200 to 2000 pps. The tube drop is primarily dependent on the electrode spacing and pulse duration.

The voltage across a gap during the first part of the discharge has been studied with the use of a capacitance voltage divider. By multiplying the values of tube drop and pulse current for each increment of time during the pulse, a curve can be obtained showing the rate at which energy

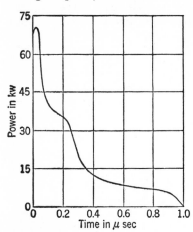

FIG. 8·31.—Power dissipated in one WX3226 gap as a function of time for a single pulse.

is dissipated in a single gap during the pulse. Figure 8·31 shows such a curve for a WX3226 gap operated in series with two other gaps at a pulse duration of 0.9 μsec and pulse current of 80 amp. Integrating this curve, a value of 15.4×10^{-3} joules is obtained as the energy dissipated per pulse in one of these gaps. A measurement of the average dissipation by means of a calorimeter gave a value of 15.5×10^{-3} joules per pulse. A comparison of other values obtained by integrating power-versus-time curves with those obtained calorimetrically also shows good agreement.

The dissipation per pulse has been found to be directly proportional to pulse current and to gap spacing. By arbitrarily assuming that an equation for dissipation per pulse involves terms including τ and τ^2, the following empirical relation has been developed:

$$D = (0.703 \times 10^{-6} + 0.420\tau - 0.0233 \times 10^6\tau^2)SI_p,$$

where D is the dissipation per gap in joules per pulse, τ is the pulse duration in seconds, S is the gap spacing in mils, and I_p is the pulse current in amperes. This equation agrees reasonably well with experimental data over the range of 0.9- to 5.0-μsec pulse duration, 0.200 to 0.440-in. spacing, and 80- to 500-amp pulse current.[1]

Time Jitter.—Attempts to make the cylindrical-electrode aluminum-cathode gap operate synchronously have not been successful. In using these gaps 1 to 3 μsec of over-all time jitter must be tolerated, depending on operating conditions and particularly on the value of the operating voltage relative to V_s and V_{min}. About 95 per cent of the pulses show a time jitter that is considerably less than 1 μsec, but an appreciable number of random pulses account for the over-all jitter of 1 to 3 μsec.

The two gaps in a set of three that are broken down by the trigger

[1] R. G. Fluharty and J. R. Dillinger, "Dissipation in Series Spark Gaps and Voltage-current Relationships During the Discharge," RL Report No. 682-1, June 26, 1945.

pulse can be made to fire accurately to within 0.1 μsec.   The primary source of jitter in a switch of this type is in the firing of the third tube, which cannot be overvolted by the trigger.   After the two triggered tubes are broken down, the full switch voltage is applied to the third tube; thus, the greater the switch voltage, the greater the overvolting of the third tube.   The jitter in this switch, therefore, decreases with increasing switch voltage.   At a given switch voltage the jitter also varies during the life of the tube because of changes in electrode-surface conditions.[1]

8·9. The Iron-sponge Mercury-cathode Gap.—A gap of this type[2] is an improvement over the cylindrical-electrode aluminum-cathode gap in at least three respects:

1. The range remains constant during life.
2. The time jitter can be maintained at a value of the order of magnitude of one per cent of the pulse duration.
3. As wide an operating range can be obtained with two of these gaps as with three of the cylindrical-electrode aluminum-cathode gaps.

For satisfactory operation, however, the reverse current must be kept very low.

The anode of this gap is a molybdenum rod with a diameter of approximately 0.060 in.   The cathode is mercury that is immobilized by an iron sponge.   This iron sponge contains about 60 per cent void space and is made by compressing iron powder into a kovar cup and sintering under appropriate conditions.   After subsequent heat treatment in a hydrogen atmosphere the sponge of a typical gap holds about 9 cm^3 of mercury when fully saturated.   The mercury that is evaporated from the surface of the cathode during operation condenses and runs down the walls back into the sponge.   Because of the surface tension of the mercury, a film of mercury is maintained over the surface of the iron sponge which prevents the erosion of the iron.   In order to minimize the time jitter, the gaps are usually filled with 100 per cent hydrogen.   Radium salts are generally omitted in order to increase the operating range and to further minimize jitter.

[1] H. L. Glick, "Triggering of High Power Spark Gaps," Westinghouse Research Report SR-307, Oct. 18, 1945.

[2] F. S. Goucher, J. R. Haynes, and E. J. Ryder, "High Power Series Gaps Having Sintered Iron Sponge Mercury Cathodes," NDRC 14-488, Bell Telephone Laboratories, Oct. 1, 1945; J. R. Dillinger, "Operation of Sintered Iron Sponge-Mercury Cathode Type Series Gaps at 5 Microsecond Conditions," RL Report No. 682-5, Nov. 28, 1945; and J. R. Dillinger, "Line-Type Modulator and HP10V Magnetron Operation at 6 Megawatts," RL Report No. 682-6, Nov. 30, 1945.

Particular Gap Designs.—Figure 8·32 shows the two tubes of this type
developed to date. The cooling fins, which are in thermal contact with
the cathodes of the tubes, can be seen. The 1B42 is shown in Fig.
8·32*a* and the Fe-I is shown in Fig. 8·32*b*. The large opaque spot just

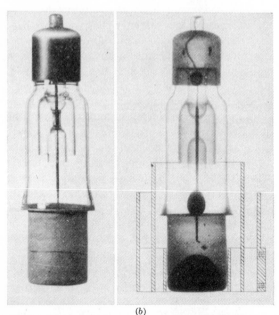

(b)

Fig. 8·32.—Photographs and X-ray prints of iron-sponge mercury-cathode gaps.
(a) The 1B42, (b) the Fe-I. (*The photographs for part (a) courtesy of the Bell Telephone
Laboratories.*)

above the kovar cup in the x-ray of the Fe-I tube is due to a globule of free mercury that collected there when the tube was placed in a horizontal position to take the x-ray.   The small spots on the walls of the kovar cup were caused by drops of mercury adhering to the kovar.   The upper portion of the anode is surrounded by glass shields in order to prevent mercury from dripping down close enough to the sparking region to affect the operation of the gap.   The 1B42 is mounted by means of a bolt extending down from the cathode, and the cooling fin is an integral part of the tube.   As shown in the sketch in Fig. 8·32b, the cooling fin of the Fe-I tube is not an integral part of the tube, but serves instead as a mounting socket.   The operation of the Fe-I tube with various electrode spacings and gas pressures has been satisfactory for a variety of conditions, the reliable life of the tube being greater than 500 hr.

Some specifications for these tubes are given in Table 8·3.   Each quantity has the same significance as in Table 8·2.   In columns containing more than one figure, the first represents the maximum and the second the minimum rating.   The value of V_{SG}, the nominal operating voltage per gap, has been obtained from data for the operation of two gaps in series.

TABLE 8·3.—RATINGS FOR TWO IRON-SPONGE MERCURY-CATHODE GAPS

No.	I_p, amp	τ, μsec	f_r, pps	I_{pav}, ma	V_{SG}, kv	τf_r	τI_p, coulombs per pulse	$f_r I_p$, amp $\times$ sec^{-1}
1B42	300—80	6.1—0.25	2000	0.250	5.0	0.0012	1.28×10^{-3}	40×10^4
Fe-I	750—100	5.5—0.5	1000	0.450	7.5	0.0011	1.5×10^{-3}	25×10^4

Operating Characteristics.—Two of these gaps are used in series as the switch in a line-type pulser because it was found that two gaps give an operating range greater than ±33 per cent, which is ample for most applications.   In general, one would expect V_{min} to be equal to the breakdown voltage of one gap and V_S to be twice this value when using two gaps in series, making the range ±33 per cent.   However, the application of the charging-voltage wave to these gaps causes a corona sheath to be formed about the anode, which changes the breakdown characteristics.   The magnitude of this change increases with the amplitude of the charging-voltage wave.   At voltages near V_{min}, the corona sheath has a small effect, and the breakdown voltage of the gap is approximately characteristic of a point-to-plane discharge, as seen from the x-rays of Fig. 8·32.   Near V_S, however, the corona sheath is large and shaped like a distorted sphere about the end of the anode, making the breakdown voltage per gap more nearly characteristic of that of a sphere-to-plane discharge.   Thus, the dynamic-breakdown voltage per gap at voltages in the region of V_s is greater than in the region of voltages near V_{min}. Therefore, the ratio of V_s to V_{min} is greater than 2 to 1 for the operation of two gaps in series. If a small amount of radium salt is inserted in these gaps, the beneficial effects of this corona sheath are destroyed, and the ratio of maximum to minimum operating voltage obtained with two gaps becomes less than 2.

For two Fe-I gaps operated at 15.5 kv, 290 amp, 300 pps, and 2 μsec, the voltage range of 10.5 to 22.5 kv is constant for more than 500 hr of operation, with V_{start} equal to 5.5 kv. The required trigger voltage is 20 kv, and the time jitter is less than 0.02 μsec at voltages above 14 kv, provided that the rate of rise of trigger voltage is 55 kv/μsec or greater. For gaps filled to higher gas pressures, ranges of 13 to 29 kv for two gaps have been maintained during more than 500 hr of operation at 24.5 kv, 925 amp, 250 pps, and 2 μsec.

Time Jitter.—In operating two gaps in circuit (*d*) of Fig. 8·9, gap G_2 is broken down by the trigger pulse, applying the full switch voltage to G_1, which is then broken down. If the delay in firing G_1 is appreciable, G_2 can partially recover and must be reignited after G_1 breaks down. As a result, there are at least three sources of uncertainty in the initiation of the discharge, which combine to produce the observed time jitter in the output pulse.

The uncertainty in the firing of G_2 by the trigger pulse can be made small compared with 0.02 μsec by making the rate of rise of the trigger voltage pulse equal to or greater than 55 kv/μsec.

The uncertainty in the firing of G_1 can be reduced by increasing the switch voltage, all of which appears across G_1 after G_2 breaks down. The time jitter introduced in reigniting G_2 has been detected, but it is negligibly small.

All three sources of time jitter, but particularly that introduced in the firing of G_1, can be reduced by improvements in the tube design. The elimination of argon from the gas filling, a reduction in the diameter of the anode, and a decrease in the gap spacing have all been found effective in reducing time jitter. It is possible to eliminate argon from these tubes because they are intended for operation at pulse currents of 100 amp and higher. A reduction in the anode diameter decreases the jitter, but increases the detrimental effects of reverse current in the tubes. The most effective way of reducing time jitter is to decrease the spacing, and to increase the gas pressure accordingly in order to obtain the desired gap breakdown voltage. However, the maximum gain that can be obtained by this method is limited because, for a gap with small spacing, the breakdown voltage increases linearly with gas pressure in the region of low values, but for high gas pressures, this voltage is not affected appreciably by a change in pressure.

Effects of Reverse Current.—Reverse current damages iron-sponge mercury-cathode tubes by eroding the electrode that is the anode for the forward pulse and the cathode for the reverse current pulse. The resulting increase in spacing during operation causes V_{min} to increase and V_S either to increase or to decrease. If considerable material is eroded from the anode and deposited on the tube walls, mercury condenses on it and partially covers the walls. This mercury may give rise to disturbances along the walls, which can lower V_S despite the increase in spacing. The increase in spacing also causes the time jitter to increase. Tests have shown that a given value of reverse current has a more detrimental effect on gap operation from the point of view of time jitter than from that of operating range. In order to specify the reverse current that can be tolerated in these tubes, limits are imposed on the maximum value of erosion per pulse and on the total erosion permissible for a life of 500 hr. The film of mercury that coats the end of the anode during operation has been found to limit the erosion rate of the anode to a value much smaller than would be obtained without this film. It is therefore necessary to limit the amount of erosion per pulse of reverse current, otherwise the mercury film could be broken through during a single pulse of reverse current, thereby exposing the molybdenum of the anode and greatly increasing the erosion rate. By placing limits on the pulse current and the pulse duration the erosion per pulse can be limited. If the total erosion during a period of 500 hr were directly proportional to the number of coulombs per pulse, it could be limited by a specification of the maximum allowable value of the average current. Although this linear relation does not hold over a wide range of pulse duration, the linearity is sufficient for general specifications. The limiting value of the average reverse current that does not affect time jitters appears to lie between 1 and 2 ma.

In addition to the need for limiting the reverse current in these tubes to a very low value because of its effect on range and time jitter, it is necessary to limit it in the tubes filled with 100 per cent hydrogen in order to eliminate amplitude jitter. In tubes containing 100 per cent hydrogen, the tube drop during the conduction of reverse currents of low peak value can be high and can fluctuate from pulse to pulse. A voltage that is sufficient to affect the next charging voltage can therefore be left on the network after the pulse. Since the amount of voltage left on the network fluctuates from pulse to pulse, amplitude jitter can result in the output pulse.

Dissipation.—As a result of calorimetric measurements made at the Bell Telephone Laboratories[1] on iron-sponge mercury-cathode gaps

---

[1] F. S. Goucher, J. R. Haynes, W. A. Depp, and E. J. Ryder, "Spark Gap Switches for Radar," *Bell System Technical Journal*, Oct. 1946.

operated over a wide range of pulsing conditions, the following empirical
formula has been established expressing the dissipation D in joules per
pulse per gap in terms of the gap parameters and the pulsing conditions:

$$D = 5.7 \times 10^{-7}I_pS + (40 + 3.9 \times 10^{-2}p^{0.4}S)I_p\tau,$$

where I_p is the pulse current in amperes, S is the gap spacing in mils, p
is the gas pressure in inches of mercury, and τ is the pulse duration in
seconds. This equation has been established from data covering the
following ranges of parameters: spacing, 40 to 350 mils; gas pressure, 28 to
50 in. of mercury; pulse duration, 1 to 6 μsec; pulse current, 45 to 1070
amp. The dissipation in watts per gap for any application may be
obtained by multiplying the value of D by the recurrence frequency.
This equation does not include the energy contributed by the trigger,
which can usually be neglected, but which can be measured independently
and added if necessary.

Dissipation is an important consideration not only from the standpoint of circuit efficiency, but also in determining whether or not forced
cooling is necessary when operating mercury-cathode gaps. Since
mercury vapor has poor deionization characteristics, there is some upper
limit to the partial pressure of mercury, and thus to the operating temperature of the gap, above which the poor deionization characteristics
of the mercury override the good characteristics of the hydrogen.

8·10. The Three-electrode Fixed Spark Gap.—In order to build a
satisfactory three-electrode gap, it is necessary to have an electrode
material such that its erosion rate at the desired operating conditions is
negligibly small in the gas to be used. Since a gap of this type has a
somewhat more complex electrode configuration than does a two-electrode gap, much less electrode erosion can be tolerated.

The Trigatron.—The trigatron[1] is a three-electrode tube filled with
approximately 95 per cent argon and 5 per cent oxygen to pressures of
about 1 to 6 atmospheres, depending on the desired operating voltage
and on particular tube design. The British CV85 and the CV125 were
the two most widely used designs. Typical operating conditions for the
CV85 are 8 kv, 1200 pps, and 1 μsec in a 70-ohm line-type pulser.
Photograph (a) of Fig. 8·33 shows a CV125 and (b) is a print of an
x-ray of this tube. The anode and cathode are of molybdenum and the
trigger pin is tungsten. The anode sleeve was found effective in making
the time jitter less than 0.1 μsec.

Oxygen is used in a trigatron principally to maintain an oxide coating

[1] J. D. Craggs, M. E. Haine, and J. M. Meek, "The Development of Triggered
Spark Gaps with Particular Reference to Sealed Gaps," Metropolitan-Vickers Electric
Co., Ltd., Report No. C-331, September 1942.

on the surfaces of the electrodes and thereby to limit the rate of electrode erosion, since there are effectively two cathodes in the tube when it is operating.   In this tube, the principal discharge does not start between the anode and cathode after the tube is triggered, but takes place from the cathode to the trigger pin to the anode.   Thus, the trigger pin must serve as both an anode and cathode, and is therefore doubly subject to erosion.   Because of the small size of the trigger pin and the other electrodes, this erosion must be minimized.   The oxygen is also needed in these gaps to quench metastable atoms of argon after the discharge.

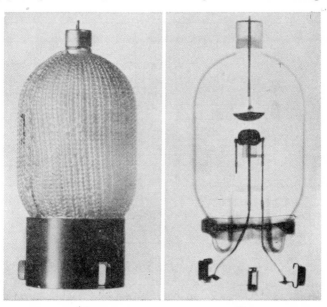

(a)   (b)

FIG. 8·33.—(a) A photograph and (b) an x-ray print of the CV125 three-electrode gap.

At a recurrence frequency of 800 pps and a pulse duration of 0.9 μsec, and in a line-type pulser with a 50–ohm network and 50–ohm load, a new CV85 trigatron has a range of about 3.5 to 11 kv with a starting voltage of 1.5 kv.   A trigger voltage of 6.5 kv is sufficient.   The curves of Fig. 8·34a show the variation in range with trigger voltage for a new CV125 operated in this circuit.   A comparison of these curves with those of Fig. 8·11 for three WX3226 gaps filled to a pressure of 110 cm of mercury and operated under the same conditions shows that the range of a new CV125 is equivalent to that of three of these gaps in series.

Figure 8·34b shows variations in range with life for a CV125 operated at 12 kv, 800 pps, and 0.9 μsec in a 50-ohm circuit.   After 375 hr of operation, this tube was found to fail to deionize at frequent intervals, agreeing with British experience. Failure of this tube is not due to electrode erosion, for it operates satisfactorily after being pumped and refilled. The failure may be due to the formation of nitrogen peroxide, which is known from experience with rotary gaps to have poor deionization characteristics, or it may be due to a reduction in the amount of oxygen to a value that is insufficient to quench metastable atoms of argon after the discharge. This reduction is caused by the combination of oxygen with the molybdenum and tungsten electrodes during operation.[1]

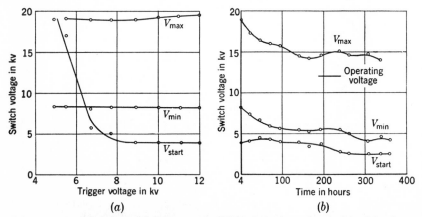

Fig. 8·34.—Variation in voltage range of a CV125 three-electrode gap (*a*) with trigger voltage (new tube), (*b*) with time.

Further comparison of the CV125 with a set of three WX3226 gaps operated under the same conditions at a pressure of 110 cm of mercury shows that a 13-kv trigger voltage is required to obtain the lowest values of V_{min} and V_{start} for the series gaps, whereas 8 kv is sufficient for the three-electrode gap. It is also to be noted that the CV125 requires a high trigger voltage primarily for good starting, whereas series gaps require a high trigger voltage to give a satisfactory operating range as well. The time jitter in the CV125 at 12 kv, 800 pps, and 0.9 μsec in a 50-ohm circuit remains less than 0.09 μsec throughout life, a value that is much less than that for cylindrical-electrode aluminum-cathode gaps. The life of series gaps under the above conditions is considerably longer than that of the CV125, and can exceed 1500 hr. Also, the deionization characteristics of the series gaps are better than those of the trigatrons,

[1] These observations are in accord with reports of work done by the British at Birmingham University. See D. T. Roberts, "Determination of Oxygen and Nitrogen Peroxide in Samples of Gas from Trigatrons Taken at Various Stages of Life," Birmingham University, C. V. D. Report BS/19, 1943.

as is evidenced by the greater decrease in V_M with increasing recurrence frequency for the trigatron than for the series gaps.[1]

Hydrogen-filled Three-electrode Gap.—It would be desirable to combine the advantages of the hydrogen or hydrogen-argon gas filling, which is stable with life, with those of a three-electrode geometry of the trigatron type. Unfortunately, the erosion rate of possible electrode materials in the absence of an oxide coating on the surface is usually high.

An attempt has been made to overcome this difficulty by using electrodes made by sintering tungsten and barium oxide together, with nickel as a binder. Statements concerning the erosion rate of these sintered mixtures have been given in Sec. 8·7. Some three-electrode tubes have been constructed with these materials, but sufficient tests have not yet been made to indicate the stability of their characteristics during life.[2]

THE HYDROGEN THYRATRON

By K. J. Germeshausen

As explained in the introductory paragraph of this chapter, work was started early in the history of the development of pulse generators in order to obtain a satisfactory switch of the thyratron type. The advantages of the thyratron are many: the switch is small and light, it can be triggered accurately by applying low-voltage pulses to the grid, it has a high efficiency, and it can operate over a wide range of plate voltages.

Experimental work was started simultaneously to improve existing mercury thyratrons and to develop tubes of new types. One disadvantage of mercury is its temperature sensitivity; this, however, can be remedied by thermostatic control of the enclosures. There are other difficulties specifically related to pulser operation, such as the long deionizing time and the low voltage drop at which ion velocities destroy the oxide cathode. To eliminate these defects, developmental work was started on a thyratron that would be particularly well suited to pulser operation. Hydrogen was chosen for the filling because it enables high pulse currents to pass through the tube without causing voltage drops great enough to destroy the cathode. Also, the structure of the tubes was designed specifically to withstand high voltages. The developmental work has been successful in creating and putting into production three tubes that provide for a continuous range of pulse power from about 10 to 2500 kw; work has also been started on a tube capable of switching

---

[1] J. R. Dillinger, "General Characteristics of Aluminum Cathode Type Series Gaps," RL Report No. 682-3, Nov. 21, 1945.

[2] K. J. Germeshausen and H. R. Zeller, "Three Electrode Triggered Gap," RL Report No. 880, Oct. 11, 1945.

pulse powers ranging from about 5 to 8 Mw, but has not been completed at the time of this writing.

8·11. General Operating Characteristics of the Hydrogen Thyratron. The use of hydrogen in place of mercury vapor or a rare gas as the filling for thyratrons,[1] appeared to have some real advantage if an adequate life could be obtained. Drewell succeeded in making hydrogen tubes for sweep circuits, but their operating voltage and life were inadequate for pulser applications. His results, however, were considered encouraging enough to warrant further development, and consequently work was started in 1941.

The primary advantage of hydrogen, when used in a thyratron, is the high fall of cathode potential that can occur without injury to the oxide cathode. The destruction voltage, or voltage corresponding to the ion velocity at which destruction of an oxide cathode sets in, is about 30 volts for mercury ions and has about the same order of magnitude for the rare gases, including helium. For hydrogen the destruction voltage is about 600 volts, or 20 times as great. This fact is of considerable importance in the design of a thyratron for operation at high voltages and high pulse currents.

A second advantage of hydrogen-filled tube is the short deionization time that is obtained. In any given circuit this deionization time is about one tenth that of mercury-, argon-, or zenon-filled thyratrons. The only other gas that provides such a short deionization time is helium, which cannot be used because of the cathode destruction previously mentioned.

A serious problem connected with the use of hydrogen in thyratrons is gas cleanup, or the disappearance of the gas during operation. Gas cleanup is caused mainly by the great chemical activity of hydrogen, which combines readily with many substances including, under certain conditions, the oxide cathode. The grade A nickel usually employed in vacuum-tube construction contains reducing agents, such as carbon and silicon, that combine with the hydrogen and promote cleanup. In addition, these nickels may contain other reducing agents, such as magnesium, which do not combine directly with hydrogen, but which can reduce the oxide cathode, releasing free barium. The free barium thus produced combines very readily with hydrogen and can cause a rapid disappearance of the gas in the tube. In order to obtain nickel free from these reducing agents, or other harmful impurities, it was necessary to develop a very pure grade of electrolytic nickel.

In addition to the use of materials of carefully controlled purity, it is important to prevent contamination resulting from improper cleaning or

[1] P. Drewell, *Zeits. f. Techn. Phys.*, **16**, 614, (1936).

handling of the parts. The successful manufacture of hydrogen thyratrons requires a much more rigid control of the various manufacturing
processes than is usual in the manufacture of radio tubes. Great care
must be taken to prevent the inclusion of any substance that can react
chemically with the hydrogen. By proper design and processing, and
by the use of selected materials, pressure cleanup has largely been eliminated and is no longer a serious limitation on tube life.

Since the reducing action of hydrogen on the oxide cathode becomes
serious at temperatures of about 900°C, it is necessary to maintain the
cathode temperature well below this value. A maximum temperature
of 850°C is permissible, but a somewhat lower value is preferable. On
the other hand, cathode emission decreases rapidly at temperatures
below about 800°C; hence, the operating range of cathode temperature
is narrow. The filament voltage must therefore be kept within close
limits, and variations in cathode temperature from tube to tube minimized. Variations in temperature
over the surface of the cathode can
be made much smaller for indirectly heated cathodes than for
filament cathodes; hence, it is desirable that hydrogen tubes have
indirectly heated cathodes.

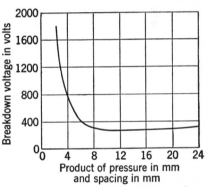

FIG. 8·35.—Plot of breakdown voltage
in hydrogen as a function of the product of
spacing and pressure.

Because of gas cleanup, the gas
pressure is raised as high as possible
by making the spacing between the
anode and grid much smaller than
in the more conventional thyratron
designs. The purpose of the small
spacing can best be explained by
referring to Fig. 8·35, which is a
plot of the breakdown voltage in hydrogen versus the product of spacing and
pressure, the familiar Paschen curve of breakdown in gases. In thyratrons the grid-to-anode spacing is such that the operating point is on the
left-hand portion of the curve, where the breakdown voltage is rising
rapidly as the product of spacing and pressure is reduced. Since the
product of spacing and pressure must be maintained at a value less than
that corresponding to the desired breakdown voltage, high gas pressures
can be obtained only by reducing the spacing. In typical hydrogen
thyratrons, the gas pressure is about 500 microns and the grid-anode
spacing is about 0.0625 to 0.090 in. Smaller spacings make the mechanical assembly difficult, and may result in field emission from the grid.
The perpendicular distance from grid to anode must not exceed the
desired spacing at any point; the grid structure is therefore placed so

that it completely surround the anode, as shown in Figs. 8·36, 8·37, and
8·38.   Long-path discharges between the anode-lead wire and the outside of the grid structure are prevented by surrounding the lead by a glass
sleeve that fits tightly into a collar attached to the grid structure.   From
Fig. 8·36 it is apparent that the distance between
the upper part of the anode lead inside the glass
sleeve and the grid structure is considerably greater
than the shortest spacing from grid to anode.
Breakdown over this relatively long path is prevented partly by the small spacing between the
glass sleeve and the anode lead, and partly by the
fact that the field between the anode lead and

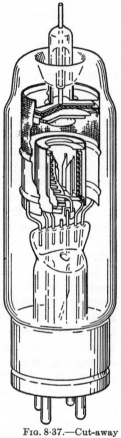

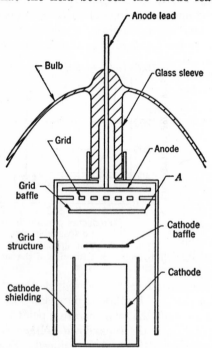

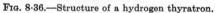

FIG. 8·36.—Structure of a hydrogen thyratron.

FIG. 8·37.—Cut-away
perspective view of the
5C22 hydrogen thyra-
tron.

the grid structure in this region is in such a direction that the acceleration of ions or electrons over the long path is prevented.

    Hydrogen thyratrons differ from the more common thyratron types
in that they are designed with a positive control-grid characteristic.
In order to trigger the tube it is necessary to drive the grid to a positive
voltage sufficient to draw grid current between the grid and the cathode.
Two considerations dictated the positive control characteristic.   First,

positive control simplifies the trigger circuit, since, for most applications, no negative bias supply is required. Second, the extensive baffling between the anode and cathode that is associated with positive control minimizes grid-emission difficulties.

In order to obtain a positive control characteristic, the cathode is completely shielded from the anode field in the manner shown in Fig. 8·36. The grid itself is a perforated, or mesh, section situated just below the anode, and beneath it is a grid baffle, which is attached to the grid. In such a structure the anode field does not extend beyond the point marked A, and there is no opportunity for the anode field to act upon electrons emitted from the cathode, most of which are confined to the region inside the cathode shield and baffle structure. In order to trigger the tube, or to start conduction, it is necessary to draw current between the grid and the cathode. This current produces electrons and ions in the region outside the cathode-shield structure, some of which reach the point A. As soon as the electron density at A is high enough, the anode field is able to produce ionization in the region above the grid baffles, and breakdown takes place. During the initial stages of the breakdown, the anode current is drawn from the grid as a glow discharge because the anode field is unable to penetrate into the grid-cathode space. This glow discharge raises the grid to a high positive potential, which quickly ionizes the grid-cathode region to an

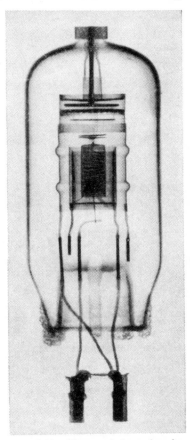

FIG. 8·38.—X-ray photograph of a hydrogen thyratron.

extent sufficient to bring the grid back almost to the cathode potential. The entire breakdown process described above occurs in 0.02 to 0.07 μsec, which is thus the ionization time.

Tube Characteristics and Operation.—Photographs of the three hydrogen thyratrons that have been developed are shown in Fig. 8·39, and their basic operating characteristics may be found in Table 8·4.

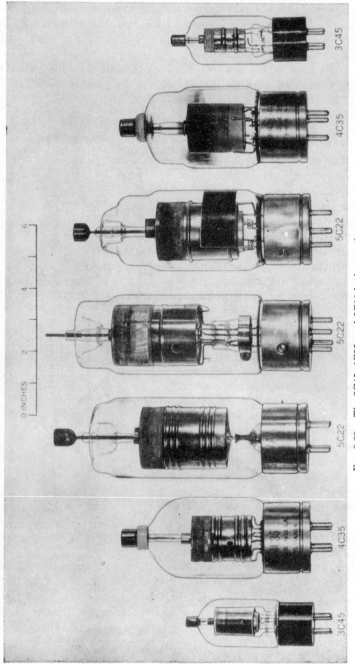

FIG. 8·39.—The 3C45, 4C35, and 5C22 hydrogen thyratrons.

TABLE 8·4.—OPERATING CHARACTERISTICS OF THE 3C45, 4C35, AND 5C22 HYDROGEN
THYRATRONS

	3C45	4C35	5C22
Maximum forward anode voltage in kv..................	3	8	16
Maximum inverse anode voltage in kv...................	3.0	8.0	16.0
Maximum value of inverse anode voltage in kv for 25 μsec after pulse...	1.5	2.5	5.0
Maximum anode pulse current in amp...................	35	90	325
Pulse power into resistance load in kw..................	50	350	2500
Maximum average anode current in ma..................	45	100	200
Cathode: indirectly heated, unipotential................			
Heater power in watts...............................	15	40	65
Heater voltage in volts (±7.5%).......................	6.3	6.3	6.3
Maximum pulse duration in μsec.......................	6	6	6
Grid bias in volts....................................	0	0	0
Minimum trigger voltage in volts......................	150	150	150
Tube weight in grams................................	64	194	273
Tube life at maximum ratings in hours.................	500	500	500

A simplified diagram of a thyratron pulser is given in Fig. 8·40.

Hydrogen thyratrons are designed to work primarily into a load impedance of 50 ohms and, in the case of the 3C45 and 4C35, maximum pulse power is obtained at this level. The 5C22 supplies its maximum pulse power at 25 ohms; however, the average power is the same as at

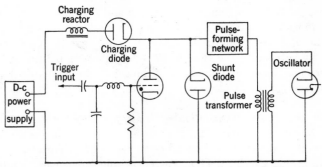

FIG. 8·40.—A typical hydrogen-thyratron pulser circuit.

50 ohms. Any desired load impedance may be used, provided that none of the maximum tube ratings are exceeded. In general, both pulse and average power are less if a load impedance of other than the optimum value is used.

The life of the thyratron depends greatly on the operating voltage, current, and recurrence frequency. A typical life of about 500 hr can be obtained at the maximum voltage and current ratings, with recurrence frequencies of 2000 pps for the 3C45 and 4C35 and 1000 pps for the 5C22. The length of life is considerably increased by reducing any of these parameters, and, in general, the operating level of thyratron pulsers should be kept somewhat below the maximum tube ratings. A much longer tube life can be obtained by operating the tubes well below these ratings; for instance, 4C35's operated at 4 kv and 45- to 50-amp pulse current usually give 2500 to 3000 hours of satisfactory service. Improvements in manufacturing methods are constantly increasing the life expectancy, which may soon be at least 1000 hr at full rating.

Since the thyratron is a unidirectional switch, negative charges are left on the network if the load impedance is too low. When the load impedance varies erratically, as in the case of a sparking-magnetron load, variable negative charges may be left, which seriously affect the forward voltage of the succeeding pulse. In order to remove these negative charges and to minimize or prevent their effect on forward voltage, it is usually desirable to connect a shunt diode across the thyratron. The problem of unidirectional-switch operation is discussed in detail in Chap. 10.

The tube heating time may be reduced by overvolting the heater by as much as 20 per cent, in which case the preheating time for the 5C22 is reduced from five to two minutes. It may also be possible to apply the anode voltage and heater power simultaneously; however, adequate tests and recommendations from the manufacturer are necessary if the present ratings and specifications are not followed exactly.

Hydrogen thyratrons may be mounted and operated in any position, but care must be taken lest the life be reduced by gas cleanup or puncture of the bulb. Gas cleanup is accelerated if the bulb temperature is lowered by subjecting the tube to forced cooling, or if intense r-f fields are present to cause the ionization of the gas. Corona extending to the glass surface causes erratic operation and, eventually, puncture of the bulb.

Series and Parallel Operation of Hydrogen Thyratrons.—It is often possible to satisfy switch requirements for which no single thyratron is suited by the operation of two tubes in series or in parallel.[1] Parallel operation provides twice the load current, while series operation provides twice the load voltage. There are a number of possible circuits, two of which are shown in Figs. 8·41 and 8·42.

In parallel operation, the principal problem that arises is to secure proper division of the current between the two tubes. When the anodes of the two tubes are connected directly, the tube that breaks down first reduces the anode voltage of the second tube so rapidly that it may not

---

[1] Experimental work on series and parallel operation has been carried out at the Evans Signal Laboratory, among other places.

break down at all.   The best way to avoid this difficulty is to use a
balanced reactor in the thyratron-anode circuit, a device that has been
used with gas-tube rectifier circuits.   The reactor is wound so that the
fields of the two halves are in opposition, and with very close coupling
between the two.   When the triggered tube is broken down, the full
anode voltage appears across its half of the reactor, producing an equal
and opposite voltage in the other half of the reactor which abruptly
raises the anode voltage of the second tube to twice its previous value.

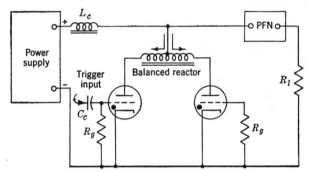

FIG. 8·41.—Parallel operation of thyratrons.

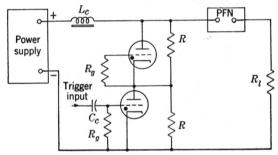

FIG. 8·42.—Series operation of thyratrons.

The grid-to-anode capacitance of the second tube is such that the grid is
pulled positive by the transient voltage, thus triggering the second tube.
Until the currents in the two halves of the reactor are equal, there is
considerable reactance in each anode circuit; however, when they become
equal the net reactance is negligible.   Any tendency of one tube to draw
more current than the other unbalances the reactor and raises the anode
voltage of the lagging tube until the anode currents are again equal.

A practical circuit for the operation of two thyratrons in series is
shown in Fig. 8·42.   Equal division of the voltage across the two thyratrons is obtained by means of the voltage divider comprising the resistors
R.   The minimum value of the resistors R is limited by the excessive

drain on the power supply and by the effect on the peak network voltage. The maximum value is limited by the effect of the thyratron capacitance on the proper division of voltage. When the lower tube is triggered, the cathode potential of the upper tube is abruptly lowered to ground, but the potential of the grid of the upper tube tends to stay fixed because of the grid-anode capacitance. As a result, a positive voltage is applied to the grid of the upper tube, which triggers it. By this means both tubes are rendered conducting.

Special problems related to the effect of pulser design on thyratron performance and, to some extent, to the effect of thyratron characteristics on pulser performance are discussed in the following sections.

8·12. The Anode Circuit. *Variation of Tube Drop with Time.*—The major tube characteristic affecting the performance of the anode circuit

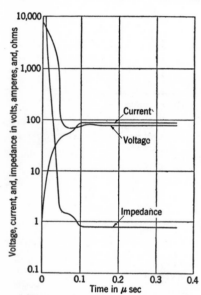

is the variation of tube drop with time. It may be divided into two regions: an initial, or ionization period, when the drop is relatively high, and a conducting period during the pulse when the tube drop is relatively low. In Fig. 8·43 is shown the relation between the tube drop, current, and impedance, as a function of time.[1] The data for the curves were obtained from oscillographic records of the operation of a 4C35 in a 50-ohm pulser circuit. The portion of the curves to the left of 0.05 μsec represent conditions in the tube during the time that the gas is being ionized. This section of the curves is called the ionization period. The portion of the curves to the right of 0.05 μsec, occurring after the gas is fully ionized, is the conducting period during which the tube drop remains relatively constant.

FIG. 8·43.—Tube drop, current, and impedance as a function of time for a 4C35 hydrogen thyratron ($V_N = 8$ kv, $I_p = 90$ amp, $\tau = 1.1$ μsec.

Ionization time and the shape of the voltage-time curve during ionization are almost entirely independent of the external circuit, that is, they are a function of tube characteristics only, mainly because of the high anode voltages employed in pulser applications, which insure that any electrons present are accelerated sufficiently to ionize the gas. The

[1] S. J. Krulikoski, "Hydrogen Thyratrons in Pulse Generator Circuits," **RL** Report No. 953, Mar. 18, 1946.

ionization time depends primarily on the probability of the collision of electrons with hydrogen molecules, and on the length of the path to be ionized.   The factors affecting ionization time are, therefore, primarily the tube dimensions and gas pressure; the quality of the cathode has little influence on this characteristic.   The ionization time is approximately

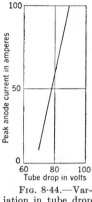

FIG. 8·44.—Variation in tube drop during the pulse with anode current.

proportional to the tube dimensions, hence large tubes have a longer ionization time than small tubes.   The ionization time is about 0.03 μsec for the 3C45, 0.045 μsec for the 4C35, and 0.07 μsec for the 5C22 at nominal operating pressures.   Gas pressure has a very marked effect on the ionization time; a high gas pressure materially reduces the time required to establish conduction, whereas a low gas pressure increases it. When the gas pressure becomes very low, the ionization time may become long enough to affect the pulse shape considerably.   Since ionization time is primarily a tube characteristic, parameters such as anode current, rate of rise of anode current, and initial plate voltage have very little effect on the time required to establish conduction.

After conduction has been established the tube drop during the pulse is a function of tube current and of the quality of the oxide cathode.   As can be seen from Fig. 8·44, the tube drop during the pulse does not vary appreciably with anode current.   On the other hand, the quality of the cathode has as much effect on the tube drop as the variations in current.   For most pulser applications, the tube drop has a negligible effect on pulser performance.

Tube Dissipation.—Since tube dissipation is one of the factors limiting tube performance, the parameters affecting it deserve considerable attention.   In Fig. 8·45, is shown a

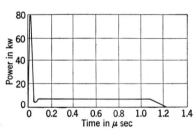

FIG. 8·45.—Plot of tube dissipation vs. time for a single pulse (4C35, $V_N = 8$ kv, $I_p = 90$ amp, $\tau = 1.1$ μsec).

plot of tube dissipation versus time for a single pulse of 1.1-μsec duration.   The data for this curve were obtained from the volt-ampere characteristics of Fig. 8·43, considering the dissipation as the product of tube drop and tube current.   The total integrated area under the curve is 9.8 $\times$ 10^{-3} joules, of which approximately 25 per cent is under the initial spike that occurs during the ioniza-

tion period.   The circuit parameters affecting tube dissipation per pulse are pulse current, pulse duration, anode voltage, and rate of rise of anode current. For short pulses, where a large proportion of the tube dissipation occurs in the initial spike, the most important parameters are the anode voltage and the rate of rise of anode current. For long pulses the factors controlling tube dissipation are the anode current and the pulse duration.

In general, tube dissipation increases with decreasing pulse duration and constant duty ratio, since the average energy dissipated in the initial spike is proportional to pulse recurrence frequency and independent of pulse duration. This effect is accelerated by the increased rate of rise of current associated with the shorter pulses. The tube dissipation for short pulses can be reduced considerably by limiting the rate of rise of anode current. For a given pulser circuit, tube dissipation is also approximately proportional to the square of the applied anode voltage. Excessive tube dissipation shortens the life of the tube and can usually be detected through excess anode heating, which causes the anode to glow with a red color. If the anode of a tube turns red, either it is being operated above the ratings, or the gas pressure is too low.

Forward Anode Voltage.—The forward anode voltage applied to the thyraton is limited by the maximum tube ratings and the method of applying it can considerably influence the maximum pulse recurrence frequency. If the pulses are spaced equally in time, linear charging, resonant charging, and diode charging are all equally satisfactory from the standpoint of obtaining a constant output pulse voltage. There is,

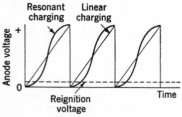

Fig. 8·46.—Anode-voltage waveforms for linear and resonant charging.

however, a significant difference between the anode-voltage waveforms for linear charging and that for resonant charging, as shown in Fig. 8·46. During the period immediately following the pulse the anode voltage is much lower for resonant charging than it is for linear charging. When a positive voltage is applied to the thyratron before it has completely deionized, the tube starts to conduct when the anode voltage reaches the critical reignition voltage, which is about 100 to 200 volts, without the application of a trigger voltage. As a result, continuous conduction in the thyratron usually occurs, which causes the pulser to draw an excessive power-supply current. With resonant charging, the time required to reach this critical reignition voltage is a maximum. Any deviation from this condition causes a decrease in the maximum pulse recurrence frequency.

Inverse Anode Voltage.—Inverse anode voltage may be divided into two types: that which appears immediately after the pulse, usually because of mismatch, and that which appears during the interpulse interval, associated with a-c resonant-charging circuits. Since effect on tube performance is somewhat different in the two cases, they are considered separately. If the load impedance is less than the network impedance, the anode potential becomes negative immediately after the pulse. The amount of this inverse voltage depends on the degree of mismatch, and it should not exceed the rating for the tube. When a high inverse voltage is applied to the anode before the ions in the grid-anode space have time to recombine, the ions are pulled into the anode with high velocity, and cause serious sputtering of the anode material. If the inverse voltage is high enough, a low-impedance arc may form between the anode and the grid, resulting in even more serious sputtering of these surfaces and, since the low-impedance arc removes the normal inverse voltage, the forward voltage of the next pulse is low. The time required for the grid-anode space to deionize is not known accurately, but it is about 5 μsec. Because of the relatively small grid-anode spacing, this time is much shorter than that required for the grid-cathode space to deionize; hence deionization problems are concerned mainly with conditions in the grid-cathode region.

If the load is short-circuited, the thyratron conducts a current twice the normal pulse current, and the inverse voltage on the tube greatly exceeds its rating. Until a means of eliminating magnetron-sparking is found, there does not seem to be any remedy for this condition; however, there is no evidence that the thyratron life is seriously shortened by the amount of sparking that is usually tolerable in a radar transmitter.

For a given circuit, the presence of inverse anode voltage increases the maximum recurrence frequency that can be obtained, before the thyratron starts to conduct continuously.[1] As is shown in Fig. 8·47, the effect of inverse voltage is to increase the time that elapses before the anode potential reaches the reignition voltage. This effect is similar to that caused by the difference between linear and resonant charging as illustrated in Fig. 8·46. Higher re-

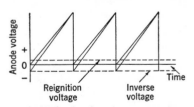

Fig. 8·47.—Anode-voltage waveform with and without inverse voltage.

currence frequencies can be obtained with resonant charging and some inverse voltage on the network. A condition to be avoided is one in which the load impedance is higher than the network impedance. With a mismatch of this type, the anode voltage may not fall below the extinction voltage of the thyratron, and continuous conduction may result.

[1] S. J. Krulikoski, "Technical Data and Operating Notes for the 5C22 Hydrogen Thyratron," RL Report No. 828, Nov. 14, 1945.

The practice of using a shunt diode in thyratron-pulser circuits changes the effect of inverse voltage on thyratron operation. A typical anode-voltage waveform, with linear charging which shows the removal of inverse voltage by a shunt diode, is given in Fig. 8·48. The impedance in the diode circuit is usually so great that the peak inverse voltage is not greatly changed, and the time required to remove the inverse voltage is long compared with the deionization time of the grid-anode space. Hence, sputtering of the anode and grid-anode breakdown are not greatly reduced by the presence of a diode. However, the diode does remove the inverse voltage quickly enough to nullify its effect on the time for deionization of the grid-cathode space, and hence lowers the maximum recurrent frequency.

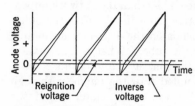

FIG. 8·48.—Anode-voltage waveform showing the removal of inverse voltage by means of a shunt diode.

A-c resonant-charging circuits apply an inverse anode voltage that is comparable to the forward voltage. The maximum inverse voltage usually occurs near the middle of the interpulse interval, after the thyratron has become completely deionized, and hence has no adverse effect on the tube. Test data indicate that life expectancy is probably as great with a-c charging as with d-c charging, except possibly at high recurrence frequencies.

Rate of Rise of Anode Current.—The rate of rise of anode current influences anode dissipation and, under some conditions, may cause cathode sparking. Anode dissipation and its relation to rate of rise of current are discussed in an earlier part of this section. Cathode sparking, although comparatively rare, may occur with very high rates of rise of anode current, particularly when the cathode temperature is low. During the development of hydrogen thyratrons, various limits were placed on the maximum rate of rise of anode current, starting as low as 600 amp/μsec. This figure was based on British experience with mercury thyratrons; however, tests on hydrogen thyratrons have indicated that they are not damaged by a high rate of rise of current, the major limitation on this rate being anode dissipation.

In general, the rate of rise of anode current depends both on the network design and on the pulser design. For type E networks it becomes lower as the number of sections is reduced, and is lower for long pulses than for short pulses. One very troublesome source of high rates of rise of current is the stray capacitance across the thyratron. As shown in Fig. 8·49, this capacitance can originate in the filament transformers for hold-off and shunt diodes, and in the capacitance between the network and its container.   Excessive cabled wiring in the thyratron circuit may also introduce appreciable stray capacitance.

When the thyratron breaks down, these capacitances discharge through the tube, the rate of rise of current being limited only by the wiring inductance and thyratron impedance.   The current flows in the

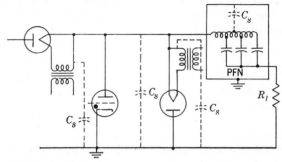

Fig. 8·49.—Typical pulser circuit showing distributed capacitance.

thyratron and not through the load; hence, in checking the thyratron pulse current and the rate of rise of current, it is important to make the measurements at the tube.   For small capacitances, the thyratron current differs only slightly from the load current, as shown in Fig. 8·50a.

Pulser designs have been encountered, however, where the difference was as great as that shown in Fig. 8·50b.   The high-frequency oscillation in the thyratron current is apparently due to oscillations between the distributed capacitance and the inductance of the circuit wiring.   The effects of distributed capacitance may be reduced to a minimum by careful design of the components and circuit layout. For type E networks, the effect of the stray capacitance between the network and the case can be reduced by connecting the coil terminal to the thyratron, thus placing a small inductance in series with

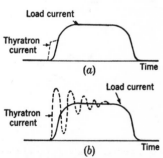

Fig. 8·50.—Waveforms showing load and thyratron current (a) for small distributed capacitances, (b) for large distributed capacitances.

the distributed capacitance of the network.   In some cases it may be necessary to add a small inductance of about 5 μh in series with the thyratron anode lead.   Such an inductance may distort the pulse shape slightly, particularly for short pulses, but it will effectively limit the rate of rise of thyratron current.

8·13. The Grid Circuit.—One of the important advantages of hydrogen thyratrons as compared with other gaseous-discharge switches is their excellent triggering properties. They can be triggered precisely, with very small delay and time jitter, by a low-voltage low-power trigger pulse that can be obtained from receiving-tube circuits. The variation in delay from tube to tube during life and with changes in operating parameters is also small. Because of the importance of precise synchronization, the triggering properties of thyratrons have been carefully studied. It has been found that the major circuit parameters affecting delay and jitter are the amplitude and rate of rise of the trigger pulse, and the thyratron anode voltage. Neither hydrogen pressure nor cathode temperature have much effect on the time delay or jitter as long as they are kept within the normal operating range. The variation in triggering characteristics with circuit parameters has been measured for a large number of tubes. Most of the data has been obtained with the 4C35, but enough tests have been conducted with the other types to demonstrate that the same general conclusions hold.

As has previously been explained, hydrogen thyratrons differ from the more common thyratron types in that they are designed with a positive grid-control characteristic. In order to trigger the tube, it is necessary to drive the grid sufficiently positive to draw grid current between the grid and cathode. The voltage required to start conduction between the grid and cathode and the time that elapses before conduction starts depend on the rate of rise of the applied grid voltage, as shown in Fig. 8·51. When conduction has been established and the grid-cathode space is ionized, the anode-grid space breaks down with a very short delay. As a result of this breakdown, the grid is momentarily raised to a high potential, falling back to a potential equal to the cathode potential plus the normal grid-cathode drop in a time comparable to the thyratron ionization time.

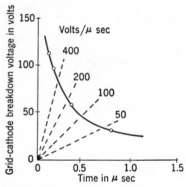

Fig. 8·51.—Grid-to-cathode breakdown voltage as a function of the rate of rise of grid voltage for a 4C35 thyratron.

A pair of synchroscope photographs of the thyratron grid voltage are shown in Fig. 8·52. Trace *A* of Fig. 8·52*a* is the open circuit trigger voltage and trace *B* is the grid voltage when grid-cathode breakdown occurs. The effect on the grid voltage of the glow discharge and subsequent entire breakdown of the anode-cathode space referred to previously, is shown in Fig. 8·52*b*. The anode fires within 0.05 μsec of the time when the grid fires. In addition, the presence of the anode voltage slightly lowers the grid-cathode breakdown voltage.   As the anode voltage is decreased, its effect on grid-cathode breakdown becomes less, and the delay between grid-cathode breakdown and anode breakdown increases; these effects combine to increase the time between the application of grid voltage and anode breakdown.   This time is considered to be the interval between the time when the grid voltage exceeds 6 volts and the time when the anode fires.

Since the delay time is important in the design of precisely synchronized equipment, it has been measured over a wide range of conditions. Figure 8·53 shows the effect of rate of rise of trigger voltage on the delay time with a constant trigger amplitude of 150 volts.   Curve C is the average delay time for a group of 78 tubes, while curves A and B represent the longest and shortest delay times observed.   From these curves it can be seen that, above about 200 to 300 volts μsec, the reduction in time delay is small compared with the increase in the rate of rise of trigger voltage.   In some applications in which a short delay time was desired, trigger pulses rising at the rate of 1200 volts/μsec have been used. For most applications, however, a rate of rise of about 200 volts/μsec is adequate.   The variation in delay time with anode voltage is relatively small, being about 0.07 μsec from full to $\frac{1}{4}$ maximum anode voltage. Decreasing the anode voltage increases the delay time.   There is also some variation in delay time with life; in general, this delay decreases

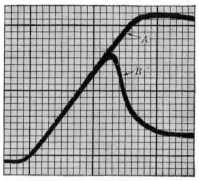

(a) Without anode voltage.

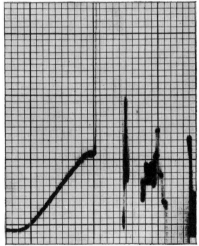

(b) With anode voltage.

FIG. 8·52.—Photographs of synchroscope traces of thyratron grid voltage.

as the tube grows older, the maximum variation in delay with life being about 0.1 μsec.   The effect of trigger impedance on the delay time has been studied over a range from a hundred to several thousand ohms.   It was found that the delay time decreased about 0.1 μsec when the impedance was changed from 2000 to 200 ohms, and that no decrease occurred for impedances less than 200 ohms. The usual trigger circuits have an internal impedance of 300 to 500 ohms.

Time jitter, or the variation in time delay from pulse to pulse, is invariably less than 0.05 µsec with the trigger voltage shown in Fig. 8·52

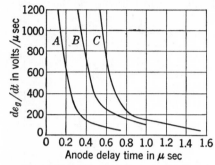

FIG. 8·53.—Effect of the rate of rise of trigger voltage on the anode delay time. Curve A is for the shortest delay, curve B is for the longest delay, and curve C is an average based on A and B and statistical data. (4C35, $V_N = 8$ kv, trigger amplitude $= 150$ v.)

and a trigger impedance of 500 ohms. Until recently, there has been no need for reducing the time jitter below this level, and no equipment for making significant measurements of shorter time intervals. There has, therefore, been no extensive investigation of time jitter, except for a few measurements on the 5C22. The results tabulated in Table 8·5 show the effect that variations in the trigger parameters have on time jitter in the breakdown of a group of twenty-five 5C22's. Trigger A has the minimum amplitude and rate of rise permitted by tube specifications. It has been observed that jitter is associated with the a-c field produced by the cathode heater; however, it can be reduced below a measurable value by the use of d-c heater power.

TABLE 8·5.—EFFECT OF VARIATIONS IN TRIGGER PARAMETERS ON TIME JITTER

Trigger	A	B
Amplitude, volts..............................	150	195
Rate of rise, volts/µsec........................	150	850
Output impedance, ohms.......................	620	230
Average time jitter for 25 5C22's, µsec...........	0.03	0.003

The trigger generator for hydrogen thyratrons may be any of the various low-level pulse generators used in other parts of the radar system. A commonly used source consists of a regenerative pulse generator with a cathode-follower output, as shown in Fig. 8·54. The major requirements are a suitable output pulse shape and a low internal impedance, preferably not more than 500 ohms. As explained in connection with Fig. 8·52b, the beginning of anode-current flow is associated with a high grid-voltage spike, which may approach the anode potential. This spike is usually of very short duration and has little energy associated with it, but it may cause the driving circuit to become unstable, or cause the electrical breakdown of the low-voltage driver components. In order to avoid these difficulties, a low-pass filter circuit is usually connected between the thyratron grid and the driver. Such a filter is essential when using a high-voltage tube like the 5C22, and is desirable with the 4C35 and 3C45. A typical filter circuit is shown in Fig. 8·54; its design is not critical, and in many cases a simple L-section filter is used. Since the voltages in the filter circuit may be very high, both the chokes and the condensers should have a rating of at least 2500 volts.

The impedance to ground in the thyratron grid circuit is important, particularly for high pulse recurrence frequencies. By keeping this impedance low, it is possible to minimize the effects of thyratron anode-grid capacitance, and to influence the deionization characteristics.

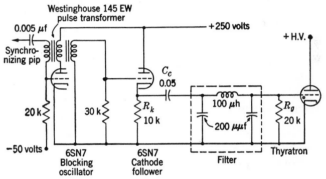

FIG. 8·54.—Typical hydrogen-thyratron trigger generator.

Because of the close grid-anode spacing, hydrogen thyratrons have a large grid-to-anode capacitance of about 10 to 15 $\mu\mu f$. This capacitance causes coupling between the grid and anode circuits, which may pull the grid positive during the anode-charging cycle and cause the tube to break down. The effect of this coupling is most serious at high pulse recurrence frequencies when the rate of rise of anode voltage is high, or under conditions where high-frequency transients may appear at the thyratron anode during the charging cycle. Essentially, the grid-to-ground impedance consists of the thyratron grid resistor in parallel with the series combination of the coupling condenser and the cathode-follower resistor. The values for these components given in Fig. 8·54 are suitable for most applications. In order to obtain a low grid-to-ground impedance, the grid resistor may be replaced by an inductance of 2 to 5 mh. The low d-c resistance of this coil and its low reactance at the charging frequencies insure negligible coupling between the grid and the anode.

At high pulse recurrence frequencies, the deionization time of the grid-cathode region may become a limiting parameter. Since deionization, or the recombination of the ions, takes place largely at the grid surface, it can be accelerated by applying a negative grid bias to pull the ions to the grid. One means of applying a bias is shown in Fig. 8·55. The time required to remove the ions depends on the degree of ionization, which is a function of the pulse current, on the bias voltage, and on the impedance in series with this voltage. In other words, a

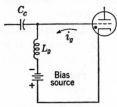

FIG. 8·55.—Thyratron grid circuit with bias.

charge represented by the ions must be removed by a current, i_g, flowing in the bias circuit. Figure 8·56 shows the grid voltage and current for a 5C22 thyratron operating with a peak anode current of 160 amp, and a bias voltage of −45 volts. Two curves are given, one for an inductance L_g of 1 mh, and one for an inductance of 5 mh; they show clearly the effect of series impedance on the rate of removal of ions. Since this rate depends on both the series impedance and the bias voltage, a

similar result can be obtained by increasing the bias voltage and maintaining L_g at 5 mh. The rate of removal of ions is such that the inductance of L_g is more important than its resistance, resistances up to 500 ohms having little effect on the deionization time.

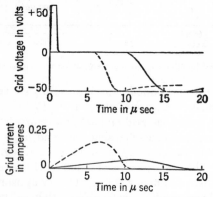

FIG. 8·56.—Thyratron grid voltage and deionization current. The solid and broken lines represent $L_g = 5$ and 1 mh respectively.

In many circuits it is desirable to couple the trigger to the thyratron grid through a transformer. Such circuits must be used with care, since the transformer secondary may present a very high grid impedance, particularly with a cathode-follower driver. After the trigger pulse the tube in the cathode-follower stage is nonconducting, and the transformer primary is shunted only by its cathode resistor, which may be of considerable magnitude. When a transformer is used either the primary or the secondary must be loaded with a suitable impedance.

CHAPTER 9

THE CHARGING CIRCUIT OF THE LINE-TYPE PULSER

By H. J. White, P. C. Edwards, and H. H. Koski[1]

In line-type pulsers, all the energy stored in the pulse-forming network is normally dissipated during the pulse and it is necessary to recharge the network during the interpulse interval. Since the voltage-fed network is used in preference to the current-fed network in the overwhelming majority of practical applications, the detailed discussion of the theory and practice of network charging given in this chapter is restricted to the voltage-fed network. The charging circuit for a voltage-fed network, as shown schematically in Fig. 9·1, consists of a power supply, charging element, pulser load, and the network.

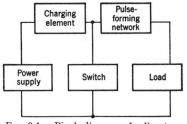

Fig. 9·1.—Block diagram of a line-type pulser.

Although the charging circuit has little effect on the output characteristics of a pulser, the design of the circuit and the choice of the circuit components are of vital importance to the over-all pulser operation and efficiency. One of the important considerations in the design of the circuit is that the same amount of energy must be stored in the network for each pulse. Another consideration is that the charging element must isolate the power supply from the switch during the pulse and for a short time immediately after the pulse. (The isolation during the pulse is necessary to minimize the current flowing from the power supply through the switch during the pulse interval, and the isolation immediately following the pulse is necessary to allow the gaseous-discharge switch to deionize and return to its nonconducting state.) Finally, since the pulsers considered here are power devices, it is important that the charging circuit be designed for high efficiency.

In general, the charging element can be either a resistance or an inductance. A resistance in series with the energy-storage condenser of a voltage-fed network and the power supply is a simple method of meeting the first two requirements stated above, but the inherent efficiency of

[1] Section 9·3 by P. C. Edwards and Sec. 9·8 by H. H. Koski, both of the General Electric Company, Pittsfield, Mass., the remainder of Chap. 9 by H. J. White.

such an arrangement is well known to be never greater than 50 per cent. The use of an inductance as the charging element, however, makes it possible to design the charging circuit for a very high efficiency and to obtain better isolation between the power supply and the switch than is possible with resistance charging under the same conditions of recurrence frequency and pulse power. As a result, inductance charging has been used almost exclusively in pulsers for microwave radar.

The power supply may be either d-c or a-c, depending on the nature of the switch to be used, the pulse power, the recurrence frequency, and the required flexibility. Since the design of the charging circuit depends on the type of power supply, it is logical to divide the discussion into two parts: inductance charging from a d-c supply, and inductance charging from an a-c supply.

INDUCTANCE CHARGING FROM A D-C POWER SUPPLY

9·1. General Analysis of D-c Charging.—It is usually possible to analyze the behavior of the charging circuit by making the following simplifying assumptions:

1. The pulse-forming network is represented by the capacitance C_N appearing between its terminals. The effect of the PFN inductances on the charging voltage wave can be neglected because the frequencies involved during the charging cycles are very low compared with the natural resonant frequency of the network meshes.
2. The pulser switch is assumed to be perfect—that is, its deionization is assumed to be instantaneous after the discharge of the network—and can be considered as an open circuit.
3. The shunt inductance of a pulse transformer used with a unidirectional load has a negligible effect compared with the inductance of the charging reactor.
4. The charging reactor is assumed to be linear, that is, its flux is assumed to be proportional to the current. Its inductance must therefore be constant.

The equivalent charging circuit can then be represented by Fig. 9·2 in which the switch S, not present in actual pulsers, is inserted as a schematic means of starting the charging cycle after the discharge of the pulse-forming network. The differential equation for this circuit, in terms of the instantaneous charge Q_N on the network, is

$$L_c \frac{d^2 q_N}{dt^2} + R_c \frac{dq_N}{dt} + \frac{q_N}{C_N} = E_{bb}, \qquad (1)$$

where R_c is the resistance of the charging inductor and E_{bb} is the power-supply voltage. If it is assumed that there is an initial current $i_c(0)$ in the charging inductance L_c and an initial voltage $v_N(0)$ across the network capacitance C_N, the initial conditions imposed on Eq. (1) are:

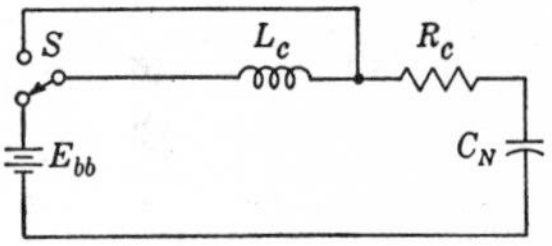

$$q_N(0) = C_N v_N(0)$$

and

$$\left(\frac{dq_N}{dt}\right)_{t=0} = i_c(0).$$

(2)

FIG. 9·2.—Equivalent charging circuit for a line-type pulser.

With these initial conditions, Eq. (1) leads to the following Laplace-transform equation:

$$q_N(p) = \frac{E_{bb}}{L_c p} \frac{1}{p^2 + \frac{R_c}{L_c} p + \frac{1}{L_c C_N}} + \frac{p + \frac{R_c}{L_c} q_N(0)}{p^2 + \frac{R_c}{L_c} p + \frac{1}{L_c C_N}}$$
$$+ \frac{i_c(0)}{p^2 + \frac{R_c}{L_c} p + \frac{1}{L_c C_N}}. \quad (3)$$

Let

$$a = \frac{R_c}{2L_c}; \qquad \omega_0^2 = \frac{1}{L_c C_N}; \qquad \omega^2 = \omega_0^2 - a^2 = \frac{1}{L_c C_N} - \frac{R_c^2}{4L_c^2}.$$

Then Eq. (3) becomes

$$q_N(p) = C_N E_{bb} \left[\frac{1}{p} - \frac{(p+a)+a}{(p+a)^2 + \omega^2}\right] + q_N(0) \frac{(p+a)+a}{(p+a)^2 + \omega^2}$$
$$+ i_c(0) \frac{1}{(p+a)^2 + \omega^2}$$

and the corresponding time function can be obtained by inverse transformation from tables of Laplace-transform pairs. For the oscillatory case, which is the only one of interest here, the time function is

$$q_N(t) = C_N E_{bb} \left[1 - e^{-at}\left(\cos \omega t + \frac{a}{\omega}\sin \omega t\right)\right]$$
$$+ q_N(0)e^{-at}\left(\cos \omega t + \frac{a}{\omega}\sin \omega t\right) + i_c(0)e^{-at}\frac{\sin \omega t}{\omega}. \quad (4)$$

The expression for the network voltage follows immediately.

$$v_N(t) = \frac{q_N(t)}{C_N} = E_{bb} + e^{-at}\left\{[v_N(0) - E_{bb}]\left[\cos \omega t + \frac{a}{\omega}\sin \omega t\right]\right.$$
$$\left. + \frac{i_c(0)}{C_N \omega}\sin \omega t\right\}. \quad (5)$$

By differentiating Eq. (4) and simplifying, the expression for current becomes

$$i_c(t) = e^{-at} \left\{ \frac{E_{bb} - v_N(0)}{L_c} \frac{\sin \omega t}{\omega} + i_c(0) \left[\cos \omega t - \frac{a}{\omega} \sin \omega t \right] \right\}. \quad (6)$$

As stated before, it is necessary that the pulse-forming network be charged to the same potential each time the discharge switch closes if all the output pulses are to be of the same amplitude. Examination of Eq. (5) indicates that, if this condition is met, and if the charging period is the same before all pulses and equal to the recurrence period T_r, the initial conditions, $v_N(0)$ and $i_c(0)$, must be the same for each cycle. The value of $v_N(0)$ depends on the load characteristics and is usually constant, except in cases of faulty load behavior discussed in Chap. 10. Because of the short pulse durations that are involved, the current in the inductance at the beginning of a charging cycle can be considered equal to that at the end of the preceding charging cycle. Then, $i_c(0) = i_c(T_r)$. From Eq. (6),

$$i_c(0) = i_c(T_r) = e^{-aT_r} \left[\frac{E_{bb} - v_N(0)}{L_c} \frac{\sin \omega T_r}{\omega} \right.$$
$$\left. + i_c(0) \left(\cos \omega T_r - \frac{a}{\omega} \sin \omega T_r \right) \right].$$

Solving,

$$i_c(0) = \frac{E_{bb} - v_N(0)}{L_c \omega} \frac{\sin \omega T_r}{e^{aT_r} + \frac{a}{\omega} \sin \omega T_r - \cos \omega T_r}, \quad (7)$$

and the following general expression for network voltage $v_N(t)$ is obtained by substituting Eq. (7) into Eq. (5):

$$v_N(t) = E_{bb} + [E_{bb} - v_N(0)]e^{-at} \left[\frac{\sin \omega t \sin \omega T_r}{\left(e^{aT_r} - \cos \omega T_r + \frac{a}{\omega} \sin \omega T_r \right) L_c C_N \omega^2} \right.$$
$$\left. - \left(\cos \omega t + \frac{a}{\omega} \sin \omega t \right) \right]. \quad (8)$$

The value of network voltage at the time of discharge is given by

$$v_N(T_r) = E_{bb} + [E_{bb} - v_N(0)]e^{-aT_r} \left[\frac{\sin^2 \omega T_r}{\left(e^{aT_r} - \cos \omega T_r + \frac{a}{\omega} \sin \omega T_r \right) L_c C_N \omega^2} \right.$$
$$\left. \cdot \left(\cos \omega T_r + \frac{a}{\omega} \sin \omega T_r \right) \right]. \quad (9)$$

By substituting Eq. (7) in Eq. (6) in the same way a general expression for the current that charges the network is obtained, that is,

$$i_c(t) = \frac{E_{bb} - v_N(0)}{L_c\omega} e^{-at} \frac{e^{aT_r}\sin\omega t + \sin\omega(T_r - t)}{e^{aT_r} + \frac{a}{\omega}\sin\omega T_r - \cos\omega T_r}. \tag{10}$$

If the resistance R_c can be neglected, that is, if there are no circuit losses, $a = 0$, the expressions (8) and (10) for voltage and current may be simplified to

$$v_N(t) = E_{bb} + [E_{bb} - v_N(0)]\frac{\sin\dfrac{2t - T_r}{2\sqrt{L_cC_N}}}{\sin\dfrac{T_r}{2\sqrt{L_cC_N}}} \tag{11}$$

and

$$i_c(t) = \frac{E_{bb} - v_N(0)}{\sqrt{\dfrac{L_c}{C_N}}}\frac{\cos\dfrac{T_r - 2t}{2\sqrt{L_cC_N}}}{\sin\dfrac{T_r}{2\sqrt{L_cC_N}}}. \tag{12}$$

(Equations (11) and (12) are not valid if $T_r/2\sqrt{L_cC_N} = n\pi$.)
The network voltage at the time of discharge given by Eq. (9) reduces to

$$v_N(T_r) = 2E_{bb} - v_N(0). \tag{13}$$

In the case of a lossless circuit, the sum of the initial and final network voltages is always equal to $2E_{bb}$, regardless of the value of the inductance chosen. Practical circuits always have losses, however, but if the "quality factor," Q, of the charging circuit is kept high—10 or more—the ratio of network to power-supply voltage is only slightly less than two, and is not greatly affected by the actual value of inductance that is used.

As a check on the previous computations, it is easy to arrive at Eq. (13) by very simple physical considerations. Again consider the circuit of Fig. 9·2, and assume $R_c = 0$ and an initial voltage $v_N(0)$ on the network. Assume that the energy stored in the inductance is the same at the end as at the beginning of the charging cycle, and that a charge q_N has been transferred from the battery to the network, resulting in a voltage $v_N(T_r)$. Then, to satisfy the law of conservation of energy,

$$q_N E_{bb} = \frac{C_N}{2}\{[v_N(T_r)]^2 - [v_N(0)]^2\}.$$

But the electric charge

$$q_N = C_N[v_N(T_r) - v_N(0)].$$

Hence,

$$q_N E_{bb} = \frac{q_N}{2}[v_N(T_r) + v_N(0)],$$

or

$$v_N(T_r) = 2E_{bb} - v_N(0). \tag{13}$$

Equation (7) indicates that the initial current in the inductance $i_c(0)$ may be either positive, zero, or negative, depending on the relative values of both the natural resonant period, $(2\pi/\omega)$, of the circuit and the pulse recurrence period. The special case where $i_c(0) = 0$ is called "resonant charging," and corresponds to the first zero of $\sin \omega T_r$ as the argument increases, obtained when

$$\omega T_r = \pi. \tag{14}$$

For resonant charging, the expressions (5) and (6) for voltage and current may be simplified to

$$v_N(t) = E_{bb} + e^{-at} [v_N(0) - E_{bb}] \left[\cos \omega t + \frac{a}{\omega} \sin \omega t \right] \tag{15}$$

and

$$i_c(t) = \frac{E_{bb} - v_N(0)}{L_c \omega} e^{-at} \sin \omega t, \tag{16}$$

giving a network voltage at the time of discharge

$$v_N(T_r) = E_{bb} + [E_{bb} - v_N(0)]e^{-aT_r}. \tag{17a}$$

This equation can be rewritten as a function of the quality factor of the circuit. Since

$$Q = \frac{\omega L_c}{R_c}, \qquad a = \frac{R_c}{2L_c}, \qquad \text{and} \qquad aT_r = \frac{\pi}{2Q},$$

the network voltage at the time of discharge is given by

$$v_N(T_r) = E_{bb} + [E_{bb} - v_N(0)]e^{-\frac{\pi}{2Q}}. \tag{17b}$$

It is evident from Eq. (15) that the rate of change of the charging voltage is small in the region of the maximum value. Hence, there are several advantages in operating near resonant charging, namely, small variation in output power even if the time jitter in the switch is large, no overvolting when the switch misfires, and a slow buildup of the voltage after the pulse, allowing a maximum length of time for the switch to deionize. The value of inductance corresponding to resonant charging is readily obtained from Eq. (14), and can be expressed, if the effect of the resistance is neglected, by

$$L_r = \frac{1}{\pi^2 f_r^2 C_N}, \qquad \text{where } f_r = \frac{1}{T_r}.$$

Since the resonant frequency of the circuit is given by

$$f_0 = \frac{1}{2\pi \sqrt{L_c C_N}}$$

it is immediately evident that

$$f_r = 2f_0.$$

For any value of inductance larger than L_r, so-called "linear charging" results, that is, the voltage on the network is still rising at the time the switch is fired. At equilibrium, the voltage is essentially the same as that obtained by resonant charging when a choke with the same Q is used. In this case, the current in the charging choke never reaches zero, and the degree of linearity of both the charging voltage and current depends on the ratio of the actual circuit inductance to that which would produce resonance. By taking advantage of linear charging the same value of inductance can be used throughout large ranges of recurrence frequencies and pulse-forming-network capacitances. Care must be taken to insure that the switch operation is free from time jitter, and that the inductance current is small enough to allow the switch to deionize. Satisfactory deionization can usually be obtained by allowing a small inverse voltage to appear on the network after the pulse.

If the value of charging inductance is made smaller than that corresponding to resonant charging, the initial current $i_c(0)$ is negative, and T_r is longer than one half the natural period of the circuit. Consequently, additional losses occur in the circuit, and the pulse-forming network must be able to withstand a voltage higher than that at which the discharge takes place. For these reasons, the pulse recurrence period is never allowed, in practice, to become more than about 10 per cent larger than one half the natural period of the circuit. If other requirements of the pulser dictate the use of a small value of charging inductance, a simple artifice is used: a charging diode is connected in series between the charging reactor and the pulse-forming network. This diode prevents reversal of current, and the voltage on the pulse-forming network assumes the shape indicated by Eq. (17) until the maximum value is reached. Except for possible leakage, the voltage remains at a maximum until the switch is fired. The shapes of charging-voltage and current waves for typical charging circuits and values of inductance are shown in Fig. 9·3 where the inductance L_r corresponds to the special case of resonant charging. It is therefore evident that inductance charging from a d-c power supply allows a great flexibility in the operation of a line-type pulser. This feature has been largely responsible for making the line-type pulser a competitor of the hard-tube pulser where variable pulse durations and recurrence frequencies are required; a pulser of this type has been produced with pulse durations varying in the ratio of one to twenty and recurrence frequencies varying in the ratio of one to eight.

Two quantities—the average and effective current—are necessary to the study of both the pulser charging circuit and charging inductance.

They can be obtained by integration over the charging period, using the well-known relations

$$I_{c_{av}} = \frac{1}{T_r} \int_0^{T_r} i_c(t) \, dt,$$

and

$$I^2_{c_{rms}} = \frac{1}{T_r} \int_0^{T_r} [i_c(t)]^2 \, dt.$$

It is easier, however, to obtain the average current by considering the

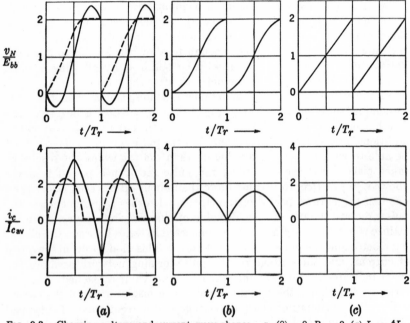

Fig. 9·3.—Charging-voltage and current wave shapes. $v_N(0) = 0$, $R_c = 0$, (a) $L_c = \frac{1}{3}L_r$, (b) $L_c = L_r$, (c) $L_c = 4L_r$. The dotted lines correspond to the use of a charging diode.

charge on the network, thus

$$I_{c_{av}} = \frac{q_N}{T_r} = f_r C_N [v_N(T_r) - v_N(0)]. \tag{18}$$

The expression for the effective value of the current is sufficiently accurate for most purposes if losses are neglected. The current $i_c(t)$ is given by Eq. (12); therefore,

$$I_{c_{rms}}^2 = \frac{1}{T_r} \int_0^{T_r} \frac{[E_{bb} - v_N(0)]^2}{\frac{L_c}{C_N} \sin^2 \frac{T_r}{2 \sqrt{L_c C_N}}} \cos^2 \frac{(T_r - 2t)}{2 \sqrt{L_c C_N}} dt$$

$$= \frac{[E_{bb} - v_N(0)]^2}{2 \frac{L_c}{C_N} \sin^2 \frac{T_r}{2 \sqrt{L_c C_N}}} \left(1 + \frac{\sqrt{L_c C_N}}{T_r} \sin \frac{T_r}{\sqrt{L_c C_N}} \right). \quad (19)$$

The ratio of $I_{c_{rms}}$ to $I_{c_{av}}$, obtained from Eqs. (19), (18), and (13), is known as the "form factor," that is,

$$\frac{I_{c_{rms}}}{I_{c_{av}}} = \frac{T_r}{\sqrt{2 L_c C_N}} \frac{\sqrt{1 + \frac{\sqrt{L_c C_N}}{T_r} \sin \frac{T_r}{\sqrt{L_c C_N}}}}{2 \sin \frac{T_r}{2 \sqrt{L_c C_N}}}. \quad (20)$$

For the special case of resonant charging, where $T_r/\sqrt{L_c C_N} = \pi$, the form factor reduces to $\pi/2 \sqrt{2} = 1.11$, the expected value for a sine wave. As the charging inductance increases, the form factor decreases and approaches unity, as is to be expected since the current approaches a constant value as the value of the inductance approaches infinity.

The efficiency of inductance charging can be readily obtained as the ratio of the energy supplied to the network during the charging cycle to the energy taken from the power supply during the same period. Thus

$$\eta_c = \frac{\frac{1}{2} C_N [v_N^2(T_r) - v_N^2(0)]}{E_{bb} I_{c_{av}} T_r}$$

Substituting $I_{c_{av}}$ from Eq. (18) and simplifying,

$$\eta_c = \frac{v_N(T_r) + v_N(0)}{2 E_{bb}} \quad (21)$$

For the case of resonant charging, $v_N(T_r)$ is given by Eq. (17b) and Eq. (21) may be simplified to

$$\eta_c = \frac{1 + e^{-\frac{\pi}{2Q}}}{2} + \frac{v_N(0)}{E_{bb}} \frac{1 - e^{-\frac{\pi}{2Q}}}{2} \approx 1 - \frac{\pi}{4Q} \left(1 - \frac{v_N(0)}{E_{bb}} \right). \quad (22)$$

In many cases, $v_N(0)$ is equal to zero, and the charging efficiency is given simply by

$$\eta_c = 1 - \frac{\pi}{4Q} \quad (22a)$$

It is seen that the efficiency varies from about 92 to 96 per cent values of Q ranging from 10 to 20, whereas for resistance charging the efficiency is only 50 per cent.

9·2. Practical D-c Charging Reactors.—The approximate ranges of values of inductance, average-current, peak-voltage, and recurrence-frequency requirements for the majority of d-c charging reactors used in microwave-radar applications are as follows:

Inductance	1 to 100 henrys
Average Current	0.01 to 1.0 amp
Peak Voltage	1 to 30 kv
Pulse Recurrence Frequency	200 to 4000 pps

The inductance and current requirements are such that it is nearly always advantageous to use iron-core inductors. Because of the high network voltages encountered and the surge voltage that appears between turns at the high-voltage end when the switch is closed, very careful insulating and processing of the units are required. Oil impregnation with hermetic sealing is used almost entirely for voltages higher than about 5 kv.

Linearity Requirements for D-c Charging Reactors.—In the theoretical treatment of d-c inductance charging, a linear reactor of constant inductance is assumed. Linear, or approximately linear, inductors are also the most satisfactory in practice. As anticipated from physical considerations, small departures from linearity affect the results only slightly. Large variations in the charging inductance produced by saturation of the iron core are usually not permissible because of the excessive power loss and the possibility of operating in a region of nonrepeating charging voltage.

In the theoretical discussion of d-c charging it is shown that, when using a linear charging choke, repeating transients may occur under all conditions. The proof is not valid when the inductance varies with the current or, more specifically, when the total magnetic flux in the reactor is not proportional to the current. For a nonlinear reactor, the differential equation for the charging current must be written in the form

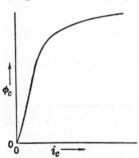

FIG. 9·4.—Flux ϕ_c as a function of current i_c for a charging reactor.

$$\frac{N_c}{10^8}\frac{d\phi_c}{dt} + R_{cc}i + \frac{1}{C_N}\int i_c\,dt = E_{bb}, \quad (21)$$

where N_c is the number of turns on the reactor and ϕ_c is the total flux, which is assumed to be confined to the core. The total flux ϕ_c is a function of the charging current, $\phi_c = \phi(i_c)$, which may be found by experiment and has the form shown in Fig. 9·4. Equation (21) may then be solved graphically or numerically for $i_c(t)$. It should be noted, however, that this method of solution does not prove that the repeating transients required for stable d-c charging exist.

At currents sufficiently below saturation, $\phi_c \approx k i_c$ and the reactor becomes approximately linear. As the core becomes saturated, the incremental inductance $N_c \dfrac{d\phi_c}{di_c}$, becomes very small, and large increases in current are necessary to maintain a given voltage across the reactor. As a result high peak currents occur in the reactor when d-c charging is used.

Experimental charging-current and voltage waveforms for a typical nonlinear reactor are shown in Fig. 9·5. At $I_{c_{av}} = 44$ ma, the charging-current waveshapes are the same as those to be expected from a linear choke. At 50 ma, their loops have become quite peaked, indicating the

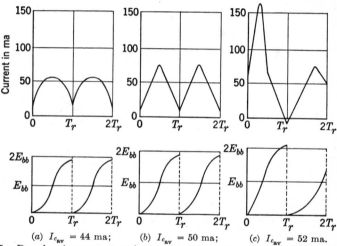

(a) $I_{c_{av}} = 44$ ma;   (b) $I_{c_{av}} = 50$ ma;   (c) $I_{c_{av}} = 52$ ma.

FIG. 9·5.—D-c charging current and network voltage obtained from nonlinear charging reactor.

onset of saturation. Finally at 52-ma average current, the loops no longer repeat from cycle to cycle, but rather repeat in alternate cycles, one cycle having a much higher peak current and condenser voltage than the other. This occurrence indicates a high degree of saturation and, of course, is not permissible in practice. A general explanation follows.

At low average currents there is no flux saturation of the iron core, and the charging waves are those for a linear reactor. As the average or direct current is raised, a point is reached where the reactor starts to become saturated at the current peaks. This saturation lowers the incremental inductance, which in turn increases the peak current. The effect tends to be regenerative and somewhat unstable, and causes the current peaks to increase rapidly in amplitude as the direct current is raised. At the same time, the period of the $L_c C_N$-circuit decreases, causing the charging voltage to overshoot and the charging current to become negative before the switch is fired. As a result, the reactor inductance remains high for a longer period on the following cycle, and the current is thereby prevented from reaching the high peak value of the preceding cycle. Since a higher inductance also means a longer charging period, the reactor current still has a positive value at the instant when the network discharges. Saturation is encouraged by this positive value of the initial current, and the high and low current loops are repeated alternately in a perfectly stable manner. The whole phenomenon occurs because the reactor has a relatively high average inductance on one cycle and a relatively low average inductance on the following cycle.

The failure to obtain cycle-to-cycle repeating transients is a good illustration of the statement made earlier that repeating transients may or may not be obtained in any case, and that the proof of their existence is limited to linear reactors. Linearity is therefore important in the design of charging reactors for pulsers; however, its advantages have to be weighed against its cost.

It is possible to make charging reactors with any desired degree of linearity, but, in general, they are larger and heavier, the stricter the linearity requirement. Thus, for use in airborne sets, they are usually made somewhat nonlinear in order to save weight and size. When weight is not an important factor, the majority of charging reactors for pulsers designed at the Radiation Laboratory satisfy the following conditions for linearity and inductance variations.

1. Linearity. The inductance shall not change by more than 5 per cent measured at rated full-load and at half the rated full-load direct current.
2. Inductance value. The inductance shall be within the tolerance range of from +6 to −2 per cent of the design value.

Charging reactors for airborne applications are usually specified on the basis of samples that are tested in an electrical model of the pulser unit. Reactors having varying degrees of nonlinearity are tried until a satisfactory compromise is obtained between linearity and heating on the one hand and weight and size on the other hand. This method of design is justified on the basis of the large amount of adjustment necessary for airborne sets, and of the very large numbers in which these sets usually are made.

Inductance Measurements.—Inductance-measuring circuits are designed to simulate the current wave shapes for d-c resonant charging, which consist of a series of half sine-wave loops. Such a current can be obtained exactly by using a line-type pulser of adequate voltage and current capacities, but this method is very awkward, inconvenient, and expensive.   The voltage and current wave shapes can be simulated by the output of a full-wave rectifier consisting of an LR-circuit of the proper ratio.[1]   This method, on the other hand, is rather slow and inaccurate because it involves adjustment of the resistance until the wave

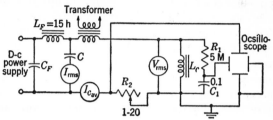

Fig. 9·6.—Circuit for measuring the inductance of a charging reactor.

becomes tangent to the zero axis on an oscilloscope.   Hence, the simulating circuit shown in Fig. 9·6 has been used in preference to both the previous methods, and its explanation follows.

Superimposed direct and 60-cycle alternating currents are passed through the reactor L_c under test, the alternating current being supplied by means of a transformer and the direct current by means of a d-c power supply to which an additional filter section $C_F L_F$ has been added.   The capacitance C provides a very low impedance path for alternating currents, and an accurate measurement of the alternating component of the current may be obtained by inserting an accurate a-c milliammeter in series with C.

In operation, the direct current is adjusted to the desired value and the alternating current is then adjusted so as to have a peak value equal to the direct current.   For this condition, assuming a perfectly linear reactor and a purely sinusoidal voltage, the current wave becomes tangent to the zero axis and rises to a peak value equal to twice the direct current, as illustrated in Fig. 9·7.

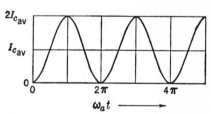

Fig. 9·7.—Current through the charging reactor in the inductance-measuring circuit.

The magnitude of the alternating current to be used is calculated from the relation

$$I_{c_{a-c}} = \frac{I_{c_{av}}}{\sqrt{2}}. \tag{22}$$

[1] A. C. Donovan, "The Measurement and Design of D-C Resonant Charging Chokes," RL Report No. 51-14, Nov. 23, 1942.

The value of L_c is given by

$$L_c = \frac{V_{\text{rms}}}{\omega_a I_{c_{\text{a-c}}}},\tag{23}$$

where the applied angular frequency $\omega_a = 377$ for 60-cycle voltage. The use of 60-cycle voltage is preferred because both the frequency and wave shape supplied by the public utilities usually are accurately controlled, and also because 60-cycle frequency allows the use of relatively low alternating voltages to obtain the necessary (and sometimes high) values of alternating current. The meters used should be accurate to 1 per cent or better in order to obtain suitable accuracy for the inductance L_c.

The ratio of peak to average current for the wave of Fig. 9·7 is 2/1, whereas the ratio obtained in the pulser circuit for a linear reactor and resonant, charging is $\pi/2 = 1.57$. The test circuit therefore imposes a higher peak current in the reactor than it will carry in actual service. The increase, which is by a factor of $4/\pi = 1.27$ for d-c resonant charging, may be regarded as a safety factor in the measurement. The factor is greater for linear charging, approaching the value 2 in the limit. Advantage may sometimes be taken of the decreased peak current occurring for linear charging in order to decrease the size of the reactor core.

When L_c is nonlinear, the method of measurement outlined above gives an approximate average value for L_c over the current range that is used. This value is satisfactory for checking inductors against the linearity and inductance conditions given in the preceding section.

The inductance-measuring equipment usually incorporates an oscilloscopic viewing system for directly observing the B-H curve for the reactor under test. In Fig. 9·6 these added elements consist of the resistor R_2, the resistor and condenser R_1 and C_1, and the oscilloscope. The voltage across R_2 at each instant is proportional to the magnetizing force of the reactor, since

$$V_{R_2} = I_c R_2 = \frac{H_c \times 10}{4\pi N_c} R_2,$$

and is applied to the horizontal deflecting plates. The voltage across C_1, which is applied to the vertical deflecting plates, is proportional to the flux density, as is shown by the following calculations. Neglecting the voltage drop across the reactor resistance, the voltage across $R_1 C_1$ is given by

$$V_{L_c} = \frac{N_c}{10^8} \frac{d\phi_c}{dt} = \frac{N_c A}{10^8} \frac{dB_c}{dt},$$

where A is the cross-sectional area of the core. If the values of R_1 and C_1 are chosen so that the current in that circuit is determined almost exclusively by the resistance, the voltage across C_1 is given by

$$V_{C_1} = \frac{1}{C_1} \int i \, dt = \frac{1}{C_1} \int \frac{V_{L_c}}{R_1} \, dt = \frac{N_c A}{R_1 C_1 \times 10^8} \int \frac{dB_c}{dt} \, dt = \frac{N_c A}{R_1 C_1 \times 10^8} B_c.$$

The degree of linearity of a charging reactor is probably best shown by means of oscillograms. For an ideal perfectly linear reactor having no losses, the *B-H* oscillogram consists simply of two straight lines enclosing zero area. The *B-H* oscillogram for a well-designed iron-core

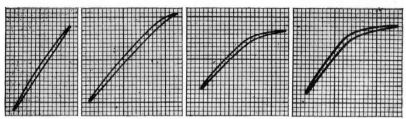

(a) $I_{c_{av}} = 0.050$
amp,
$L_c = 31.6$
henrys.

(b) $I_{c_{av}} = 0.100$ amp,
$L_c = 28.1$ henrys.

(c) $I_{c_{av}} = 0.125$ amp,
$L_c = 22.5$ henrys.

(d) $I_{c_{av}} = 0.150$ amp,
$L_c = 18.8$ henrys.

$$I_{c_{a-c}}/I_{c_{av}} = 0.70$$

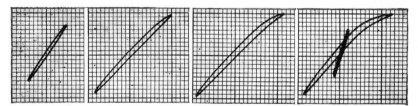

(e) $I_{c_{av}} = 0.050$
amp,
$L_c = 31.1$
henrys,

(f) $I_{c_{av}} = 0.100$ amp,
$L_c = 28.0$ henrys,

(g) $I_{c_{av}} = 0.125$ amp,
$L_c = 25.9$ henrys,

(h) $I_{c_{av}} = 0.150$ amp,
$L_c = 22.5$ henrys.

$$I_{c_{a-c}}/I_{c_{av}} = 0.40.$$

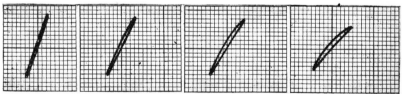

(i) $I_{c_{av}} = 0.100$
amp,
$L_c = 29.0$
henrys.

(j) $I_{c_{av}} = 0.125$ amp,
$L_c = 26.5$ henrys.

(k) $I_{c_{av}} = 0.175$ amp,
$L_c = 23.9$ henrys.

(l) $I_{c_{av}} = 0.200$ amp,
$L_c = 19.2$ henrys.

$$I_{c_{a-c}}/I_{c_{av}} = 0.10.$$

Fig. 9·8.—*B-H* oscillograms for a typical d-c charging reactor rated at $I_{c_{av}} = 0.10$ amp, *B* is vertical and *H* is horizontal.

reactor departs only slightly from the ideal case as it consists of two slightly bowed lines that form a narrow *B-H* loop of small area. A good example of such a *B-H* loop for a reactor tested at half-rated direct cur-

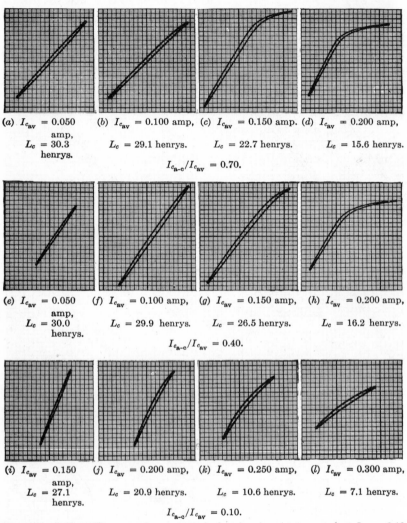

(a) $I_{c_{av}}$ = 0.050 amp, L_c = 30.3 henrys. (b) $I_{c_{av}}$ = 0.100 amp, L_c = 29.1 henrys. (c) $I_{c_{av}}$ = 0.150 amp. L_c = 22.7 henrys. (d) $I_{c_{av}}$ = 0.200 amp, L_c = 15.6 henrys.

$$I_{c_{a-c}}/I_{c_{av}} = 0.70.$$

(e) $I_{c_{av}}$ = 0.050 amp, L_c = 30.0 henrys. (f) $I_{c_{av}}$ = 0.100 amp, L_c = 29.9 henrys. (g) $I_{c_{av}}$ = 0.150 amp, L_c = 26.5 henrys. (h) $I_{c_{av}}$ = 0.200 amp, L_c = 16.2 henrys.

$$I_{c_{a-c}}/I_{c_{av}} = 0.40.$$

(i) $I_{c_{av}}$ = 0.150 amp, L_c = 27.1 henrys. (j) $I_{c_{av}}$ = 0.200 amp, L_c = 20.9 henrys. (k) $I_{c_{av}}$ = 0.250 amp, L_c = 10.6 henrys. (l) $I_{c_{av}}$ = 0.300 amp, L_c = 7.1 henrys.

$$I_{c_{a-c}}/I_{c_{av}} = 0.10.$$

FIG. 9·9.—*B-H* oscillograms for a typical d-c charging reactor rated at $I_{c_{av}}$ = 0.19 amp, *B* is vertical and *H* is horizontal.

rent is shown in Fig. 9·8a. The onset of saturation of the reactor core when the direct current is increased to the rated value is shown in Fig. 9·8b. Further increases in the current produce core saturation over a greater range of the *B-H* loop (Fig. 9·8c and 9·8d.)

The saturated portion of the loop has a slope that is characteristic of the inductance of the equivalent air-core reactor. For example, in Fig. 9·8d the relative slope of the steep to the flat portion of the *B-H* loop is about 20/1, which indicates that the inductance is increased by a factor of about 20 when the air core is replaced by an iron core of the same size. The corresponding ratio for the curve of Fig. 9·9d for another reactor is about the same.

The oscillograms in Fig. 9·8 are all for the same reactor, but are taken for different values of the current ratio $I_{c_{a\text{-}c}}/I_{c_{av}}$, the ratios being 0.70 for Fig. 9·8d, 0.40 for Fig. 9·8e–h and 0.10 for Fig. 9·8i–l. The $I_{c_{a\text{-}c}}/I_{c_{av}}$ current ratio of 0.70 corresponds to the test condition, the ratio of 0.40 to sine-wave or d-c resonant charging, and the ratio of 0.10 to nearly linear charging.   In the case of linear charging, it should be noted that the *B-H* loops for large direct currents (Figs. 9·8k and l) do not show the two-slope character, but rather are relatively linear.   This linearity is a characteristic of the *B-H* loops that is to be expected when the component of alternating current is relatively small.[1]

The oscillograms of Fig. 9·9 are similar to those of Fig. 9·8, but are for a reactor of somewhat different design.   The latter reactor is definitely nonlinear when operated at its rated current of 0.190 amp.   In a pulser circuit it will therefore give rise to a charging wave of the same general character as that previously shown in Fig. 9·5.   It is therefore unsuitable as a d-c resonant-charging reactor for a current of 0.190 amp, although for currents of 0.100 amp, or possibly 0.125 amp, it would be satisfactory.

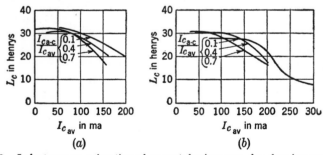

FIG. 9·10.—Inductance as a function of current for iron-core d-c charging reactors, (a) linear reactor (see Fig. 9·8), (b) nonlinear reactor (see Fig. 9·9).

The *B-H* oscillograms thus serve as a rapid and rather sensitive visual test of the linearity of a reactor and of its suitability as a charging choke; however, they should always be supplemented by meter measurements in

[1] For a discussion of the magnetic characteristics of iron under these circumstances, see Members of the Staff of the Department of Electrical Engineering, Massachusetts Institute of Technology, *Magnetic Circuits and Transformers*, Wiley, New York, 1943, pp. 197–202.

order to determine the numerical value of the inductance. Figure 9·10 shows the results of such measurements for the same two reactors.

The inductance of d-c charging reactors can also be measured by a power bridge.[1] The voltage supplied to the bridge circuit is obtained by the addition of a-c and d-c voltages in such a way that the peak alternating current is equal to the direct current. Inductance and quality-factor measurements made with the power bridge can be accurate to within $\frac{1}{2}$ and 1 per cent respectively.

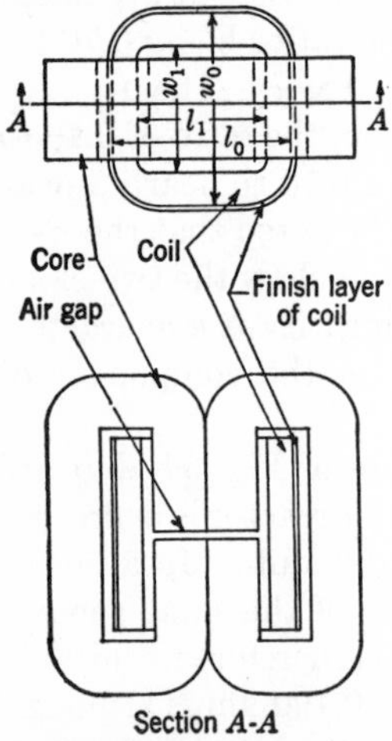

9·3 The Design of D-c Charging Reactors[2]. Figures 9·11 and 9·12 show the usual form of the d-c resonant-charging reactor. The essential elements of a complete reactor are the coil, the core, the air gap in the core, and the enclosing case. Accuracy in both design and manufacture is necessary to obtain reactor characteristics that are within specified limits.

Core Design.—The degree of linearity of the inductance is determined by the relationship between the characteristics of the core material and those of the air gap. The following limits, however, have been found to apply generally to core steels:

1. Maximum flux density in the core = 55 kilolines/in[2].

2. Ratio of the air-gap spacing to the mean length of the magnetic path ≥ 0.6 per cent.

Section *A-A*
FIG. 9·11.—Sketch of d-c resonant-charging reactor.

If the current density in the copper and the flux density in the core are held constant, a larger gap requires a greater number of turns in the coil and a smaller cross section for the core in order to produce a given inductance. Thus, as long as the above limits are met, the designer has the freedom to reduce the weight of either the copper or the iron. The ratio of copper to iron in the reactor is important from the standpoint of low cost and high operating efficiency.

Laminations 0.014 in. thick can be operated at frequencies up to 600 cycles/sec, but for frequencies up to 15 kc/sec the thickness should not exceed 0.005 in. For any given operating frequency and steel thickness the designer can control the core loss by varying the peak operating flux density. The operating frequency to be used in the design is the resonant frequency of the charging circuit of the pulser.

Coil Design.—Coils for resonant-charging reactors as well as for a-c

---

[1] *Standard Handbook for Electrical Engineers*, 7th ed., McGraw-Hill, New York, 1941, pp. 180–185.

[2] By P. C. Edwards of the General Electric Company, Pittsfield, Mass.

resonant-charging transformers (see Sec. 9·8) must withstand continued electrical impulses, as the voltage across the coil reverses in polarity in a few microseconds when the pulser switch closes. This condition is considerably more severe than that to which normal reactors and transformers are subjected.

The distributed capacitance that occurs between the coil turns and the winding layers has several effects upon the circuit: it increases the losses by the dissipation of the stored energy, $\frac{1}{2}C_sV_N^2$, at the time the switch closes; it tends to detune the charging circuit, an effect which is small except for very short pulses; in the case of d-c charging, it causes some impulse voltage to be applied to the rectifier circuit; and, during

FIG. 9·12.—Core-and-coil assembly of a resonant-charging reactor. (*Courtesy of General Electric Co.*)

the discharge of the pulse-forming network, it produces an uneven voltage distribution throughout the coil, thus placing an undue stress on certain parts of the coil conductor and layer insulation.

The distribution of impulse voltage can be improved by designing a coil so that the radial build is about $\frac{1}{2}$ to $\frac{2}{3}$ the length of the coil winding layer. This ratio is a compromise between that needed for good impulse-voltage distribution and that for a low coil capacitance. As the ratio of the coil dimensions decreases the voltage distribution improves, but the capacitance becomes greater. It is possible to control the distribution of impulse voltage by means of an electrostatic shield that is applied over the finish layer of the coil and connected to the output lead, as shown in Fig. 9·11. This shield can be either a metallic wire screen or a conductor on the last layer of the coil.

Methods of Treating, Tanking, and Sealing.—In addition to the magnetic and electrical design requirements outlined above, the reactors and transformers developed for radar applications have to meet general specifications for humidity and temperature, acceleration, insulation, mechanical handling, and life. Accordingly, the higher-voltage units are usually built in hermetically sealed tanks, and special techniques of handling oil expansion, vacuum treatment, insulation, and heating are used.

Varnished units are used whenever conditions of ambient temperature and humidity are not severe, voltages are not high, and low cost and light weight are of prime importance; new types of dry insulation recently developed have shown great promise up to 10 to 15 kv (see Sec. 14·3).

When the reactor is enclosed in a hermetically sealed case, some type of filling compound or oil is required to aid in the process of cooling the core and coils, and to provide the necessary insulation between the coil and grounded parts. When used with vacuum-treating technique, oil has the advantage over the compounds now available in that it is able to fill all voids and remain free from cracks at normal operating temperatures. Since the initial corona discharge that is usually the starting point for insulation failure is often associated with air pockets and voids in the insulation (see Sec. 6·5), the flow of oil into the vicinity of the spark immediately after the internal flashover helps to prevent recurrence of such a breakdown, and the solid insulation does not become carbonized.

When used with a hermetically sealed case, oil provides a durable, reliable, and long-lasting insulation, even at continuous operating temperatures as high as 115°C. Compounds provide an inexpensive, though not so reliable, filling medium for high-voltage units. The decision whether to use oil or compound is usually made on the basis of the applied voltage and reliability desired.

Practical values usually accepted as the maximum allowable voltage gradients for a satisfactory reactor and transformer are listed in Table 9·1.

TABLE 9·1.—MAXIMUM ALLOWABLE VOLTAGE GRADIENTS

Quantity	Working stress, peak volts/mil
Solid insulation coil to ground	100
Solid layer insulation	100
No. 10-C transformer oil	75
Surface creep from coil to ground	20
Surface creep inside coil	20

Representative charging reactors are shown in Fig. 9·13, and Table 9·2 gives their significant design values.

Heating.—The reactor losses produce heat in the core and coil. Excessive coil temperatures not only damage conductors, but also cause deterioration of the usual organic insulating materials.

Oil expansion and contraction give rise to forces on the sides of the tank, which may result in mechanical damage to the seams. Several methods have been used to limit the pressure built up in the tank.

1. The amount of expansion can be reduced by the use of sand to displace part of the oil, and the pressure may sometimes be limited to a practical value by combining this method with a flexible tank.
2. An air space at the top of the tank has been used to limit the pressure by compression of the air.

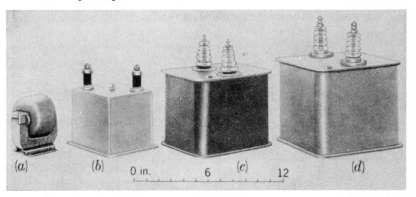

Fig. 9·13.—Representative d-c charging reactors.

3. Various mechanical expansion chambers have been used which reduce the pressure to its lowest possible value. The most satisfactory mechanical device is the metal bellows provided that the resultant increase in case size can be tolerated. An empirical equation for calculating the final oil temperature and pressure for a given design is given in Sec. 9·8.

TABLE 9·2.—SIGNIFICANT DESIGN INFORMATION FOR REACTORS OF FIG. 9·13

No.	Type of service	Weight, lb	Over-all height, in.	D-c current rating, amp	Peak voltage rating, kv	L rating, henrys
a	Airborne	$5\frac{3}{4}$	5	0.050	8	98
b	Ground or ship	$11\frac{3}{4}$	$7\frac{3}{4}$	0.100	8	24
c	Ground or ship	45	10	0.200	17	28
d	Ground or ship	$71\frac{1}{2}$	$11\frac{1}{4}$	0.400	17	19

Testing.—A preliminary test is conducted prior to sealing the core-and-coil assembly into the case in order to insure that, as far as possible,

376 THE CHARGING CIRCUIT OF THE LINE-TYPE PULSER [SEC. 9·3

the final sealed unit will meet the inductance specifications, and thus to avoid the necessity of opening the case to adjust the reactor. A final test is also made in order to determine whether or not the reactor insulation has been damaged, the inductance and d-c resistance have changed, or the power loss or Q factor have varied excessively during the processing. A 1 per cent change in inductance can result from the treating process, which apparently modifies the gap spacing in the core slightly.

The insulation tests consist of an applied-voltage test and an induced-voltage test. In the applied-voltage test, which is used to check the major insulation of the reactor, a 60-cycle voltage, the rms value of which is

$$\frac{4\eta_c E_{bb} + 1000}{\sqrt{2}},$$

is applied for one minute between ground and the two short-circuited reactor terminals. The induced-voltage test, in which the voltage is applied between the reactor terminals, checks the insulation between the turns and layers of the coil. In standard practice, the test duration is 7200 cycles, and the rms value of the induced voltage is $1.5\eta_c E_{bb}/\sqrt{2}$.

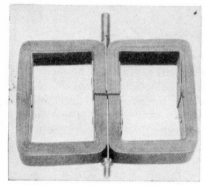

FIG. 9·14.—Reactor core formed of pre-cut strip steel. (*Courtesy of General Electric Co.*)

The test is made at frequencies from 400 to 800 cycles/sec, depending upon the equipment available.

A comparison of the preliminary and final values of either the power loss or the quality factor indicates whether or not the unit has passed the induced-voltage test. This change is usually not over 5 per cent. Turn-to-turn failure in the coil is readily distinguished by an increase in power loss or decrease in Q, whereas the measured inductance does not change appreciably, especially when the number of turns involved in the failure is small compared with the total number of coil turns.

Finally, the d-c resistance of the coil is measured in order to make certain that the coil conductor is continuous and that the coil contains about the proper number of turns of the specified wire size.

Sample Design.—The following sample calculations demonstrate two general design procedures. Figure 9·14 shows the core and Fig. 9·12 shows the core-and-coil assembly in the mounting clamps. The specifications applying to this unit are

D-c power-supply voltage: 13 kv.

Inductance and tolerance: 7.4 henrys, -2 to $+6$ per cent at full-load current and less than 5 per cent variation from 50 per cent to full-load current.

Average charging current: 0.274 amp.   Ratio of rms current to average current $= 1.11$.

Recurrence frequency: 1170 pps.

Core frequency: 585 cycles/sec.

Peak-charging-wave voltage on pulse-forming network: 25 kv.

Allowable minimum quality factor at rated core frequency: 25.

Ambient temperature range: $0°$ to $+60°$C.

Resonant charging.

Bidirectional switch (triggered gap).

Matched pulse load, that is, $v_N(0) = 0$.

Reactor design is usually based on experience.   However, in the absence of suitable previous experience the design process can be started mathematically.[1]   If the ratio of air-gap length to magnetic-path length is 0.6 per cent or more, and the flux change is large compared with the d-c flux, the energy stored per unit volume of core may be equated to the magnetizing force and flux density in the core steel, that is,

$$\frac{\frac{1}{2}L_{\mathrm{Fe}}(I_{c\mathrm{peak}})^2}{v} = \frac{1}{2} B_{\mathrm{Fe}} \frac{N_c I_{c\mathrm{peak}}}{l_m \times 10^8},$$

where

L_{Fe} = that portion of the inductance of the reactor associated with the flux in the core steel (the flux that threads the coil turns but does not flow through the complete length of the core is disregarded in the initial design calculation),

$I_{c\mathrm{peak}}$ = peak rated amperes flowing in the reactor,

v = core volume in in.^{3} $= l_m A_{\mathrm{Fe}}$,

l_m = length of average magnetic path in in.,

A_{Fe} = net cross-sectional area of the steel in in.^{2},

B_{Fe} = flux density in core steel in lines/in.^{2},

and

$\dfrac{(N_c I_{c\mathrm{peak}})}{l_m}$ = peak ampere-turns/in.

Note that $\frac{1}{2}L_{\mathrm{Fe}}(I_{c\mathrm{peak}})^2$ is the maximum instantaneous **magnetic** energy, in watt-seconds, stored in the core.   Since about 98 per cent of the total number of ampere-turns are required to produce the flux in the air gap, the energy in the reactor is predominantly associated with this

---

[1] C. R. Hanna, "Design of Reactances and Transformers Which Carry Direct Current," *J. Amer. Inst. Elect. Engrs.*, **46**, 128 (1927).

part of the magnetic circuit.   For simplicity in the calculation, however, the energy is apportioned to the complete core volume including the air gap.   For a charging reactor using normal core steels, the value of $(N_c I_{cpeak})/l_m$ is approximately 85 when the flux density in the steel is 55,000 lines/in.² and the gap length is 0.6 per cent.   This figure is adjusted somewhat to allow for flux-fringing at the air gap.   The value is increased or reduced in inverse proportion to the fringing effect. Using the above figure,

$$\frac{\frac{1}{2}L_{Fe}(I_{cpeak})^2}{v} = 0.023 \text{ watt-seconds/in.}^3$$

of core, including the gap.   Thus, the core volume is

$$v = \frac{\frac{1}{2}L_{Fe}(I_{cpeak})^2}{0.023} \text{ in.}^3$$

The number of turns can be calculated from $N_c = 85 \, l_m/I_{cpeak}$.   For minimum size, the reactor coil and insulation should fully utilize the area of the core window.

Experience has shown that about 80 per cent of the total flux threading the coil turns is in the core steel; the remainder is leakage flux. Hence, an approximate value may be obtained by considering $L_{Fe} = 0.8L_c$.

The energy $\frac{1}{2}L_c(I_{cpeak})^2$ stored in the reactor determines the core size and the operating voltage gives an indication of the additional space required for insulation.

Graduated sizes of reactor cores can be designed and tabulated.   The data required are: core dimensions, net cross-sectional area, weight, volume per unit of stack, length of magnetic path, and the maximum number of ampere-turns that can be wound into the window for different thicknesses of insulation (that is, various voltage levels).

The designer can readily determine core dimensions, coil turns, and insulation thicknesses by trying two or three cores from the standard list prepared as above.   In the following example, it is assumed that the reactor core and coil sizes have been determined, and that this calculation is the final check on the design.   Note that the adjustment in core cross-sectional area and coil turns must be made previously because the amount of leakage flux has been assumed.   The actual values must be calculated, and used to determine the inductance.

As a result of the design calculations, the coil is to be constructed of 3394 turns.   The major portion of the coil conductor is 0.0253 in. DEC wire that has a cross section of 0.000503 in.²   The last layer, shown as the finish layer in Fig. 9·11, is wound of 6/30 AWG tinned-copper cable insulated with paper to give an insulation layer thickness of 0.012 in. which adds 0.024 in. to the diameter of the stranded conductor.   The cable is finished with a 0.007-in. layer of cotton. The resulting dimensions for a rectangular coil are:

$$l_i = 2.063 \text{ in.} \qquad w_i = 2.438 \text{ in.}$$
$$l_o = 5.813 \text{ in.} \qquad w_o = 6.188 \text{ in.}$$

length of winding layer $l_w = 2.875$ in.

The core, Fig. 9·14, uses 0.014 in. by $1\frac{1}{2}$ in. low-loss precut formed steel strips built up to $\frac{9}{16}$ in. The center leg gross cross-sectional area is the strip width w_2 times the total buildup h_2, or 1.688 in.² Assuming a space factor of 90 per cent the net steel cross-sectional area, A_{Fe}, is 1.519 in.², and the windows for the coil are $4\frac{1}{4}$ in. by $2\frac{13}{16}$ in. The mean length of the magnetic circuit l_m is

$$l_m = 2(h_1 + w_1) + \frac{9}{16}\pi = 15.9 \text{ in.}$$

where h_1 is the height and w_1 the width of the window, and $\frac{9}{16}\pi$ is the corner allowance.

If the length of the core gap l_g is chosen to be 0.114 in.,

$$\frac{l_g}{l_m} = 0.0072,$$

and the net area of the air gap, including fringing, is given by

$$A_g = w_2 h_2 + \tfrac{2}{3}(h_2 + w_2)l_g = 1.89 \text{ in.}^2,$$

where $h_2 = 1\frac{1}{8}$in. and $w_2 = 1\frac{1}{2}$ in.

The area of the coil for leakage flux is given by

$$A_{lk} = \frac{2w_i l_i + w_o l_o}{3} - A_g = 13.5 \text{ in.}^2$$

The ampere-turns in the steel are determined as 20 (rms value) consisting of 1.15 ampere-turns/in. for the steel at 50,000 lines/in.², and 1.7 ampere-turns for the core joint. Finally, the design-center voltage across the reactor is obtained from

$$V_a = 2\pi f_0 L_a I_{crms} = 8450 \text{ volts},$$

where

$$f_0 = \frac{f_r}{2} = 585 \text{ cycles/sec.},$$

L_a = design-center inductance, or rated value adjusted to be at the center of tolerance range = $1.02 \times 7.4 = 7.55$ henrys,

and

$I_{crms} = 1.11 \times 0.274 = 0.304$ amp.

Checks on the design are then obtained by computing the inductance by either the a-c or the d-c method.

By the a-c method, the voltage across the reactor is obtained from

$$V_a = 4.44\phi_T N_c f_0 \times 10^{-8} \text{ volts,}$$

where ϕ_T, the total flux, is the sum of the flux in the core ϕ_{Fe} and the leakage flux ϕ_{lk}. The total number of ampere-turns (rms value) is

$$N_c I_{crms} = 3394 \times 0.304 = 1032,$$

of which 20 are in the steel, and 1012 across the gap. Then, the flux in the gap and steel is given by

$$\phi_{Fe} = 4.51 \frac{A_g}{l_g} 1012 = 76,000 \text{ lines,}$$

$$\phi_{lk} = 4.51 \frac{A_{lk}}{l_w} 1032 = 21,900 \text{ lines,}$$

and

$$\phi_T = 97,900 \text{ lines.}$$

where 4.51 is the permeability of air in lines per square inch per rms ampere-turn per inch from which $V_a = 8600$ volts, which is within the manufacturing tolerance since the design-center voltage is 8450 volts.

By the d-c method, the peak ampere-turns is

$$N_c I_{cpeak} = \frac{\pi}{2} I_{cav} 3394 = 1460 \text{ ampere-turns,}$$

resulting in a total flux of 97,900 lines, which corresponds to an inductance

$$L_c = \frac{N_c \phi_T}{I_{cpeak}} 10^{-8} = 7.7 \text{ henrys.}$$

This value again checks closely with the value for the design-center inductance obtained above.

INDUCTANCE CHARGING FROM AN A-C SOURCE

9·4. General Analysis of A-c Charging.—The energy-storage condenser of a voltage-fed network may be recharged from an a-c voltage source whose frequency is integrally related to the recurrence frequency of the pulse generator. Some intermediate element must be interposed between the pulse-forming network and the a-c voltage source; otherwise, it is impossible to discharge the network at a voltage peak and at the same time retain stable conditions. For example, if the network is connected directly to the terminals of an ordinary high-voltage transformer and then discharged at the peak of the transformer voltage, the network tends to recharge immediately, and the transformer is short-circuited for the remainder of the half cycle under consideration.

Perhaps the most obvious means of avoiding this difficulty is to use a hold-off diode between the network and the transformer, and to discharge the network on the following half cycle, which has a polarity opposite to that of the charging half cycle. Under these conditions the network does not recharge immediately; consequently, the circuit action is stable, but the utilization factor for the high-voltage transformer and a-c source is low (see Sec. 9·9).

The other simple method for recharging the network from an a-c source is to interpose a series inductance between the high-voltage transformer and the network. By the proper adjustment of the value of this inductance, the PFN capacitance, and the voltage phase, the network may be discharged at a voltage peak and stable circuit action retained. The series inductance also isolates the network from the power supply for an appreciable time after the pulse, allowing the switch restriking voltage to increase faster than the applied voltage.

The conditions for a-c inductance charging are considerably more complicated than those for d-c charging, primarily because there are more variables to consider. These variables include the voltage phase angle at which the network is discharged, and the relation between charging period and impressed frequency. The equations for a-c inductance charging are therefore more difficult to derive and apply, and a reasonably complete study of all the possible variations is lengthy and somewhat cumbersome.

The simplest type of a-c inductance charging (as well as the one most often used in practice in this country) is a-c resonant charging, in which the charging circuit is tuned to resonance at the impressed a-c frequency. The network voltage reaches a maximum value when the impressed sinusoidal voltage is passing through zero. The pulses therefore occur whenever the impressed voltage is zero. Although the pulse recurrence frequency is usually equal to the impressed a-c frequency, it is sometimes double the impressed frequency, in which case there is one pulse for each half cycle of the applied-voltage wave. The disadvantage of a-c resonant charging is that the voltage across the network continues to build up if the switch misses one or several pulses. Considerable work on a-c charging has also been done by the British, who often use nonresonant charging to alleviate this disadvantage.

A-c inductance charging has the advantage of simplicity, and permits a net saving in weight and size, particularly since the inductance is usually built into the high-voltage transformer. On the other hand, it generally requires a special motor-alternator for each design in order to supply the proper frequency, with a resultant lack of flexibility. The disadvantage of requiring a special motor-alternator is offset to a certain extent by the advantage of being able to control the pulser power output by varying the relatively small field current of the alternator. In contrast, the power output of a high-voltage d-c rectifier, such as used in d-c inductance charging, must usually be controlled by a large motor-driven induction regulator or a set of motor-driven variacs, which necessitates an increase in weight and a more complicated circuit.

A-c charging pulsers having rotary-gap switches are used extensively where relatively high powers and low recurrence frequencies are specified. Rotary spark gaps, however, require self-synchronous triggers and also introduce a time jitter of about 25 μsec or more. Triggered fixed spark gaps or thyratrons produce very little time jitter, but, because a more complicated circuit is needed, they have not been used to any great extent in a-c charging pulsers.

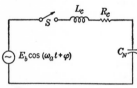

Fig. 9·15.—Schematic circuit for a-c inductance charging.

The equations for a-c charging require the general solution of the series-LRC circuit for an applied a-c voltage of arbitrary frequency and phase. The following method of solution for the circuit of Fig. 9·15 is based on the use of complex quantities and numbers.

The differential equation for the circuit in terms of the charge q_N on the network is

$$L_c \frac{d^2 q_N}{dt^2} + R_c \frac{dq_N}{dt} + \frac{1}{C_N} q_N = E_b \cos(\omega_a t + \varphi) = \text{Re}\,(\bar{E}_b e^{j\omega_a t}). \quad (51)$$

(Hereafter, the abbreviation "Re" meaning "real part of" is usually omitted.) As usual, $\bar{E}_b = E_b e^{j\varphi}$, so that E_b is the magnitude and φ the phase angle of $\bar{E}_b$. The bar notation is used in this section to denote complex numbers.

By inspection, the particular or steady-state integral of Eq. (51) has the form

$$q_1(t) = \bar{Q}_N e^{j\omega_a t},$$

where $\bar{Q}_N$ is determined by substitution in Eq. (51), that is,

$$\bar{Q}_N = \frac{C_N \bar{E}_b}{1 - L_c C_N \omega_a^2 + j R_c C_N \omega_a}.$$

The complementary or transient integral is the same as that already found for the d-c charging circuit, namely,

$$q_2(t) = \bar{A} e^{\bar{p}t},$$

where $\bar{A}$ is a complex constant of integration and

$$\bar{p} = -a + j\omega = -\frac{R_c}{2L_c} + j\sqrt{\frac{1}{L_c C_N} - \left(\frac{R_c}{2L_c}\right)^2}$$

As in the case of d-c charging, only the oscillatory solution need be considered. The complete solution is then

$$q_N(t) = q_1(t) + q_2(t) = \bar{Q}_N e^{j\omega_a t} + \bar{A} e^{\bar{p}t}. \tag{52}$$

Assume the initial or boundary conditions at $t = 0$ to be

$$q_N(t) = q_N(0)$$
$$i_c(t) = i_c(0).$$

Substituting these values in Eq. (52) and the time derivative of Eq. (52),

$$q_N(0) = \text{Re}(\bar{Q}_N + \bar{A}) = Q_1 + A_1$$
$$i_c(0) = \text{Re}(j\omega_a \bar{Q}_N + \bar{p}\bar{A}) = -\omega_a Q_2 - aA_1 - \omega A_2.$$

Solving for A_1 and A_2,

$$A_1 = q_N(0) - Q_1$$
$$A_2 = -\frac{1}{\omega}\{i_c(0) + \omega_a Q_2 + a[q_N(0) - Q_1]\}. \tag{53}$$

Now let

$$A = |\bar{A}| = |A_1 + jA_2|,$$
$$\psi = \text{phase angle of } \bar{A} = \tan^{-1}\frac{A_2}{A_1},$$
$$Q_N = |\bar{Q}_N| = |Q_1 + jQ_2|,$$
$$\theta = \text{phase angle of circuit} = \tan^{-1}\frac{R_c C_N \omega_a}{1 - L_c C_N \omega_a^2}.$$

The expression for $\bar{Q}_N$ is then

$$\bar{Q}_N = Q_N e^{j(\varphi - \theta)}.$$

The solution for $q_N(t)$ may then be written

$$q_N(t) = \text{Re}(\bar{Q}_N e^{j\omega_a t} + \bar{A} e^{\bar{p}t})$$
$$= Q_N \cos(\omega_a t + \varphi - \theta) + A e^{-at} \cos(\omega t + \psi). \tag{54}$$

Differentiating,

$$i_c(t) = \omega_a Q_N \cos\left(\omega_a t + \varphi - \theta + \frac{\pi}{2}\right) + \omega_0 A e^{-at} \cos(\omega t + \psi + \beta), \tag{55}$$

where

$$Q_N = \left|\frac{C_N E_b}{1 - L_c C_N \omega_a^2 + jR_c C_N \omega_a}\right| = |Q_1 + jQ_2|,$$
$$\omega = \text{angular frequency of circuit},$$
$$\beta = \tan^{-1}\frac{\omega}{-a},$$

and

$$\omega_0 = \sqrt{\omega^2 + a^2}.$$

As in the case of d-c charging, one condition necessary for obtaining repeating transients is that the magnitude of the current in the inductance must be the same at the beginning and at the end of the charging period. In addition, the charging period must be an integral multiple of the half period of the applied voltage, that is,

$$\omega_a T_r = n\pi \qquad \text{where } n = 1, 2, 3, \cdot\cdot\cdot.$$

For the case of an even number of half cycles,

$$i_c(0) = i_c(T_r).$$

In the case where n is odd, that is, for an odd number of half cycles of applied voltage, the condition becomes

$$i_c(0) = -i_c(T_r).$$

The most general condition that must be satisfied in order to obtain repeating transients is then

$$i_c(n\pi) \pm i_c(0) = \omega_a Q_N \left[\cos\left(n\pi + \varphi - \theta + \frac{\pi}{2} \right) \pm \cos\left(\varphi - \theta + \frac{\pi}{2} \right) \right]$$
$$+ \omega_0 A \left[e^{-n\pi\frac{a}{\omega_a}} \cos\left(n\pi \frac{\omega}{\omega_a} + \psi + \beta \right) \pm \cos\left(\psi + \beta \right) \right] = 0, \quad (56)$$

where the plus sign applies to n odd, the minus sign to n even. This equation is transcendental, and can be solved exactly by appropriate means. For the present discussion, however, it is sufficiently accurate to assume that a approaches zero, and to solve the simpler equation, provided that $\omega \neq \omega_a$. The relation

$$\cos\left(n\pi \frac{\omega}{\omega_a} + \psi + \beta \right) \pm \cos\left(\psi + \beta \right) = 0, \qquad (57a)$$

can be written in product form,

$$\left. \begin{array}{ll} -2 \sin\left(\dfrac{n\pi}{2} \dfrac{\omega}{\omega_a} + \psi + \beta \right) \sin \dfrac{n\pi}{2} \dfrac{\omega}{\omega_a} = 0 & n \text{ even,} \\[3mm] 2 \cos\left(\dfrac{n\pi}{2} \dfrac{\omega}{\omega_a} + \psi + \beta \right) \cos \dfrac{n\pi}{2} \dfrac{\omega}{\omega_a} = 0 & n \text{ odd.} \end{array} \right\} \qquad (57b)$$

For n even, the following solutions are obtained

$$\frac{\omega}{\omega_a} = \frac{2m}{n} \qquad \text{where } m = 0, 1, 2, \cdot\cdot\cdot,$$

and

$$\frac{\omega}{\omega_a} = \frac{2}{n}\left(m - \frac{\psi + \beta}{\pi} \right), \qquad \text{where } m = 0, 1, 2, \cdot\cdot\cdot.$$

For n odd,

$$\frac{\omega}{\omega_a} = \frac{m}{n} \qquad \text{where } m = 1, 3, \cdots ,$$

$$\frac{\omega}{\omega_a} = \frac{1}{n}\left[m - \frac{2}{\pi}(\psi + \beta) \right], \qquad \text{where } m = 1, 3, \cdots .$$

It is evident that $\omega/\omega_a = 0$ is a trivial solution. The resonant solution is $\omega/\omega_a = 1$, which must be examined because losses were neglected in deriving Eqs. (57b). The solutions for ω/ω_a can be put in direct terms by noting that

$$\psi + \beta = \tan^{-1}\left\{ \frac{-\left[\dfrac{i_c(0)}{\omega} + \dfrac{\omega_a}{\omega}Q_2\right]}{q_N(0) - Q_1} + \frac{\pi}{2} \right\} = \tan^{-1}\left[\frac{q_N(0) - Q_1}{\dfrac{i_c(0)}{\omega} + \dfrac{\omega_a}{\omega}Q_2} \right]$$

$$= \tan^{-1}\left[\frac{q_N(0) - Q_N \cos\varphi}{\dfrac{i_c(0)}{\omega} + \dfrac{\omega_a}{\omega}Q_N \sin\varphi} \right]$$

when losses are neglected. Making this substitution and simplifying, the following condition equations are obtained. For n even,

$$\frac{q_N(0) - Q_N \cos\varphi}{\dfrac{i_c(0)}{\omega} + \dfrac{\omega_a}{\omega}Q_N \sin\varphi} = \tan\left(m\pi - \frac{n\pi}{2}\frac{\omega}{\omega_a} \right) = -\tan\frac{n\pi}{2}\frac{\omega}{\omega_a}, \qquad (58a)$$

and for n odd,

$$\frac{q_N(0) - Q_N \cos\varphi}{\dfrac{i_c(0)}{\omega} + \dfrac{\omega_a}{\omega}Q_N \sin\varphi} = \tan\left(\frac{m\pi}{2} - \frac{n\pi}{2}\cdot\frac{\omega}{\omega_a} \right) = +\cot\frac{n\pi}{2}\frac{\omega}{\omega_a}. \qquad (58b)$$

The quantities $q_N(0)$, $i_c(0)$, φ and ω/ω_a may be considered to be the variables in Eqs. (58). In practice, three of these quantities must be specified or determined by special considerations. For example, if $i_c(0)$ and $q_N(0)$ are specified to be zero and ω/ω_a is given, the values of the phase angle φ calculated from Eqs. (58) are those necessary to obtain the repeating transients when n is even and odd respectively.

There are a great number of special cases that are of interest. In general, these may be divided into two groups, depending on whether resonant or nonresonant charging is used. Resonance is defined by the relation

$$1 - L_c C_N \omega_a^2 = 0.$$

If losses can be neglected, this relation is equivalent to $\omega = \omega_a$; otherwise, the natural resonant frequency is less than the resonant frequency defined by the above relation. For most applications, the difference between ω and ω_a is negligible, and it is sufficiently accurate to set $\omega = \omega_a$. The following two sections treat separately the cases of resonant and non-resonant a-c charging.

9·5. A-c Resonant Charging.—As defined in Sec. 9·4 the condition for a-c resonant charging is

$$1 - L_c C_N \omega_a^2 = 0$$

With $\omega = \omega_a$, Eq. (54) becomes

$$q_N(t) = Q_N \cos(\omega_a t + \varphi - \theta) + A e^{-at} \cos(\omega_a t + \psi)$$

where

$$\bar{Q}_N = \frac{E_b}{R_c \omega_a} e^{i(\varphi - \theta)} = Q_N \sin \varphi - j Q_N \cos \varphi,$$

$$\theta = \frac{\pi}{2}$$

$$\bar{A} = q_N(0) - Q_N \sin \varphi - j \left[\frac{i_c(0)}{\omega_a} - Q_N \cos \varphi + \frac{a}{\omega_a}(q_N(0) - Q_N \sin \varphi) \right]$$

$$\psi = \tan^{-1}\frac{A_2}{A_1} = \tan^{-1}\left[\frac{-\left(\dfrac{i_c(0)}{\omega_a} - Q_N \cos \varphi\right)}{(q_N(0) - Q_N \sin \varphi)} - \frac{a}{\omega_a} \right].$$

Making these substitutions and reducing, the equation for q_N becomes

$$q_N(t) = Q_N(1 - e^{-at}) \sin(\omega_a t + \varphi) + e^{-at}\bigg[q_N(0) \cos \omega_a t$$

$$+ \left(\frac{i_c(0)}{\omega_a} + \frac{a q_N(0)}{\omega_a} - \frac{a}{\omega_a} Q_N \sin \varphi \right) \sin \omega_a t \bigg]. \quad (59)$$

The condition for repeating transients, namely, $i_c(n\pi) - i_c(0) = 0$, must be examined separately for the resonant case. The current can be obtained from Eq. (55) or by differentiating Eq. (59), and is

$$i_c(t) = \frac{E_b}{R_c}(1 - e^{-at}) \cos(\omega_a t + \varphi)$$

$$+ e^{-at}\left(i_c(0) \cos \omega_a t - \omega_a q_N(0) \sin \omega_a t + \frac{E_b}{2 L_c \omega_a} \sin \omega_a t \cos \varphi \right)$$

$$+ \frac{a}{\omega_a} e^{-at}\left[\frac{E_b}{2 L_c \omega_a} \sin \varphi - i_c(0) - a q_N(0) \right] \sin \omega_a t. \quad (60)$$

For repeating transients, $\omega_a t = n\pi$, and for n even,

$$i_c(n\pi) = \frac{E_b}{R_c}(1 - e^{-\frac{n\pi a}{\omega_a}}) \cos \varphi + i_c(0) e^{-\frac{n\pi a}{\omega_a}} = i_c(0).$$

For n odd, that is, for a charging period containing an odd number of half cycles, the condition for repeating transients is $i_c(n\pi) = -i_c(0)$. Since two successive charging periods correspond to an even number of half cycles, the initial current returns to its original value, and it is apparent that the above condition is correct, and is equivalent to that for full-cycle charging. For n odd,

$$i_c(n\pi) = -\frac{E_b}{R_c}\left(1 - e^{-\frac{n\pi a}{\omega_a}}\right)\cos\varphi - e^{-\frac{n\pi a}{\omega_a}}i_c(0) = -i_c(0).$$

Solving for $i_c(0)$ for n odd or even,

$$i_c(0) = \frac{E_b}{R_c}\cos\varphi, \tag{61}$$

and the expression for $q_N(t)$ becomes

$$q_N(t) = \frac{E_b}{R_c\omega_a}\left(1 - e^{-at}\sin(\omega_a t + \varphi)\right.$$
$$+ e^{-at}\left\{q_N(0)\cos\omega_a t + \left[\frac{E_b}{R_c\omega_a}\cos\varphi - \frac{C_N E_b}{2}\sin\varphi + \frac{R_c}{2L_c\omega_a}q_N(0)\right]\sin\omega_a t\right\}.$$

Introducing the quality factor $Q = \dfrac{L_c\omega_a}{R_c} = \dfrac{1}{R_c C_N\omega_a}$,

$$q_N(t) = QC_N E_b\left(1 - e^{-\frac{\omega_a t}{2Q}}\right)\sin(\omega_a t + \varphi)$$
$$+ e^{-\frac{\omega_a t}{2Q}}\left[q_N(0)\cos\omega_a t + \left(QC_N E_b\cos\varphi - \frac{C_N E_b}{2}\sin\varphi + \frac{1}{2Q}q_N(0)\right)\sin\omega_a t\right]. \tag{62}$$

Differentiating, the current is

$$i_c(t) = QC_N E_b\omega_a\left(1 - e^{\frac{-\omega_a t}{2Q}}\right)\cos(\omega_a t + \varphi)$$
$$+ e^{-\frac{\omega_a t}{2Q}}\left\{QC_N E_b\omega_a\cos\varphi\cos\omega_a t - \left[C_N E_b\omega_a\left(\frac{q_N(0)}{C_N E_b} - \frac{1}{4Q}\sin\varphi\right)\right.\right.$$
$$\left.\left. - \frac{q_N(0)\omega_a}{4Q^2}\right]\sin\omega_a t\right\}$$
$$= QC_N E_b\omega_a\left(\left(1 - e^{\frac{-\omega_a t}{2Q}}\right)\cos(\omega_a t + \varphi)\right.$$
$$\left. + e^{\frac{-\omega_a t}{2Q}}\left\{\cos\varphi\cos\omega_a t - \left[\frac{q_N(0)}{QC_N E_b}\left(1 - \frac{1}{4Q^2}\right) - \frac{1}{4Q^2}\sin\varphi\right]\sin\omega_a t\right\}\right),$$

which, to a close approximation, is

$$i_c(t) = QC_N E_b\omega_a\left\{\left(1 - e^{\frac{-\omega_a t}{2Q}}\right)\cos(\omega_a t + \varphi)\right.$$
$$\left. + e^{\frac{-\omega_a t}{2Q}}\left[\cos\varphi\cos\omega_a t - \frac{q_N(0)}{QC_N E_b}\sin\omega_a t\right]\right\}. \tag{63}$$

For some purposes Eq. (62) is more convenient when written in terms of the network voltage $v_N = q_N/C_N$, that is,

$$\frac{v_N(t)}{E_b} = Q \left\{ (1 - e^{-\frac{\omega_a t}{2Q}}) \sin(\omega_a t + \varphi) \right.$$

$$\left. + e^{-\frac{\omega_a t}{2Q}} \left[\frac{q_N(0)}{Q C_N E_b} \cos \omega_a t + \left(\cos \varphi - \frac{1}{2Q} \sin \varphi + \frac{1}{2Q^2} \cdot \frac{q_N(0)}{C_N E_b} \right) \sin \omega_a t \right] \right\}.$$

$$(64)$$

If the losses can be considered negligible, that is, if $R_c \rightarrow 0$, Eq. (60) becomes

$$\lim_{R_c \rightarrow 0} i_c(t) = \frac{E_b}{R_c} (at) \cos(\omega_a t + \varphi) + i_c(0) \cos \omega_a t$$

$$+ \left[\frac{E_b}{2L_c \omega_a} \cos \varphi - \omega_a q_N(0) \right] \sin \omega_a t$$

$$= \frac{E_b t}{2L_c} \cos(\omega_a t + \varphi) + i_c(0) \cos \omega_a t + \left[\frac{E_b}{2L_c \omega_a} \cos \varphi - \omega_a q_N(0) \right] \sin \omega_a t,$$

$$(65)$$

and

$$i_c(n\pi) = \pm \left[\frac{n\pi E_b}{2L_c} \cos \varphi + i_c(0) \right],$$

where the plus sign applies to n even, the minus sign to n odd. Obviously, the only solution for the condition for repeating transients is

$$\cos \varphi = 0 \quad \text{or} \quad \varphi = \pm \frac{\pi}{2},$$

and therefore

$$i_c(0) = 0.$$

Equations (61), (63), and (64) are the fundamental expressions for a-c resonant charging. Equation (64) gives the voltage stepup ratio at the discharge point as

$$\frac{v_N(n\pi)}{E_b} = \pm \left[Q \left(1 - e^{-\frac{n\pi}{2Q}} \right) \sin \varphi + \frac{q_N(0)}{C_N E_b} e^{-\frac{n\pi}{2Q}} \right], \quad (66a)$$

where the plus sign applies to n even, the minus sign to n odd. For the case $n\pi/2Q \ll 1$, the exponentials may be expanded to give

$$\frac{v_N(n\pi)}{E_b} \approx \frac{n\pi}{2} \left(1 - \frac{n\pi}{4Q} \right) \sin \varphi + \frac{q_N(0)}{Q E_b} \left(1 - \frac{n\pi}{2Q} \right). \quad (66b)$$

For the particular case of zero initial charge on the condenser and negligible losses, the expression becomes

$$\frac{v_N(n\pi)}{E_b} = \frac{n\pi}{2} \sin \varphi.$$

Hence, for $n = 2$, or one-cycle charging, the maximum network voltage at the time of discharge is π times the maximum applied voltage.

The curves of Fig. 9·16 illustrate typical voltage and current wave shapes for $Q = 10$, and $\varphi = 90°$. The values for average and effective current, circuit utilization factor, and efficiency are of interest in transformer design. They can be obtained as follows.

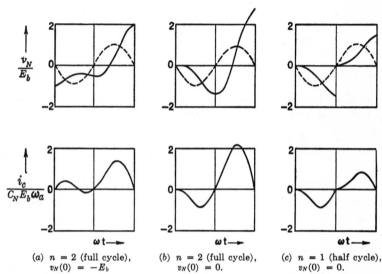

(a) $n = 2$ (full cycle),
$v_N(0) = -E_b$.

(b) $n = 2$ (full cycle),
$v_N(0) = 0$.

(c) $n = 1$ (half cycle),
$v_N(0) = 0$.

FIG. 9·16.—Voltage and current wave shapes for a-c resonant charging. The broken line is the impressed voltage.

Average-current Component.—The average current is zero for any charging cycle involving an odd number of half cycles; if n is even it is calculated from Eq. (63), using the definition

$$I_{cav} = \frac{1}{T_r} \int_0^{T_r} i_c \, dt,$$

where T_r is the recurrence period and can be considered equal to the charging period, since $\tau \ll T_r$.
Then

$$I_{cav} = \frac{1}{T_r} \int_0^{T_r} QC_NE_b\omega_a \left\{ (1 - e^{-\frac{\omega_a t}{2Q}}) \cos (\omega_a t + \varphi) \right. $$
$$\left. + e^{-\frac{\omega_a t}{2Q}} \left[\cos \varphi \cos \omega_a t - \frac{q_N(0)}{QC_NE_b} \sin \omega_a t \right] \right\} dt.$$

Noting that $T_r = n\pi/\omega_a$ and letting $x = \omega_a t$,

$$I_{c_{av}} = \frac{QC_N E_b \omega_a}{n\pi} \int_0^{n\pi} \left\{ (1 - e^{-\frac{x}{2Q}}) \cos(x + \varphi) \right. $$
$$\left. + e^{-\frac{x}{2Q}} \left[\cos \varphi \cos x - \frac{q_N(0)}{QC_N E_b} \sin x \right] \right\} dx.$$

The integral is calculated in a straight-forward manner and evaluated as follows:

$$I_{c_{av}} = \frac{QC_N E_b \omega_a}{n\pi} \frac{(1 - e^{-\frac{n\pi}{2Q}}) \left(\sin \varphi - \frac{q_N(0)}{QC_N E_b} \right)}{1 + \frac{1}{4Q^2}}, \qquad n \text{ even.} \quad (67a)$$

If $n\pi/2Q \ll 1$, the expression for $I_{c_{av}}$ can be closely approximated by expanding the exponential to three terms and neglecting $1/4Q^2$. Thus,

$$I_{c_{av}} \approx \frac{C_N E_b \omega_a}{2} \left(1 - \frac{n\pi}{4Q} \right) \left[\sin \varphi - \frac{q_N(0)}{QC_N E_b} \right], \qquad n \text{ even.} \quad (67b)$$

Rms or Effective Current in the Charging Circuit.—The rms current is calculated from the definition, using the value of i_c given by Eq. (63), that is,

$$I_{c_{rms}}^2 = \frac{1}{T_r} \int_0^{T_r} i_c^2(t) \, dt$$
$$= \frac{1}{T_r} \int_0^{T_r} (QC_N E_b \omega_a)^2 \left\{ (1 - e^{-\frac{\omega_a t}{2Q}}) \cos(\omega_a t + \varphi) \right.$$
$$\left. + e^{-\frac{\omega_a t}{2Q}} \left(\cos \varphi \cos \omega_a t - \frac{q_N(0)}{QC_N E_b} \sin \omega_a t \right) \right\}^2 dt.$$

But $T_r = n\pi/\omega_a$ and letting, $x = \omega_a t$, the expression becomes

$$I_{c_{rms}}^2 = \frac{(QC_N E_b \omega_a)^2}{n\pi} \int_0^{n\pi} \left\{ (1 - e^{-\frac{x}{2Q}}) \cos(x + \varphi) \right.$$
$$\left. + e^{-\frac{x}{2Q}} \left(\cos \varphi \cos x - \frac{q_N(0)}{QC_N E_b} \sin x \right) \right\}^2 dx.$$

The calculation of this integral is tedious and is not given here. The result, after applying certain very close approximations, is

$$I_{c_{rms}}^2 = \frac{(QC_N E_b \omega_a)^2}{2} \left[1 + \frac{Q}{n\pi} (1 - e^{-\frac{n\pi}{Q}}) \left(\sin \varphi - \frac{q_N(0)}{QC_N E_b} \right)^2 \right.$$
$$\left. + \frac{4Q}{n\pi} (1 - e^{-\frac{n\pi}{2Q}}) \left(\frac{1}{4Q} \cos \varphi - \sin \varphi \right) \left(\sin \varphi - \frac{q_N(0)}{QC_N E_b} \right) \right]. \quad (68)$$

For no initial voltage on the network,

$$I^2_{c_{\text{rms}}} = \frac{(QC_NE_b\omega_a)^2}{2}\left[1 + \frac{Q}{n\pi}(1 - e^{-\frac{n\pi}{Q}})\sin^2\varphi\right.$$
$$\left. + \frac{4Q}{n\pi}(1 - e^{-\frac{n\pi}{2Q}})\left(\frac{1}{4Q}\cos\varphi - \sin\varphi\right)\sin\varphi\right]. \quad (69a)$$

The exponentials in Eq. (69a) must, in certain cases, be calculated to 5 or 6 significant figures in order to obtain sufficiently accurate results. A more convenient formula is obtained by expanding the exponentials for the case where $n\pi/2Q \ll 1$, that is,

$$I^2_{c_{\text{rms}}} = \frac{(C_NE_b\omega_a)^2}{2}\left[Q^2\cos^2\varphi + \frac{n^2\pi^2}{12}\sin^2\varphi + \frac{Q}{4}\left(1 - \frac{n\pi}{4Q}\right)\sin 2\varphi\right]. \quad (69b)$$

It is of interest to find the value of φ for a minimum $I_{c_{\text{rms}}}$. By the usual method,

$$\frac{\partial I^2_{c_{\text{rms}}}}{\partial\varphi} = \frac{(C_NE_b\omega_a)^2}{2}\left[\left(\frac{n^2\pi^2}{12} - Q^2\right)\sin 2\varphi + \frac{Q}{2}\left(1 - \frac{n\pi}{4Q}\right)\cos 2\varphi\right] = 0,$$

or

$$\tan 2\varphi = \frac{\dfrac{Q}{2}\left(1 - \dfrac{n\pi}{4Q}\right)}{Q^2 - \dfrac{n^2\pi^2}{12}}.$$

If Q is reasonably large, for example, $Q > 10$,

$$\tan 2\varphi \approx \frac{1}{2Q}.$$

The solutions are, to a very close approximation,

$$\varphi = \frac{1}{4Q} \pm \frac{m\pi}{2}, \qquad \text{where } m = 0, 1, 2, \cdots.$$

The solution $\varphi = 1/4Q$ corresponds to the maximum $I_{c_{\text{rms}}}$, while the solutions $\varphi = \dfrac{1}{4Q} + \dfrac{\pi}{2}$ correspond to the minimum $I_{c_{\text{rms}}}$. Thus,

$$(I_{c_{\text{rms}}})_{\text{max}} \approx \frac{QC_NE_b\omega_a}{\sqrt{2}} \qquad (70a)$$

$$(I_{c_{\text{rms}}})_{\text{min}} \approx \frac{n\pi C_NE_b\omega_a}{2\sqrt{6}}\sqrt{1 + \frac{6}{n^2\pi^2}}. \qquad (70b)$$

To obtain the minimum rms current with no initial voltage on the network, φ must thus be made nearly equal to $\pi/2$.

Circuit Utilization Factor (C.U.F.).—This factor is defined as

$$\text{C.U.F.} = \frac{\text{power input to network}}{\text{volt-amperes input}} = \frac{P_N}{E_{b_{\text{rms}}} \cdot I_{c_{\text{rms}}}}$$

$$= \frac{\dfrac{C_N \omega_a (V_N)^2 n\pi}{2n\pi}}{\dfrac{E_b}{\sqrt{2}} \cdot \dfrac{C_N E_b \omega_a}{\sqrt{2}} \sqrt{Q^2 \cos^2 \varphi + \dfrac{n^2\pi^2}{12} \sin^2 \varphi + \dfrac{Q}{4}\left(1 - \dfrac{n\pi}{4Q}\right) \sin 2\varphi}}.$$

$$\text{C.U.F.} \approx \frac{n\pi\left(1 - \dfrac{n\pi}{2Q}\right) \sin^2 \varphi}{4\sqrt{Q^2 \cos^2 \varphi + \dfrac{n^2\pi^2}{12} \sin^2 \varphi + \dfrac{Q}{4}\left(1 - \dfrac{n\pi}{4Q}\right) \sin 2\varphi}}. \tag{71}$$

For $\varphi = \pi/2$, corresponding to the most common operating condition for a-c resonant charging,

$$\text{C.U.F.} = \frac{\sqrt{3}}{2}\left(1 - \frac{n\pi}{2Q}\right).$$

Charging-circuit Efficiency.—By definition, the efficiency η_c is

$$\eta_c = \frac{P_N}{P_N + I_{c_{\text{rms}}}^2 R_c} = \frac{1}{1 + \dfrac{I_{c_{\text{rms}}}^2 R_c}{P_N}}, \tag{72}$$

where

$$\frac{I_{c_{\text{rms}}}^2 R_c}{P_N} = \frac{\dfrac{(C_N E_b \omega_a)^2}{2}\left[Q^2 \cos^2 \varphi + \dfrac{n^2\pi^2}{12} \sin^2 \varphi + \dfrac{Q}{4}\left(1 - \dfrac{n\pi}{4Q}\right) \sin 2\varphi\right]\dfrac{1}{QC_N\omega_a}}{\dfrac{C_N \omega_a v_N^2 (n\pi)}{2n\pi}}$$

$$= \frac{4\left[Q^2 \cos^2 \varphi + \dfrac{n^2\pi^2}{12} \sin^2 \varphi + \dfrac{Q}{4}\left(1 - \dfrac{n\pi}{4Q}\right)\sin 2\varphi\right]}{Qn\pi\left(1 - \dfrac{n\pi}{2Q}\right) \sin^2 \varphi}$$

$$= \frac{4\left[Q \cot^2 \varphi + \dfrac{n^2\pi^2}{12Q} + \dfrac{1}{2}\left(1 - \dfrac{n\pi}{4Q}\right) \cot \varphi\right]}{n\pi\left(1 - \dfrac{n\pi}{2Q}\right)}. \tag{73}$$

The maximum efficiency occurs when $I_{c_{\text{rms}}}^2 R_c/P_N$ is a minimum. This minimum is obtained, to a very close approximation, when

$$\cot \varphi = -\frac{1}{4Q} \qquad \text{or} \qquad \varphi = \pm\frac{\pi}{2} + \frac{1}{4Q}.$$

Thus for maximum efficiency φ is very nearly equal to $\pm\pi/2$, in which case

$$\frac{I_{c_{\mathrm{rms}}}^2 R_c}{P_N} = \frac{\dfrac{4n^2\pi^2}{12Q}}{n\pi\left(1 - \dfrac{n\pi}{2Q}\right)} = \frac{\dfrac{n\pi}{3Q}}{1 - \dfrac{n\pi}{2Q}},$$

and the maximum charging efficiency is given by

$$\eta_c = \frac{1 - \dfrac{n\pi}{2Q}}{1 - \dfrac{n\pi}{6Q}} \approx 1 - \frac{n\pi}{3Q}. \tag{74}$$

9·6. A-c Nonresonant Charging.—In resonant charging the voltage rise or gain may be considered a result of ordinary resonance multiplication. In nonresonant charging, $1 - L_cC_N\omega_a^2 \neq 0$, there is also a voltage gain which, if the duration of the transient is limited to one or two cycles, may even exceed that for resonant charging. The voltage gain for non-resonant charging may be considered a result of beats that occur between the steady-state voltage of angular frequency ω_a and the transient voltage of angular frequency ω. The voltage rises to high peak values for a few cycles, and then subsides to the steady-state values as the transient dies out. In resonant charging, on the other hand, the voltage rises to higher and higher peak values, and the steady-state value is limited in magnitude only by damping. It is clear, therefore, that damping cannot be important for nonresonant charging, except when resonance is approached, that is, when $\omega \approx \omega_a$. For transients with durations of one or two cycles, however, damping may be neglected without making serious errors, at least when calculating wave shapes.

Neglecting losses, the network charge as given by Eq. (54) may be simplified to

$$q_N(t) = Q_N \cos(\omega_a t + \varphi - \theta) + A \cos(\omega t + \psi), \tag{75}$$

where

$$Q_N = \left| \frac{C_N E_b}{1 - \dfrac{\omega_a^2}{\omega^2}} \right|$$

and

$$\theta = \lim_{R_c \to 0} \tan^{-1}\frac{R_c C_N \omega_a}{1 - \dfrac{\omega_a^2}{\omega^2}} = \begin{cases} 0 & \text{for } \dfrac{\omega_a}{\omega} < 1, \\ \pi & \text{for } \dfrac{\omega_a}{\omega} > 1. \end{cases}$$

Full-cycle Charging.—The condition for repeating transients for full-cycle charging [see Eq. (58a)] gives, for n even,

$$\cot \frac{n\pi}{2} \cdot \frac{\omega}{\omega_a} = \frac{-\left(\dfrac{i_c(0)}{\omega} + \dfrac{\omega_a}{\omega} Q_N \sin \varphi\right)}{q_N(0) - Q_N \cos \varphi} = \tan \psi$$

when $R_c = 0$ (that is, $a = 0$).   Then

$$\psi = \frac{\pi}{2} - \frac{n\pi}{2} \cdot \frac{\omega}{\omega_a}, \text{ or } \psi = \frac{3\pi}{2} - \frac{n\pi}{2} \frac{\omega}{\omega_a},$$

and Eq. (75) becomes

$$q_N(t) = Q_N \cos (\omega_a t + \varphi - \theta) \pm A \sin \frac{\omega}{\omega_a}\left(\omega_a t - \frac{n\pi}{2}\right). \tag{76}$$

When $t = 0$, the following expression may be obtained for A:

$$\pm A = \frac{Q_N \cos (\varphi - \theta) - q_N(0)}{\sin \dfrac{n\pi}{2} \dfrac{\omega}{\omega_a}}.$$

Equation (76) can now be rewritten

$$q_N(t) = Q_N \cos (\omega_a t + \varphi - \theta)$$

$$+ [Q_N \cos (\varphi - \theta) - q_N(0)] \frac{\sin \dfrac{\omega}{\omega_a}\left(\omega_a t - \dfrac{n\pi}{2}\right)}{\sin \dfrac{\omega}{\omega_a} \cdot \dfrac{n\pi}{2}}$$

$$= \frac{C_N E_b}{1 - \dfrac{\omega_a^2}{\omega^2}} \left[\cos (\omega_a t + \varphi) + \frac{\sin \dfrac{\omega}{\omega_a}\left(\omega_a t - \dfrac{n\pi}{2}\right)}{\sin \dfrac{\omega}{\omega_a} \cdot \dfrac{n\pi}{2}} \cos \varphi \right]$$

$$- q_N(0) \frac{\sin \dfrac{\omega}{\omega_a}\left(\omega_a t - \dfrac{n\pi}{2}\right)}{\sin \dfrac{\omega}{\omega_a} \cdot \dfrac{n\pi}{2}}. \tag{77}$$

The current equation obtained by differentiating Eq. (77) is

$$i_c(t) = \frac{C_N E_b \omega_a}{1 - \dfrac{\omega^2}{\omega^2}} \left[\frac{\dfrac{\omega}{\omega_a} \cos \dfrac{\omega}{\omega_a}\left(\omega_a t - \dfrac{n\pi}{2}\right)}{\sin \dfrac{\omega}{\omega_a} \cdot \dfrac{n\pi}{2}} \cos \varphi - \sin (\omega_a t + \varphi) \right]$$

$$- q_N(0) \left[\frac{\omega \cos \dfrac{\omega}{\omega_a}\left(\omega_a t - \dfrac{n\pi}{2}\right)}{\sin \dfrac{\omega}{\omega_a} \cdot \dfrac{n\pi}{2}} \right]. \tag{78}$$

The network voltage is derived from Eq. (77) and may be expressed in ratio form v_N/E_b, that is,

$$\frac{v_N(t)}{E_b} = \frac{1}{1 - \frac{\omega_a^2}{\omega^2}}\left[\cos(\omega_a t + \varphi) + \frac{\sin\frac{\omega}{\omega_a}\left(\omega_a t - \frac{n\pi}{2}\right)}{\sin\frac{\omega}{\omega_a}\cdot\frac{n\pi}{2}}\cos\varphi\right]$$
$$- \frac{v_N(0)}{E_b}\frac{\sin\frac{\omega}{\omega_a}\left(\omega_a t - \frac{n\pi}{2}\right)}{\sin\frac{\omega}{\omega_a}\cdot\frac{n\pi}{2}}. \quad (79)$$

The voltage stepup ratio at the time $(\omega_a t = n\pi)$ when the network discharges is

$$\frac{v_N(n\pi)}{E_b} = \frac{2\cos\varphi}{1 - \frac{\omega_a^2}{\omega^2}} - \frac{v_N(0)}{E_b}, \quad (80)$$

where φ is related to $i_c(0)$, $q_N(0)$, and ω/ω_a by the relation

$$\sin\varphi = -\frac{ab \pm \sqrt{a^2 - 4ab^2 + 1}}{a^2 + 1}, \quad (81)$$

in which

$$a = \frac{\omega_a}{\omega}\tan\frac{n\pi}{2}\frac{\omega}{\omega_a}, \qquad b = \left(\frac{q_N(0)}{aC_N E_b} + \frac{i_c(0)}{\omega_a C_N E_b}\right)\left(1 - \frac{\omega_a^2}{\omega^2}\right).$$

When $i_c(0) = 0$ and $q_N(0) = 0$, the value of φ reduces to

$$\tan\varphi = \frac{\omega}{\omega_a}\cot\frac{n\pi}{2}\frac{\omega}{\omega_a}, \quad (82)$$

and the equation for voltage stepup ratio at the instant of discharge may be written as a function of ω/ω_a alone, giving

$$\frac{v_N(n\pi)}{E_b} = \frac{2\cos\varphi}{1 - \frac{\omega_a^2}{\omega^2}} = \frac{2}{\left(1 - \frac{\omega_a^2}{\omega^2}\right)\sqrt{1 + \frac{\omega^2}{\omega_a^2}\cot^2\frac{n\pi}{2}\frac{\omega}{\omega_a}}}. \quad (83)$$

The values of the stepup ratio and of φ are plotted for one-cycle charging $(n = 2)$ as functions of ω_a/ω in Fig. 9·17. The steady-state value of the network-voltage stepup ratio, neglecting losses, is also plotted here. When resonance is approached, that is, when $\omega \approx \omega_a$, the steady-state voltage ratio rises to high values. The transient-voltage gain is greater than the steady-state gain for certain values of ω_a/ω, illustrating the phenomenon of beats.

The maximum stepup ratio for the transient case is about 3.66, and occurs at $\omega_a/\omega \approx 0.7$ and $\varphi \approx 21°$.

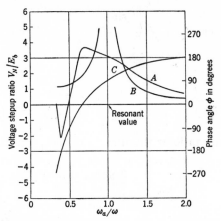

Fig. 9·17.—Voltage stepup ratio and phase angle as a function of ω_a/ω for a-c inductance charging (circuit losses are neglected).
Curve A is the voltage stepup ratio for $n = 2$ (one cycle charging).
Curve B is the voltage stepup ratio for $n = \infty$.
Curve C is the phase angle ϕ.

Again it is of interest to obtain the average and effective values of the transformer currents. The d-c current may be obtained by integrating Eq. (78) over the charging period $T_r = n\pi/\omega_a$. Thus,

$$I_{c_{av}} = \frac{1}{T_r} \int_0^{T_r} i_c(t) \, dt = \frac{1}{n\pi} \int_0^{n\pi} i_c(t) \, d(\omega_a t) = \frac{1}{n\pi} \int_0^{n\pi} i_c(x) \, dx,$$

where $\omega_a t = x$ for convenience. Then

$$I_{c_{av}} = \frac{1}{n\pi} \int_0^{n\pi} \left\{ \left[\frac{\left(\dfrac{C_N E_b \omega \cos \varphi}{1 - \dfrac{\omega_a^2}{\omega^2}} \right) - q_N(0)\omega}{\sin \dfrac{\omega}{\omega_a} \cdot \dfrac{n\pi}{2}} \right] \cos \frac{\omega}{\omega_a} \left(x - \frac{n\pi}{2} \right) \right.$$

$$\left. - \left(\frac{C_N E_b \omega_a}{1 - \dfrac{\omega_a^2}{\omega^2}} \right) \sin(x + \varphi) \right\} dx.$$

Straightforward integration gives, for n even,

$$I_{c_{av}} = \frac{2}{n\pi} \left[\frac{C_N E_b \omega_a \cos \varphi}{1 - \dfrac{\omega_a^2}{\omega^2}} - \omega_a q_N(0) \right]. \tag{84}$$

The rms current is calculated using the definition

$$I_{c_{rms}}^2 = \frac{1}{T_r} \int_0^{T_r} i_c^2(t)\, dt = \frac{1}{n\pi} \int_0^{n\pi} i_c^2(t)\, d(\omega_a t).$$

The evaluation of this integral is long and is not carried out here. The result, however, is

$$I_{c_{rms}}^2 = \frac{1}{2n\pi} \left(\frac{C_N E_b \omega_a}{1 - \frac{\omega_a^2}{\omega^2}} \right)^2 \left[k^2 \left(n\pi \pm \frac{\omega_a}{\omega} \sin n\pi \frac{\omega}{\omega_a} \right) + n\pi \right.$$
$$\left. + \frac{8 \frac{\omega_a^2}{\omega^2} k \cos \varphi \cos \frac{n\pi}{2} \frac{\omega}{\omega_a}}{1 - \frac{\omega_a^2}{\omega^2}} \right], \quad (85)$$

where

$$k = \frac{\cos \varphi - \frac{q_N(0)}{C_N E_b} \left(1 - \frac{\omega_a^2}{\omega^2} \right)}{\frac{\omega_a}{\omega} \sin \frac{n\pi}{2} \frac{\omega}{\omega_a}}.$$

Half-cycle Charging.—Following the same procedure that was used for full-cycle charging, the condition for repeating transients when n is odd is

$$\psi = -\frac{n\pi}{2} \frac{\omega}{\omega_a}, \quad \text{or} \quad \psi = \pi - \frac{n\pi}{2} \frac{\omega}{\omega_a}.$$

Substitution in Eq. (54) gives

$$q_N(t) = Q_N \cos (\omega_a t + \varphi - \theta) \pm A \cos \frac{\omega}{\omega_a} \left(\omega_a t - \frac{n\pi}{2} \right). \quad (86)$$

An expression for A may be obtained when $t = 0$,

$$\pm A = \frac{q_N(0) - Q_N \cos (\varphi - \theta)}{\cos \frac{n\pi}{2} \cdot \frac{\omega}{\omega_a}}.$$

Equation (86) can now be rewritten

$$q_N(t) = Q_N \cos (\omega_a t + \varphi - \theta)$$
$$+ \left[\frac{q_N(0) - Q_N \cos (\varphi - \theta)}{\cos \frac{n\pi}{2} \frac{\omega}{\omega_a}} \right] \cos \frac{\omega}{\omega_a} \left(\omega_a t - \frac{n\pi}{2} \right)$$
$$= \frac{C_N E_b}{1 - \frac{\omega_a^2}{\omega^2}} \left[\cos (\omega_a t + \varphi) - \frac{\cos \varphi}{\cos \frac{n\pi}{2} \frac{\omega}{\omega_a}} \cos \frac{\omega}{\omega_a} \left(\omega_a t - \frac{n\pi}{2} \right) \right]$$
$$+ q_N(0) \frac{\cos \frac{\omega}{\omega_a} \left(\omega_a t - \frac{n\pi}{2} \right)}{\cos \frac{n\pi}{2} \frac{\omega}{\omega_a}}. \quad (87)$$

The equation for current is obtained by differentiating Eq. (87). Thus,

$$\frac{i_c(t)}{C_N E_b \omega_a} = -\frac{1}{1 - \frac{\omega_a^2}{\omega^2}} \left\{ \sin(\omega_a t + \varphi) - \frac{\cos \varphi}{\cos\left(\frac{n\pi}{2} \frac{\omega}{\omega_a}\right)} \frac{\omega}{\omega_a} \sin\left[\frac{\omega}{\omega_a}\left(\omega_a t - \frac{n\pi}{2}\right)\right] \right\}$$

$$- \frac{q_N(0)}{C_N E_b} \frac{\omega}{\omega_a} \frac{\sin \frac{\omega}{\omega_a}\left(\omega_a t - \frac{n\pi}{2}\right)}{\cos \frac{n\pi}{2} \frac{\omega}{\omega_a}}. \quad (88)$$

The network voltage is derived from Eq. (87) and may be expressed in ratio form, that is,

$$\frac{v_N(t)}{E_b} = \frac{1}{1 - \frac{\omega_a^2}{\omega^2}} \left[\cos(\omega_a t + \varphi) - \frac{\cos \varphi}{\cos \frac{n\pi}{2} \frac{\omega}{\omega_a}} \cos \frac{\omega}{\omega_a}\left(\omega_a t - \frac{n\pi}{2}\right) \right]$$

$$+ \frac{q_N(0)}{C_N E_b} \cdot \frac{\cos \frac{\omega}{\omega_a}\left(\omega_a t - \frac{n\pi}{2}\right)}{\cos \frac{n\pi}{2} \frac{\omega}{\omega_a}}. \quad (89)$$

The voltage stepup ratio at the time ($\omega_a t = n\pi$) when the network discharges is

$$\frac{v_N(n\pi)}{E_b} = -\frac{2 \cos \varphi}{1 - \frac{\omega_a^2}{\omega^2}} + \frac{v_N(0)}{E_b}, \quad (90)$$

where φ is related to $i_c(0)$, $q_N(0)$, and ω/ω_a by

$$\frac{\frac{\omega_a}{\omega} \sin \varphi + \frac{i_c(0)}{\omega C_N E_b}\left(1 - \frac{\omega_a^2}{\omega^2}\right)}{-\cos \varphi + \frac{q_N(0)}{C_N E_b}\left(1 - \frac{\omega_a^2}{\omega^2}\right)} = \tan \frac{n\pi}{2} \frac{\omega}{\omega_a}. \quad (91)$$

For the special case where both the network voltage and charging current are zero at time $t = 0$, this relation may be simplified to

$$-\tan \varphi = \frac{\omega}{\omega_a} \tan \frac{n\pi}{2} \frac{\omega}{\omega_a}. \quad (92)$$

The direct component of current must, of necessity, be zero if n is odd by reason of symmetry. The rms current is obtained by integrating

$$I_{c_{rms}}^2 = \frac{1}{T_r} \int_0^{T_r} i_c^2(t) \, dt.$$

The result of evaluating this integral is

$$I^2_{c_{\text{rms}}} = \frac{1}{2n\pi}\left(\frac{C_N E_b \omega_a}{1 - \dfrac{\omega_a^2}{\omega^2}}\right)^2 \left[n\pi + k^2\left(n\pi - \frac{\omega_a}{\omega}\sin n\pi \frac{\omega}{\omega_a}\right) \right.$$

$$\left. + \frac{8k \dfrac{\omega_a}{\omega}\sin\varphi\cos\dfrac{n\pi}{2}\dfrac{\omega}{\omega_a}}{1 - \dfrac{\omega_a^2}{\omega^2}} \right], \quad (93)$$

where

$$k = \frac{1}{\dfrac{\omega_a}{\omega}\cos\dfrac{n\pi}{2}\dfrac{\omega}{\omega_a}}\left[\frac{q_N(0)}{C_N E_b}\left(1 - \frac{\omega_a^2}{\omega^2}\right) - \cos\varphi\right].$$

Figure 9·18 gives representative voltage and current wave shapes for a-c nonresonant charging; (c) and (b) correspond to zero initial current and network voltage for half-cycle and full-cycle charging respec-

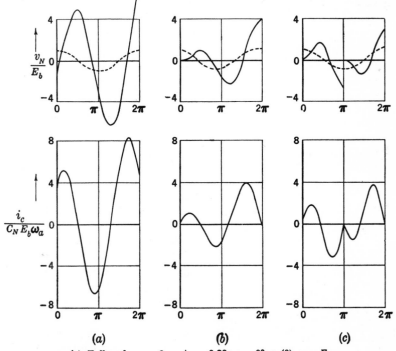

(a)   (b)   (c)

(a) Full cycle, $n = 2$; $\omega_a/\omega = 0.80$; $\varphi = 0°$; $v_N(0) = -E_b$.
(b) Full cycle, $n = 2$; $\omega_a/\omega = 0.70$; $\varphi = 21°$; $v_N(0) = 0$.
(c) Half cycle, $n = 1$; $\omega_a/\omega = 0.50$; $\varphi = 0°$; $v_N(0) = 0$.

FIG. 9·18.—Voltage and current wave shapes for a-c nonresonant charging. The broken line is the impressed voltage.

tively, and (*a*) is a special case of full-cycle charging. Figure 9·18*b* corresponds to the case of maximum voltage stepup ratio for full-cycle charging.

9·7. Practical A-c Charging Transformers.—In all practical cases, the charging inductance used for a-c charging pulsers is built as leakage inductance into the transformer supplying the high voltage. A major component is therefore eliminated, with resultant savings in the weight and size of the pulser. The majority of a-c charging transformers fall within the following range of ratings:

Leakage inductance: 1 to 25 henrys.
Secondary rms current: 0.05 to 1 amp.
Secondary peak voltage: 5 to 30 kv.
Kilovolt-amperes: 0.5 to 10 kva.
A-c frequency: 60 to 800 cycles/sec.

The leakage inductance of a transformer increases when the ratio of the primary flux cut by the secondary to the total primary flux decreases. This decrease can be achieved in several ways:

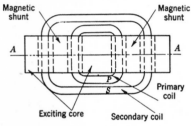

1. By a physical separation of the primary and secondary windings on the core.
2. By the use of a magnetic shunt.
3. By the use of a leakage core.
4. By a combination of the above methods.

High-reactance transformers that have a magnetic shunt or a leakage core are commonly used because the leakage flux is more easily controlled by these means. Figure 9·19 shows a typical magnetic-shunt transformer. The normal flux path through the exciting core of the transformer is indicated by *FFF*. The magnetic shunts that provide a path for the leakage-reactance flux are located between the primary coil *P* and the secondary coil *S*. These shunts are

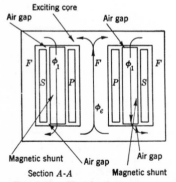

Fig. 9·19.—Sketch of an a-c resonant-charging transformer with a magnetic shunt; ϕ_e is the exciting flux and ϕ_1 is the reactance flux. (*Courtesy of General Electric Co.*)

composed of iron laminations of the same quality and thickness as those used in the main transformer core. By increasing or decreasing the spacing of the air gaps at the ends of the magnetic shunts, the leakage reactance of the transformer can be adjusted.

The magnetic-shunt transformer is simple in design and construction. There are certain current phase conditions on capacitive loads, however, under which the leakage-reactance flux and the exciting flux add in such a way as to increase the flux density in the two outside legs of the transformer core. This increase may cause magnetic saturation of the iron in the core legs, with a corresponding increase in core loss and decrease in inductance for the large values of secondary current.

Figure 9·20 shows a transformer having a separate leakage-reactance core. The design comprises a primary coil *P* and the secondary coil *S* which are linked by a normal exciting core as shown. In addition, a leakage-reactance core containing an air gap is provided in order to link the secondary winding and to serve as a magnetic path for the leakage flux. The spacing of this air gap controls the reactance and its physical shape determines the reactance-versus-current characteristics of the transformer. An air gap is also provided in the exciting core in order to prevent its saturation by the direct-current component in the secondary winding.

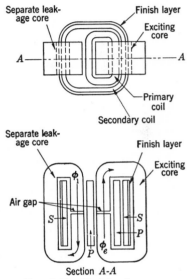

Fig. 9·20.—Sketch of an a-c resonant-charging transformer with separate leakage core; ϕ_e is the exciting flux and ϕ_1 is the reactance flux. (*Courtesy of General Electric Co.*)

The separate-leakage-core transformer has an advantage over the magnetic-shunt transformer because it provides a separate path for the leakage flux, and therefore prevents the leakage flux and the normal exciting flux from adding to produce saturation of the steel. A transformer of this type requires two separate cores, but is comparable to the magnetic-shunt transformer in simplicity of design and construction. A transformer having a separate leakage core requires approximately 10 per cent more space than that having a magnetic shunt, but the additional space has not limited its applications. Figure 9·21 shows the assembly of cores and coils for a transformer with a separate leakage core. The various parts can be recognized by comparison with Fig. 9·20.

Linearity Requirements for A-c Charging Transformers.—The switches used in a-c charging pulsers are nearly always rotary spark gaps, which have complex operating characteristics. Perhaps the most important complicating factor encountered with rotary-gap pulsers is the increase in spark length with power level. This increase in gap length changes the a-c voltage phase at which the spark occurs, thereby disturbing the charging-circuit conditions. The phase of the a-c voltage may also be changed by the effect of the load current on the alternator magnetic field.

As a result, transformers having constant leakage inductance for all currents in the operating range usually do not give the best overall performance. Since an exact analysis is difficult, the final adjustment of the inductance characteristic of the charging transformer is always made by experimental observation on an electrical sample of the pulser circuit, including the alternator.

The leakage inductances of charging transformers are measured by the same methods as those used for d-c charging reactors (Sec. 9·2). The transformer primary is short-circuited and superimposed a-c and d-c currents are passed through the secondary.

Fig. 9·21.—Core-and-coil assembly of a high-reactance transformer. (*Courtesy of General Electric Co.*)

In the case of half-cycle a-c charging, the direct current in the transformer is zero. When testing full-cycle resonant charging transformers, the a-c to d-c current ratio is taken as 2.9, but for nonresonant charging the ratio is larger. The value of 2.9 is derived as follows. For full-cycle charging ($n = 2$) Eq. (70b) reduces to

$$(I_{crms})_{min} \approx \frac{\pi C_N E_b \omega_a}{\sqrt{6}} \tag{94}$$

The corresponding average current from Eq. (67a) is

$$I_{cav} = \frac{Q C_N E_b \omega_a}{2\pi} \left(\frac{1 - e^{\frac{-\pi}{Q}}}{1 + \frac{1}{4Q^2}} \right)$$

$$\approx \frac{C_N E_b \omega_a}{2} \left(1 - \frac{\pi}{2Q} \right). \tag{95}$$

Hence,

$$(I_{crms})_{min} = \frac{2\pi I_{cav}}{\sqrt{6} \left(1 - \frac{\pi}{2Q} \right)}.$$

The a-c component of the secondary current is given by

$$I_{c_{a-c}}^2 = (I_{c_{\mathrm{rms}}}^2)_{\min} - I_{c_{av}}^2 = I_{c_{av}}^2 \left[\frac{4\pi^2}{6\left(1 - \frac{\pi}{2Q}\right)^2} - 1 \right]$$

Hence the a-c to d-c current ratio is

$$\frac{I_{c_{a-c}}}{I_{c_{av}}} = \sqrt{\frac{4\pi^2}{6\left(1 - \frac{\pi}{2Q}\right)^2} - 1}. \qquad (96)$$

Using representative value for the quality factor, that is, $Q = 10$, the a-c to d-c current ratio is found to be 2.9. For zero circuit loss, that is, $Q = \infty$, the ratio is reduced to 2.37.

The charging-current wave for the case of a-c resonant charging with zero initial voltage on the condenser and zero current is shown in Fig. 9·16b, where the form of the a-c component of the current is seen to be approximately sinusoidal. The maximum value for this a-c component is $1.62 C_N E_b \omega_a$, whereas the peak value of the corresponding sine wave, calculated for $Q = 10$, is $1.84 C_N E_b \omega_a$. Since the inductance-measuring method closely simulates the current under operating conditions the values of leakage-inductance determined by this method may be considered to be significant.

The inductance of the charging circuit includes that of the a-c alternator or other a-c voltage source. The effective inductance of the special alternators used with a-c charging pulsers may be from 10 to 20 per cent of the total inductance, and must be subtracted from the calculated value in order to obtain the net leakage inductance required in the charging transformer. The effective alternator inductance is difficult to calculate in any given case and is also difficult to measure, except when it is used directly in a pulser circuit.

A transformer to be used with an a-c charging rotary-gap pulser usually gives the best over-all performance if its leakage inductance decreases slightly with increasing current. The leakage-inductance characteristics for two representative transformers are shown in Fig. 9·22, that in Fig. 9·22a having a magnetic shunt, and that in Fig. 9·22b a leakage-reactance core. As is to be expected, the transformer using a leakage-reactance core has the more linear characteristic. The allowable amount of decrease in the inductance characteristic is estimated by experience, and the final adjustment is always made on an actual test pulser.

B-H Oscillograms for Typical A-c Charging Transformers.—The leakage-inductance characteristics may be shown by graphs such as those in Fig. 9·22. The B-H oscillograms, however, are more fundamental, and reveal in detail the effects of transformer-core saturation. Two complete sets of B-H oscillograms for the same transformers as those of Fig. 9·22 are shown in Fig. 9·23 and Fig. 9·24.

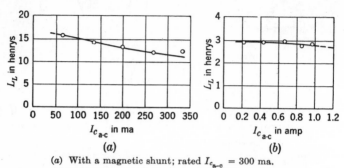

(a) With a magnetic shunt; rated $I_{c_{a-c}} = 300$ ma.

(b) With a separate leakage core; rated $I_{c_{a-c}} = 1.2$ amp.

FIG. 9·22.—Leakage inductance vs. secondary a-c current for typical a-c charging transformers.

An ideal a-c charging transformer is one that has zero internal loss, as well as a constant stepup ratio and leakage inductance over the range of voltage and currents used. The B-H oscillograms for such a transformer would consist of straight lines enclosing zero areas, instead of the loops enclosing finite areas that are actually observed. The leakage-inductance B-H oscillograms for well-designed charging transformers always enclose small areas, indicating that the losses are relatively small. The linearity of the B-H loops depends to a great extent upon the type of leakage-flux path used in the transformer. Transformers with magnetic shunts usually show the greatest saturation effects.

The oscillograms in Fig. 9·23 are good examples of this tendency since there is a slight amount of saturation even at one-third rated load current when direct current is present. The curvature of the remaining B-H loops increases, although not markedly, with increasing current. As indicated by theory, the removal of the direct-current component lessens the degree of saturation. The other oscillograms in the same figure show the secondary exciting current when the primary is open-circuited. Since the areas of these loops are considerably greater than those for the leakage inductance, it is evident that the core losses are greater. The high degree of saturation induced by both the over-voltage and the direct current is indicated by comparison with normal B-H loops for the transformer-exciting current.

The set of B-H oscillograms shown in Fig. 9·24 are for a transformer with a separate leakage core, and form an interesting comparison. The leakage-flux oscillograms indicate very slight saturation of the leakage-

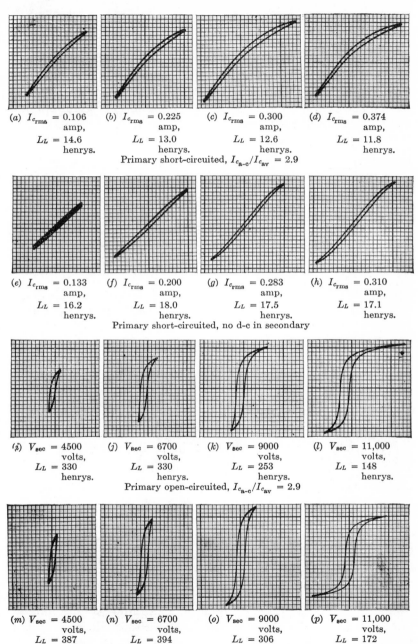

(a) $I_{c_{rms}} = 0.106$ amp, $L_L = 14.6$ henrys.

(b) $I_{c_{rms}} = 0.225$ amp, $L_L = 13.0$ henrys.

(c) $I_{c_{rms}} = 0.300$ amp, $L_L = 12.6$ henrys.

(d) $I_{c_{rms}} = 0.374$ amp, $L_L = 11.8$ henrys.

Primary short-circuited, $I_{c_{a-c}}/I_{c_{av}} = 2.9$

(e) $I_{c_{rms}} = 0.133$ amp, $L_L = 16.2$ henrys.

(f) $I_{c_{rms}} = 0.200$ amp, $L_L = 18.0$ henrys.

(g) $I_{c_{rms}} = 0.283$ amp, $L_L = 17.5$ henrys.

(h) $I_{c_{rms}} = 0.310$ amp, $L_L = 17.1$ henrys.

Primary short-circuited, no d-c in secondary

(i) $V_{sec} = 4500$ volts, $L_L = 330$ henrys.

(j) $V_{sec} = 6700$ volts, $L_L = 330$ henrys.

(k) $V_{sec} = 9000$ volts, $L_L = 253$ henrys.

(l) $V_{sec} = 11,000$ volts, $L_L = 148$ henrys.

Primary open-circuited, $I_{c_{a-c}}/I_{c_{av}} = 2.9$

(m) $V_{sec} = 4500$ volts, $L_L = 387$ henrys.

(n) $V_{sec} = 6700$ volts, $L_L = 394$ henrys.

(o) $V_{sec} = 9000$ volts, $L_L = 306$ henrys.

(p) $V_{sec} = 11,000$ volts, $L_L = 172$ henrys.

Primary open-circuited, no d-c in secondary

Fig. 9·23.—B-H oscillograms for an a-c charging transformer with a magnetic shunt Transformer rated at 0.300 amp rms and 9000 volts secondary voltage.

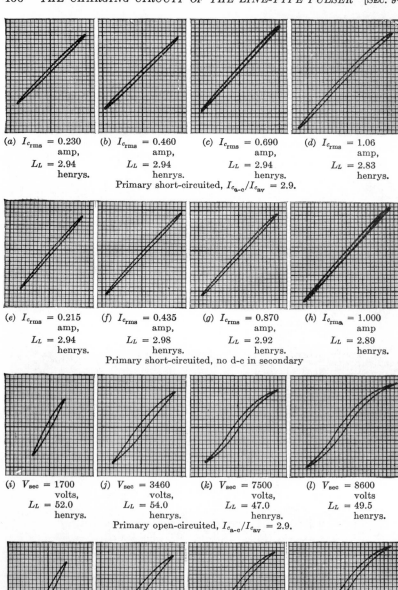

(a) $I_{c_{\mathrm{rms}}} = 0.230$ amp, $L_L = 2.94$ henrys.

(b) $I_{c_{\mathrm{rms}}} = 0.460$ amp, $L_L = 2.94$ henrys.

(c) $I_{c_{\mathrm{rms}}} = 0.690$ amp, $L_L = 2.94$ henrys.

(d) $I_{c_{\mathrm{rms}}} = 1.06$ amp, $L_L = 2.83$ henrys.

Primary short-circuited, $I_{c_{\mathrm{a-c}}}/I_{c_{\mathrm{av}}} = 2.9$.

(e) $I_{c_{\mathrm{rms}}} = 0.215$ amp, $L_L = 2.94$ henrys.

(f) $I_{c_{\mathrm{rms}}} = 0.435$ amp, $L_L = 2.98$ henrys.

(g) $I_{c_{\mathrm{rms}}} = 0.870$ amp, $L_L = 2.92$ henrys.

(h) $I_{c_{\mathrm{rms}}} = 1.000$ amp $L_L = 2.89$ henrys.

Primary short-circuited, no d-c in secondary

(i) $V_{\mathrm{sec}} = 1700$ volts, $L_L = 52.0$ henrys.

(j) $V_{\mathrm{sec}} = 3460$ volts, $L_L = 54.0$ henrys.

(k) $V_{\mathrm{sec}} = 7500$ volts, $L_L = 47.0$ henrys.

(l) $V_{\mathrm{sec}} = 8600$ volts $L_L = 49.5$ henrys.

Primary open-circuited, $I_{c_{\mathrm{a-c}}}/I_{c_{\mathrm{av}}} = 2.9$.

(m) $V_{\mathrm{sec}} = 1730$ volts, $L_L = 54.0$ henrys.

(n) $V_{\mathrm{sec}} = 3460$ volts, $L_L = 52.0$ henrys.

(o) $V_{\mathrm{sec}} = 7500$ volts, $L_L = 48.4$ henrys.

(p) $V_{\mathrm{sec}} = 8600$ volts, $L_L = 46.6$ henrys.

Primary open-circuited, no d-c in secondary.

Fig. 9·24.—*B-H* oscillograms for an a-c charging transformer with a separate leakage core. Transformer rated at 1.20 amp and 7500 volts secondary voltage.

flux core.   Likewise, the direct-current component has only a very small effect on the measured values of the leakage inductance.   The oscillograms for the secondary exciting current are also of a somewhat different character than those for a transformer of the magnetic-shunt type.   The direct-current component has less effect on the degree of core saturation in the latter case.   Unfortunately, however, limitations in the measuring apparatus prevented the overvolting of the secondary, and it was therefore impossible to obtain a complete set of comparative data for the latter transformer.

9·8. The Design of High-reactance Transformers.[1]—Only the design problems specifically related to high-reactance transformers are discussed here since those common to both d-c charging reactors and a-c charging transformers are treated in Sec. 9·3.

The determination of the effective voltage stepup ratio and the inductance of the transformer is made by calculation and by experiment. Theoretically, the total reactance in an a-c resonant-charging circuit of the full-wave type should be about 194 per cent, that is,

$$\sqrt{2}\,\frac{\omega_a L_c I_{crms}}{E_b} \approx 1.94.$$

The series reactances of the power supply and the high-reactance transformer are combined to give this reactance.   Nonlinearity of the transformer inductance may be provided by extending the length of a few of the laminations on the leakage core, thus providing a short gap of small cross section in parallel with the main gap.

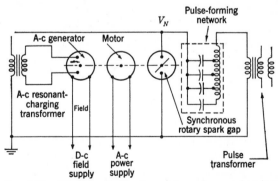

Fig. 9·25.—Diagram of a line-type pulser using a-c charging.

Figure 9·25 shows the general circuit in which a-c resonant-charging transformers are used.   The pulse transformer shown does not contribute in any way to the characteristics of the charging circuit; hence, for most

[1] By H. H. Koski of the General Electric Company, Pittsfield, Mass.

purposes, the impedance of the pulse transformer can be considered to be zero, except during pulsing.

Figure 9·26 shows the equivalent circuit of the diagram given in Fig. 9·25. The induced voltage, usually sinusoidal, in the generator armature is shown by V_G. This voltage is applied to the resistance and reactance components of the a-c generator, resonant-charging transformer, and the capacitance C_N in the pulser circuit.

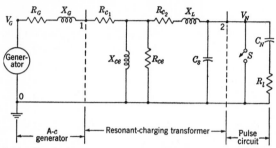

FIG. 9·26.—Equivalent circuit of a line-type pulser using a-c charging.

Typical oscillograms of the voltage output of the transformer in a full-wave charging circuit are shown in Fig. 9·27. The exponential decay in the voltage after the pulse is caused by the time constant of the viewing circuit that is used in conjunction with a cathode-ray oscilloscope to observe the charging waveform.

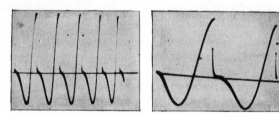

(a) Slow sweep.   (b) Fast sweep.

FIG. 9·27.—Charging voltage wave shapes in an a-c charging line-type pulser.   (*Courtesy of General Electric Co.*)

Sample Design.—The following sample calculations show the general procedure followed in the design of a transformer having the following specifications:

Input: 115-volt, 635-cycle.
Effective turns ratio: 1/49.
Inductance: 6.2 henrys ± 5 per cent.
Current in high-voltage winding: 0.330 amp rms, 0.114 amp d-c.
Recurrence frequency: 635 pps.
Peak charging voltage: 21.8 kv.

Full-cycle charging circuit.

Efficiency: 90 per cent.

Ambient temperature range: $-40°C$ to $+50°C$.

For shipboard use.

Hermetically-sealed unit, dimensions not specified, mounting to be by means of a clamp over the top edge of the tank.

PFN capacitance: 0.0091 μf.

Generator impedance: 3.9 ohms.

For this case, tests indicated that an actual turns ratio of 1/44 was required instead of the theoretical value 1/49; in the same way, the necessary transformer inductance was found to be 6.2 henrys as against 5 henrys indicated by the original computations.

This transformer was designed to have a separate leakage core (Fig. 9·20), but the calculations can, in general, be applied to one having a magnetic shunt. Figure 9·21 shows the core and coil of the assembled unit. The design calculation is started by choosing values of maximum flux densities compatible with previous experience. Selecting 27,000 and 40,000 lines/in.^{2} for the flux in the main and leakage cores respectively, and a cross section of 3 in. by $\frac{7}{8}$ in. for the main core, the voltage per turn may be found by the formula

$$V_t = \frac{2\pi}{\sqrt{2}} f_r \times B_c \times A_c \times 10^{-8},$$

where A_c is the net area of steel or the cross section multiplied by the space factor. Assuming a value of 0.88 for this factor gives

$$V_t = 4.44 \times 635 \times 27,000 \times 3 \times \tfrac{7}{8} \times 10^{-8} \text{ volts}$$
$$= 1.76 \text{ volts}.$$

Hence, the coils require 65 and 2860 turns respectively.

The leakage-reactance core can now be determined. Its flux is given by

$$\phi_{lk} = \frac{L_c \times I_{c\max} \times 10^8}{N},$$

where $I_{c\max} = 1.8 I_{c\mathrm{rms}}$, and N = number of high-voltage turns. Then

$$\phi_{lk} = \frac{6.2 \times 0.33 \times 1.8 \times 10^8}{2860}$$
$$= 129,000 \text{ lines}.$$

Past experience indicates that about 20 per cent of this flux is external to the leakage core, leaving only 103,000 lines in the core. The cross section of the leakage core at 40,000 lines/in.^{2} equals

$$\frac{103,000}{40,000} = 2.58 \text{ in.}^2$$

This value closely approximates that for the main-core cross section. For mechanical reasons, the same section is used for both cores, giving a flux density

$$B_c = \frac{103,000}{2.36} = 44,600 \text{ lines/in.}^2$$

in the leakage core. This value is approximate and must be corrected later when the flux external to the core is calculated.

The coils can now be designed. In order to stay within the allowable current density at full load (assumed to be 1300 amp/in.^{2}), the secondary conductor must be 0.0179 in. in diameter, and the primary 0.120 in. by 0.090 in. The latter cross section corresponds to the equivalent value of the a-c component of the high-voltage current plus the core-exciting current. The conductor shape is determined solely by the complete coil-shape desired and the wire sizes on hand.

The low-voltage wire is chosen with paper insulation, making the over-all insulated size 0.131 in. by 0.101 in. Two layers are necessary for the coil and a sheet of 0.015-in. insulation between the layers serves as mechanical support for the second layer.

In order to reduce the voltage induced in the primary by the discharge of the pulse-forming network and thus to minimize radio-noise interference, a grounded electrostatic shield is interposed between the windings. This shield consists of a brass screen insulated from the coil by a sheet of 0.015-in. layer insulation forming one open turn around the coil. It is bonded to the core clamp and hence to ground. Some insulation must be between the ends of the shield to prevent a short-circuit.

The high-voltage wire is constructed with double enamel and cotton covering, which makes its nominal over-all diameter equal to 0.0246 in. In order to distribute the voltage stresses more evenly under the impulse conditions of operation, the last layer is made of more heavily insulated wire, as shown in Figs. 9·19 and 9·20. This wire insulation consists of $\frac{1}{32}$-in. black varnished cambric insulation, which needs only a few turns for a full layer; thus, the number of turns of the 0.0179-in. wire is reduced accordingly.

The insulation in the transformer consists of the coil cylinders, paper-layer insulation in the coils, pressboard collars and barriers, wooden spacers, and oil.

Because of the mechanical strength required, the coil cylinders present no problem in electrical insulation. The layer insulation in the coils, the creepage distance around the ends of the layers, the collars and barriers between the high-voltage coil and the cores, and the insulation of leads are all determined from the corresponding applied voltages and the limiting values of stress. Some of these values are calculated directly, but others must be obtained from a scale layout of the transformer. Another reason for using a scale layout is the necessity of measuring the cross-sectional areas of the coils and the area between coils in order to calculate the air and iron fluxes more accurately.

Leakage-reactance-core Gap.—The preliminary calculation of the flux in the leakage-reactance core was based on an estimate of the flux in the air external to the core. The air flux is now calculated from the actual dimensions of the transformer in order to give a more accurate value of core flux for use in determining the gap in the leakage-reactance core.

The flux ϕ_1 external to the core is[1]

$$\phi_1 = \frac{3.19 \left(\dfrac{A_h}{3} + A_{(h-l)} + \dfrac{A_l}{3} \right) NI_{cmax}}{0.65 l_h},$$

where

A_h = cross-sectional area of the high-voltage coil in in.[2],

A_l = cross-sectional area of the low-voltage coil in in.[2],

$A_{(h-l)}$ = area between the coils in in.[2],

l_h = length of winding on the high-voltage coil in in.,

and

$$\phi_1 = \frac{3.19 \left(\dfrac{2.2}{3} + 5.85 + \dfrac{15.3}{3} \right) (2860)(0.330)(1.8)}{(0.65)(4.25)}$$

$$= 23{,}200 \text{ lines.}$$

Since a total flux of 129,000 lines was previously calculated, 105,800 lines are left in the core.

Because of the effect of "fringing," the calculation of the core gap is a trial-and-error process. The actual length of the gap is used, but its cross-sectional area is increased by an empirical amount that is a function of the length.

First, the ratio of effective area to length of the leakage-reactance core is calculated;

$$\frac{A_g}{l_g} = \frac{\phi_2}{(3.19)(NI_m)}$$

where A_g = effective gap area, l_g = gap length, and ϕ_2 = core flux.

[1] The factor 0.65 in the denominator is empirical and depends on the coil configuration. Its value may vary from 0.6 to 1.1.

There results

$$\frac{A_g}{l_g} = \frac{105,800}{(3.19)(2860)(0.330)(1.8)} = 19.5 \text{ in.}$$

Assuming a gap length of 0.160 in., the effective area is calculated from

$$A_g = A_a + \frac{l_g \times p_g}{3},$$

where A_a is the actual cross-sectional area of the gap, and p_g is the periphery of the gap.

Therefore

$$A_g = 3 \times \frac{7}{8} + \frac{(0.160)(7.75)}{3}$$
$$= 3.03 \text{ in.}^2$$

Checking,

$$\frac{A_g}{l_g} = \frac{3.03}{0.160} = 19.0 \text{ in.}$$

A gap length of 0.155 in. would almost exactly check the value calculated for A_g/l_g but the value 19.0 is within the design limits.

A gap of this length is satisfactory, but a nonlinear inductance gives more stable operation. The ordinary gap gives an almost linear inductance. By experiment, a nonlinear inductance is obtained by making the gap with several of the outside laminations extending into the gap. At low currents the short gap between the extended laminations gives a high inductance, but at high currents these extended laminations become saturated, causing the effective length of the gap to increase. The inductance at high current is therefore decreased by some value depending on the proportions of the gap. The final design has about a 15 per cent drop in inductance from $\frac{1}{3}$ to full current. This gap construction requires preliminary tests on the cores in order to adjust the spacing to the right value.

Losses.—The losses in the transformer are important not only from the standpoint of resonant-voltage rise but also from the point of view of efficiency and heating. The losses, shown in Table 9·3, consist of I^2R- and eddy-current losses in the windings, core loss, and stray loss, which is an all-inclusive term covering indeterminate losses in the insulation, the clamps, and the tank.

The ratio of the expected voltage rise to the applied a-c voltage in a resonant-charging circuit is given by the relation (66b) which, in this case, reduces to

$$\frac{V_N}{E_b} = \frac{n\pi}{2}\left(1 - \frac{n\pi}{4Q}\right),$$

where

$$Q = \frac{\omega_a L_c}{R_c} = \frac{\omega_a L_c}{P_e} I_{c_{rms}}^2$$
$$= \frac{635 \times 2\pi \times 6.9}{90.16} \times (0.33)^2 = 30.$$

Hence, for full-cycle charging.

$$\frac{V_N}{E_b} \approx 2.98.$$

The leakage-core loss is calculated by assuming that the wave is unsymmetrical, that is, the first peak has only half the voltage of the second peak.   The stray loss depends greatly on the mechanical proportions of the transformer and can be estimated only from experience; in a transformer of this type it is usually about equal to the total copper loss.

TABLE 9·3.—TRANSFORMER LOSSES

Loss	Watts full load, a-c resonant-charging circuit
In primary coil I^2R plus eddy-current loss..................	13.45
In secondary coil ⎰ I^2R plus eddy.........................	17.71
Leakage-core loss.......................	29.0
⎱ Stray loss..............................	30.
Total loss in charging circuit, P_c..........................	90.16
In exciting core..	24.4
Total transformer loss...................................	114.56

Heating and Oil Expansion.—The operating temperature of the windings, core, and oil is determined by computing empirically the temperature drop from the wire and core to the tank surface through the insulation, the oil, and the contact surfaces.   In this particular example, the losses correspond to approximately 0.2 watts/in.^{2} of tank, giving a temperature rise of 25°C from ambient air to oil.   The temperature rise in the oil from tank to coil depends on conduction and convection, and may amount to 15°C in this transformer; the rise from the coil to the windings amounts to about 10°C for a coil construction of the particular type used in this case.   The temperature rise of the core above oil, resulting from a dissipation of about 0.25 watts in.^{2}, is also about 10°. The temperature rise of both coils and core above the external ambient temperature is therefore about 50°C.

In this particular transformer, an air space is provided in order to limit changes in pressure inside the tank, resulting from temperature variations that cause the oil to expand or contract.   The expected pressure is then calculated from the following empirical formula:

$$P = \frac{1470 V_{25} T + 65.4 T}{29{,}800 V_T + 0.0147 T^2},$$

where

   P = absolute pressure in lb/in.²,
   T = final gas and oil temperature absolute in °C,
   V_{25} = ratio of air volume to oil volume at 25°C,
   V_T = ratio of air volume to oil volume at T°C.

If a final oil temperature of 80°C is assumed, $V_{25} = 0.0715$ and V_T = 0.0276, giving a pressure of 22.7 lb/in.² if there is no flexing in the tank. In practice, the elasticity of the sides of the tank reduces that pressure appreciably.

9·9. Miscellaneous Charging Circuits.   *A-c Diode Charging.*—A simple method for a-c charging, mentioned in Sec. 9·4, is to insert a hold-off

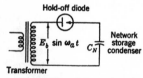

Hold-off diode

$E_b \sin \omega_a t$ C_N Network storage condenser

Transformer

FIG. 9·28.—Schematic circuit diagram for a-c charging using a hold-off diode.

diode between the high-voltage transformer and the network as shown in Fig. 9·28. As illustrated by Fig. 9·29, the voltage on the network builds up to almost the peak positive value of the transformer voltage. The hold-off diode prevents the reverse flow of current, and therefore maintains the charge on the network until the switch is fired. The discharge of the network is timed to take place during the negative half cycle of the transformer voltage in order to insure a long deionization time for the switch.

   The equations for a-c diode charging are developed on the assumptions (1) that the transformer has zero leakage inductance and (2) that

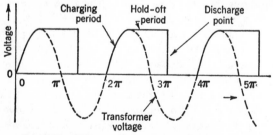

FIG. 9·29.—Voltage relations for a-c diode charging.

the diode loss can be represented by an equivalent resistance. The differential equation and initial conditions for the network charge q_N during the charging period are

$$R_c \frac{dq_N}{dt} + \frac{q_N}{C_N} = E_b \sin \omega_a t,$$

$$q_N(0) = 0,$$

$$\left(\frac{dq_N}{dt}\right)_{t=0} = 0.$$

The corresponding Laplace-transform equation is

$$R_c p q_N(p) + \frac{1}{C_N} q_N(p) = \frac{E_b \omega_a}{p^2 + \omega_a^2}.$$

Solving for $q_N(p)$,

$$q_N(p) = \frac{E_b \omega_a}{R_c} \cdot \frac{1}{\left(p + \dfrac{1}{R_c C_N}\right)(p^2 + \omega_a^2)}. \tag{98}$$

The inverse transform giving $q_N(t)$ is

$$q_N(t) = \frac{C_N E_b}{1 + R_c^2 C_N^2 \omega_a^2} \left(R_c C_N \omega_a e^{\frac{-\omega_a t}{R_c C_N \omega_a}} - R_c C_N \omega_a \cos \omega_a t + \sin \omega_a t\right). \tag{99}$$

By differentiating, the current may be found to be

$$i_c(t) = \frac{C_N E_b \omega_a}{1 + R_c^2 C_N^2 \omega_a^2} \left(R_c C_N \omega_a \sin \omega_a t + \cos \omega_a t - e^{\frac{-\omega_a t}{R_c C_N \omega_a}}\right). \tag{100}$$

The maximum voltage on the condenser occurs either for $i_c(t) = 0$, or for a value of $t = t_1$ given by setting Eq. (100) equal to zero. Then t_1 is a solution of

$$R_c C_N \omega_a \sin \omega_a t_1 + \cos \omega_a t_1 - e^{-\frac{\omega_a t_1}{R_c C_N \omega_a}} = 0. \tag{101}$$

By substituting Eq. (100) into Eq. (99), the relation

$$(q_N)_{\text{max}} = C_N E_b \sin \omega_a t_1$$

is obtained. For most practical cases of a-c diode charging, $R_c C_N \omega_a \ll 1$. For example, if $R_c C_N \omega_a = 0.04$, the exponential term in Eq. (101) is negligible, and $\omega_a t_1$ is given approximately by

$$\tan \omega_a t_1 = \frac{-1}{R_c C_N \omega_a} \qquad \text{or} \qquad \omega_a t_1 \approx \frac{\pi}{2} + R_c C_N \omega_a.$$

Using this value of $\omega_a t_1$, $(q_N)_{\text{max}}$ becomes

$$(q_N)_{\text{max}} = \frac{C_N E_b}{\sqrt{1 + R_c^2 C_N^2 \omega_a^2}} \approx C_N E_b, \tag{102}$$

to a very close approximation. When $R_c C_N \omega_a$ is not small compared with unity, the more exact equations must be used. For the remaining calculations, it is assumed that $R_c C_N \omega_a \ll 1$, and the average and effective currents are found to be

$$I_{c_{\mathrm{av}}} = \frac{C_N E_b \omega_a}{2\pi}$$

and

$$I_{c_{\mathrm{rms}}} = \frac{C_N E_b \omega_a}{2\sqrt{2}}$$

respectively.

The transformer utilization factor, T.U.F., or ratio of power output to transformer volt-amperes, is then

$$\text{T.U.F.} = \frac{\dfrac{\omega_a}{2\pi} \cdot \dfrac{1}{2} C_N E_b^2}{\dfrac{E_b}{\sqrt{2}} \cdot \dfrac{C_N E_b \omega_a}{2\sqrt{2}}} = \frac{1}{\pi} = 0.32, \tag{103}$$

and the charging efficiency, η_c, is given by

$$\eta_c = \frac{\text{power output}}{\text{power input}} = \frac{\dfrac{\omega_a}{2\pi} \cdot \dfrac{1}{2} C_N E_b^2}{\dfrac{\omega_a}{2\pi} \cdot \dfrac{1}{2} C_N E_b^2 + \dfrac{C_N^2 E_b^2 \omega_a^2}{8} R_c} = \frac{1}{1 + \dfrac{\pi}{2} R_c C_N \omega_a}, \tag{104}$$

if the core loss in the transformer is neglected. Both the diode resistance and the transformer effective resistance must be included in R_c.

A-c diode charging normally has a high efficiency if a suitable diode is used. The method has the advantage of being simple and requiring no adjustments. On the other hand, it has the disadvantage of having a very low T.U.F. and requiring a high-voltage diode. These disadvantages limit its use to relatively low-power circuits.

A variation of the a-c diode-charging circuit is one in which a resonating inductance is included in order to increase the network voltage. Neglecting losses, the maximum voltage on the condenser is increased by a factor of $\pi/2$ and the T.U.F. is likewise increased. This circuit has no advantage over the a-c resonant-charging circuit, however, except in the case where the a-c and the recurrence frequencies are subject to considerable variation.

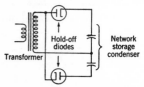

Fig. 9·30.—Two-diode charging circuit.

The a-c diode-charging method may be extended to full-wave charging by using two diodes in a manner similar to the ordinary voltage-doubler rectifier circuit. The two-diode charging circuit is shown in Fig. 9·30.

CHAPTER 10

PERFORMANCE OF LINE-TYPE PULSERS

By J. V. Lebacqz

In the preceding chapters the behavior and performance of the various components of the pulser and of the discharging and charging circuits are considered separately. In most of the discussions it is also assumed that the pulser load stays constant, both from pulse to pulse and during one pulse. In practice, however, the load is not always the same from pulse to pulse, and there are special conditions that require a consideration of the entire pulser circuit. Faults can occur in some of the components or in the load, and it is necessary to devise protective measures in order to limit the resulting damage to the other components. Some magnetrons exhibit spurious characteristics, such as mode-changing or sparking, which can be alleviated by careful pulser design.

The purpose of this chapter is to indicate some of the principles to be followed in the design of the pulser as a whole in order to obtain the most satisfactory operation that is compatible with the load characteristics.

10·1. Effects of Changes in Load Impedance.—The purpose of this section is to discuss the effect on the pulser circuit of sudden variations in load impedance, either from pulse to pulse, or during one pulse. Small variations in load impedance usually have little effect on the operation of the circuit. This fact can easily be understood by the considerations of power transfer, discussed in Sec. 7·2, which show that little change in output power is introduced by a slight mismatch between the impedances of the load and the pulse-forming network. This statement, however, must be qualified when the entire pulser circuit, including the charging circuit, is considered. It can then be shown that the effect may not be negligible if a unidirectional switch is used.

Of more direct concern are the effects of large variations in load impedance which are usually produced by faulty operation of the load, such as an open circuit or a short circuit. Either one of these conditions may occur for an indefinite length of time, for only one or a few pulses in succession, or—as, for instance, with some sparking magnetrons—they may be expected to repeat at irregular but frequent intervals. The general measures taken to protect the circuit against such load behavior are considered in this section, and a more complete analysis of the operation of the pulser with a sparking magnetron is given in Sec. 10·3.

417

Effect of Load on Pulser Operation.—In Sec. 7·1 it is shown that the current and voltage supplied by an ideal pulser discharging a pulse-forming network of impedance Z_N into a resistance R_l are given by

$$I_l = \frac{1}{R_l + Z_N} V_N \tag{1}$$

and

$$V_l = \frac{R_l}{R_l + Z_N} V_N. \tag{2}$$

The voltage left on the network at the end of the pulse is given by

$$V_{N-1} = \frac{R_l - Z_N}{R_l + Z_N} V_N. \tag{3}$$

If $R_l > Z_N$, V_{N-1} has the same polarity as V_N, and the voltage left on the network discharges through the load, giving reflected pulses of amplitude

$$V_{ln} = \frac{R_l}{R_l + Z_N} \left(\frac{R_l - Z_N}{R_l + Z_N}\right)^n V_N,$$

where V_{ln} is the voltage of the nth reflected pulse following the principal pulse. Obviously, if the load is a biased diode, the reflected pulses in the load appear only as long as the voltage left on the network V_{N-n} is greater than the bias voltage V_s, and the value of R_l changes with each successive step. If $V_s > V_{N-n}$, the discharge takes place entirely through shunt paths in the pulse transformer.

If $R_l < Z_N$, three cases must be considered. If the load is a resistance and the switch is perfectly bidirectional, voltage left on the network discharges through the load in the same fashion as when $R_l > Z_N$, and reflected pulse voltages appear across the load, the successive voltages being of opposite polarity. If the switch is unidirectional the voltage given in Eq. (3) is left on the network, since its discharge requires a current of polarity opposite to that of the main pulse flowing through the switch. This voltage affects the amplitude of the network voltage at the end of the following charging cycle in the manner described below.

If the switch is imperfectly bidirectional—that is, normally passes current in either direction but may hold off some voltage of either polarity because deionization sets in—this voltage affects the following charging cycles and, since it is random in nature, may also cause random variations in the peak network voltage.

The following discussion applies to the relatively simple but very important case of a pulser using d-c resonant charging and a unidirectional switch. A constant load resistance R_l is assumed, instead of a biased diode load.   The voltage at the end of the nth charging period is given by

$$V_{N_n} = E_{bb} + (E_{bb} - V_{J_{n-1}})e^{-\frac{R_c T_r}{2L_c}} \qquad n = 1, 2 \cdot \cdot \cdot , \qquad (9·17a)$$

where $V_{J_n} = V_{N_{n-1}}$ is the voltage left on the network by the mismatch as derived from Eq. (3) and shown in Fig. 10·1.
and

$$T_r = \frac{1}{f_r} = \frac{2\pi}{\omega_r},$$

Thus

$$V_{N_n} = E_{bb} + (E_{bb} - V_{J_{n-1}})e^{-\frac{\pi}{2Q}},$$

where

$$Q = \frac{\omega L_c}{R_c} = \frac{\omega_r}{2}\frac{L_c}{R_c}.$$

This equation can be rewritten

$$V_{N_n} = E_{bb}(1 + e^{-\frac{\pi}{2Q}}) - V_{J_{n-1}}e^{-\frac{\pi}{2Q}}$$

or, letting $\gamma = e^{-\frac{\pi}{2Q}}$ and considering the charging cycle following the first pulse,

$$V_{N_2} = E_{bb}(1 + \gamma) - \gamma V_{J_1}. \qquad (4)$$

If the value of $V_{J_1} = V_{N-1}$ is introduced from Eq. (3), and

$$\kappa = \frac{R_l - Z_N}{R_l + Z_N},$$
$$V_{J_1} = \kappa V_N = \kappa E_{bb}(1 + \gamma).$$

Thus

$$V_{N_2} = E_{bb}(1 + \gamma)(1 - \gamma\kappa).$$

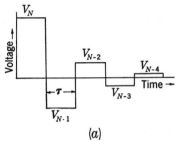

(a)

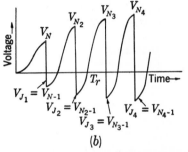

(b)

FIG. 10·1.—Network voltages if the load resistance is smaller than the network impedance. (a) Bidirectional switch; successive reflections. (b) Effect of inverse voltage on successive charging cycles with a unidirectional switch and d-c resonant charging.

At the end of the second pulse, the voltage left on the network is given by

$$V_{J_2} = \kappa V_{N_2},$$

and at the end of the third charging cycle the network reaches the voltage

$$V_{N_3} = E_{bb}(1 + \gamma) - \gamma\kappa V_{N_2} = E_{bb}(1 + \gamma)(1 - \gamma\kappa + \gamma^2\kappa^2).$$

Similarly,

$$V_{J_3} = \kappa V_{N_3}$$

and

$$V_{N_4} = E_{bb}(1 + \gamma)(1 - \gamma\kappa + \gamma^2\kappa^2 - \gamma^3\kappa^3). \qquad (5)$$

When it is assumed that $R_l < Z_N$, κ is always negative, and Eq. (5) can be rewritten

$$V_{N_4} = E_{bb}(1 + \gamma)(1 + \gamma|\kappa| + \gamma^2|\kappa|^2 + \gamma^3|\kappa|^3).$$

After the nth pulse, the network recharges to a voltage

$$V_{N_{(n+1)}} = E_{bb}(1 + \gamma)(1 + \gamma|\kappa| + \gamma^2|\kappa|^2 + \cdots + \gamma^n|\kappa|^n),$$

which can be rewritten

$$V_{N_{(n+1)}} = E_{bb}\frac{1 + \gamma}{1 - \gamma|\kappa|}(1 - \gamma^{n+1}|\kappa|^{n+1}).$$

When n approaches infinity, the equilibrium network voltage is given by

$$V_{N_\infty} = E_{bb}\frac{1 + \gamma}{1 - \gamma|\kappa|} = E_{bb}\frac{1 + \gamma}{1 + \gamma\kappa}. \tag{6}$$

This equation brings out the fact that, for unidirectional switches, the network voltage can easily be more than twice the supply voltage. If, for instance, it is assumed that $\gamma = 0.91$ and $\kappa = -0.1$, corresponding to a normal charging circuit and a 20 per cent mismatch between the load and the network (which is perfectly admissible from power-transfer considerations),

$$\frac{V_{N_\infty}}{E_{bb}} = \frac{1.90}{0.90} = 2.11.$$

Such charging stepup ratios are common in line-type pulsers using unidirectional switches when no measures are taken to discharge the inverse voltage left on the network. In general, it is not necessary to provide a discharging path except when misbehavior of the load is expected.

The effect of a mismatch such that $R_l < Z_N$ on the over-all operation of the pulser using a unidirectional switch may be considered briefly by determining the voltage and current input to the pulser circuit required for a given pulse output.

If a unidirectional switch is used, the peak forward network voltage is given by Eq. (6).
Since

$$V_l = V_{N_\infty}\frac{R_l}{R_l + Z_N} = V_{N_\infty}\frac{1 + \kappa}{2},$$

Eq. (6) can be rewritten

$$E_{bb} = V_l\frac{2}{1 + \gamma}\frac{1 + \kappa\gamma}{1 + \kappa}. \tag{7}$$

The power-supply current, given by Eq. (9·19), is

$$I_{c_{av}} = f_r C_N(V_{N_\infty} - V_{J_\infty}) = f_r C_N 2V_l\frac{1 - \kappa}{1 + \kappa},$$

and the average power supplied to the pulser is

$$P_i = E_{bb}I_{c_{av}} = f_r C_N \frac{4V_l^2}{1 + \gamma} \frac{(1 + \gamma\kappa)(1 - \kappa)}{(1 + \kappa)^2}. \tag{8}$$

For a pulser using a bidirectional switch to supply the same power to the same load

$$V_N = E'_{bb}(1 + \gamma)$$

or

$$E'_{bb} = \frac{2V_l}{(1 + \gamma)(1 + \kappa)}$$

$$I'_{c_{av}} = f_r C_N V_N = f_r C_N \frac{2V_l}{1 + \kappa},$$

and

$$P'_i = f_r C_N \frac{4V_l^2}{(1 + \gamma)(1 + \kappa)^2}. \tag{9}$$

The ratio of Eqs. (8) and (9), which is the ratio of the power inputs to the pulser required to obtain the same output into the same load, is

$$\rho = (1 + \gamma\kappa)(1 - \kappa). \tag{10}$$

Since the unidirectional switch conserves energy on the network after each pulse, the ratio ρ might be expected to be always less than unity. As can be seen by examination of Eq. (10), however, ρ can be greater than one because of the decrease in charging efficiency when inverse voltage is present on the network. If $\gamma = 1$ (100 per cent charging efficiency),

$$\rho = 1 - \kappa^2 < 1.$$

For any other value of γ between 0 and 1, the expression (10) can be rewritten

$$\rho = 1 - \gamma\kappa^2 - \kappa(1 - \gamma).$$

Since κ is always negative for $R_l < Z_N$, the second term is negative, but the third term of the expression is positive. Accordingly, ρ is smaller than unity only when

$$\gamma\kappa^2 > \kappa(1 - \gamma),$$

$$\gamma > \frac{1}{1 - \kappa},$$

or

$$e^{-\frac{\pi}{2Q}} > \frac{R_l + Z_N}{2Z_N}.$$

The considerations outlined above are based on the assumption of an ideally simplified circuit consisting of a network, a switch, and a resistance load. If a biased-diode load is considered, the analytical expressions become more complicated because of the change in operating point with change in network-charging voltage, which causes the coefficient κ to decrease slightly after each pulse. Some equilibrium network voltage is eventually reached, however, because the quality factor of the charging reactor is not independent of the applied voltage, resulting in a decrease in γ with an increase in $(V_N - E_{bb})$.

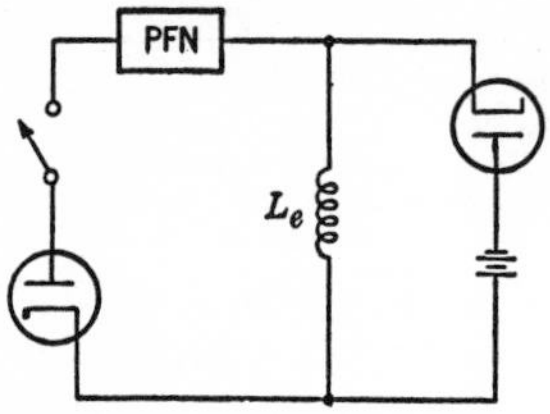

FIG. 10·2.—Equivalent discharging circuit used to study inverse network voltage.

If a pulse transformer and a biased-diode load are considered, network inverse voltage appears even though the operating point of the load matches the network impedance, as can be seen by considering Fig. 10·2 in which all disturbing elements except the shunt inductance of the pulse transformer have been neglected.

At the end of the rectangular pulse of amplitude V_l and duration τ, the current flowing in this inductance can be expressed by $i_{L_e} = \dfrac{V_l}{L_e}\tau$, and the energy stored in it by

$$\frac{1}{2} L_e i_{L_e}^2 = \frac{V_l^2 \tau^2}{2L_e}.$$

At the end of the pulse, this energy charges the storage condenser of the pulse-forming network to a voltage V_J such that

$$\frac{1}{2} C_N V_J^2 = \frac{1}{2} \frac{V_l^2 \tau^2}{L_e}.$$

For matched conditions,

$$V_l = \frac{V_N}{2},$$

$$C_N V_J^2 = \frac{V_N^2 \tau^2}{4L_e},$$

and

$$\left(\frac{V_J}{V_N}\right)^2 = \frac{1}{4}\frac{\tau^2}{L_e C_N}.$$

However,

$$\tau = 2C_N Z_N = 2\sqrt{L_N C_N},$$

and hence, to a first approximation,

$$\frac{V_J}{V_N} = -\sqrt{\frac{L_N}{L_e}}, \tag{11}$$

where the sign is determined by the direction of current flow.   Assuming $\tau = 2.5$ μsec, $Z_N = 1200$ ohms, and $L_e = 45$ mh,

$$L_N = \frac{Z_N\tau}{2} = 1.5 \times 10^{-3} \text{ henrys},$$

and

$$\frac{V_J}{V_N} = -\sqrt{\frac{1.5}{45}} = -\sqrt{\frac{1}{30}} = -\frac{1}{5.5} = -0.18.$$

The values obtained from Eq. (11) are usually greater than those obtained experimentally because losses in the circuit and in the distributed capacitances normally absorb or dissipate part of the energy that has been assumed to be returned to the network capacitance.   These values are sufficiently accurate, however, for use in the preliminary design of a pulser.

10·2. Short Circuits in the Load.—Two cases must be considered when studying the operation of a pulser when the load is short-circuited:

1. That for a unidirectional switch.
2. That for a bidirectional switch.

The fundamental concepts of operation discussed earlier in Sec. 10·1 are now amplified.

Circuit Using a Undirectional Switch.—It has been shown that the equilibrium output voltage is given by Eq. (7), that is,

$$V_l = E_{bb}\frac{1 + \gamma}{2}\frac{1 + \kappa}{1 + \kappa\gamma}$$

where $\gamma = e^{-\frac{\pi}{2Q}}$ is determined by the charging circuit, and $\kappa = \dfrac{R_l - Z_N}{R_l + Z_N}$ is a measure of the mismatch present.

In the following discussion, however, the output voltage has to be considered in a slightly different way because, obviously, if $R_l = 0$, $V_l = 0$.   If the entire series resistance (including switch resistance and series losses) in the discharging circuit is considered instead of only the load resistance,

$$\kappa' = \frac{R_l + R_p - Z_N}{R_l + R_p + Z_N} = \frac{R_p - Z_N}{R_p + Z_N} \qquad \text{for } R_l = 0$$

and

$$V_l' = E_{bb}\frac{1 + \gamma}{2}\frac{1 + \kappa'}{1 + \kappa'\gamma}.$$

The term V_l' is still referred to as "output voltage," even though it is not possible to measure any such voltage across short-circuited output terminals. The voltage on the pulse-forming network just before the switch is made conducting is given by

$$V_N = E_{bb}(1 + \gamma)[1 - \gamma\kappa' + (\gamma\kappa')^2 - \cdots + (\gamma\kappa')^n]$$

or, if equilibrium is reached,

$$V_{N_\infty} = E_{bb} \frac{1 + \gamma}{1 + \gamma\kappa'}. \tag{12}$$

It is of interest to plot the network voltage for successive pulses for a typical case in which a short circuit is suddenly applied to the output.

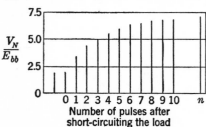

FIG. 10·3.—Increase in network voltage with a short circuit in the load when the switch is unidirectional.

If it is assumed that $\gamma = 0.9$ and $R_p/Z_N = 0.10$, or $\kappa' = -0.82$, Fig. 10·3 gives the ratio of the network voltage to the power-supply voltage, for the first ten consecutive pulses after application of the short circuit, as well as the equilibrium voltage that would be reached by the network after a large number, n, of successive pulses on a short-circuited load. After only two consecutive operations of the pulser with the short-circuited load, the network voltage is more than twice its normal value under matched conditions, and after four such consecutive pulses, it is very nearly three times its normal value. These conclusions may vary slightly depending on the values of γ and κ', but the order of magnitude stays the same, indicating how quickly voltages dangerous to the circuit components can be reached if preventive measures are not taken.

The average pulser current taken from the power supply, given by Eq. (9·19), is

$$I_{cav} = f_r C_N(V_N - V_J) = f_r C_N V_N(1 - \kappa').$$

Hence, for any given conditions of load mismatch, the power-supply average current increases proportionally with the peak forward network voltage. In practice, the power-supply output voltage, E_{bb}, must therefore decrease, since no d-c rectifier can be built with perfect regulation, and the final network voltage is lower than the value indicated in Fig. 10·3. A complete analysis is outside the scope of this book, but the interrelation of all the components in a pulser—from the power supply to the load—is important enough to be mentioned here.

Bidirectional Switches.—When bidirectional switches are used, all the energy stored in the pulse-forming network is dissipated in the resistance R_p by a series of pulses of amplitudes

$$V'_{ln} = \frac{1 + \kappa'}{2} (\kappa')^n V_N, \qquad n = 0, 1, 2, 3, \cdots$$

$$I'_{ln} = \frac{1 - \kappa'}{2Z_N} (\kappa')^n V_N,$$

and

$$P'_{ln} = \frac{V_N^2}{4Z_N}(1 - \kappa'^2)\kappa'^{2n}.$$

For practical values of κ' (of the order of magnitude of -0.8 or less), most of the energy in the pulse-forming network is generally dissipated in less than ten consecutive reflections, the voltage left on the network after fifteen to twenty reflections is only a few per cent of the maximum forward voltage, and the switch usually begins to deionize at this time. Since the total time interval required by ten to twenty reflections is, for most radar pulsers, only one or two per cent of the charging period, the current in the charging reactor at the end of this interval has not yet reached a value which can prevent switch deionization, and the charging cycle proceeds normally with almost zero initial charge on the network capacitance. Hence, both the peak forward network voltage and the average power-supply current have the same value for short-circuited as for normal load operation. All the energy supplied by the power supply, however, is now dissipated in the components of the pulser discharging circuit, instead of in a load. The heating that results from the additional losses in the components has caused the failure of enough pulse transformers and networks to necessitate the introduction of protective devices.

In conclusion, it can be said that the damage to pulser components resulting from a short-circuited load is caused primarily by overvoltage for unidirectional switches, and by overheating for bidirectional switches.

The way in which the circuit components are protected against short circuits in the load must depend on the type of switch. The final choice of protective device in any practical pulser is determined partly by the particular application for which it is designed. For instance, airborne systems usually carry less protection than ground or ship pulsers in order to keep the size and weight to a minimum. The frequency with which faults in the load can be expected is also an important factor to consider. Some magnetrons used in radar applications may have normally high sparking rates, perhaps as high as one per few hundred pulses. The protective device then becomes a circuit element, especially if the pulser uses a unidirectional switch, and if the tendency of the load to spark is enhanced by an increase in network power, as is usually the case. The two methods of protection described below apply specifically to this case. General protection by relays is discussed later.

The Shunt Diode.—The overvoltage on the pulse-forming network at the end of the charging cycle immediately following a short circuit in the load can be eliminated in several ways. One method would be to insert a resistance $R_l = Z_N$ in series with the load at the very instant at which the load is short-circuited, thus preventing the appearance of inverse voltage on the network. Although no practical solution has been reached by this method, it is theoretically possible to achieve the proposed result by connecting a saturating reactor or a nonlinear resistance in series with the load. Another way in which the network-charging voltage may be kept constant is to remove the inverse voltage so rapidly that its effect on the following charging cycle is negligible. If a

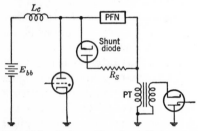

FIG. 10·4.—Pulser with a shunt diode across the network.

resistance $R_l = Z_N$ were connected in parallel with the network at the end of a short-circuited pulse, the inverse voltage, V_J, would be removed in a time τ, and the charging cycle would proceed as if no short circuit had occurred.

This procedure is closely approximated by the shunt-diode circuit of Fig. 10·4. In practice, however, it has not been possible to obtain diodes having internal resistances as low as the impedance of the pulse-forming network. It is hoped that some day a gaseous-discharge diode that may be used to great advantage in this position will be available. Most diodes available at present have an internal resistance of about ten or more times the network impedance, and additional series resistance often has to be inserted in order to obtain satisfactory life for the diode. Accordingly, the time constant for the discharge of the network capacitance through the shunt diode becomes an appreciable fraction of the charging period. The effectiveness of the diode is therefore impaired, since an appreciable current may already be flowing in the charging reactor at the time when the network voltage reaches zero.

The addition of a series inductance L_s in series with the shunt diode offers advantages that can best be understood by simple physical considerations. If a small inductance is used in series with a diode of zero resistance, the inverse network voltage reverses rapidly because of the resonant action of the shunt circuit. Since the losses are neglected, the network is now charged to a voltage $-\kappa' V_N$ that is of the same polarity as E_{bb}, but is greater than E_{bb} for values of κ' assumed previously (≈ -0.8). Under these conditions, the network voltage at the end of the first charging cycle following a short circuit in the load is given by $E_{bb}(1 + \gamma)(1 + \gamma\kappa')$, and is smaller than E_{bb} if $-\kappa' > 1/(1 + \gamma)$. It is therefore possible to reduce the output voltage for the pulse immediately following a short circuit to a value much smaller than normal.

Since a pulser circuit that does not incorporate a shunt diode produces an output voltage for the pulse immediately following a short circuit which is much greater than normal, there must be a combination of values of elements—including charging reactor, pulse-forming-network capacitance, and shunt circuit—for which the network voltage is maintained at its normal value after a short circuit in the load.

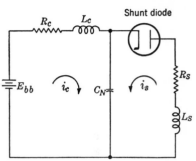

The circuit behavior can best be analyzed by considering Fig. 10·5, in which the network is replaced by its capacitance C_N, and the total resistance in the diode circuit is R_S. The effect of post-pulse inverse voltage on the network, produced by the release of energy stored in the inductances in parallel with the load, is neglected in the following analysis.   The equations for the circuit are

FIG. 10·5.—Equivalent circuit for the analysis of the effectiveness of the shunt diode.

$$L_c \frac{di_c}{dt} + R_c i_c + \frac{1}{C_N} \int (i_c + i_s)\, dt = E_{bb},$$

$$L_s \frac{di_s}{dt} + R_s i_s + \frac{1}{C_N} \int (i_c + i_s)\, dt = 0.$$

If resonant charging is assumed,

$$(i_c)_{t=0} = 0,$$
$$(i_s)_{t=0} = 0,$$
$$(v_N)_{t=0} = V_J.$$

Solving by the Laplace-transform method,

$$v_N(p) = V_J \left[\frac{1}{p} + \frac{p\left(L_s \dfrac{E_{bb}}{V_J} - L_c - L_s\right) + R_s \dfrac{E_{bb}}{V_J} - R_c - R_s}{L_c L_s C_N D(p)} \right],$$

$$i_s(p) = -V_J \frac{\left(p^2 + \dfrac{R_c}{L_c} p + \dfrac{E_{bb}}{V_J} \dfrac{1}{L_c C_N}\right)}{L_s D(p)},$$

$$i_c(p) = (E_{bb} - V_J) \frac{p^2 + \dfrac{R_s}{L_s} p + \dfrac{E_{bb}}{E_{bb} - V_J} \dfrac{1}{L_s C_N}}{L_c D(p)},$$

where

$$D(p) = p\left[p^3 + \left(\frac{R_cL_s + L_cR_s}{L_cL_s}\right)p^2 + \frac{L_c + L_s + R_cR_sC_N}{L_cL_sC_N}p + \frac{R_c + R_s}{L_cL_sC_N}\right].$$

The time functions $v_N(t)$, $i_c(t)$, and $i_s(t)$, corresponding to the transforms above, assume different forms depending on the nature of the roots of $D(p) = 0$. Let these roots be

$$p_1 = 0,$$
$$p_2 = -a,$$
$$p_3 = -b + c,$$

and

$$p_4 = -b - c,$$

where a and b are real positive numbers and c may be real, zero, or imaginary. If c is real (aperiodic case), the time functions are of the form

$$F(t) = A + Be^{-at} + Ce^{-(b+c)t} + De^{-(b-c)t}.$$

If c is zero (critically damped case),

$$F(t) = A + Be^{-at} + (C + D)e^{-bt}.$$

If c is imaginary (oscillatory case),

$$F(t) = A + Be^{-at} + e^{-bt}(C \cos \omega t + D \sin \omega t),$$

where A, B, C, and D are constants that depend on the initial conditions and the values of the circuit elements, and may be evaluated from the transforms given above.

The time t_1 at which the current $i_s(t)$ reaches zero can be found, in each particular case, by a series of trial values. After that time, the circuit reduces to a single mesh containing R_c, L_c, and C_N in series, $i_c(t_1)$ and $v_N(t_1)$ being the initial values of current in the inductance and voltage on the condenser, respectively. The expression for the network voltage is then

$$v_N(t) = E_{bb}[1 + e^{-a_1t}(A \sin \omega_1 t + B \cos \omega_1 t)],$$

where t is measured from the instant t_1 and

$$a_1 = \frac{R_c}{2L_c},$$

$$\omega_1 \approx \sqrt{\frac{1}{L_cC_N}}.$$

$$A \approx L_cC_N\left[\frac{i_c(t_1)}{C_NE_{bb}} - \frac{R_c}{2L_c}\left(1 - \frac{v_N(t_1)}{E_{bb}}\right)\right],$$

$$B = -\left[1 - \frac{v_N(t_1)}{E_{bb}}\right].$$

The term $(R_c/2L_c)^2$ has been considered negligible compared with $1/L_cC_N$. The time at which the network voltage reaches its maximum may be obtained by differentiation,

$$t_m = \frac{1}{\omega_1} \tan^{-1} \frac{A\omega_1 - Ba_1}{Aa_1 + B\omega_1},$$

and the maximum value of network voltage can thus be ascertained.

The expressions obtained are obviously too complex to allow general conclusions to be drawn as to the optimum values of R_S and L_S for any given value of $v_N(t_m)$ which are desired. In order to keep the peak network forward voltage after a short circuit the same as that obtained after a normal pulse, the necessary condition is

$$e^{-a_1t_m}(A \sin \omega_1t_m + B \cos \omega_1t_m) = e^{-\frac{\pi}{2Q}} = e^{\frac{a_1\pi}{\omega_1}}.$$

The values of R_S and L_S enter into this expression only inasmuch as they determine the initial conditions $i_c(t_1)$ and $v_N(t_1)$. A typical example is treated more completely in the following section, when magnetron sparking is considered.

Nonlinear Circuits.—Although nonlinear elements have not been used to date to prevent the buildup of inverse voltage on the network, they have been used to control the network-charging voltage even though inverse voltage is present. One proposed system uses a vacuum tube (triode or tetrode) connected from network to ground. The grid bias is controlled by feedback from the pulser operation in such a way that the tube is cut off for a normal pulse current, but is made conducting during the charging period immediately following a short circuit. The charge is thus permitted to leak off the network. Another suggestion was to increase the charging-circuit losses after a short circuit in the load by inserting a tetrode with a normally low resistance in series with the charging reactor, and with the grid biased by feedback from the short-circuit current to reduce the charging stepup ratio during the following charging cycle.

The use of thyrite was also suggested, and computations and tests proved the method satisfactory when the tendency of the load to become short-circuited was not

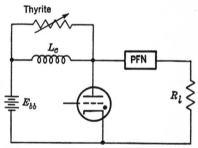

Fig. 10·6.—Pulser using thyrite for network-voltage control.

greatly affected by a power increase of 20 to 30 per cent. Since the thyrite current characteristic is of the form $i = kv^n$, it is connected in the circuit as shown in Fig. 10·6 in order to obtain the highest possible voltage increase across it after short circuit. During normal operation, the voltage across the thyrite never exceeds E_{bb}, but after a short circuit,

with the values considered in previous examples, it reaches a value

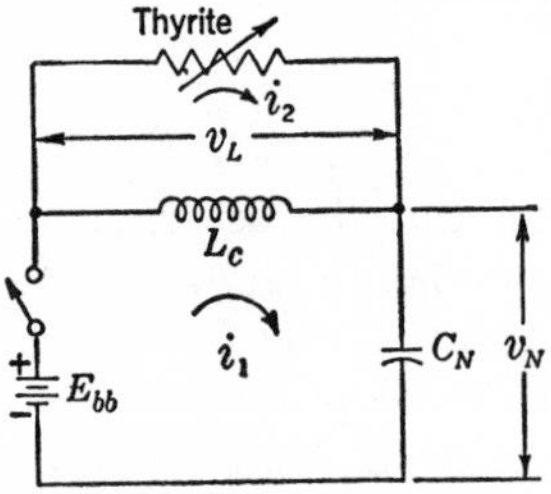

$$E_{bb} - V_{J_1} = E_{bb}[1 - \kappa'(1 + \gamma)] = 2.56E_{bb}.$$

Thyrite can be obtained for which the exponent n is 6 or more, in which case the initial current flowing through the thyrite after a short circuit is about 250 times the maximum current under normal conditions. Detailed computations were carried out as explained below, using the equivalent charging circuit given in Fig. 10·7. Assuming negligible losses in the charging reactor, and replacing the network by its capacitance C_N, the equations for the circuit can be written

$$E_{bb} = v_L + v_N,$$

$$v_L = L_c\left(\frac{di_1}{dt} - \frac{di_2}{dt}\right),$$

$$v_N = \frac{1}{C_N}\int i_1\,dt,$$

and

$$i_2 = kv_L^n.$$

These equations can be combined into the following differential equation

$$\frac{d^2h}{d\xi^2} + Kh^{(n-1)}\frac{dh}{d\xi} + h = 0,$$

where

$$K = kn\sqrt{\frac{L_c}{C_N}}\,E_{bb}{}^{n-1},$$

$$h = \frac{v_L}{E_{bb}},$$

and

$$\xi = \frac{t}{\sqrt{L_cC_N}}.$$

The presence of h^{n-1} in the equation necessitates a point-by-point integration, which was used to solve a specific problem. Resonant charging was assumed, with $E_{bb} = 7$ kv, $L_c = 20$ henrys, $C_N = 3 \times 10^{-8}$ farads, T_r and the charging period $= 2500$ μsec. For the thyrite characteristic, values of k and n were chosen so that they had little effect during normal operation, but a large effect when there was an inverse voltage on C_N.

Fig. 10·7.—Equivalent charging circuit of a pulser using thyrite for network-voltage control.

These values were $k = 1.1 \times 10^{-25}$ and $n = 6$. For the initial conditions corresponding to a spark after normal operation, the current through the inductance is $i_1 - i_2 = 0$, and $V_{J_1} = -1.5V_N = -0.75(2E_{bb})$. The

curve of V_N against t for this case is shown in Fig. 10.8. The value of V_N at the end of the period is $2.28E_{bb}$, or approximately 15 per cent higher than the value for normal operation. If a second spark follows on the next pulse, the initial conditions are

$$i_1 - i_2 = 0.05 \text{ amp,}$$

determined from the previous calculations, and

$$V_J = -0.75(2.28E_{bb}) = -1.71V_N.$$

Although V_J initially has a larger inverse voltage for this case, the slope of the curve is also greater, and the entire curve of v_N/E_{bb} against t follows very closely that of Fig. 10·8. The value of V_N at

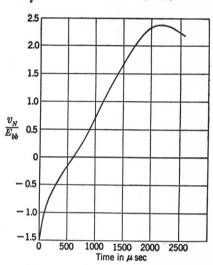

Fig. 10·8.—Charging wave of a pulser using thyrite for network-voltage control after a short circuit in the load.

the end of the period is the same as that obtained in the previous computation, indicating that there is no further buildup of network voltage if the short circuit in the load lasts for a large number of consecutive pulses.

These results were checked experimentally with a pulser having very nearly the same characteristics as were used in the computation, and the agreement was remarkably good. Obviously, the advantage of thyrite appears mostly in systems where the charging period is long.

10·3. Open Circuits and Protective Measures.—The discussion of the effect of an open circuit can be divided into several examples, depending on the connections from the output of the pulser to the load, and on the exact location of the fault. Assume first that a pulse transformer is used, and that an open circuit takes place either in the secondary winding or between the transformer and the load. The primary winding constitutes a discharging path of very high impedance for the pulse-forming network, and, since $R_e \gg Z_N$, most of the network voltage appears across the open terminals. If no breakdown occurs in the pulse transformer or in the output connection of the network because of this overvoltage (which is usually about twice the normal operating voltage), the network discharges slowly through the pulse-transformer shunt path as shown in Fig. 10·9. Since the inductance L_e is, in general, many times greater than the network inductance, the discharging circuit acts as a resonant circuit of period

$$T_d = 2\pi \sqrt{C_N L_e}$$

if the effect of shunt and series resistance is neglected.

The circuit behavior then depends on the switch used and on the ratio T_d/T_r. If this ratio is large (about 0.1) and the switch is a hydrogen thyratron, the current in the charging inductance may build up to a value

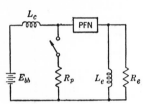

Fig. 10·9.—Equivalent pulser circuit for an open circuit at the secondary of the pulse transformer.

that can prevent thyratron deionization before the network is completely discharged. The power supply is then short-circuited by the charging inductance. If the ratio T_d/T_r is small, the thyratron has time to deionize, but a high inverse voltage V_J is left on the network. The situation is then essentially the same as that already discussed for a short circuit in the load. If the switch is bidirectional, the energy stored on the network is dissipated in the pulser components, unless the duration of the oscillations produced in the discharging circuit is long enough to prevent deionization, in which case the power supply is again short-circuited by the charging reactor. For a rotary-gap switch, the arc is usually interrupted by the increasing separation of the electrodes, but both the voltage left on the network and the charging period are erratic, resulting in a variable network voltage at the time of firing.

If no pulse transformer is used or the open circuit takes place in the primary winding, the equivalent circuit is given by Fig. 10·10, in which the capacitance C_s represents all stray capacitances from the anode of the switch to ground. If a triggered switch is used, this capacitance is suddenly discharged by the switch, and immediately begins to recharge through the charging inductance L_c. The charging period in this case is usually so short, however, that the switch is not able to deionize before the anode voltage

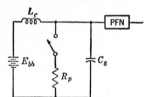

Fig. 10·10.—Equivalent pulser circuit for an open circuit at the primary of the pulse transformer.

reaches a value high enough to maintain conduction. The switch therefore goes into continuous conduction and short-circuits the power supply through the charging reactor. For a rotary-gap switch, the current may again be interrupted by electrode separation, but at best the operation is equivalent to a rapid succession of short circuits of short duration across the power supply.

One more special case may be considered, in which the open circuit takes place at the primary of the pulse transformer and a long cable connects the pulser to the pulse transformer. The equivalent circuit is then given by Fig. 10·11, where the cable is considered as a pulse-forming network. The discharging circuit then consists of two pulse-forming networks of the same impedance but different pulse durations, connected in series, which are short-circuited by the switch when it operates. The result is then again comparable to that obtained with a short-circuited load.

Protection of Circuit Elements by Relays.—In line-type pulsers overcurrent, undercurrent, and reverse current relays are used for the protection of circuit elements against load variations, as well as against the possible failure of some of the elements themselves.

It has been shown that an open circuit in the load often causes the switch tube to conduct continuously. The protective device should therefore be an overload relay in the power-supply circuit. For d-c charging, the usual practice has been to connect a relay in the ground return of the power supply, the contacts opening the connections to the primary of the transformer. Undercurrent relays in the load are also used for this purpose.

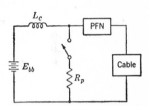

FIG. 10·11.—Equivalent pulser circuit for an open circuit at the end of a long cable.

In order to devise effective protection against short circuits in the load it is necessary to consider the type of switch and the nature of the circuit being used. If the switch is unidirectional and auxiliary circuits are not included to prevent the buildup of network voltage after a short circuit, the average power-supply current increases with the network voltage and an overload relay in the grounded side of the power supply will readily disconnect the primary power input. If bidirectional switches are used, or if a shunt diode or similar system is used to maintain the network voltage very nearly constant, the average pulser input current is almost unchanged by the short circuit in the load. On the other hand, the ratio of peak load currents for short-circuit and normal operation usually does not exceed two, and the increase in average load current is large only if the short circuit in the load is unidirectional. Although an overload relay in the load does not operate under certain conditions, it was widely used as long as no better system was available. Protective devices whose operation depends on reverse current have proved the most satisfactory.

The first of these devices was designed specifically for use in pulsers employing shunt diodes. As has been explained above, the shunt diode does not normally conduct any current, but, when a short circuit occurs, it carries the average pulser current. Some device for averaging the diode current must, of course, be used; it can be either a thermal relay, or a capacitance connected in parallel with a magnetic relay.   The time constants of the available magnetic relays and condensers cannot usually be made long enough to delay the operation of the relay for more than ten consecutive short-circuited pulses.   Since such rapid action is not necessary for protection of the components, thermal relays are generally preferred.   Relays are chosen that will operate either after one or two seconds during which short circuits occur at every pulse, or when the rate of sparking in the magnetron exceeds a predetermined limit for a longer time.   This limit is determined by the ratings of the shunt diode and other circuit components.   Experience with pulsers used in microwave-radar applications indicates that the thermal relay should operate when the load is short-circuited on 15 to 25 per cent of the pulses during a 15- to 30-sec interval.   It must be noted that the thermal relay operates

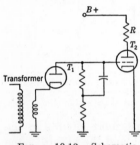

as a function of the effective, not the average, value of the current, and that the ratio of these values varies with the design of the shunt-diode circuit.   It must also be pointed out that the relay in this position becomes less effective if the cathode emission of the shunt diode decreases.

Fig.   10·12.—Schematic diagram of a protective circuit using reverse current.

The second type of reverse-current protection was designed specifically for a spark-gap pulser, but is applicable to all pulsers using bidirectional switches.   It should not be used in place of the method described above because its operation depends on a large peak reverse current, which is not obtained with the shunt diodes available at present.

The principle of operation is as follows (See Fig. 10·12).   The polarity of the main pulse current flowing through the primary of the pulse transformer T is such that, for normal pulses, the cathode of T_1 is driven positive with each pulse.   Hence, the grid of T_2 is maintained at ground potential, and a certain current normally flows through R.   A pulse of opposite polarity, however, drives the cathode of T_1 and the grid of T_2 negative, reducing the current through R.   The resistance R can easily be replaced by a relay, and the circuit constants made such that the relay is de-energized when reverse current flows through the transformer for one or several pulses.

The transformer T actually used in one radar system consists of a small steel ring fitted at the cable connector in such a way that the pulse current passes through the axis of the ring.   One turn of wire is looped around the ring, and the voltage generated is sufficient to operate the protective device.   Simplifications were introduced in the circuit of

Fig. 10·12 by eliminating the plate-voltage supply; tube T_2 then acts as a grid-controlled rectifier, and the load consists of the relay bypassed by a condenser.   An auxiliary contact introduces an additional voltage on the grid, which keeps the relay de-energized until a reset button is pushed. This system of protection has proved very satisfactory.

PULSER PERFORMANCE WITH A MAGNETRON LOAD

10·4. Normal Operation of the Magnetron.—This section discusses qualitatively the operation of a pulser with actual magnetron loads, and attempts to point out the difference between operation with a magnetron and with a perfect biased diode.   Particular attention is paid to some of the characteristics of the magnetron which may, under some conditions,

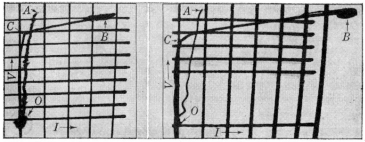

FIG. 10·13.—Magnetron-input characteristics illustrated by *V-I* oscillograms.

make it an unstable device, and to some of the corrective methods which have been used to improve the performance of the over-all transmitter.

The magnetron input characteristics can best be analyzed from a study of the voltage-current characteristic curves.   Some oscillograms of such characteristics are given in Fig. 10·13, the time sequence of the curves being given by OABCO.   Any portion of the curve corresponding to negative voltages is due to post-pulse backswing and need not be considered here.

The part of the curve *OA* corresponds to the buildup of the voltage. In general, only capacitance current is drawn by the magnetron during this time, although leakage current may be present in some cases.   The time necessary for the voltage buildup is usually between 0.05 and 0.2 μsec, depending on the pulser characteristics.   The portion AB corresponds to the buildup of current in the magnetron.   There is usually little or no increase in voltage corresponding to the current buildup; there may even be a slight decrease.   The time necessary for current buildup has not yet been measured very accurately, but it is always very short and has been estimated to be as low as 5×10^{-9} sec for some low-voltage X-band magnetrons (2J42).   Point *B* corresponds to the so-called "flat" portion of the pulse, where both voltage and current remain constant except for small oscillations.

From B to C both current and voltage decay at the end of the pulse, the line BC giving the diode characteristic of the load, which has been used before. Any slow variations of voltage and current, such as oscillations up to perhaps 10 Mc/sec, follow very nearly the same curve once the magnetron is operating. Corrections may have to be made, however, for the transit time between the plates of the cathode-ray tube or other viewing-system defects at higher oscillation frequencies. The average slope of this curve thus gives the dynamic resistance of the magnetron. From C to O, the voltage is gradually decreasing to zero, and again capacitance current may cause the curve to deviate slightly from the axis. This deviation is much smaller than that resulting from the volt-

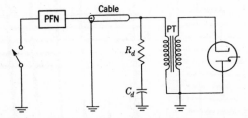

Fig. 10·14.—Line-type pulser with a despiking RC-network.

age buildup, however, because of the much smaller rate of change of voltage.

The assumption that the load acts as a biased diode does not hold during the starting period of the pulse after the voltage has reached an amplitude corresponding to C. It can be assumed, however, either that the magnetron impedance is infinite until the voltage reaches a value A, and then drops suddenly (in about 10^{-8} sec) to the normal operating value, or that during the buildup of oscillations, that is, from points O to B, the magnetron is a biased diode of nearly zero internal resistance. The value of the voltage at A is, unfortunately, not constant, but depends to some extent on the time required for the voltage to build up to this value. Hence, no general analysis of the problem can be made. It can be stated, however, that the sudden rush of current through the load tends to produce unduly high oscillations by means of the shock excitation of the LC-circuits in the pulse transformer connecting the pulser to the load.

One satisfactory method of decreasing the resulting mismatch is to introduce an RC-circuit in parallel with the primary of the transformer, as shown in Fig. 10·14. Its purpose is to minimize the "spike" that often appears at the beginning of both voltage and current pulses because of the magnetron characteristics discussed above. If a unit function of voltage is applied to the despiking network, its instantaneous impedance as a function of time is given by

$$z_d = R_d e^{t/R_d C_d}.$$

The instantaneous impedance that the pulse transformer presents to a unit voltage until the magnetron starts to oscillate is a complicated function of time. A satisfactory approximation can be obtained, however, by reducing the pulse transformer to its leakage inductance and distributed capacitance, L_L and C_D, respectively. Its instantaneous impedance can then be expressed as

$$z_T = \sqrt{\frac{L_L}{C_D}} \csc \frac{t}{\sqrt{L_L C_D}}.$$

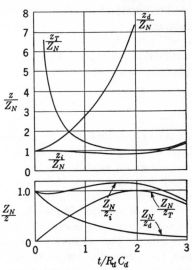

The effect of the despiking RC-circuit on the instantaneous output impedance of the pulser can best be seen by a graph such as that of Fig. 10·15. For the sake of uniformity, the instantaneous output impedances are referred to the network impedance Z_N, and the following assumptions are made,

$$Z_N = R_d = \sqrt{\frac{L_L}{C_D}}$$

and

$$\sqrt{L_L C_D} = \frac{1}{R_d C_d} \frac{\pi}{4}.$$

Fig. 10·15.—Instantaneous output impedances of a pulser with a despiking RC network.

The time scale can then be $t/R_d C_d$, and the impedance scale z/Z_N. The curve z_T/Z_N is the pulse-transformer instantaneous impedance, and obviously starts at infinity. The resulting instantaneous mismatch produces a reflection of voltage to the pulse-forming network through the cable linking the pulser to the load, and further reflections at the network-cable junction may produce undue oscillations in the load voltage.

The instantaneous impedance to which the pulser is connected when a despiking RC-circuit is used in parallel with the pulse-transformer primary is given by

$$\frac{1}{z_i} = \frac{1}{z_d} + \frac{1}{z_T}.$$

When the curves Z_N/z_d and Z_N/z_T are plotted and added graphically, Z_N/z_i is obtained. The reciprocal of Z_N/z_i is then taken, giving the instantaneous impedance of the load for the constants used. It can readily be seen that, for the particular example treated, the values of z_i do not vary from Z_N by more than 13 per cent for any time $t < 2.75R_dC_d$. In practice, the magnetron usually starts to conduct before the current in the leakage inductance of the pulse transformer has decreased to 70 per cent of its peak value (corresponding to $t = 3R_dC_d$ in this scale). At that time, the simplified equivalent circuit considered here is no longer valid, and matching of the load to the pulse-forming network is assured by the magnetron itself.

This method of eliminating instantaneous mismatch has been used extensively with very good results. It has the further advantage of tending to decrease the voltage rate of rise at the magnetron before the oscillations start, since the instantaneous voltage applied to the input of the pulse transformer is given by

$$v_i = V_N \frac{z_i}{z_i + Z_N}.$$

At the first instant, $v_i = V_N$ if no despiking circuit is used, and $v_i = V_N/2$ if a despiking circuit containing $R_d = Z_N$ is used. The disadvantage of the despiking circuit is a power loss in the additional capacitance C_d, which can be estimated by the method described in Sec. 7·3, and the introduction of two additional elements in the pulser circuit.

10·5. Magnetron Mode-changing.—Some magnetrons, unfortunately, do not always operate in the intended mode of oscillation once the voltage is applied. The reasons are obviously outside the scope of this chapter,[1] but, since remedial measures can be introduced in the pulser to prevent some magnetrons from· selecting the wrong mode of oscillation, a brief explanation of some possible mode-changing processes is given here. A common type of mode change from pulse to pulse (called mode-skipping) may be most readily understood by a study of the voltage-current characteristics of a magnetron exhibiting such behavior. Figure 10·16 shows oscillograms of the voltage-current input to a magnetron that is skipping modes. First, it may be noted that the operating characteristics of the unwanted mode are such that the voltage is higher and the current lower than the values corresponding to the normal mode of operation. Of particular interest is the fact that mode selection is determined at the very beginning of the current pulse. Looking at the voltage rise, it is seen that, at a point corresponding to A of Fig. 10·13, the magnetron current tends to increase, but succeeds in reaching the operating point

---

[1] See Vol. 6, Chap. 8.

only occasionally. In other cases, the voltage continues to increase until the current starts to build up the oscillations in the unwanted mode.

For the purpose of this section, it is sufficient to say that a mode skip can take place if the voltage applied to the magnetron is allowed to reach a region in the *V-I* plot where the unwanted mode may start.

Obviously, if the voltage is never allowed to reach the region where instability may develop, the problem of mode-skipping does not arise. By increasing the voltage-rise time through the region where the magnetron starts in the desired mode to a value greater than the magnetron-starting time, the voltage can be kept out of the region of instability.

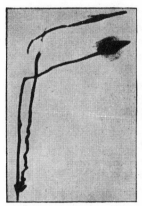 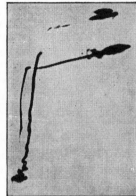 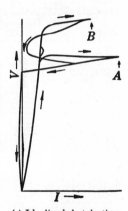

(a) First tube.   (b) Second tube.   (c) Idealized sketch; time follows arrows; *A* is the normal operating mode; *B* is the unwanted mode.

Fig. 10·16.—*V-I* Characteristics of mode-skipping magnetron.

This condition alone is not necessarily sufficient, however, since the magnetron-starting time itself may vary, depending on the voltage rate of rise itself, and possibly on pulser circuit conditions.

The increase in voltage-rise time—or decrease in the rate of rise of the voltage—can be accomplished, as explained before, by addition of a despiking *RC*-circuit in parallel with the pulse-transformer primary. It can be achieved, however, more simply and directly by adding either a capacitance in parallel with the magnetron (increasing C_D) or an inductance in series with the pulse-forming network and the pulse transformer (increasing L_D). If the simplified pulse-transformer circuit is considered, an increase in either of those quantities by the same percentage should have very nearly the same effect on the front edge of the voltage pulse. Experimental results agree with this conclusion, but also indicate that the tendency to skip modes is not always affected in the same way by a given decrease in rate of rise of voltage if this decrease is a result of additional inductance rather than additional capacitance.

For the 2J42 magnetron, for example, a greater decrease in dv/dt is necessary in order to bring about the same proportional reduction in mode-skipping if an inductance is used. This result can be explained by a consideration of the instantaneous impedance of the pulser output circuit and of the time necessary for current to build up in the magnetron, which has been estimated to be as low as 0.005 μsec for some of these magnetrons.

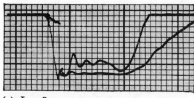

(a) $L = 0$.

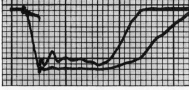

(b) $L = 5\mu\text{h}$.

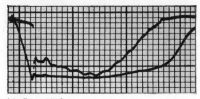

(c) $L = 15\mu\text{h}$.

Fig. 10·17.—Magnetron voltage and current pulses (lower and upper traces respectively) showing the effect of series inductance between the pulse transformer and the pulse-forming network.

Additional capacitance in parallel with the magnetron has two effects: (1) it increases the maximum value of current in the leakage inductance of the pulse transformer, and (2) it stores added energy in parallel with the load. The combined result is that a greater instantaneous current can be supplied to the load. Additional inductance in series with the pulse-transformer leakage inductance, on the other hand, decreases the maximum instantaneous current flowing through that inductance. Hence, less current is available to permit the magnetron to start in the desired mode, and a very much larger decrease in voltage rate of rise is necessary before the tendency to skip modes can be corrected.

In practice, however, a capacitance cannot always be chosen that will correct for mode-skipping in magnetrons. The principal objection to the use of a capacitance in the circuit is the resulting decrease in pulse duration and efficiency. Series inductance generally tends to lengthen the pulse duration and to decrease the efficiency by a smaller amount. The amount of inductance used, however, must not be so large that the shape of the current pulse deteriorates appreciably. Figure 10·17 is an example chosen at random from many photographs showing the magnetron voltage and current pulses (lower and upper traces respectively) as a function of added inductance. For all these pulse photographs, $V_l = 5.4$ kv and $I_l = 4.6$ amp. The rate of rise of voltage was reduced from 59 kv/μsec (Fig. 10·17a) to 46 kv/μsec (Fig. 10·17b) by the addition of a 5-μh inductance in series with the network and pulse transformer, and to 40 kv/μsec (Fig. 10·17c) by a 15-μh inductance. Actually, a marked improvement in current pulse shape is observed between Figs. 10·17a and b but the slope of the current in Fig. 10·17c is detrimental to the r-f spectrum.

Other types of mode changes may be possible in magnetrons. In some cases the magnetron may be able to operate in an unwanted mode that starts at a voltage lower than that of the desired mode. A possible remedy may then be to decrease the time of rise of the voltage through the starting region for the unwanted mode to a value lower than the starting time for that mode by increasing the number of sections in the pulse-forming network and reducing the leakage inductance and distributed capacitance of the pulse transformer. Finally, mode-shifting—or a change in operating mode during a pulse—may occur. In general, little can be done to the pulser to prevent this behavior.

10·6. Magnetron Sparking.—Sparking difficulties have occurred frequently in the magnetrons used in radar systems,[1] principally because of the war-imposed necessity of rating the operating point of the tubes with an insufficient factor of safety. The following discussion summarizes the present knowledge of the effect of line-type-pulser characteristics on magnetron sparking, as well as the effect of magnetron sparking on pulser operation. The experimental study of the causes and effects of sparking has been conducted primarily on a statistical basis. Some pictures of individual current and voltage pulses during sparking are shown in Fig. 10·18. These records were taken on a rapidly moving film in order to obtain the desired separation between pulses, and the blur in the pictures is caused by the persistence of the fluorescent screen of the cathode-ray tube. Figure 10·18a shows a series of voltage pulses from a medium-power magnetron, Fig. 10·18b shows current pulses on the same magnetron, and Fig. 10·18c current pulses on a high-power magnetron. The line drawings in Fig. 10·19 show schematically the conditions occurring in a few of the oscillograms of Fig. 10·18. The immediate conclusions that can be drawn from observation of the individual pulse pictures are:

1. Sparks may take place at any time during the pulse.
2. A spark can be initiated in several ways, corresponding in some cases to a rapid ncrease in current to almost twice the normal value, and in some cases to a reasonably slow breakdown of voltage and increase in pulse current.

[1] See Vol. 6, Chap. 12.

3. After the spark is initiated, it can have the character of an arc (as indicated by pictures in which the voltage stays very nearly zero), or it can show unstable characteristics, possibly caused by oscillations in the external circuit.   These characteristics are shown by pictures in which the voltage trace at the zero axis is broken,

indicating temporary high potentials between anode and cathode after which the spark again breaks down the cathode-anode space.

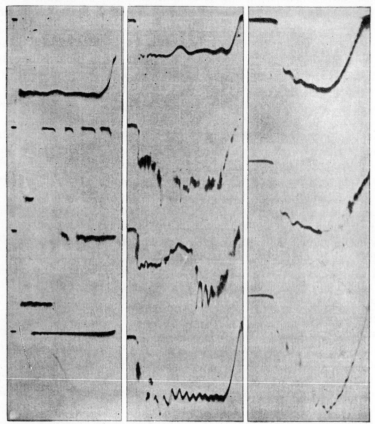

(a) Voltage pulses, 4J52   (b) Current pulses, 4J52   (c) Current pulses, HK7
    magnetron.   magnetron.   magnetron.
Fig. 10·18.—Oscillograms showing the effect of magnetron sparking on voltage and current pulse shapes.   The first trace in each series is a normal pulse.

There are many causes for the initiation of a spark in the magnetron, as evidenced by oscillograms similar to those shown here.   In some cases, the spark is presumably caused by bursts of gas in the magnetron.   A very high percentage of sparks occurs in some tubes during pulses when the magnetron is operating in an unwanted mode at a higher voltage and a lower current than the normal values. In other cases, sparking is presumably associated with cathode fatigue during the pulse;[1] many photographs of individual voltage traces indicate that the current decreases and the voltage rises slowly (in a few tenths of a μsec) to a value that is 10 to 20 per cent greater than normal before the tube breaks down.

The assumptions made in the study of the effects of sparks on pulser operation should cover a wide range of possibilities. The variable nature of the sparks—from an almost perfect short circuit to a very nearly normal pulse—result in values of κ (the mismatch coefficient) ranging from -1 to 0, if the losses in the circuit are neglected.

For pulsers using bidirectional switches, the protective systems described in Sec. 10·3 are satisfactory; for pulsers using unidirectional switches, a diode circuit in parallel with the pulse-forming network has proved to be particularly effective. The effectiveness of the shunt-diode circuit depends to a certain extent, however, on the value of κ. A typical example has been worked out using the general method outlined in Sec. 10·2, and the most significant results are given in Figs. 10·20, 10·21, and 10·22.[2] The circuit con-

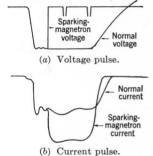

(a) Voltage pulse.

(b) Current pulse.

FIG. 10·19.—Schematic representation of the pulse shapes of Fig. 10·18.

stants are those of a medium-power airborne pulser, rated at 200-kw pulse-power input to a 4J52 magnetron, with pulse durations ranging from 0.25 to 5.4 μsec. Since sparking was most prevalent for the long pulses, the following values of parameters were used:

Charging inductance $L_c = 16$ henrys,
Charging circuit $Q = 15$,
Network capacitance $C_N = 0.0525$ μf.

For the study, a range of values were considered for the shunt-diode circuit. Figure 10·20 shows some typical charging waves for normal operation and after a spark ($\kappa = -0.8$) for several values of the shunt-diode circuit parameters Fig. 10·20a shows the first part of the charging wave on an expanded time scale. Figure 10·21 gives the percentage increase of network voltage over its normal value as a function of the mismatch coefficient for several combinations of series inductance and

[1] Volume 6, Chap. 12.

[2] O. T. Fundingsland and Anna Walter, "Analysis of Line Modulator Behavior with a Sparking Magnetron Load," RL Report No. 765, Aug. 10, 1945.

resistance in the diode circuit. At first glance, the circuits containing inductance seem highly preferable because they maintain the network voltage nearer to the normal value, and can be designed to produce a reduction in this voltage.

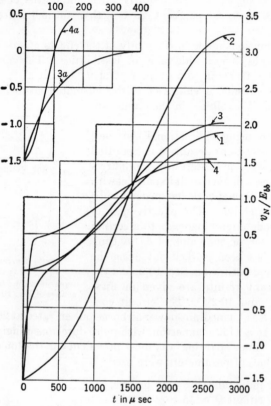

Fig. 10·20.—Computed charging waves for normal and sparking operation of the load. Circuit constants: $L_c = 16$ henrys, $R_c = 1200$ ohms, $Q = 15$, $C_N = 0.0525\mu f$. Curve (1): Normal operation, $\kappa = 0$. Curve (2): Sparking operation, $\kappa = -0.8$, no shunt diode circuit ($R_S = \infty$). Curves (3) and (3a): Sparking operation, $\kappa = -0.8$, $R_S = 2000$ ohms, $L_S = 0$. Curves (4) and (4a): Sparking operation, $\kappa = -0.8$, $R_S = 700$ ohms, $L_S = 45$ mh.

If an *RL*-circuit is used to obtain negative regulation (that is, a decrease in the network voltage from normal after a spark), the instantaneous power-supply regulation may be such that the second pulse following the spark is higher than normal, and the advantage of the good initial regulation is thus lost. This high pulse occurs because the current drain from the power supply is smaller during the charging period that produces a network voltage smaller than normal, and thus leaves a higher voltage on the power-supply filter condenser. The following charging cycle therefore produces a correspondingly higher voltage on the network.

Some sample curves of magnetron sparking rates versus pulse current are given later. Over the range of currents studied, they are of the general form

$$S = ke^{\lambda I_l} + K,$$

where S is the number of sparks per unit time, I_l is the pulse current, and k, λ, and K are constants that depend on the magnetron and the pulser circuit. Then $dS/dI_l = \lambda k e^{\lambda I_l}$. If the increase in sparking as a function of pulse current is large for the normal value of

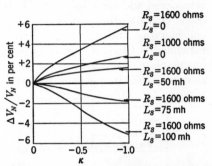

FIG. 10·21.—Percentage increase of network voltage over its normal value as a function of the mismatch coefficient for several combinations of series inductance and resistance in the diode circuit.

pulse current considered, every effort should be made to keep the network voltage as nearly constant as possible, lest an accidental spark should initiate a long burst of sparks. If dS/dI_l is small, the chances of an

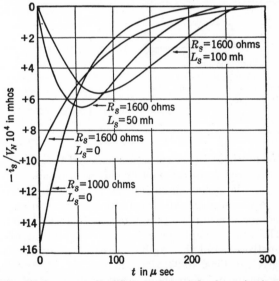

FIG. 10·22.—Diode currents for different values of the shunt-circuit constants.

accidental spark starting a series are minimized even though the current on the next pulse may be higher than normal, and the network-voltage regulation need not be as good as in the first case.

Another item to be considered is the peak current in the shunt diode. Figure 10·22 shows the diode currents for the shunt-circuit constants considered and for $\kappa = -0.8$. It is seen here that the peak currents in diode circuits using series inductance are much smaller. Finally, some consideration must be given to the switch-tube deionization. As explained in Chap. 8, it may be helpful to maintain some inverse voltage on the plate of a thyratron for some time after the pulse. When such is the case, the time constant of the shunt-diode circuit must not be so

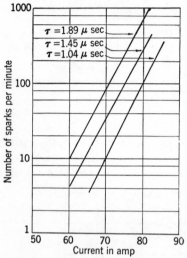

FIG. 10·23.—Sparking rate vs. current for variable pulse durations. In all cases, $dv/dt = 200$ kv/μsec at 60 amp.

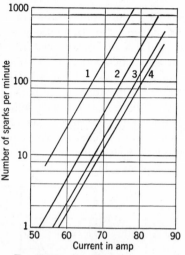

FIG. 10·24.—Sparking rate vs. current for different networks of identical pulse duration and variable dv/dt.
Network 1: $dv/dt = 307$ kv/μsec at 70 amp.
Network 2: $dv/dt = 252$ kv/μsec at 70 amp.
Network 3: $dv/dt = 208$ kv/μsec at 70 amp.
Network 4: $dv/dt = 175$ kv/μsec at 70 amp.

short that the normal inverse voltage is removed before the thyratron is completely deionized, lest continuous conduction result.

The effect of the pulser circuit on the magnetron sparking rate in a particular case was studied experimentally by means of electronic spark counters, and by varying the pulser parameters one by one whenever possible. The most reliable data have been obtained on high-power S-band magnetrons,[1] and the results, insofar as they may affect pulser design, are given in Figs. 10·23, 10·24, and 10·25. An exponential curve fits the data obtained for sparking rate as a function of pulse current. It can also be seen that an increase in pulse duration and an increase in rate of rise of voltage both increase the sparking rate. In general, the

[1] H. L. Rehkopf and R. E. Nysewander, "Sparking of HK7 Magnetrons as a Function of Pulse Forming Network," RL Internal Report 51-9/24/45.

pulse duration and the pulse current are determined by the system requirements, and the designer of the pulser for the system has little or no control over these quantities.   Changes in voltage rate of rise may be introduced, however, as long as the pulse shape is not affected to the extent that the r-f spectrum becomes unacceptable.   For this particular magnetron, the sparking rate can be reduced by a factor of 10 if the rate of rise of voltage at the magnetron is decreased from 300 to 200 kv/μsec.

Some magnetrons, however, tend to operate in a high-voltage mode if the rate of rise of voltage is low, and, as has been indicated, the change in mode is often accompanied by sparking.   The possible result is indicated

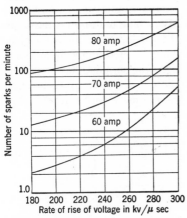

FIG. 10·25.—Sparking rate vs. rate of rise of voltage for several pulse currents at $\tau = 1.89\mu$sec.

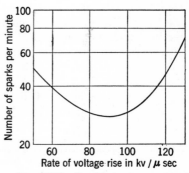

FIG. 10·26.—Sparking rate vs. rate of rise of voltage (average of six 4J52 magnetrons).

by Fig. 10·26, which shows the average trend of sparking rate for six medium-power X-band magnetrons (4J52) as a function of rate of rise of voltage at a constant pulse duration and pulse current.   It is seen, in this case, that the value of dv/dt cannot be decreased indiscriminately in order to minimize sparking.

If the rate of rise of voltage is decreased by connecting a capacitance in parallel with the magnetron, the sparking rate may be increased instead of decreased, presumably because of cathode phenomena in the magnetron.   For normal operation of a line-type pulser the short-circuit current does not exceed twice normal value, but, if a capacitance is connected across the magnetron terminals, the instantaneous current produced by the discharge of that capacitance when a spark occurs may be many times the normal current.   This high current may, in turn, damage the cathode to a point where the probability of a spark occurring on the following pulse is much greater than normal, resulting in a long burst of sparks.

CHAPTER 11

PARTICULAR APPLICATIONS

By R. S. Stanton, J. V. Lebacqz, L. G. Kersta, and H. J. White

11·1. A High-power Rotary-gap Pulser.[1]—Early in 1942 there was a need for a pulser that would be simple, compact, and rugged, and would have a pulse-power output as high as 3 Mw. The high-power hard-tube pulsers did not fulfill this need because of their large size and necessarily complicated design. Line-type pulsers using d-c charging were in limited use by this time, but although their design was simpler they required a rectified high-voltage supply. The simplest conceivable pulser consists of a source of alternating current, a transformer, and a rotary spark

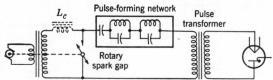

Fig. 11·1.—Schematic diagram of a high-power line-type pulser using a rotary-spark-gap switch and a-c resonant charging.

gap. The secondary of the transformer supplies a voltage equal to the desired charging voltage on the condensers of a pulse-forming network, and the rotary spark gap is synchronized with the supply frequency and phased so as to discharge the pulse-forming network into the load at the end of each full charging cycle, as discussed in Sec. 9·4. The source of alternating current is a motor-generator because commercial supply frequencies are not high enough to give the required pulse recurrence frequencies for most radar applications. When a special generator is used as the source, the obvious method of synchronizing the rotary gap is to mount the rotor on an extension of the generator shaft. Higher efficiency and less amplitude jitter can be obtained by the addition of an inductance in series to make the charging circuit resonant at the supply frequency. In practice, the charging inductance L_c is built into the transformer as leakage inductance. The basic circuit of this pulser is shown in Fig. 11·1.

Design.—The following specific requirements were set up for this pulser:

[1] By R. S. Stanton.

448

Pulse power output: 3 Mw.
Pulse duration: 0.9 μsec.
Recurrence frequency: 400 pps.
Load impedance: 50 ohms.

Supply voltage: 220 volts, 3 phase, 60 cycles/sec.
The quantities important to the pulser design are obtained from these requirements and from the relationships between the various pulser parameters that are developed in the preceeding chapters.

The pulse voltage for a 50-ohm load is

$$V_l = \sqrt{P_l Z_l} = \sqrt{3 \times 10^6 \times 50} = 12.3 \text{ kv,}$$

where P_l is the pulse-power output and Z_l is the load impedance. When the network impedance is equal to 50 ohms, the total capacitance of the network becomes

$$C_N = \frac{\tau}{2Z_N} = 0.009 \ \mu\text{f,}$$

and the network voltage is

$$V_N = \sqrt{\frac{4P_l Z_l}{\eta_d}} = \sqrt{\frac{4 \times 3 \times 10^6 \times 50}{0.85}} \approx 26.5 \text{ kv,}$$

where η_d, the efficiency of the discharging circuit, is assumed to be 85 per cent. The average power taken from the network is given by

$$P_N = \frac{P_l \tau f_r}{\eta_d} = \frac{3 \times 10^6 \times 0.9 \times 10^{-6} \times 400}{0.85} \approx 1260 \text{ watts.}$$

Choosing full-cycle charging ($n = 2$, $\varphi = 90°$), the secondary voltage of the charging transformer, from Eq. (9.66), is

$$E_{b\text{rms}} = \frac{\dfrac{V_N}{\sqrt{2}}}{Q(1 - e^{-\frac{n\pi}{2Q}})}.$$

For an assumed value of $Q = 12$,

$$E_{b\text{rms}} \approx \frac{0.707 \times 26.5 \times 10^3}{12(1 - e^{-\frac{\pi}{2Q}})} = 6.8 \text{ kv,}$$

and the current in the transformer secondary, obtained from Eq. (9.94), is

$$I_{c\text{rms}} \approx \frac{n\pi C_N E_b \omega_a}{2\sqrt{6}},$$

where E_b is the peak applied voltage. For this example,

$$I_{crms} \approx \frac{\pi(0.009 \times 10^{-6})\,\sqrt{2}(6.8 \times 10^3)(2\pi \times 400)}{\sqrt{6}} \approx 0.285 \text{ amp,}$$

so

$$E_{brms} \times I_{crms} \approx 1940 \text{ volt-amp.}$$

The average current is obtained from Eq. (9.95);

$$I_{cav} \approx \frac{C_N E_b \omega_a}{2}\left(1 - \frac{n\pi}{4Q}\right) \approx 0.44 C_N E_b \omega_a \approx 0.097 \text{ amp.}$$

The charging inductance is given by

$$L_c = \frac{1}{C_N \omega_a^2} = \frac{1}{(0.009 \times 10^{-6})(2\pi \times 400)^2} = 17.4 \text{ henrys.}$$

Although this value is the total necessary inductance, the source inductance, transformed by the square of the transformer turns ratio, must be

Fig. 11·2.—High-power line-type pulser of Fig. 11·1, side view.

considered when designing the transformer because it supplies an appreciable part of this total. In this high-power pulser, the source inductance is approximately 0.001 henry, and the equivalent secondary inductance is about 3.5 henrys. With the usual circuit Q, the value of the resonating inductance is not critical, and it can vary ± 5 per cent without seriously affecting the operation.

Description.—The motor-generator and rotary gap are mounted on vibration-absorbing mounts in a small framework. The contactor box that houses the control apparatus and the oil tank enclosing the a-c resonant transformer and pulse-forming network are mounted on top of this frame directly over the motor-generator. Except for phase adjustment the pulser is adjusted by remote control, and meters are provided to measure the generator voltage, oscillator average current, and operating time.

The power level is adjusted by a variac in the control box, which varies the generator-field excitation. Over a small range the power output can be controlled entirely by this variac, but, if a large change in output power is required, it is also necessary to rephase the rotary gap by means of a knurled knob on the side of the gap housing.

The complete pulser, which weighs approximately 700 lb, is shown in Fig. 11·2. Figures 11·3 and 11·4 are photographs of some of the pulser

FIG. 11·3.—Contactor box for the high-power pulser, top view.

FIG. 11·4.—Compartment for the high-voltage components of high-power pulser.

components. Figure 11·5 is a complete schematic diagram showing both pulser circuits and control.[1]

Performance.—Typical performance data[2] for this pulser are given in Table 11·1 with a magnetron load and a pulse transformer having a turns ratio of 3/1.

When operating under the proper conditions, the inaccuracy in pulse-timing that results from the use of the rotary spark gap normally amounts to ± 25 μsec. An additional winding on the pulse transformer supplies a trigger pulse for self-synchronous operation of the radar system.

The normal shape of the voltage pulse delivered to a magnetron through the pulse transformer and a 50-ohm pulse cable is shown in

[1] P. C. Bettler, "Instruction Manual for Model 6 Modulator," RL Report No. M-153, Feb. 18, 1944.

[2] P. C. Bettler, "Model 6 Modulator Performance Tests," RL Report No. 549, Apr. 22, 1944.

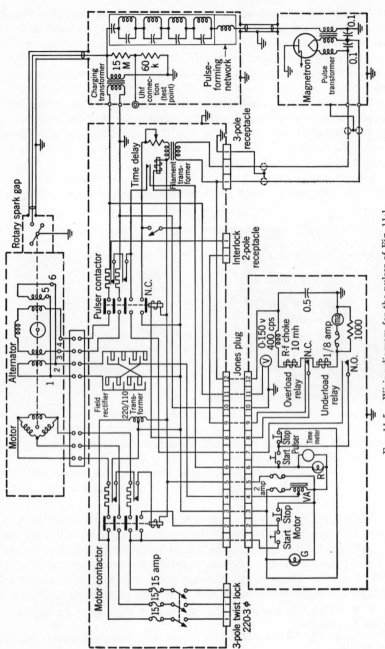

FIG. 11·5.—Wiring diagram for the pulser of Fig. 11·1.

TABLE 11·1.—TYPICAL PERFORMANCE DATA FOR A HIGH-POWER ROTARY-GAP PULSER

Test No.	Supply-line power	Generator output		Pulse-forming network		Magnetron input			
	P_S, watts	V_G, volts	P_i, watts	V_N, kv	P_N, watts	V_l, kv	I_{lav}, ma	$V_l \cdot I_{lav}$, watts	P_l, Mw
1	1225	68	535	15.5	505	25.8	12.3	313	0.99
2	1680	85	855	19.4	762	28.9	18.0	520	1.53
3	2090	98.5	1135	21.9	1010	31.8	22.4	712	2.11

Test No.	Pulser efficiency $\dfrac{V_l \cdot I_{lav}}{P_i} \times 100$, per cent	Over-all pulser efficiency from motor generator to magnetron $\dfrac{V_l \cdot I_{lav}}{P_S} \times 100$, per cent
1	59	26
2	62	31
3	63	34

Fig. 11·6. The pulse rate of rise is too steep for certain magnetrons and causes mode-changing. In these cases, pulse shape is usually modified by means of "despiking" components in the output circuit. A typical circuit for this purpose consists of a 12-mh inductance in series with the output (at the input to the pulse cable) and a 1600-$\mu\mu$f capacitance in series with a 50-ohm noninductive resistance connected in parallel with the primary of the pulse transformer. A better solution would be to substitute a network that was designed to deliver a pulse to fit the particular type of magnetron used, but this

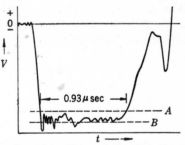

FIG. 11·6.—Voltage-pulse shape from the high-power pulser of Fig. 11·1, A is 90 per cent of the average pulse amplitude, B is the average pulse amplitude.

procedure is usually impractical in a general-purpose pulser.

This high-voltage rotary-gap pulser has been used extensively for component development, life-testing, and magnetron-seasoning. For these uses no alterations were necessary except a modification of the output pulse shape in order to adapt it to particular magnetrons. This pulse generator also served as the system field-test pulser for several of the modern ground-based microwave-radar systems.

11·2. A High-power Airborne Pulser.[1]—The pulser described in this section[2] was designed to supply a pulse power of 600 kw to a 4J50 magnetron at a duty ratio of 0.1 per cent. Since the pulser was intended for airborne use, it was imperative to keep the weight and size of the package as small as was compatible with a reasonable operating life, and it was also necessary to provide an airtight housing, which introduced additional elements to be considered in the design. Accordingly, in addition to electrical design and performance, the following discussion includes a brief outline of mechanical design with particular reference to the problems of heat dissipation. The completed pulser weighed less than 100 lb and had an over-all efficiency (including blower and control circuits) of about 40 per cent.

Electrical Design Requirements.—The specific requirements for this pulser were as follows:

Pulse-power output at full-power operation: 600 kw (22 kv at 27 amp).
Pulse-power output at reduced power (starting): 400 kw (21 kv at 19 amp).
Pulse durations: 0.5 and 2.5 μsec.
Recurrence frequencies: 2000 and 400 pps.
Supply voltages: 115 v at 400 to 2400 cycles/sec and 24 v d-c.

The requirements of multiple values of pulse duration, recurrence frequency, and pulse-power output made it necessary to use the most flexible circuit possible. Accordingly, d-c inductance charging with a hold-off diode and a hydrogen-thyratron switch was chosen. A pulse-forming-network impedance of 50 ohms was adopted.

Voltage on the Pulse-forming Network and Switch.—If the discharging efficiency, η_d, is assumed to be 75 per cent, the peak forward pulse-forming-network voltage is given by

$$V_N = \sqrt{\frac{4Z_N P_l}{\eta_d}} = 2\sqrt{\frac{50 \times 0.6}{0.75}} \times 10^3 \approx 12.6 \text{ kv.}$$

Since this value is well within the specifications of the 5C22 hydrogen thyratron, this tube was then selected as the switch.

Network Capacitance.—The approximate network capacitance is given by

$$C_N = \frac{\tau}{2Z_N}.$$

[1] By J. V. Lebacqz.
[2] S. Siegel, A. P. Kruper, and H. L. Glick, Westinghouse Research Report SR-316, Nov. 1, 1945.

For the 0.5-μsec pulse,

$$C_{N_1} = \frac{0.5 \times 10^{-6}}{100} = 5000 \ \mu\mu f,$$

and for the 2.5-μsec pulse,

$$C_{N_2} = 25,000 \ \mu\mu f.$$

Charging Inductance.—In order to insure the best operation of the 5C22 at 2000 pps, nearly resonant charging should be achieved. Then $f_r = 1/\pi \sqrt{L_c C_N}$, and

$$L_c = \frac{1}{\pi^2 f_r^2 C_{N_1}} \approx \frac{1}{10 \times 4 \times 5 \times 10^{-3}} = 5 \text{ henrys,}$$

which is the value of charging inductance used in this pulser.

Shunt-diode Circuit.—In order to maintain a constant peak forward voltage on the network after an accidental short circuit in the load, it is necessary to dissipate the inverse voltage left on the network after such a short circuit as rapidly as possible by means of a shunt-diode circuit across the network. For maximum effectiveness, the time constant of the network capacitance and resistance of the shunt circuit should be as small as possible compared with the charging period. Since most magnetron sparking takes place with long pulses, the charging period to be considered is

$$T_c = \pi \sqrt{L_c C_{N_2}} \approx 1100 \ \mu sec.$$

In general, the diode circuit proves reasonably effective if its time constant is about 1 per cent of the charging period. Then

$$R_S C_{N_2} = 11 \times 10^{-6},$$
$$R_S = \frac{11 \times 10^{-6}}{25 \times 10^{-9}} \approx 450 \text{ ohms.}$$

A resistance of this value can be obtained by using two 3B26's in parallel, each in series with a 500-ohm resistance. The maximum ratings of the tubes are not exceeded because, for the peak inverse voltage of 13 kv (rating = 15 kv), the peak current after a complete short circuit is $\frac{1}{2}$ 13000/900 = 7.2 amp, and decreases in 5 μsec to less than 4.5 amp (rating = 8 amp). For a continuous short circuit only the rating for plate dissipation is exceeded. This excess dissipation can be corrected by the protective relay discussed later.

Power Supply.—The power supply was designed as a standard full-wave rectifier with a choke input filter to minimize the effect of the input-voltage waveform on the pulser output. The d-c voltage required for normal operation can be arrived at by the use of an estimated charging ratio; 1.85 was chosen. Then

$$E_{bb} = \frac{V_N}{1.85} = \frac{12.6}{1.85} = 6.8 \text{ kv.}$$

For starting,

$$E_{bb} = \frac{2}{1.85} \sqrt{\frac{50 \times 0.4}{0.75}} = 5.6 \text{ kv.}$$

The average current from the power supply is approximately

$$I_{cav} = \frac{P_l}{E_{bb} \times \eta_d \times \eta_c} = \frac{600}{6800 \times 0.75 \times 0.925} = 126 \text{ ma,}$$

or

$$I_{cav} = C_N V_N f_r = 5 \times 2000 \times 12.6 \times 10^{-6} = 126 \text{ ma.}$$

A total of eight output voltages was provided, in two groups of four. Each group was given by two taps connected near one end of the primary winding to allow for the change from low (starting) to high (running) power. For each operating power level, four adjustments were provided over a voltage range of approximately ± 5 per cent in order to accommodate possible variations in the 4J50 input requirements from tube to tube, as well as to compensate easily for changes in input-voltage waveform.

No particular difficulties were encountered with the power supply, with the possible exception of the filter inductance. Because of the waveforms supplied by aircraft generators, the peak voltage across the inductance was, for some conditions, greater than 1.5 times the expected value for a sinusoidal voltage. Both the insulation stresses and the core loss were therefore increased, and the design required special care.

Hold-off Diode.—The maximum expected peak current through the charging circuit occurs for the long pulse duration and is given approximately by

$$I_{cpeak} \approx \sqrt{2} \times 126 \times \tfrac{2500}{1100} \approx 400 \quad \text{ma.}$$

Since the 705A diode satisfies both the peak- and average-current requirements in addition to the voltage requirement for the hold-off diode, it was used in this position as well as in the rectifier.

Pulse-duration Switching.—When the pulse duration is changed, it is necessary to shut off the high-voltage supply for a short time before, during, and after the switching operation in order to prevent the buildup of excessive voltage on the network and to eliminate sparking at the switch contacts. In this particular instance, two auxiliary relays (K_5 and K_7) actuate the main connector relays K_2 and K_3 as well as the high-voltage network switch (K_7), designed especially on a Rototrol mechanism. (See Fig. 11·7.) The main power supply is cut off before the pulse duration is changed, and the power is restored as soon as the high-voltage switch is again in operating position.

Protection.—Protection against short circuits in the load is normally achieved by the shunt-diode circuit, which prevents dangerous overvolting of any pulser component and keeps the average current very nearly constant. For prolonged short circuits, it is desirable either to turn off the pulser, or at least to change its output from high to low power. Since the largest current change resulting from a fault occurs in the shunt-diode circuit, a protective relay is introduced in this circuit. A thermal relay (TK_1 of Fig. 11·7) was selected for this function because of its long operating delay. The relay chosen in this particular case operates in approximately one second in case of a short circuit in the load (see Sec. 10·3), but takes five seconds to return to its normal position. The resultant decrease in the average plate dissipation in the diode to one sixth of the expected value enables the 3B26 to be operated within ratings.

The pulser components are protected against the effects of an open circuit in the load, or a short circuit across the power supply caused by a fault in the pulser, by means of an overload relay (K_4 in Fig. 11·7). This relay is of the "flapper" type, and releases when the high voltage is shut off. When the trouble condition is continuous, final protection is assured by overloading the fuses through the resistance R_1.

Trigger Amplifier.—The trigger pulse supplied by the radar system to the pulser may vary in amplitude from 7 to 150 volts, and in duration from 0.5 to 10 μsec. Because of the trigger and bias requirements of the 5C22 hydrogen thyratron, a special power supply was needed for its grid circuit. The trigger amplifier is shown in Fig. 11·7. A double triode is used, one half of which serves as an amplifier and limiter, and the other half as the tube in a regenerative pulser. The trigger pulse for the 5C22 is obtained from the cathode-follower output from the regenerative pulser tube.

Insulation.—All magnetic components used in this pulser have been designed with Fosterite insulation in order to reduce their weight to a minimum and to enable operation at ambient temperatures higher than those that standard equipment would normally withstand. Results so far have been very satisfactory. It was also desired to use diaplex as network insulation to further reduce the weight. Because of corona difficulties occurring at the operating-voltage levels, a satisfactory diaplex network was not available, and a network with oil-impregnated paper insulation was used instead. By careful location of the network in the air flow, it was possible to reduce its temperature rise and thus insure satisfactory life.

The complete wiring diagrams of the pulser and its control box are given in Fig. 11·7.

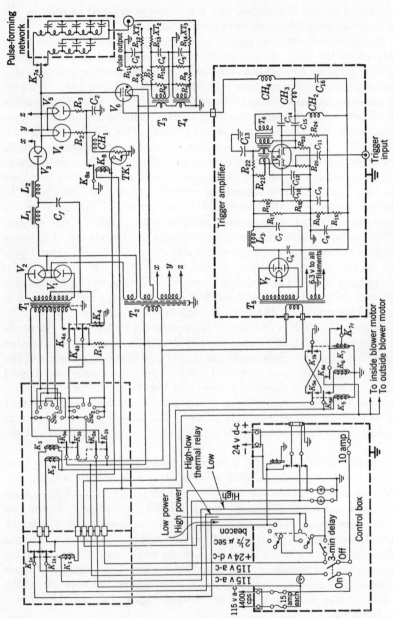

Fig. 11·7.—Circuit diagram for the high-power airborne pulser.   (Courtesy of the Westinghouse Research Laboratories.)

Mechanical Design and Dissipation of Heat.—A preliminary study and estimates of efficiency indicated that the pulser components could probably be contained in a cylinder less than 15 in. in diameter and 17 in. long, but that the total losses would be 600 to 700 watts. Hence, the ultimate size of the pulser might be determined by temperature-rise considerations and heat transfer through the airtight container. Cooling studies give heat-transfer coefficients of 6 milliwatts per square inch per degree centigrade for turbulent (low-velocity) air on either side of the container, and about 16.8 milliwatts for high-velocity air.[1]

If a value of 95°C is assumed for the maximum air temperature in the container, the maximum temperature rise allowable is 24°C above the

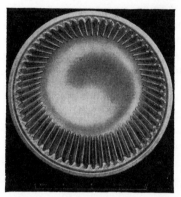

FIG. 11·8.—Interior view of the corrugated can. (*Courtesy of the Westinghouse Research Laboratories.*)

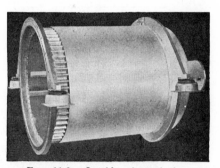

FIG. 11·9.—Outside view of the completed can showing mounting rings and shock mounts. (*Courtesy of the Westinghouse Research Laboratories.*)

value of 71.1°C specified as the ambient operating temperature. Then, the required cooling area for the best conditions of heat transfer is

$$\text{Area} = \frac{700}{16.8 \times 24} \approx 1750 \text{ in.}^2$$

In order to obtain a high-velocity air flow along the entire area of the airtight can, a triple-walled can is necessary. A tentative design, based on the estimated size of the pulser components size and of the axial-flow blower, gave an area of about 1200 in.^{2} for the center (airtight) can. By forming the cylinder out of a corrugated sheet rather than a smooth sheet, it was possible to increase the total cooling area to about 1750 in.^{2} without increasing the outside dimensions of the unit; furthermore, the mechanical rigidity was increased. Figures 11·8 and 11·9 show the airtight corrugated can alone, and mounted with the jackets that assure a

[1] A. E. Vershbow and E. L. Czapek "Cooling of Pressure Tight Containers," RL Report No. 462, Mar. 14, 1944.

high-velocity flow of air along the corrugations, and Fig. 11·10 gives a comparison of cooling efficiency between plain and corrugated cans.   The temperature rise is higher here than expected because the correct blowers were not available for tests, causing a decrease in air velocity from 2500 to 1500 ft/min for the outside air.

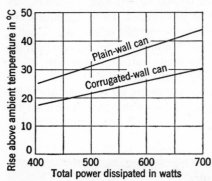

Fig. 11·10.—Comparison of the heat dissipation of a plain-wall can versus that of a corrugated-wall can. (*Courtesy of the Westinghouse Research Laboratories.*)

Chassis.—The pulser components are mounted on a T-shaped chassis welded to the circular-front pressure plate; channel-shaped sections serve as reinforcement and runners for sliding on the guides of the inner can.   The location of components on the chassis has been chosen with regard to weight distribution, short connections, and the elimination of electrical noise.   Most heavy components are located near the front plate in order to relieve strains on the chassis, the parts have been grouped by functions, and the "noisy" elements of the pulse-forming circuit have been kept in a section by themselves.

Fig. 11·11.—Top view of the chassis.   (*Courtesy of the Westinghouse Research Laboratories.*)

Relays, tap switches, and line noise filters for all power leads are contained in a relay box on the front of the pressure plate, and the line filters are mounted on a partition that provides a completely shielded input compartment for the control-box connector.   Separate shielded cables are provided for both input and output trigger pulses, and a special pulse-cable connector is also used.   Figures 11·11 and 11·12 show the chassis

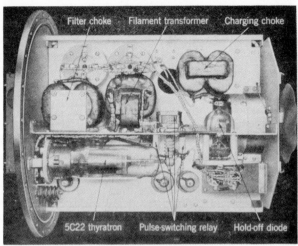

FIG. 11·12.—Bottom view of the chassis. (*Courtesy of the Westinghouse Research Laboratories.*)

FIG. 11·13.—View of the chassis partially slid into the can.   (*Courtesy of the Westinghouse Research Laboratories.*)

layout, and Fig. 11·13 shows a general view of the pulser with the cover partly removed.

Performance.—Some data covering electrical performance are given in Table 11·2, corresponding to several taps on the input transformer for both short and long pulses. Measurements applying to all cases are:

1. Short pulse. Recurrence frequency = 2000 pps. Pulse duration = 0.43 μsec, measured at half amplitude of magnetron current pulse.
2. Long pulse. Recurrence frequency = 400 pps. Pulse duration = 2.4 μsec, measured at half amplitude of magnetron current pulse.

The tabulated magnetron input voltage in Table 11·2 has been obtained by plotting an average *V-I* characteristic from the actual data, and correcting the voltage readings to make the points follow a smooth curve. In no case was the correction greater than 2.5 per cent, which is a reasonable error for voltage measurements with a capacitance divider.

TABLE 11·2.—PERFORMANCE DATA FOR HIGH-POWER AIRBORNE PULSER

Trans-former tap	A-c input power P_s, watts	Input to pulser circuit			Magnetron input				Pulser-circuit efficiency $\dfrac{P_{l_{av}}}{P_i} \times 100$, per cent
		E_{bb}, kv	$I_{c_{av}}$, ma	P_i, watts	I_l, amp	V_l, kv	P_l, kw	$P_{l_{av}}$, watts	
				Short pulse					
1	710	5.20	86	446	17.0	20.6	350	300	68
3	780	5.56	92	511	20.6	21.2	435	375	73
5	950	6.30	105	660	24.3	21.8	530	455	69
6	1000	6.50	108	702	26.6	22.2	590	505	72
7	1070	6.78	112	760	27.4	22.3	610	525	69
				Long pulse					
3	825	5.5	100	550	19.2	20.9	400	385	70
6	1040	6.5	112	728	23.4	21.6	505	485	67

The circuit efficiency is approximately 70 per cent for all operating conditions; however, the over-all pulser efficiency—from a-c input to pulse output—is only about 50 per cent at the higher power levels. If the drain of blower motors and d-c relays are included, the best efficiency available is about 40 per cent. Thus, it is seen that the fixed losses—cathode power, cooling, etc.—account, in general, for more than half the total losses in the pulser.

The pulse input to the magnetron and the r-f spectrum are given in Fig. 11·14.

Heat runs on the finished pulser at full output indicated a hot-spot temperature on the can of the network that was 32°C above the external ambient temperature, and a 35°C temperature rise for the core of the charging reactor.   These values are about equal to those expected from the design considerations.

11·3. Multiple-network Pulsers.[1]—In the conventional line-type pulser the load is matched to the network impedance in order to obtain

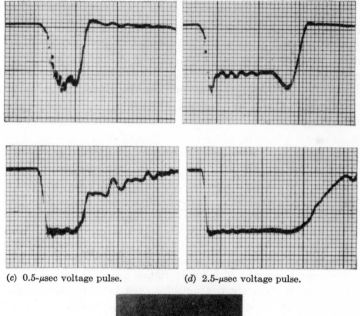

(c) 0.5-μsec voltage pulse.   (d) 2.5-μsec voltage pulse.

(e) R-f spectrum for the 0.5-μsec pulse.

FIG. 11·14.—Oscilloscope traces of pulses obtained with the high-power airborne pulser and the 4J50 magnetron.   (*Courtesy of the Westinghouse Research Laboratories.*)

optimum power transfer, resulting in a load voltage equal to one half the network voltage before discharge.   The use of pulse transformers, of course, enables the load voltage to be stepped up or down by a factor of five, and possibly ten in some cases.   It is possible to obtain load voltages equal to or higher than the network voltage without pulse transformers by using several networks in the discharging circuit.   Circuits were developed both in England and in this country to accomplish this

[1] By R. S. Stanton.

result. The British used a two-network system called the "Blumlein circuit," and a general scheme for the use of n networks was devised by S. Darlington of the Bell Telephone Laboratories. The general principle on which these circuits are based is essentially that of charging the networks in parallel and discharging them in series.

The Darlington Circuit.—A simplified schematic diagram of the Darlington circuit is shown in Fig. 11·15. It consists of $(n - 1)$ four-terminal networks. The nth network can be of the two-terminal type. One obvious requirement to obtain a single pulse across the load is that all the networks have the same delay time and phase characteristics. In order to obtain a single pulse across the load resistance R_l, some definite relations between the network impedances are required. These impedance relationships may be obtained by making use of a steady-state theorem on equivalent circuits, and applying it to the impulse system.

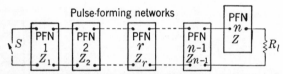

FIG. 11·15.—Schematic diagram of the Darlington discharging circuit.

This theorem states that a circuit consisting of an ideal transformer in series with a load resistance and a four-terminal network is equivalent to another circuit consisting of a four-terminal network and series resistance, provided that certain relationships exist between the transformer ratio, the series resistances, and the network impedances. By applying this theorem to the discharging circuit of a conventional pulser and introducing a delay line of the same electrical characteristics as that of the original network, an equivalent two-network circuit is obtained. The process is repeated until the n-network system is developed for which the expression for the impedance of the rth network is given by

$$Z_r = R_l \left[\frac{r(r + 1)}{n^2} \right],$$

and the impedance of the nth network is given by $Z_n = R_l/n$.

Energy considerations show that all the energy stored in the network is dissipated in one pulse in the load resistance when these values are adopted. Hence, the reflections taking place between networks must of necessity cancel each other, and a single pulse be obtained at the load. The voltage of that pulse is equal to $n/2$ times the network voltage. The series discharge is obtained by short-circuiting the first network of the series by switch S. By simple transmission-line theory, short-circuiting one end of a network is equivalent to reversing the potential of the network, thus putting it in series with the second network. The voltage-reversal process is continued until the pulse appears across the load. It must be noted that the reversal process results in a fixed time delay between the firing of the switch and the appearance of the pulse at the load. The recharging of the network can be accomplished by the same methods as have been discussed in the case of a conventional line-type pulser.

The Blumlein Circuit.—If the relations for the network impedance obtained above are applied to the case where only two networks are used, $Z_1 = R_l/2$, $Z_2 = R_l/2$. For two networks, however, the constraining

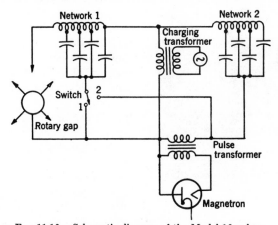

Fig. 11·16.—Schematic diagram of the Model 16 pulser.

conditions are not as severe as in the general case described above, and matched conditions are obtained if the sum of the network impedances is equal to the load impedance, or $Z_1 + Z_2 = R_l$. In this way it is possible to match a high-impedance load directly to a low-impedance network by the addition of another network.

Some advantages can be derived from using two networks of equal impedance. For instance, the practical pulser described hereafter uses two networks of equal impedance, which can either be connected in series as in the Blumlein circuit to obtain a pulse power of 10 Mw for a pulse duration of 1 μsec, or connected in tandem to obtain a pulse power of 5 Mw for a pulse duration of 2 μsec by connecting the switch as indicated in Fig. 11·16. A-c resonant charging was used, and the rotary spark gap was mounted on an extension of the generator shaft and provided with phasing control. The networks have impedances equal to one half the load impedance (magnetron impedance divided by the square of the pulse-transformer turns ratio). The specifications for the pulser were:

Recurrence frequency: 350 pps.

Power output: 10 and 5 Mw.

Pulse durations: 1 and 2 μsec.

Supply voltage: 60-cycle 3-phase.

The following protective devices were introduced in the circuit: (1) a magnetron-average-current underload relay, (2) a pulse reverse-current relay, (3) a thermal overload relay on motor and charging transformer, and (4) fuses for average-current meter, under-current relay, and control circuit. The magnetron-filament voltage may be adjusted by means of a

FIG. 11·17.—Photograph of the Model 16 pulser.

variac, and an automatic two-minute time delay is introduced before the high voltage can be applied to the circuit. The pulser is built as a single unit, approximately 30 in. by 60 in. by 69 in. and weighs about 1700 lb. A photograph of the completed pulser is reproduced in Fig. 11·17.

Design Calculations.—For the conventional circuit having a network impedance of 25 ohms, the pulse-power output is 5 Mw and the pulse duration is 2 μsec. When the Blumlein circuit is used, the network impedance is 50 ohms, the pulse output is 10 Mw, and the pulse duration is 1 μsec. For both arrangements of the circuit the recurrence frequency is 350 pps and the average power is 3500 watts. On the basis of the conventional circuit arrangement, the capacitance for the network is

$$C_N = \frac{\tau}{2Z_N} = \frac{2 \times 10^{-6}}{2 \times 25} = 40,000 \ \mu\mu f.$$

If the discharging efficiency η_d is assumed to be 70 per cent, the network voltage is

$$V_N = \sqrt{\frac{4P_l Z_N}{\eta_d}} = 2\sqrt{\frac{5 \times 10^6 \times 25}{0.7}} \approx 27 \text{ kv},$$

and the average power taken from the network is

$$P_N = \frac{P_l \tau f_r}{\eta_d} \approx 5100 \text{ watts.}$$

The rms voltage across the transformer secondary for $n = 2$ and $Q = 12$ is

$$E_{b_{rms}} = \frac{\frac{V_N}{\sqrt{2}}}{Q(1 - e^{\frac{-n\pi}{2Q}})} \approx \frac{0.707 \times 27 \times 10^3}{2.76} = 6920 \text{ volts,}$$

and the rms current in the transformer secondary is

$$I_{c_{rms}} \approx \frac{n\pi C_N E_b \omega_a}{2\sqrt{6}} = 1.1 \text{ amp.}$$

Therefore,

$$E_{b_{rms}} \times I_{c_{rms}} \approx 6920 \times 1.1 = 7.6 \text{ kv-amp.}$$

The average current in the transformer secondary is

$$I_{c_{av}} \approx \frac{C_N E_b \omega_a}{2}\left(1 - \frac{n\pi}{4Q}\right) \approx 0.44 C_N E_b \omega_a = 0.378 \text{ amp.}$$

The charging inductance is given by

$$L_c = \frac{1}{C_N \omega_a^2} = 5.15 \text{ henrys.}$$

This value is the total inductance, but allowance must be made for the source inductance transformed by the square of the turns ratio of the charging transformer. According to experimental tests, a transformer

TABLE 11·3.—TYPICAL OPERATING CHARACTERISTICS FOR THE MODEL 16 PULSER

Generator volts, V_G	Charging current $I_{c_{av}}$, ma.	Pulse voltage, kv	Pulse power, Mw
Blumlein circuit			
150	220	13.6	3.7
155	240	15.4	4.7
160	260	16.4	5.4
165	280	18.2	6.6
170	300	19.1	7.2
185	320	20.2	8.2
187	340	21.4	9.2
195	360	22.6	10.2
197	380	23.6	11.2
Conventional circuit			
185	250	8	2.5
190	300	9.9	3.9
205	340	10.9	4.8
215	375	12.0	5.7

leakage inductance of 3.6 henrys is necessary in order to obtain a total circuit inductance of 5.15 henrys.

Typical operating characteristics with resistance load for the Blumlein and conventional circuits are given in Table 11·3.

11·4. The Anger Circuit.[1]—In the conventional line-type pulser in use in this country, the pulse-forming network is charged slowly to a potential V_N, and then is suddenly discharged through a load whose impedance is very nearly equal to the characteristic impedance of the pulse-forming network.

The Anger circuit was developed in this country by H. O. Anger, in 1942.[2] The British have used the same circuit in some of their pulse generators. In this circuit the network is charged to a po-

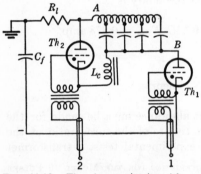

tential V_N through a load of impedance very nearly equal to the characteristic impedance of the network, and the pulse appears across the load during the charging of the network.

The Anger circuit also differs from that of the d-c charging line-type pulser in that it is necessary either to discharge the network or to reverse the polarity of the network voltage during the interpulse interval. The network can be discharged by connecting a suitable resistance across its terminals, corresponding to conventional resistance charging. The polarity of the network voltage can be reversed by connecting an inductance across its terminals, and the same possibilities of resonant, hold-off diode, or linear operation exist as in the conventional inductance-charging circuit.

Fig. 11·18.—The Anger circuit with a hold-off thyratron.

The fundamental circuit as originally designed is given in Fig. 11·18. Assume that thyratron Th_1 has been made conducting, so that point B is at potential $-E_{bb}$. If some time later, thyratron Th_2 is made conducting, (Th_1 nonconducting), it closes a resonant circuit formed by the capacitance of the pulse-forming network and the inductance L_c. Since the current cannot reverse in the circuit because of the unidirectional property of the thyratron, a charge is left on the network that is nearly equal in magnitude, but opposite in polarity, to that left on it after the pulse.

[1] By J. V. Lebacqz.

[2] J. V. Lebacqz, H. O. Anger, and T. W. Jarmie, "Mechanical Vacuum Switches, Transmission Line and RC Pulsing Circuits," NDRC 14-156, U. of Calif., June 1, 1943,

Before thyratron Th_1 is made conducting a second time, a potential almost equal to $2E_{bb}$ appears across it. At the time of firing, the equivalent circuit is that shown in Fig. 11·19. The current flowing through the circuit when the switch is closed is given by

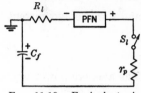

$$I_l = \frac{V_N + E_{bb}}{R_p + R_l + Z_N},$$

and the voltage appearing across the load is

$$V_l = I_l R_l = \frac{V_N + E_{bb}}{R_p + R_l + Z_N} R_l.$$

FIG. 11·19.—Equivalent circuit at the start of the pulse.

Assuming matched conditions ($Z_N = R_l$) and neglecting losses ($R_p = 0$),

$$V_l = \frac{V_N + E_{bb}}{2}.$$

After the pulse, the pulse-forming network again has a voltage E_{bb} across it, and the schematic diagram of the potential-reversing circuit is given by Fig. 11·20. The pulse-forming network can be represented by its capacitance C_N, if the resonant period of L_c and C_N is large compared with the pulse duration.

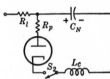

FIG. 11·20.—Schematic diagram of the potential-reversing circuit.

Then, one half cycle after switch S_2 is closed,

$$V_N = E_{bb}e^{-\frac{\pi}{2Q}},$$

where $Q = \omega L_c/R_c$, and R_c is the resistance of the potential-reversing inductance and switch S_2 in series.

The load voltage for the following pulses can then be written, for matched conditions and no losses in the switch S_1,

$$V_l = E_{bb}\frac{1 + e^{-\frac{\pi}{2Q}}}{2}.$$

For a value of Q of approximately 15,

$$e^{-\frac{\pi}{2Q}} \approx e^{-0.1} = \frac{1}{1.105} = 0.9,$$

and

$$V_l \approx 0.95E_{bb}.$$

In general, V_l can be written

$$V_l = E_{bb}(1 + e^{-\frac{\pi}{2Q}})\frac{R_l}{R_p + R_l + Z_N}.$$

The peak current taken from the power-supply filter condenser is

$$I_l = \frac{E_{bb}(1 + e^{-\frac{\pi}{2Q}})}{R_p + R_l + Z_N},$$

and the average current is

$$I_{c_{av}} = \frac{E_{bb}(1 + e^{-\frac{\pi}{2Q}})}{R_p + R_l + Z_N} \cdot \tau \cdot f_r.$$

The average power output is given by

$$P_{l_{av}} = V_l I_l \tau f_r = \frac{E_{bb}^2(1 + e^{-\frac{\pi}{2Q}})^2}{(R_p + R_l + Z_N)^2} R_l \tau f_r,$$

the average power input is

$$P_{i_{av}} = E_{bb} \cdot I_{c_{av}} = \frac{E_{bb}^2(1 + e^{-\frac{\pi}{2Q}})}{R_p + R_l + Z_N} \tau f_r,$$

and the pulser-circuit efficiency is given by

$$\eta = \frac{(1 + e^{-\frac{\pi}{2Q}})}{R_p + R_l + Z_N} R_l.$$

It can be seen from these relations that the performance of this circuit is essentially the same as that of the conventional line-type pulser.

A modification of this circuit was introduced a little later in order to eliminate the necessity of the thyratron Th_2 The value of the inductance L_c was increased until the natural period of oscillation of the L_cC_N-combination was exactly twice the pulse recurrence period. Under these conditions the network potential-reversing process occupies the full interval between pulses, corresponding to normal resonant charging of the standard pulser circuit. A circuit diagram is given in Fig. 11·21.

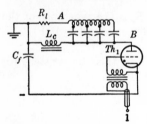

Fig. 11·21.—The revised Anger circuit.

Further investigation also showed that the value of the inductance could be made larger than that corresponding to resonance. In this case, the current in L_c never drops to zero, and the potential across the pulse-forming network reverses in a more linear fashion, corresponding to linear d-c charging of the normal line-type pulser circuit.

Since the Anger circuit gives essentially the same performance as the circuit discussed in Chap. 9, the reasons for using it must depend on practical considerations. Probably the principal disadvantage is that the rectifier-output filter capacitance must be able to withstand the additional heat produced by the pulse current flowing through it, and must also be large enough to prevent an appreciable drop in the pulse voltage. From a practical standpoint, a capacitance ten times the pulse-forming-network capacitance should prove ample. In general, it is found that this value is also required to keep the rectifier ripple within reasonable limits.

The principal advantage of the circuit is apparent in applications requiring high voltages in crowded places. It may be noted that, in the Anger circuit, the maximum instantaneous voltage to ground at any point in the circuit does not exceed the d-c supply voltage, whereas, in the usual line-type circuit, it is twice the d-c supply voltage.

Little difference in the transformers may be expected, the rectifier filaments are at ground potential instead of E_{bb}, but the thyratron cathode is at $-E_{bb}$ instead of ground potential, requiring, of course, the addition of an insulated trigger transformer for the thyratron grid.

11·5. The Nonlinear-inductance Circuit.[1]—This section is concerned with pulse generators in which nonlinear inductances are used as the switching elements. These pulsers can produce a high voltage across the load from a low-voltage power supply without the use of a pulse transformer. By suddenly reducing the current in a linear inductance to zero, the energy stored in the associated magnetic field is transferred to a capacitance. The resultant high voltage across the condenser causes a large current to build up in a nonlinear inductance, which soon reaches current saturation. Upon saturation, the inductance of the nonlinear coil immediately diminishes to a very small value and, together with the capacitance, acts as a high-impedance pulse-forming network and delivers the pulse to the load.

The coil has a toroidal winding on a spirally wound molybdenum permalloy tape core. The tape has a thickness of about 1 mil and an initial permeability of at least 10,000. The switching impedance ratio and the time of saturation of the coil are controlled by the proper proportioning of both the weight of the core material and the diameter and number of turns on the coil. For a typical coil the inductance changes from approximately 1.5 h to 100 μh at a pulse recurrence frequency of 3600 pps, and the time jitter can be held to less than 0.05 μsec.

The nonlinear-inductance pulser operates in the following manner. The tube T_1 (shown in Fig. 11·22), which is normally cut off, is made conducting by means of a rectangular-wave grid excitation (E_g in Fig. 11·23). Plate current from a high-voltage source flows through the linear inductance L_1, and the tube is allowed to conduct for a time sufficient to permit this plate current to build up to a point nearing current saturation (I_{L_1} in Fig. 11·23). This duration is made equal to approximately 25 per cent of the interval between pulses. At the time

[1] By L. G. Kersta of the Bell Telephone Laboratories.

when the current is built up to the greatest usable amplitude for the
excitation applied, the tube is suddenly cut off. Peak current amplitudes
between 0.5 and 3.5 amp are obtained in L_1, depending on the output
requirements. A 5D21 tetrode is very satisfactory as tube T_1 for a
pulser output of about 200 kw. During the time the tube conducts, the
nonlinear inductance L_2 operates in the linear region where its inductance is about 1 to 1.5 henrys. At the cutoff instant the energy in the
inductance L_1 begins to transfer to the capacitance C_1, and current of
the opposite sign begins to build up in the nonlinear inductance. This
inductance is designed so that the
time required for the core to saturate
is equal to the time for the condenser
to become fully charged. At this
instant the condenser suddenly discharges and energizes the magnetron
(I_{NL} in Fig. 11·23). The pulse applied to the magnetron from the
pulse-shaping elements has a trapezoidal shape (E_{MAG} in Fig. 11·23);

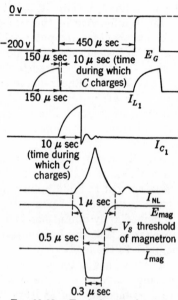

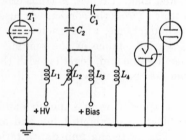

Fig. 11·22.—Basic circuit for a
nonlinear-inductance pulser. (*Courtesy
of the Bell Telephone Laboratories.*)

Fig. 11·23.—Typical wave shapes in a
nonlinear-inductance pulser. (*Courtesy of
the Bell Telephone Laboratories.*)

the voltage pulse has a base about 1 μsec long and a flat top of about
0.3 μsec duration. For the operating conditions shown in Fig. 11·23, the
threshold voltage for the magnetron is about 11 kv. Therefore, it is
apparent that both the current pulse and r-f pulse have a base time
duration equal to the duration of the voltage pulse at the threshold
value (E_{MAG} and I_{MAG} in Fig. 11·23). The resultant r-f pulse has a
base about 0.5 μsec long and a top 0.3 μsec long.

It may be noted, from Fig. 11·24, that the nonlinear inductance is
operated with a d-c bias. For circuit simplicity an external bias source
is shown here, and circuit arrangements that require no external bias
source are described later. With the application of bias, the cycle of

operation is started with the nonlinear inductance in saturation, as shown on the B-H characteristic of Fig. 11·25 at point I_B. When the tube T_1 starts to conduct, current flows through the tube from two sources: (1) the linear inductance L_1, and (2) C_2 and the nonlinear inductance L_2. Current flows from source (2) because C_2 has assumed

the full voltage of the high-voltage power supply (1200 volts) during the cutoff period. This current is in a direction opposite to the bias current and causes the nonlinear inductance to move its operating point to the linear range as shown by the arrow indicating a rising B. The bias current is adjusted to limit the maximum B to a value just below the saturation point shown on the positive side of the characteristic.

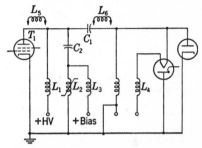

FIG. 11·24.—Nonlinear-inductance pulser with external bias. (*Courtesy of the Bell Telephone Laboratories.*)

The pulse-shaping circuit (Fig. 11·26) was evolved from the attempt to use an equivalent of the Guillemin circuit, a pulse-shaping circuit that can be represented by sections of series-tuned circuits in parallel. The variation attempted here was an equivalent circuit that used the nonlinear inductance and capacitance in series for the first section, and introduced shunt-tuned circuits in series with the above combination.

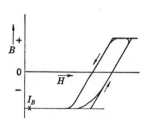

FIG. 11·25.—Hysteresis loop of a nonlinear inductance. (*Courtesy of the Bell Telephone Laboratories.*)

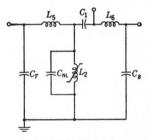

FIG. 11·26.—Pulse-forming network for a nonlinear-inductance pulser. (*Courtesy of the Bell Telephone Laboratories.*)

This attempt to square the pulse left much to be desired because of parasitic effects introduced by component proximities. In its final form, which was determined experimentally, the first element in the network consisted of a nonlinear inductance and its shunt capacitance in series with C_1. The inductance L_5 was adjusted to tune to a higher harmonic of the pulse recurrence frequency with the tube capacitance C_T, and L_6

was adjusted similarly to tune with the capacitance of the diode and magnetron. The resultant circuit is effectively a three-terminal network in which C_1, C_T, and C_{NL} are charged to the full circuit voltage. Upon saturation of L_2, the condenser C_{NL} discharges through L_2 and defines the slope of the pulse voltage up to the threshold value of the magnetron. The voltage from threshold is maintained by the energy in C_1, and declines at a rate that depends on the product of the higher order elements in the network. The final pulse shape resulted from a compromise between the desire for a rectangular pulse and that for simplicity in the network.

Dependent on the application, three basic transmitter circuits have been used. The first, see Fig. 11·22, is described with the operation of

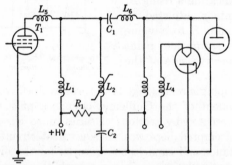

FIG. 11·27.—Diagram showing a method to supply the bias for the nonlinear inductance from an *RC*-circuit. (*Courtesy of the Bell Telephone Laboratories.*)

the basic circuit, and uses an external source of bias supply. The other two circuits use no external power for the supply of bias, and, as a consequence, they have been more widely used in practical applications. The first of these, shown in Fig. 11·27, is called the dynamic-bias circuit. It employs the combination R_1C_2 to provide the bias. The values are so chosen that the charge which accumulates on C_2 during the cutoff time and is dissipated during the period of tube conduction does not saturate the nonlinear inductance. Also, C_2 must be so large compared with C_1 that appreciable energy is not lost during the discharging period. Likewise, R_1 must be large enough to limit the tube current through the nonlinear inductance to a value that is less than the saturation value. During the discharge, the value of C_2R_1 must be such that the current in the nonlinear inductance builds up to the saturation value in a time equal to the charging time of C_1. It is found possible to meet these requirements with relatively noncritical values of C and R. The second internal-bias circuit shown in Fig. 11·28 is called the multifilar-bias circuit. The biasing circuit is very similar to that shown in Fig. 11·22, the difference being that the average plate current of the tube T_1 supplies the bias for the nonlinear inductance. Since the plate current is predetermined by the operating conditions, the proper biasing point is obtained by adjusting the number of turns on the nonlinear inductance until the proper number of ampere-turns of bias is obtained. Since this number of turns is greater than the optimum number for the discharge, the additional turns are obtained by winding them in multifilar fashion with the winding value that is optimum for the discharging circuit. As a result, the nonlinear inductance has between two and four filar windings, depending on the power-output requirement. Since the proper bias polarity is opposite in direction to the normal plate-current flow, the current must be supplied through a linear inductance in order to allow current reversal in the

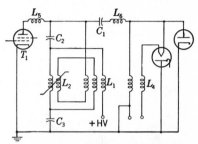

FIG. 11·28.—Diagram showing the elimination of external bias by multifilar windings in the inductances. (*Courtesy of the Bell Telephone Laboratories.*)

nonlinear inductance. The linear inductance is also proportioned by multifilar means in order to allow a division of inductance between the elements of the nonlinear inductance. An auxiliary consideration is that the voltage across the nonlinear and choke coils be kept at a minimum; this is also accomplished by the multifilar windings.

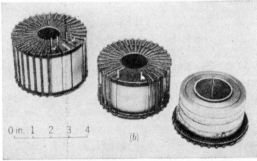

FIG. 11·29.—Photographs of nonlinear-inductance coils. (*Courtesy of the Bell Telephone Laboratories.*)

A photograph of the nonlinear inductance used in the circuit of Fig. 11·27 is reproduced in Fig. 11·29a, and three stages in the construction of a multifilar-winding coil for the circuit of Fig. 11·28 are shown in Fig. 11·29b. The core for the coil shown in Fig. 11·29a weighs about 400 grams, and the finished unit weighs about 1.5 lb for a pulser having a pulse-power output of about 200 kw. Photographs of the assembly of the pulser components for the circuit of Fig. 11·27 are reproduced in Fig. 11·30a and b. The completed assembly is enclosed by an oiltight box, and contains all of the components shown in the diagram with the exception of the tubes and the resistor R_1.

In pulse generators using a nonlinear inductance as the switching element, it is possible to obtain small time jitter, and to operate continuously at high pulse recurrence frequencies (greater than 4000 pps) if necessary. The pulser operates also at pulse durations longer than those mentioned above, but for durations greater than 1 μsec the efficiency becomes poor compared with that of conventional line-type and hard-tube pulsers.

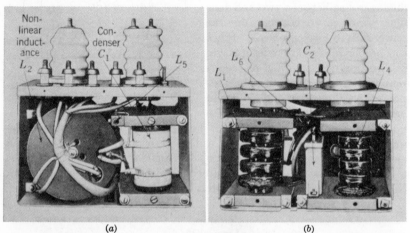

(a)   (b)

FIG. 11·30.—Photographs of the component assembly for the nonlinear-inductance pulser circuit of Fig. 11·27. (*Courtesy of the Bell Telephone Laboratories.*)

11·6. Special-purpose Output Circuits.[1] *Half-wave Single-phase Charging.*—The a-c resonant pulsers described previously in this chapter have full-wave, or single-cycle, charging circuits. In these circuits a simple switch that is synchronized with the supply frequency and made conducting in proper phase relation with the charging voltage serves to deliver a unidirectional pulse to the load, and the pulse recurrence frequency is, in general, equal to the supply frequency.

For half-wave charging, discussed in Chap. 9, the pulse recurrence frequency is twice the supply frequency, but the charge on the network is of opposite polarity on alternate pulses. Accordingly, a conventional discharging circuit would lead to output pulses of alternating polarity. Two special switching arrangements have been used in order to obtain a series of unidirectional pulses across the load by rectifying action.

The first of these is shown in Fig. 11·31, in which the rotary gap G

[1] By R. S. Stanton.

is of a special design that provides the rectifying element in the circuit as follows. When the network voltage assumes a maximum value with terminal a positive and b negative, the switch assumes the position shown in the figure; a is therefore connected to ground, and a negative voltage appears at the terminal c of the load. One half cycle later, the polarity on the network is reversed, the switch connects b to ground and a to the load at c, and again a negative pulse appears across the load.

One pulser based on the circuit described above was required to deliver 5-μsec pulses to a load impedance of 450 ohms at a maximum pulse power of 1.8 Mw. The pulse recurrence frequency was 120 pps, and the a-c supply was a 115-volt 60-cycle single-phase line. The rotary-gap switch was driven by an 1800-rpm synchronous motor with electrical means for automatically selecting the phase required to deliver a negative

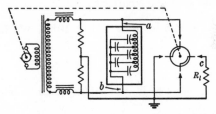

FIG. 11·31.—Pulser using a-c resonant half-wave charging.

pulse. A special transformer was designed to provide the correct inductance for resonant charging.

Design Calculations.—The requirements for the pulser are:
Pulse power P_l: 1.8 Mw.
Pulse duration τ: 5 μsec.
Pulse voltage V_l: 28.5 kv.
Load impedance Z_l: 450 ohms.
Average power: 1080 watts.
Pulse recurrence frequency $f_r = 120$ pps.

Assuming a pulse-forming-network impedance of 50 ohms to match the pulse-cable impedance, the following values are obtained:
Pulse-forming-network capacitance $C_N = 0.05$ μf.

Pulse-transformer stepup ratio $\sqrt{\dfrac{Z_l}{Z_N}} = \dfrac{3}{1}$.

Discharging efficiency $\eta_d = 70$ per cent (assumed). Using the above values, the network voltage is given by

$$V_N = \sqrt{\frac{4 P_l Z_N}{\eta_d}} = \sqrt{\frac{4 \times 1.8 \times 10^6 \times 50}{0.7}} \approx 23 \text{ kv},$$

and the power to be taken from the network is

$$P_N = \frac{P_l \tau f_r}{\eta_d} = \frac{1.8 \times 10^6 \times 5 \times 10^{-6} \times 120}{0.7} \approx 1580 \text{ watts.}$$

The transformer-secondary voltage is

$$E_{b_{\text{rms}}} = \frac{\dfrac{V_N}{\sqrt{2}}}{Q\left(1 - e^{-\frac{n\pi}{2Q}}\right)};$$

with $n = 1$ (half-cycle charging) and $Q = 12$,

$$E_{b_{\text{rms}}} \approx \frac{0.707 \times 23 \times 10^3}{1.47} \approx 11 \text{ kv,}$$

and the transformer-secondary current is

$$I_{c_{\text{rms}}} \approx \frac{n\pi C_N E_b \omega_a}{2\sqrt{6}} = \frac{\pi \times 5 \times 10^{-8} \times 11 \times 10^3 \times \sqrt{2}\,(2\pi)60}{2 \times 2.45}$$

$$\approx 0.19 \text{ amp.}$$

Therefore,

$$E_{b_{\text{rms}}} \times I_{c_{\text{rms}}} \approx 2100 \text{ volt-amp.}$$

The charging inductance is

$$L_c = \frac{1}{C_N \omega_a^2} = \frac{1}{(5 \times 10^{-8})(2\pi \times 60)^2} = 138 \text{ henrys.}$$

This value was used in designing the a-c resonant transformer because the source inductance could be neglected.

The Thyratron Bridge.—A thyratron bridge can be used instead of the rotary gap to obtain pulses of identical polarity, as indicated in Fig. 11·32.

When terminal a of the pulse-forming network has reached its maximum positive charge, a trigger pulse is supplied to $VT1a$ causing it to conduct. Its plate is thus brought very nearly to ground potential, and a negative impulse is applied to the cathode of $VT1b$ through the capacitance of the pulse-forming network. Because of interelectrode capacitance, the grid does not become negative as rapidly as does the cathode. Thus, $VT1b$ is also made conducting, and the discharging circuit is completed through R_l, $VT1b$, the pulse-forming network, and $VT1a$. At the peak of the next charging cycle (the succeeding half-cycle of supply voltage), $VT2a$ and $VT2b$ are made to conduct in a similar manner. Thus, the thyratron bridge serves the same purpose as the rectifying rotary gap switch.

Assuming perfect voltage division across the bridge, the network voltage may be twice the voltage rating for a single tube and, since each pair of tubes conducts at only half of the output pulse recurrence frequency, the duty ratio may be twice that for a single tube. The pulse current is limited to the current rating of a single tube, so the maximum average power output may be four times that for a single thyratron switch.

A special trigger-pulse generator is required for use with the thyratron-bridge circuit. It must supply alternate trigger pulses to $VT1a$ and $VT2a$ spaced exactly 180° in the supply cycle, and phased with respect to the charging voltage so that each tube is caused to conduct when the network voltage reaches a maximum.

An experimental pulser was constructed and tested at the Radiation Laboratory using 4C35 thyratrons and a 400-cycle a-c supply. The

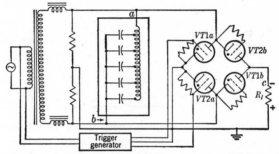

FIG. 11·32.—Schematic diagram of the thryratron-bridge circuit.

pulse recurrence frequency was therefore 800 pps. The 4C35 thyratrons have maximum pulse ratings of 8 kv and 90 amp, but, since the two tubes are in series, the maximum allowable network voltage is 16 kv. Assuming matched load, the value of Z_N that causes the pulse current to fall within the maximum rating is

$$Z_N = \frac{1}{2}\frac{V_N}{I_l} = 89 \text{ ohms.}$$

The network and load impedances were chosen as 100 ohms each, the load being a noninductive resistance. For a pulse duration of 0.9 μsec, the pulse-forming network had a measured capacitance of 4550 μμf.

The charging-transformer characteristics were as follows:
Transformer-secondary voltage,

$$E_{b_{rms}} = \frac{\dfrac{V_N}{\sqrt{2}}}{Q(1 - e^{-\frac{n\pi}{2Q}})} \approx 7.7 \text{ kv.}$$

Transformer-secondary rms current,

$$I_{c_{\mathrm{rms}}} \approx \frac{n\pi C_N E_b \omega_a}{2\sqrt{6}} \approx 0.8 \text{ amp.}$$

Transformer-secondary average current, $I_{c_{\mathrm{av}}} = 0$.

Charging inductance, $L_c = \dfrac{1}{C_N \omega_a^2} = 34.8$ henrys.

Typical operating data for this pulser are given in Table 11·4.

TABLE 11·4.—TYPICAL OPERATING DATA FOR AN A-C RESONANT HALF-WAVE-CHARGING THYRATRON-BRIDGE PULSER

Supply line	Pulse-forming network		Load						Efficiency
P_i, watts	V_N, kv	P_N, watts	V_l, kv	I_l, amp	$I_{l_{\mathrm{av}}}$, ma	P_l, kw	$P_{l_{\mathrm{av}}}$, watts	$P_{l_{\mathrm{av}}} \times 100/P_i$, per cent	
150	6.8	84	4.1	38.0	25	156	63	42	
280	9.4	161	5.4	50.0	35	270	123	44	
428	11.7	247	6.7	62.0	45	415	202	47	

Multiple-load Pulser.—In 1942 the need arose for a pulser to supply pulse power to two magnetrons simultaneously. At that time the problem was solved satisfactorily by placing the two loads in parallel on the output of the pulser described in Sec. 11·1, using separate pulse transformers. With this system the magnetrons and magnets had to be selected carefully in order to assure the equality of load impedance and a reasonably uniform power distribution. When the production system

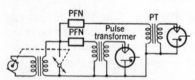

FIG. 11·33.—Schematic diagram of a multiple-load pulser.

was designed, a circuit was developed that had a common charging circuit and rotary-gap switch, but separate pulse-forming networks and pulse transformers. The problem of power distribution to the two loads does not arise with this arrangement because there is almost no coupling between the output circuits during the pulse interval. Each network, pulse transformer, and magnetron combination behaves essentially as a separate pulser circuit. Figure 11·33 is a simplified schematic diagram of this circuit.

When a pulser was planned for a system requiring five simultaneous outputs of 2-Mw pulse power each, this circuit was extended to make a five-network pulser. Complete schematic diagrams of this pulser, its

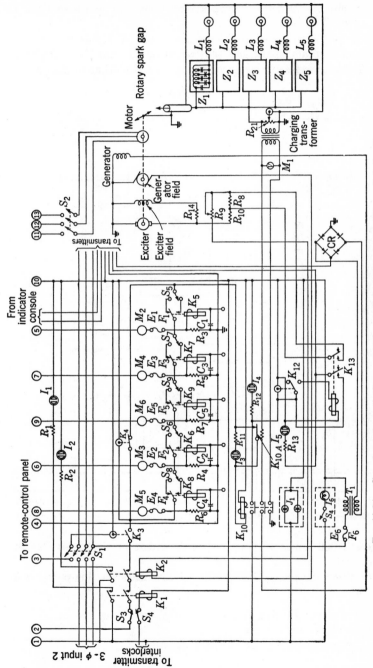

Fig. 11·34.—Complete schematic diagram of the multiple-load pulser and its control circuit.

control circuits, and its remote-control panel are shown in Figs. 11·34 and 11·35.

One of the principal problems associated with this pulser was the design of a rotary spark gap that could handle the high current (1070 amp) without excessive electrode wear. A switch that would operate for

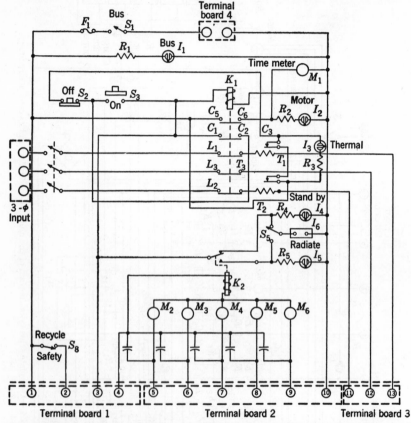

Fig. 11·35.—Complete schematic diagram of the remote-control panel for the multiple-load pulser.

at least 1000 hours without the replacement of electrodes was finally developed.

Electrical Design.—The specific requirements for this pulser were as follows:

Pulse power, P_l: five outputs of 2 Mw each.
Pulse duration, τ: 1 μsec.
Average power, $P_{l_{av}}$: 3500 watts (total).

Pulse recurrence frequency, f_r: 350 pps.
Load impedance, Z_l: 450 ohms.
Pulse-forming-network impedance, Z_N: 50 ohms.
Total network capacitance, C_N: 0.05 × 10⁻⁶ farads.
Pulse-transformer stepup ratio: $\sqrt{Z_l/Z_N} = 3/1$.

If the discharging efficiency, η_d, is assumed to be 70 per cent, the network voltage is

$$V_N = \sqrt{\frac{4P_lZ_N}{\eta_d}} = \sqrt{\frac{4 \times 2 \times 10^6 \times 50}{0.7}} \approx 24 \text{ kv},$$

and the average power taken from each network is

$$P_N = \frac{P_l \tau f_r}{\eta_d} = \frac{2 \times 10^6 \times 10^{-6} \times 350}{0.7} \approx 1000 \text{ watts}.$$

The rms voltage across the transformer secondary for $n = 2$ and $Q = 12$ is

$$E_{b_{\text{rms}}} = \frac{\dfrac{V_N}{\sqrt{2}}}{Q(1 - e^{-\frac{n\pi}{2Q}})} = \frac{0.707 \times 24 \times 10^3}{2.76} \approx 6.2 \text{ kv},$$

and the rms current in the transformer secondary is

$$I_{c_{\text{rms}}} \approx \frac{n\pi C_N E_b \omega_a}{2\sqrt{6}}$$
$$= 1.28(0.05 \times 10^{-6})(6.2 \times 10^3)\sqrt{2}\,(2\pi \times 350) = 1.2 \text{ amp}.$$

Therefore,

$$E_{b_{\text{rms}}} \times I_{c_{\text{rms}}} \approx 6.2 \times 10^3 \times 1.2 = 7.6 \text{ kv-amp}.$$

The average current in the transformer secondary is

$$I_{c_{\text{av}}} \approx \frac{C_N E_b \omega_a}{2}\left(1 - \frac{n\pi}{4Q}\right) \approx 0.44\,C_N E_b \omega_a$$
$$\approx 0.44(0.05 \times 10^{-6})(6.2 \times 10^3)\sqrt{2}\,(2\pi \times 350) \approx 0.42 \text{ amp}.$$

The charging inductance is

$$L_c = \frac{1}{C_N \omega_a^2} = \frac{1}{(0.05 \times 10^{-6})(2\pi \times 350)^2} = 4.14 \text{ henrys (total)}.$$

(Only 2.85 henrys of this total value were designed with the a-c resonant transformer; the remainder was provided by the equivalent inductance of the source.)

Typical performance data for this multiple-load pulser are given in Table 11·5, and photographs of the equipment are reproduced in Figures 11·36 and 11·37.

(a)
(b)

FIG. 11·36.—(a) Motor-generator and rotary-gap switch for the multiple-load pulser.
(b) Rotary spark gap.

TABLE 11·5.—TYPICAL PERFORMANCE DATA FOR A MULTIPLE-LOAD PULSER

Test No.	f_r, pps	Generator output			Pulse-forming networks		Efficiency
		V_G, volts	I_G, amp	P_i, kw	V_N, kv	ΣP_N, kw	$\dfrac{P_N}{P_i} \times 100$, per cent
1	356	158	23.1	3.27	18.8	3.11	95
2	355	179	27.4	4.27	22.0	4.22	98
3	354	198	28.0	5.10	23.1	4.61	91

Test No.	Magnetron No. 1				Magnetron No. 2				Magnetron No. 3			
	V_l, kv	$I_{l_{av}}$, ma	$P_{l_{av}}$, watts	P_l, Mw	V_l, kv	$I_{l_{av}}$, ma	$P_{l_{av}}$, watts	P_l, Mw	V_l, kv	$I_{l_{av}}$, ma	$P_{l_{av}}$, watts	P_l, Mw
1	28.0	14.1	395	1.15	28.0	13.5	378	1.08	27.4	14.7	403	1.15
2	29.0	17.7	514	1.50	29.0	16.9	490	1.41	28.2	18.5	522	1.49
3	29.7	20.0	594	1.73	30.0	18.8	564	1.63	29.2	20.8	607	1.73

Test No.	Magnetron No. 4				Magnetron No. 5				$\Sigma P_{l_{av}}$, kw	Efficiency in per cent	
	V_l, kv	$I_{l_{av}}$, ma	$P_{l_{av}}$, watts	P_l, Mw	V_l, kv	$I_{l_{av}}$, ma	$P_{l_{av}}$, watts	P_l, Mw		$\dfrac{\Sigma P_{l_{av}}}{\Sigma P_N} \times 100$	$\dfrac{\Sigma P_{l_{av}}}{P_i} \times 100$
1	27.9	13.5	377	1.09	27.4	14.6	400	1.14	1.95	63	60
2	28.9	17.2	497	1.44	28.7	18.5	530	1.51	2.55	61	60
3	29.8	19.3	576	1.67	29.2	20.7	605	1.73	2.94	65	60

11·7. Multiple-pulse Line-type Pulsers.[1]—The problem of obtaining a rapid succession of pulses from a line-type pulser is complicated by the fact that all gaseous-discharge tubes known to date have a deionization time that is too long to enable the network to become recharged if the pulse interval is to be less than approximately 100 μsec. Hence, in order to obtain multiple pulses from a line-type pulser, it is necessary to use artifices.

The following three methods have been tried, one of which is used in practice: (1) a multiple-switch multiple-network circuit, (2) a multiple-switch single-network circuit, and (3) a single-switch multiple-network

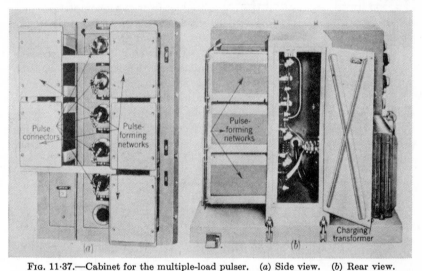

FIG. 11·37.—Cabinet for the multiple-load pulser. (a) Side view. (b) Rear view.

circuit. The three methods are discussed separately, and their possible uses and respective advantages are compared.

Multiple-switch Multiple-network Circuit.—The schematic diagram given in Fig. 11·38 applies where a double-pulse output is required. As can be seen, this circuit is simply a combination of two identical line-type pulsers connected to the same load. When thyratron Th_1 is fired, the network PFN_1 discharges through the load resistance R_l, giving the first pulse of the series. When Th_2 is fired, the second pulse is produced in the load by the discharge of PFN_2. More circuits can similarly be fired in succession to produce so-called "codes" of three or more pulses. Additional stray capacitance, which may affect the pulse shape, occurs across the load when all the pulse-forming networks are connected to the load, or to the primary of the pulse transformer. Also,

[1] By J. V. Lebacqz.

the plates of all the thyratrons are coupled together through the pulse-forming networks. Hence, all output pulse voltages appear, essentially, at the plates of the untriggered tubes. As long as the pulse voltage is

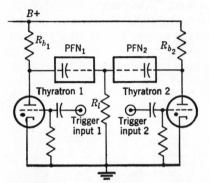

FIG. 11·38.—Circuit diagram for a multiple-switch multiple-network circuit.

negative, no trouble can result. If, however, post-pulse oscillations appear because of the nature of the load or the pulse transformer, difficulties may arise either from exceeding the peak forward voltage of the thyratrons that have not yet been fired, or from the incomplete deionization of the thyratrons that have already been fired.

The spacing between successive pulses of the same code can be obtained in many ways. A practical method is to use a delay circuit that is energized when one thyratron is fired and produces the trigger for the successive pulse. A low-power coded pulser was built on this principle, whose schematic diagram is shown in Fig. 11·39. A brief summary of the design considerations follows.

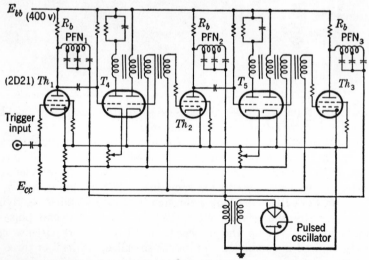

FIG. 11·39.—Basic circuit diagram for a pulser producing a three-pulse code.

When thyratron Th_1 is fired, the first pulse of the code is sent to the load, and, at the same time, the grid of the first half of T_4 is driven well beyond cutoff. When the grid potential again rises to allow the tube to conduct, the sudden increase in plate current causes a positive trigger to appear on the grid of the second half of T_4, starting the regenerative pulser action and applying a trigger to the grid of Th_2. The operation is then repeated to trigger Th_3. The spacing between pulses can easily be controlled by adjusting the cathode bias of the triodes T_4 and T_5.

Resistance charging of the pulse-forming network was chosen because this particular pulser was required to operate at random recurrence frequencies from 0 to 2000 pps. Resistance charging presents some special design problems that are discussed here.

When the thyratron is fired, and until it is completely deionized, the charging element short-circuits the power supply. Hence, a current E_{bb}/R_c flows through the tube after the pulse-forming network is discharged. If this current becomes too large, the thyratron does not deionize properly. Even before it stops completely, the deionization becomes erratic and may occasionally take as long as 500 μsec, resulting in improper charging for the next cycle.

In order to prevent large variations in pulse power when the recurrence frequency is changed, it is necessary that the pulse-forming network be charged nearly to the power-supply voltage at the time of triggering when the highest recurrence frequency is used.

If T_r is the recurrence period, and T_k is the deionizing time corresponding to the chosen value of R_c, the network voltage at the time of firing is given by

$$V_N = E_{bb}(1 - e^{-\frac{T_r - T_k}{R_c C_N}}),$$

where C_N is the network capacitance. Thus,

$$e^{-\frac{T_r - T_k}{R_c C_N}} = \frac{E_{bb} - V_N}{E_{bb}},$$

and

$$C_N = \frac{T_r - T_k}{R_c \ln \dfrac{E_{bb}}{E_{bb} - V_N}}.$$

If a variation of X per cent in the network voltage is allowed, V_N is within $(1 - X/100)$ of E_{bb}, and the pulse output power does not vary by more than $2X$ per cent; the maximum network capacitance is then given by

$$C_N = \frac{T_{r_{\min}} - T_k}{R_c \ln \dfrac{100}{X}}.$$

Under these conditions, the maximum energy per pulse in the load is

$$P_{l\tau} = \frac{1}{2} C_N V_N^2 \eta_d = \frac{E_{bb}^2}{2} \frac{(T_{r_{min}} - T_k)}{R_c \ln \dfrac{100}{X}} \left(\frac{100 - X}{100}\right)^2 \eta_d.$$

As has previously been shown, R_c depends on the maximum current that the switch tube can pass and still deionize satisfactorily. If I_l is the value of this current, $R_c = E_{bb}/I_k$, and

$$P_l = \frac{E_{bb}I_k}{2} \frac{(T_{r_{min}} - T_k)}{\ln \dfrac{100}{X}} \left(\frac{100 - X}{100}\right)^2 \eta_d.$$

Thus, from a design standpoint, the maximum energy per pulse that can be obtained is proportional to the supply voltage and to the minimum charging time $(T_{r_{min}} - T_k)$ of the pulse-forming network.

Double-switch Single-network Circuit.—The schematic diagram of this circuit is given in Fig. 11·40. Assume that the pulse transformer is an

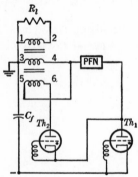

FIG. 11·40.—Circuit diagram for a double-switch single-network pulser.

ideal transformer of turns ratio 1/1/1 and that $R_l = Z_N$ (matched conditions). Assume also that the filter condenser is charged to a potential E_{bb} and that the pulse-forming network is completely discharged. If losses are neglected, the pulse-forming network becomes charged to a potential $V_N = E_{bb}$ when the thyratron Th_1 is triggered. Because of the properties of pulse-forming networks, a pulse of voltage $E_{bb}/2$ appears across R_l during the charging of the network. During the pulse both the plate and the cathode of thyratron Th_2 are driven negative to $-E_{bb}$, the plate by the addition of the voltage at point 4 and that induced in the transformer winding 5–6. At the end of the pulse, however, a voltage equal to E_{bb} suddenly appears from anode to cathode of Th_2, and, to keep this tube from firing, it is necessary to prevent the grid from becoming more than a few volts positive with respect to the cathode. The use of negative grid bias and the addition of capacitance between grid and cathode easily accomplishes this result.

Until thyratron Th_2 is triggered both the filter condenser and the network are charged to a voltage E_{bb}. When Th_2 is triggered, the pulse-forming network discharges through winding 5–6 of the pulse transformer, and a pulse of amplitude $E_{bb}/2$ again appears across R_l.

Although the circuit itself is very simple and flexible because any recurrence frequency that allows enough time for thyratron deionization is permissible, the auxiliary triggering circuit is complex.   One such circuit that has been operated successfully consists essentially of an electronic switch designed to operate at the shortest interpulse spacing required; its output causes two regenerative pulsers to operate in succession, triggering the thyratrons Th_1 and Th_2 alternately.

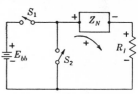

In general, the simplified equivalent circuit of Fig. 11·41 can be analyzed by the following equations.   Let the network voltage be zero when the switch S_1 is first closed.

Fig. 11·41.—Equivalent circuit for a double-switch single-network pulser.

The amplitude of the first pulse across the load is then

$$V_{l_1} = E_{bb} \frac{R_l}{R_l + Z_N},$$

and the voltage left on the network is

$$V_{N_1} = E_{bb} \frac{2Z_N}{R_l + Z_N}.$$

When switch S_2 is closed, the second pulse has an amplitude

$$V_{l_2} = -V_{N_1} \frac{R_l}{R_l + Z_N} = -E_{bb} \frac{R_l}{R_l + Z_N} \frac{2Z_N}{R_l + Z_N},$$

and the voltage left on the network is

$$V_{N_2} = -\frac{2Z_N}{R_l + Z_N} V_{N_1} + V_{N_1} = E_{bb} \frac{2Z_N}{R_l + Z_N} \left(1 - \frac{2Z_N}{R_l + Z_N}\right).$$

For simplicity, assume, as in Chap. 7, that

$$\kappa = \frac{R_l - Z_N}{R_l + Z_N}.$$

Then

$$1 - \kappa = \frac{2Z_N}{R_l + Z_N}$$

and

$$1 + \kappa = \frac{2R_l}{R_l + Z_N},$$

and the equations become

$$V_{l_1} = E_{bb} \frac{R_l}{R_l + Z_N} = \frac{E_{bb}}{2}(1 + \kappa),$$

$$V_{N_1} = E_{bb} \frac{2Z_N}{R_l + Z_N} = E_{bb}(1 - \kappa),$$

$$V_{l_2} = -\frac{E_{bb}}{2}(1 - \kappa)(1 + \kappa),$$

and

$$V_{N_2} = E_{bb}\kappa(1 - \kappa).$$

The third voltage pulse is

$$V_{l_3} = (E_{bb} - V_{N_2})\frac{1 + \kappa}{2} = \frac{E_{bb}}{2}[1 - \kappa(1 - \kappa)](1 + \kappa),$$

and the voltage left on the network after the third pulse is

$$V_{N_3} = (E_{bb} - V_{N_2})(1 - \kappa) + V_{N_2},$$

or

$$V_{N_3} = E_{bb}(1 - \kappa)(1 + \kappa^2).$$

The fourth pulse is given by

$$V_{l_4} = -V_{N_3}\frac{1 + \kappa}{2} = -\frac{E_{bb}}{2}(1 - \kappa)(1 + \kappa)(1 + \kappa^2),$$

and the voltage left on the network after the fourth pulse is

$$V_{N_4} = -V_{N_3}\frac{2Z_N}{R_l + Z_N} + V_{N_3} = E_{bb}\kappa(1 - \kappa)(1 + \kappa^2).$$

In general, for any pulse,

$$V_{l_{(2n)}} = -\frac{V_{N_{(2n-1)}}}{2}(1 + \kappa)$$

$$V_{l_{(2n+1)}} = \frac{E_{bb} - V_{N_{(2n)}}}{2}(1 + \kappa),$$

$$V_{N_{(2n)}} = \kappa V_{N_{(2n-1)}},$$

and

$$V_{N_{(2n+1)}} = (1 - \kappa)E_{bb} + \kappa V_{N_{(2n)}}.$$

These values can now be rewritten in the form of series as follows:

$$V_{l_{(2n)}} = -\frac{E_{bb}}{2}(1 + \kappa)(1 - \kappa)(1 + \kappa^2 + \kappa^4 + \cdots + \kappa^{2n-2}).$$

$$V_{l_{(2n+1)}} = \frac{E_{bb}}{2}(1 + \kappa)[1 - \kappa(1 - \kappa)(1 + \kappa^2 + \kappa^4 + \cdots + \kappa^{2n-2})].$$

$$V_{N_{(2n)}} = E_{bb}\kappa(1 - \kappa)(1 + \kappa^2 + \kappa^4 + \cdots + \kappa^{2n-2}).$$

$$V_{N_{(2n+1)}} = E_{bb}(1 - \kappa)(1 + \kappa^2 + \kappa^4 + \cdots + \kappa^{2n-2}).$$

Since κ is smaller than one, the series are all convergent and the equations can be rewritten

$$V_{l_{(2n)}} = -\frac{E_{bb}}{2}(1 + \kappa)\frac{1 - \kappa^{2n}}{1 + \kappa} = -\frac{E_{bb}}{2}(1 - \kappa^{2n}),$$

$$V_{l_{(2n+1)}} = \frac{E_{bb}}{2}(1 + \kappa)\left(1 - \kappa\frac{1 - \kappa^{2n}}{1 + \kappa}\right) = \frac{E_{bb}}{2}(1 + \kappa^{2n+1}),$$

$$V_{N_{(2n)}} = E_{bb}\kappa\frac{1 - \kappa^{2n}}{1 + \kappa},$$

and

$$V_{N(2n+1)} = E_{bb} \frac{1 - \kappa^{2n}}{1 + \kappa}.$$

As n increases, the value of κ^{2n} or κ^{2n+1} becomes rapidly negligible compared with one, and the voltage across the load becomes

$$V_l = \pm \frac{E_{bb}}{2},$$

the plus sign corresponding to odd pulses and the minus sign to even pulses. As has been explained before, a polarity reversal on alternate

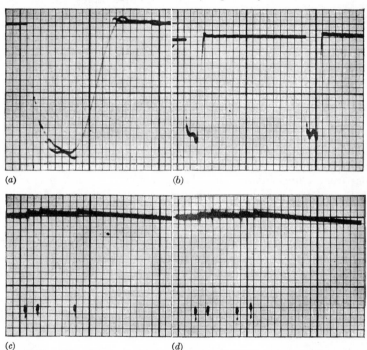

(a)   (b)

(c)   (d)

Fig. 11·42.—Pulse shapes obtained on a resistance load with multiple-switch single-network circuit. (a) Circuit arranged for single-pip operation with uniform interpulse intervals. (b) Circuit arranged for two-pip operation, (c) for three-pip operation, and (d) for four-pip operation.

pulses can easily be accomplished by the use of a pulse transformer. The network voltage at the end of the charging period is given by

$$V_N = E_{bb} \frac{1}{1 + \kappa},$$

and that at the end of the discharging period by

$$V_N = E_{bb} \frac{\kappa}{1 + \kappa}.$$

The applications of this circuit are not limited to obtaining coded pulses from line-type pulsers. Although it is equally well suited for the constant recurrence frequencies that are common in radar systems, its advantages become particularly impressive when the pulser is required to trigger at random intervals. As was pointed out before, the principal disadvantages are due to the complicated auxiliary circuits required for triggering the two tubes alternately, and to the precautions necessary to prevent the tubes from going into continuous conduction. It is believed, however, that where irregularly spaced high-power pulses are required these disadvantages are outweighed by the great flexibility of operation and the high efficiency. Oscillograms of pulse shapes obtained by this method are shown in Fig. 11·42. Figure 11·42*a* was taken for a single pulse in order to show the slight difference in pulse shape that results, in practice, from the charging or discharging of the network.

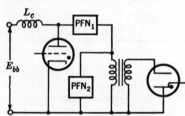

Fig. 11·43.—Circuit diagram for single-switch multiple-network pulser.

Single-switch Multiple-network Circuit.—The following circuit has been tried and found very successful in obtaining two very closely spaced pulses from a line-type pulser. The principle of operation is identical with that of a regular line-type pulser, but an open-ended delay line is connected in parallel with the load, as indicated in Fig. 11·43. Assume that δ_2, the delay time of PFN_2, is greater than δ_1, the delay time of PFN_1. When the thyratron is fired, a pulse appears across the load and the delay line. This pulse travels down the line and is reflected at the open end. After a time equal to $2\delta_2$, the reflected pulse appears at the load and gives a second signal.

Simple considerations indicate the conditions under which the two pulses have the same amplitude. The voltage amplitude of the first pulse is given by

$$V_{l_1} = V_{N_1} \frac{\dfrac{R_l Z_{N_2}}{R_l + Z_{N_2}}}{Z_{N_1} + \dfrac{R_l Z_{N_2}}{R_l + Z_{N_2}}},$$

and that of the second pulse is

$$V_{l_2} = a V_{l_1} \left(1 + \frac{R_l - Z_{N_2}}{R_l + Z_{N_2}} \right),$$

where

$$a = e^{-\alpha l},$$

α is the attenuation factor, and l is the length of the delay line. The two pulses that appear across the load have equal amplitude when

$$1 + \frac{R_l - Z_{N_2}}{R_l + Z_{N_2}} = \frac{1}{a},$$

or

$$Z_{N_2} = R_l(2a - 1).$$

To obtain matched conditions for the discharge of the pulse-forming network, PFN_1, the additional condition

$$Z_{N_1} = \frac{R_l Z_{N_2}}{R_l + Z_{N_2}} = R_l \frac{2a - 1}{a}$$

must be satisfied.

Some limitations of the system become obvious immediately. If $2a$ approaches 1, the values of Z_{N_1} and Z_{N_2} approach zero. The total attenuation of the line PFN_2 increases rapidly with the length of
the line, or the time delay between
pulses; hence, a limit on maximum
pulse separation is soon reached.
Figure 11·44 shows the similarity
between the two successive pulses
obtained by this method for a
delay time of approximately 3
μsec.

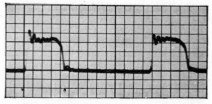

FIG. 11·44.—Oscillogram showing r-f envelope of pulses obtained wi h the circuit of
Fig. 11·43.

If, however, the time delay in PFN_2 is made less than half that in PFN_1, the wave reflected from the end of the delay line appears at the load before the main pulse is ended. If the delay line is open-circuited, the polarity of the reflected voltage is the same as that of the pulse already appearing across the load, and an increase in pulse amplitude results. If the delay line is short-circuited, the reflected voltage is of opposite polarity, and produces a decrease in the amplitude of the main pulse.

General Comparison.—The multiple-switch multiple-network circuit is the most flexible one that produces multiple pulses; there are almost no limitations on the spacings that can be obtained. The main disadvantage is the large number of components that are necessary because a complete pulser circuit is required for each pulse. The double-switch single-network circuit is almost as flexible as the multiple-switch multiple-network circuit, except that the minimum spacing between successive pulses is limited by the deionization time of the particular switch. This time can be decreased somewhat by operating the thyratrons at voltages and currents below the rated values. The main disadvantage of this circuit is the complex electronic switching circuit that is necessary to pulse the two switches alternately, and the necessity of having a power-supply voltage that is equal to the network voltage (instead of half this voltage, as is usually the case for d-c inductance charging). The high-insulation trigger transformers may also cause some difficulty, but some of these disadvantages are outweighed by the absence of any charging circuit.

The single-switch multiple-network circuit is the least flexible of the three. It has been described here because it represents a very simple method of obtaining two closely spaced pulses, or pulses of irregular step shape.

11·8. Multiple-switch Circuit for Voltage Multiplication.[1]—For high-power line-type pulsers having high-impedance networks, the voltages on the networks tend to become high, and may reach values of 50 kv or more. Such high voltages usually lead to engineering difficulties, and some form of impulse-voltage multiplication is therefore desirable. The Marx multiplier circuit may easily be adapted to this use. The basic circuit uses the Type A pulse-forming network and is shown in Fig. 11·45 for three-stage multiplication.

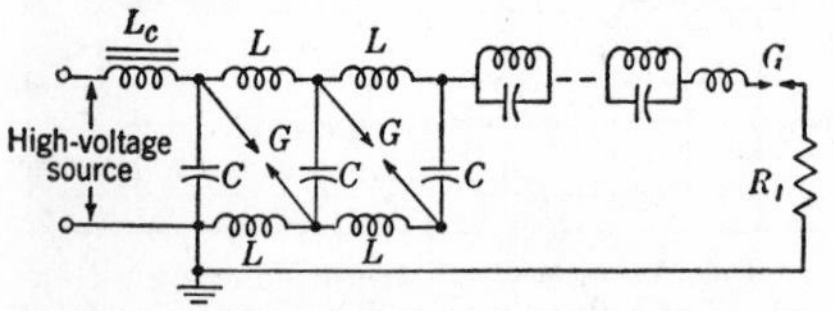

FIG. 11·45.—Three stage Marx circuit adapted to the line-type pulser for multiplication of pulse voltage.

The condensers C comprise the storage capacitance of the Type A network. Since these condensers are in series, each one must have a capacitance of nC_N, where n is the number of stages and C_N is the required capacitance for the network storage condenser. The voltage multiplication is obtained by charging the condensers in parallel and discharging them in series. In the ideal case, the voltage stepup ratio for an n-stage circuit is n. In practice, however, about 10 per cent of the voltage is usually lost because of currents flowing through the inductances L. The pulse discharge is initiated by firing the spark gaps G, which may, of course, be replaced by any other suitable switch. The isolating chokes L serve to prevent the condensers from being short-circuited through the gaps during the pulse.

It is clear that the isolating chokes L must have inductance that is sufficient to prevent an undue portion of the pulse current from being lost through them. An estimate of the required inductance may be made by calculating the circulating currents that flow during the discharge period. Some loss may also occur because of circulating currents if the gaps do not fire simultaneously. Under most conditions, however, the time lag in the firing of the gaps is less than the pulse duration τ, and the approximate calculation remains valid. Triggered switches

[1] By H. J. White.

such as thyratrons or fixed spark gaps usually have very small time lags. For the purpose of an approximate calculation, it is sufficiently accurate to consider the current flowing through one inductance L and one condenser C in series, the condenser being initially charged to a voltage V_N. The current is then

$$i_{LC} = V_N \sqrt{\frac{C}{L}} \sin \frac{t}{\sqrt{LC}}.$$

The period of the LC-circuit must be large compared with the pulse duration τ, and, on the basis of this assumption,

$$i_{LC} \approx V_N \sqrt{\frac{C}{L}} \cdot \frac{t}{\sqrt{LC}} = \frac{V_N t}{L}.$$

The maximum value that i_{LC} could have during the pulse if the condenser were not otherwise discharged is

$$(i_{LC})_{\max} = \frac{V_N \tau}{L},$$

and the pulse current in the load is given by

$$I_l = \frac{n V_N}{2 Z_N}.$$

Eliminating V_N between these two equations, the expression for L is found to be

$$L = \frac{2 Z_N \tau}{n \left[\dfrac{(i_{LC})_{\max}}{I_l} \right]}.$$

As an example of the order of magnitude of L, let

$$Z_N = 1000 \text{ ohms}, \qquad \tau = 10^{-6} \text{ sec}, \qquad n = 3, \qquad \frac{(i_{LC})_{\max}}{I_l} = 0.01.$$

Then

$$L = \frac{2 \times 1000 \times 10^{-6}}{3 \times 0.01} = 67 \text{ mh.}$$

Experimental data on the effect of the isolating-choke inductance on the current efficiency are given in Fig. 11·46 for a two-stage circuit. Current efficiency is defined as the ratio of n times the average load current to the input average current, where n is the number of stages, or $2(I_{l_{\mathrm{av}}}/I_{c_{\mathrm{av}}})$. If there were no circulating currents in the isolating chokes, the current efficiency, by Kirchhoff's law, would be 100 per cent.

Unequal storage-condenser capacitances C also cause circulating currents, which produce losses in the gaps and the condensers as well as in the chokes. The isolating chokes usually have an iron core, and, for high-power circuits, they can be mounted conveniently in the tank of the pulse-forming network.

A variation of the circuit of Fig. 11·45 that is particularly applicable to the two-stage Marx circuit is shown in Fig. 11·47. Here the highest

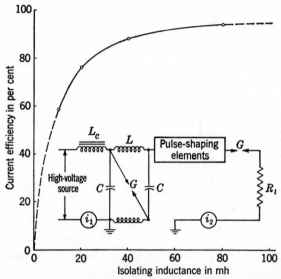

Fig. 11·46.—Effect of isolating inductance in the Marx circuit on the current efficiency.

voltage to ground at any instant is equal to the load pulse voltage, and the problem of insulation is therefore simpler than that imposed by the original circuit. The rotary spark gap can easily be adapted for use as the switch in a Marx circuit by mounting the rotating electrodes on an

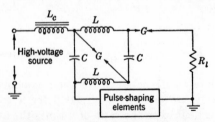

Fig. 11·47.—Variation of the Marx circuit to reduce voltages to ground.

insulating rotor and using one set of fixed electrodes for each gap required. An n-stage Marx circuit would have n sets of fixed electrodes. The gaps come simultaneously into firing position, and very smooth operation is obtained when the switch is well built.

PART III

PULSE TRANSFORMERS

CHAPTER 12

ELEMENTARY THEORY OF PULSE TRANSFORMERS

By W. H. Bostick

12·1 General Transformer Theory.—Of the devices that have been developed for the transformation of energy and power the electromagnetic transformer, which changes the ratio of voltage and current while maintaining their product constant, has proved one of the most useful. Electromagnetic transformers in general and pulse transformers in particular have been used—

1. To transfer or control energy by raising a voltage above a threshold or barrier level.
2. To invert the sign of voltage.
3. To effect "d-c isolation" between source and load.
4. To deliver the correct amount of power to a load of a given resistance by changing the voltage to the proper value.
5. To effect maximum transfer of energy (or power) from source to load by a transformation of energy to the proper impedance level.

It is possible to conceive of a perfect electromagnetic transformer (see page 504 of Sec. 12·1) which would operate successfully over any range of frequency, impedance, and power levels. For various reasons, which are discussed later, such a perfect transformer cannot be built. Any transformer that can be built has certain limitations in its range of operation and should be designed to give optimum performance under the conditions of operation for which it is intended.

Many different types of transformers have been developed to perform the many functions and to cover the various ranges of operation of electromagnetic transformers. For example, there are filament and "power" transformers, which operate steadily on a sinusoidal input at the various standard power frequencies and voltages. There are audio transformers, which are designed to operate over the audible range of frequencies, some at high-power levels and others at low-power levels. There are r-f transformers, which, when used in the circuits for which they are intended, pass only a narrow frequency band of r-f energy.

The development of pulsed radar created a need for a relatively new type of transformer—a transformer that transforms the energy in a pulse having a more or less rectangular shape and a duration of the order of magnitude of 1 μsec.

In general, such pulse transformers are used to perform any or all of the functions listed at the beginning of this chapter. One individual pulse transformer is often used over a fairly wide range of pulse durations, voltages, and impedances.

Pulse transformers are also used extensively (usually at low power) in one type of pulse-generating circuit, the regenerative pulse generator or blocking oscillator, in which energy is introduced from the plate to the grid circuit so that the polarity of the voltage is inverted and regeneration occurs. Transformers designed for regenerative pulse generators frequently have extra windings that can be used to transfer power to other circuits.

Pulse transformers are effectively used as interstage coupling and inverting devices in pulse and video amplifiers. These transformers usually operate at medium or low power.[1]

Perhaps the most important use of pulse transformers, however, has been the transformation of the energy in a pulse from a pulse generator to the impedance level of an r-f oscillator, which is frequently a magnetron. The pulse-power level at which these output transformers operate is usually between 10 kw and 10 Mw, and it is these transformers with which Part III of this book is primarily concerned.

Discussions of the properties of pulse transformers, the problems of their design, and the use of materials in their design are found in Chaps. 12, 13, 14, and 15.

Since one of the most important functional uses of a transformer is the matching of the impedances of the source and the load, it is well to review the facts relating to the maximum power transfer from source to load.

Maximum Power Transfer in the Steady State.—When a system is being energized steadily at a given frequency, the power absorbed by the load is $I_{rms}^2 R_l$, where

$$I_{rms}^2 = \frac{\int_0^t ie\,dt}{R_l t},$$

i and e are respectively the current in and the voltage across the load, and R_l is the load resistance. Maximum power transfer from source to load obtains when the value of $I_{rms}^2 R_l$ is a maximum.

If the load impedance is fixed, it may easily be shown that the maximum power transfer for the steady state occurs when—

---

[1] For a discussion of low-power pulse transformers see F. N. Moody, "A Treatise on the Design of Pulse Transformers for Handling Small Powers," TRE Technical Monograph 5A.

1. The reactive components of the source and load impedances are equal in magnitude and opposite in sign.
2. The resistive component of the source impedance is kept to a minimum.

If the source impedance is fixed, maximum power transfer for the steady state occurs when—

1. The reactive components of the source and load impedances are equal in magnitude and opposite in sign.
2. The resistive component of the load impedance is *equal* to that of the source impedance.

The condition that the reactances of load and source should be equal in magnitude and opposite in sign is merely the condition for which, on the average or at the respective peak values, the energy stored in the source reactance is equal to the energy stored in the load reactance.

This fact is easily recognized when a simple system such as that whose equivalent circuit is shown in Fig. 12·1 is considered. The peak "kinetic" or inductive energy stored in this system is $\frac{1}{2}L_G I_{peak}^2$, and the peak potential or capacitive energy is $\frac{1}{2}I_{peak}^2/(\omega^2 C_l)$. These two energies are equal when $L_G = 1/(\omega^2 C_l)$, which is the condition for which the reactances of source and load are equal and opposite, and therefore, as previously mentioned, a condition for maximum power transfer from source to load.

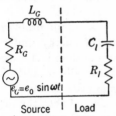

FIG. 12·1.—Simple source-load system that may be used to demonstrate the thermodynamical relationship involved in the problem of the maximum transfer of power in the steady state.

By a process of reasoning formally analogous to that used in thermodynamics, this source-load system may be considered to possess two degrees of freedom. One degree of freedom may be considered to result from the kinetic energy, the other degree from the potential energy, as in a solid made up of one-dimensional linear oscillators.[1] The "equilibrium thermodynamical state," or the lowest energy state of this system, may then be considered to occur when there is, on the average, equipartition of energy between these two degrees of freedom.[2] Thus, by way of this thermodynamical analogue, it may be stated that both the lowest energy state and the maximum transfer of energy are achieved, as far as the reactances are concerned, when the designer of the circuit makes the proper choice of C_l if L_G is fixed, or of L_G if C_l is fixed, or of transformation ratio if a transformer is available (see p. 504).

---

[1] The theorem of the equipartition of energy is usually applied to a system containing many particles or oscillators. In the formal analogue here suggested, however, it is being applied to only one oscillator.

[2] See G. Joos, *Theoretical Physics*, Stechert, New York, 1934, p. 560.

As already indicated, the resistances of the system should be chosen to give a maximum transfer of energy from the source from which the energy is available to the load in which it is dissipated.[1]

Although this process of reasoning by thermodynamical analogue may seem irrelevant and trivial, it proves useful in designing a pulse transformer that stores a minimum of energy in itself and transfers maximum pulse energy to the load. This process of reasoning may also prove useful in the design of transformers of other types inasmuch as its conclusions predict the general shape, size, maximum flux density, and number of turns resulting from good present-day audio-, video-, and pulse-transformer design practice.

It is difficult to state the general conditions for maximum energy transfer in an arbitrary time for load and source systems containing arbitrary arrangements of mass, stiffness, and resistance (or inductance, capacitance, and resistance). This difficulty exists because it is impossible to characterize accurately the behavior of such a set of circuit elements under transient conditions by a concept as simple as that of impedance.

A simple problem in determining the conditions for maximum transfer of energy under transient conditions in a frictionless, gravitationless system is, for example, a man of mass M_G who is capable of exerting an impulse $f\tau$ and wishes to impart maximum kinetic energy to a load of mass M_l by means of a transformer of adjustable force ratio n. It is assumed that the man must move his own mass in imparting motion to the load mass, and also that he has at his disposal no elements having compliance. It can easily be shown that the velocity attained by the load is

$$u_l = \frac{f n \tau}{M_G n^2 + M_l},$$

and that the kinetic energy of the load is

$$\frac{1}{2} M_l \left(\frac{f n \tau}{M_G n^2 + M_l} \right)^2.$$

It is desired to maximize the kinetic energy imparted to the load with respect to n. Thus,

$$\frac{d}{dn} \left(\frac{f n \tau}{M_G n^2 + M_l} \right)^2 = 0, \qquad \text{or} \qquad \frac{d}{dn} \left(\frac{n}{M_G n^2 + M_l} \right)^2 = 0.$$

The roots of this equation are

---

[1] Such a choice of resistance may be considered, from the point of view of the thermodynamical analogue, to effect a maximum rate of degradation of energy from source to load.

$$n = 0,$$

and

$$n = \sqrt{\frac{M_l}{M_G}},$$

the latter of which gives a maximum for the kinetic energy and has physical significance. Thus, maximum transfer of energy in this example occurs when the masses of the source and the load, referred to the same side of the transformer, are equal, and when the kinetic energies of source mass and load mass are equal. If the thermodynamical analogue is again invoked, the kinetic energies of source and load may be considered to be proportional to the "temperatures" of the source and the load. For maximum transfer of energy these temperatures are equal and therefore constant throughout the system. Constancy of temperature throughout an isolated system is, however, one of the properties of the state of lowest energy.[1]

The choice of source and load resistance for the maximum transfer of energy to a resistive load under transient conditions is similar to that under steady-state conditions.

From the foregoing examples employing a formal analogy with thermodynamics the general conclusion may be drawn that devices which transfer maximum energy from source to load, under either transient or steady-state conditions, are so designed that the elements of the system in which energy is stored are in a state of thermodynamical equilibrium or lowest energy.

The general conclusion concerning the state of lowest energy and the examples on which the conclusion is based are used in Sec. 13·2 as a plausibility argument to justify the assertion that a pulse transformer should be designed in such a way that the electromagnetic-energy densities of core and coil are approximately equal.

The General Equivalent Circuit for a Transformer.—Electromagnetic power is equal to the product of voltage and current (or more precisely $\mathbf{E} \times \mathbf{H}$), but the form or impedance level of the electromagnetic power is characterized by the ratio of voltage and current.

In considering the basic relationships involved in the transformation of electromagnetic power, it is often useful to introduce the concept of the perfect transformer. A transformation of power wherein no energy is stored or lost in the transformer is considered to be brought about by a perfect transformer. A perfect transformer is represented schematically

---

[1] In this particular case there is only one degree of freedom since there is no energy being stored as potential energy, and therefore considerations of equipartition of energy between two degrees of freedom have no significance.

504   *ELEMENTARY THEORY OF PULSE TRANSFORMERS*   [Sec. 12·1

in Fig. 12·2, where e_1 and i_1 may be any functions of time. In such a perfect transformer, energy and power are transferred immediately from input to output, that is,

$$e_1 i_1 = e_2 i_2,$$
$$e_2 = n e_1,$$

and

$$i_2 = \frac{i_1}{n}.$$

A perfect transformer reproduces at the output any voltage and current at the input, except for a factor n or $1/n$.

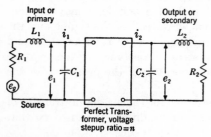

Fig. 12·2.—A source-load system employing a perfect transformer.

It is often convenient to refer circuit elements that are connected to the primary to the impedance level of the secondary, and vice versa. For example, calculations may be simplified by removing R_2 from the secondary side of the circuit in Fig. 12·2 and placing in the primary a resistance R_2' of such value that the energy and power relationships of the complete circuit are unaltered. Thus,

$$i_1^2 R_2' = i_2^2 R_2,$$

or

$$R_2' = \frac{R_2}{n^2}.$$

Furthermore,

$$\tfrac{1}{2} C_2' e_1^2 = \tfrac{1}{2} C_2 e_2^2,$$

or

$$C_2' = n^2 C_2.$$

Also

$$\tfrac{1}{2} L_2' i_1^2 = \tfrac{1}{2} L_2 i_2^2,$$

or

$$L_2' = \frac{1}{n^2} L_2.$$

If the system is energized at a constant frequency, for a source and a load of impedances Z_1 and Z_2 respectively,

$$Z_2' = \frac{Z_2}{n^2}.$$

If R_1' is defined as R_1 referred to the secondary,

$$R_1' = n^2 R_1,$$

$$C_1' = \frac{C_1}{n^2},$$

$$L_1' = n^2 L_1,$$

and

$$Z_1' = n^2 Z_1.$$

In describing the properties of an actual electromagnetic transformer it is customary to employ the lumped quantities L_1, L_2, and M, which are, respectively, the self inductances of coils 1 and 2, and the mutual

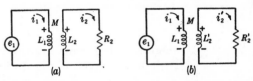

Fig. 12·3.—(*a*) Circuit illustrating the transfer and transformation of power from source to load by means of the mutual inductance M and the circuit elements L_1 and L_2. (*b*) The equivalent of the circuit shown in (*a*).

inductance shown in Fig. 12·3. Kirchhoff's voltage-law equations for the two loops of the circuit shown in Fig. 12·3 are

$$L_1 \frac{di_1}{dt} - M \frac{di_2}{dt} = e_1$$

$$-M \frac{di_1}{dt} + \left(L_2 \frac{d}{dt} + R_2\right) i_2 = 0.$$

If $i_2' = n i_2$,

$$L_1 \frac{di_1}{dt} - \frac{M}{n} \frac{di_2'}{dt} = e_1,$$

and

$$-\frac{M}{n} \frac{di_1}{dt} + \left(\frac{L_2}{n^2} \frac{d}{dt} + \frac{R_2}{n^2}\right) i_2' = 0.$$

These last two expressions are the Kirchhoff voltage-law equations for the circuit shown in Fig. 12·3*b*, where $M_1 = M/n$, $L_2' = L_2/n^2$, and $R_2' = R_2/n^2$. The mutual inductance M referred to the secondary of the transformer is

$$M_2 = n^2 M_1 = nM.$$

If suitable additions to and subtractions from the last two equations are performed, there results

$$(L_1 - M_1) \frac{di_1}{dt} + M_1 \frac{d}{dt}(i_1 - i_2'') = e_1,$$

and

$$\left[(L_2' - M_1)\frac{d}{dt} + R_2'\right] i_2' + M_1 \frac{d}{dt}(i_2' - i_1) = 0,$$

which are Kirchhoff's voltage-law equations for the two loops of the equivalent circuit shown in Fig. 12·4a. Equations identical in form can be written in which all elements are referred to the secondary; the equivalent circuit derived therefrom is given in Fig. 12·4b.

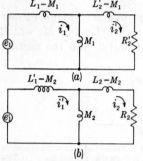

If L_1 and L_2 are wound close together on the same core (as they are in nearly all pulse transformers),

$$L_1 \approx \frac{L_2}{n^2} = L_2',$$

where n is the turns ratio of the two coils. Then, in the circuit of Fig. 12·4a,

$$L_1 - M_1 \approx L_2' - M_1.$$

Fig. 12·4.—Circuits equivalent to those shown in Fig. 12.3.

The inductance $2(L_1 - M_1)$, customarily termed "the leakage inductance," is a series inductance in the equivalent circuit through which the load current in R_2' must flow.

It is customary to define the constant k that is called the "coupling coefficient" by the following equation:

$$k = \frac{M}{\sqrt{L_1 L_2}} \approx \frac{M_1}{L_1} \approx \frac{M_2}{L_2}.$$

Thus for most pulse transformers the shunt inductance referred to the primary is $M_1 \approx kL_1$, and referred to the secondary is $M_2 \approx kL_2$; the leakage inductance referred to the primary is

$$2(L_1 - M_1) = 2L_1(1 - k),$$

and referred to the secondary is

$$2(L_2 - M_2) = 2L_2(1 - k).$$

If $2(L_1 - M_1) = 0$ (that is, the leakage inductance is zero), or, what is the same thing, if $k = 1$, a condition known as "perfect coupling" obtains. Under such circumstances there can be no magnetic energy stored anywhere in or about the transformer by the load current in either the primary or the secondary. Hence any magnetic flux associated with the primary load current must be negated completely by flux associated with the secondary load current. Literature on transformers usually defines the condition wherein $k = 1$ as that in which all the flux associated with the current in the primary links the secondary, and vice versa.

Transformers always have a certain amount of distributed capacitance between primary and secondary; to a first approximation the equivalent circuit for a transformer with distributed capacitance is shown in Fig. 12·5a, where C is some suitably chosen fraction of the total capacitance between the primary and the secondary. The equivalent circuit shown in Fig. 12·5b, in which all elements are referred to the primary winding, is an approximation to that shown in Fig. 12·5a. It can be shown by an application of Eqs. (6) and (7) of Sec. 12·2 that the capacitance C_2', which

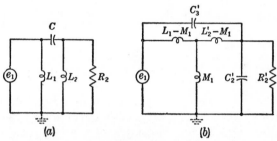

FIG. 12·5.—(a) Equivalent circuit representing the effect of distributed capacitance along the transformer winding. (b) Circuit approximately equivalent to that shown in (a).

accounts for the energy stored in C when the voltage stepup ratio n is different from 1, is given by

$$C_2' = (n - 1)^2 C = \frac{(n - 1)^2}{3} C_o,$$

where C_o is the d-c capacitance between primary and secondary, when the transformer has a single-layer primary winding and a single-layer secondary winding whose adjacent ends are connected. When the opposite ends of the two windings are connected,

$$C_2' = (n - 1)^2 C = \frac{(n^2 - n + 1)}{3} C_o.$$

The capacitance C_3', which accounts for the current that can flow directly from the source to the load without traversing the leakage inductance and for the capacitive energy stored when a voltage is developed across the leakage inductance, is given approximately by $C_3' = C$. From the foregoing expressions for C_2' and C_3' it is evident that when $0 < n < 1$, C_3' is large and C_2' is relatively unimportant, but that when $n \gg 1$ or $n \ll 0$, C_2' becomes large and C_3' is relatively unimportant.

Usually the core and case of the pulse transformer are grounded, as indicated in Figs. 12·5 and 12·6, and one terminal of the primary and one of the secondary are grounded. Consequently, there is usually some stray capacitance of the secondary winding to ground, and this capacitance may be lumped into C_2', which will now be called C_D' (or C_D when referred to the high-voltage winding which is usually the secondary). There is also stray capacitance of the primary winding to ground, and this capacitance may be represented by C_C (see Fig. 12·6).

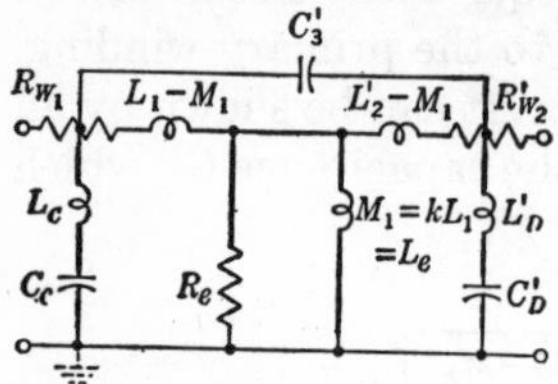

FIG. 12·6.—Approximate equivalent circuit for most nonperfect electromagnetic transformers.

Furthermore, even when C_D' is charged by application of voltage to the secondary (or C_C by application of voltage to the primary), the charging current has associated with it a magnetic field, and the energy in this field may be taken into account by the insertion of the inductances L_D' and L_C, through which the charging currents must flow, in the circuit of Fig. 12·6. (See Sec. 12·2.)

The effect of the winding resistance can be taken into account by the insertion of resistances R_{w_1} and R_{w_2} in the circuit of Fig. 12·6.

Finally, the effect of the dissipation of energy in the core of the transformer may be taken into account approximately by the insertion of R_e.

The lumped-parameter circuit of Fig. 12·6 is then, to a good approximation, the equivalent circuit for most nonperfect electrical transformers.

Equivalent Circuit of a Pulse Transformer.—From the phenomenological point of view, the generator e_1 shown in Fig. 12·3 can be considered to be a pulse generator having internal resistance R_G and producing a voltage pulse $e(t)$ that remains different from zero for a time that is short compared with the time between pulses. The usual problem is to design a pulse transformer that will transform the energy in this pulse to the proper impedance level with a minimum amount of energy absorbed or stored in the pulse transformer, and therefore with a maximum amount of pulse energy transferred to the load and a minimum distortion of the pulse shape. It is evident from the circuit of Fig. 12·6 that, in order to accomplish this purpose, the designer should strive to make the shunt inductances and resistances high, the shunt capacitances low, and the series resistances and inductances low.

From a more general point of view, a pulse is a spatial concentration of electromagnetic energy that is in the process of being propagated, the mode of propagation being determined by the disposition of conductors in the vicinity of the pulse. The pulse-transformer designer attempts to design a device that will change the ratio of $\dfrac{|\mathbf{E}|}{|\mathbf{H}|}$ in this concentration of electromagnetic energy with a minimum increase in the entropy of the system (excluding resistance load).   Such a device must be so constructed that, at the end of the pulse, it is in a state of energy lower than that of any other device that could possibly be built.

A method whereby an optimum set of values for the circuit elements of Fig. 12·6 can be chosen to effect a maximum transfer of energy, and a method whereby a transformer can be designed so that these values are achieved, are given in Chap. 13.   Methods of calculating and measuring the values of these circuit elements for a given transformer are described in Sec. 12·2.

Pulse transformers are used, however, in many special circuits and applications where the pulse shape, and not the maximum transfer of energy, is the primary consideration.   Often, for example, certain limits are placed upon the rate of rise, the percentage of droop throughout the pulse, and the shape and magnitude of the backswing voltage.   Frequently, especially at low-power levels, pulse transformers (for example, trigger transformers) and differentiation transformers[1] are purposefully designed to distort the pulse shape extensively in a particular manner. If it is desired to shape a pulse with a transformer, it is necessary to investigate the effect on pulse shape of the various parameters in the equivalent circuit of a pulse transformer, a discussion of which is given in Chap. 14.

The circuit of Fig. 12·6 has too many elements to be of practical value, and therefore it is well to try to eliminate or combine some of these elements.   For a pulse transformer designed to deliver 11-kv pulses of 0.5- to 2.0-μsec duration to a load of 1250-ohm impedance, and for which $n = 5$, the following values (all referred to the secondary) achieved in practice are typical:

$$R'_{w1} + R_{w_2} \approx 0.5 \text{ ohm,}$$

which is negligible compared with R_2 and R'_1.

$$L_2 = 25 \times 10^{-3} \text{ henrys.}$$
$$L_L = 2(L_2 - M_2) = 50 \times 10^{-6} \text{ henrys.}$$

Then

$$k = \frac{M}{L_1 L_2} = \frac{M_2}{L_2} = 1 - \frac{L_L}{2L_2} = 1 - \frac{0.025 \times 10^{-3}}{25 \times 10^{-3}},$$

or

$$k = 1 - 0.001 = 0.999,$$

and

$$M = kL_1 \approx L_1.$$

Also

$$C_D = 40 \ \mu\mu\text{f,}$$
$$C_3 = 0.10 \ \mu\mu\text{f,}$$

[1] Moody, *op. cit.*

and

$$C_C' = 0.50 \ \mu\mu f.$$

Therefore C_3 and C_C' may be neglected in comparison with C_D.

From the foregoing discussion it is evident that a suitable approximation for the equivalent circuit of such a voltage-stepup pulse transformer is that of Fig. 12·7. Since the emphasis of the

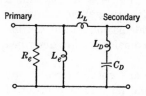

FIG. 12·7.—Approximate equivalent circuit for a pulse transformer.

discussion in Part III is on high-power pulse transformers, which are, for the most part, stepup transformers, the circuit of Fig. 12·7 is used and is discussed extensively in Chaps. 12, 13, and 14. For voltage-stepdown transformers (that is, for $0 < n < 1$, or for $n \approx 1$, the equivalent circuit of Fig. 12·6 may again be simplified, but C_3' should be retained, and in some instances it may prove necessary to

retain C_C. For pulse transformers where L_L becomes appreciable with respect to L_e ($= kL_1$) it is necessary to use the equivalent circuit of Fig. 12·4 or that of Fig. 12·6.

12·2. Values of Elements in the Equivalent Circuit.—The elements in the simplified equivalent circuit shown in Fig. 12·7 can be calculated from the geometrical constants of the transformer, the dielectric constant of the insulation, and the permeability of the core material. Various methods of measuring these elements have been developed.

Primary Inductance.—If the core is in the form of a toroid and if the effective pulse permeability of the core during operation is assumed to be a constant, μ_e (see Sec. 15·1), R_e, and L_e in the equivalent circuit shown in Fig. 12·7 may be supplanted by one inductance L_p, which is called the primary inductance. Then

$$L_p = \frac{4\pi}{10^9} \frac{N^2 A \mu_e}{l} \qquad \text{henrys},$$

where N is the number of turns, A is the cross-sectional area in square centimeters, and l is the mean magnetic-path length in centimeters.

If a more precise evaluation of the performance of the core is desired and R_e and L_e are used instead of L_p in the equivalent circuit shown in Fig. 12·7, and if μ is the d-c permeability (see Sec. 15·1, Fig. 15·2) which is effective over the range of operation of the core, the values of L_e and R_e as defined in Sec. 15·1 are

$$L_e = \frac{4\pi N^2 A \mu}{10^9 l} \qquad \text{henrys} \qquad (15·29)$$

and

$$R_e = \frac{12 N^2 A \rho}{d^2 l}, \qquad (15·30)$$

where ρ is the resistivity of the core material in ohm-centimeters, and d is the thickness of the lamination in centimeters.

A still more precise equivalent circuit for the core is a ladder network of LR-rungs, infinite in number, but this circuit is too complex to be of any practical use and, therefore, either the L_e and R_e parallel elements or the L_p element in the equivalent circuit is used to represent the core.

Measurement of L_p, or of L_e and R_e, is performed by applying the voltage pulse from a pulse generator to the primary or secondary terminals of the transformer (with the other terminals open-circuited) in such a way as to simulate the actual operating conditions of the transformer with regard to voltage, pulse duration, and reverse current, and by measuring the exciting current i_m on a synchroscope as shown in Fig. 12·8.

In general, the shape of the trace may be approximated by the sum of a rectangle and a triangle, if the initial oscillations are neglected, and the

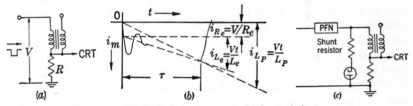

FIG. 12·8.—Method of measurement of primary inductance.

effective shunt resistance R_e and inductance L_e may be determined as shown in Fig. 12·8. However, if $R_e > 10L_e/\tau$, i_{R_e}, for practical purposes, is negligible in comparison with i_{L_e} at $t = \tau$. The effect of L_e and R_e may then be approximated by the primary inductance L_p, determined as shown in Fig. 12·8b.

If the transformer is rated to operate with a reverse current between pulses, the circuit shown in Fig. 12·8c must be used in the measurement of L_p (or L_e and R_e), and the pulse generator should be of approximately the same design as the one with which the transformer is to be used.

Leakage Inductance.—Formulas for the calculation of leakage inductance for coils of almost all shapes and types may be obtained from many different sources. This discussion of leakage inductance is confined to windings of the type commonly used in power-output pulse transformers.

Most pulse transformers for regenerative pulse generators and interstage work have very simple single-layer, noninterconnected windings, and the calculation of the leakage inductance is very simple. However, many of the pulse transformers that have been evolved have been used to pulse the cathode of an oscillator tube. To accomplish this purpose several different types of winding arrangement have been used.

In order to simplify the measurement of oscillator current, the secondary windings of output transformers are isolated from the primary windings with respect to direct current. Furthermore, in order to supply the oscillator filament current through the pulse transformer from a low-voltage-insulated filament transformer, two secondary windings that are isolated from each other with respect to direct current are provided. The two secondaries are identical and are usually separated from each other by a minimum amount of insulation; thus they are closely coupled as far as pulses are concerned. A portion of each secondary winding equal to the primary in number of turns may be placed near the primary winding in a similar fashion; the resultant close coupling makes such a transformer the equivalent of an autotransformer for pulse conditions.

The simplest type of winding consists of a one-layer primary (low-voltage) winding and a one-layer secondary (high-voltage) winding. A second type consists of a one-layer primary and a secondary broken into two equal layers, both outside the primary. (Or, the secondary may be broken into three or more layers.) A third general type consists of a primary interleaved between two equal layers of a secondary. Two two-layer coils can be put on the two legs of a transformer, and (1) the primaries and secondaries both connected in parallel, (2) the primaries and secondaries both connected in series, or (3) the primaries connected in parallel and the secondaries in series. Two-leg variations on the second and third general type can also be constructed. Each of the above winding arrangements can be constructed as an isolation (or "iso") or an "auto" version (that is, iso or auto for pulse operation).

The calculation of leakage inductance as a lumped parameter follows the process of reasoning wherein a given amount of load current I is assumed to be flowing in the coils and the total magnetic energy resulting from this load current is computed and equated to $\frac{1}{2}L_LI^2$. In computing the leakage inductance of a transformer on this basis the first example to be considered is a transformer with a one-layer primary and a one-layer secondary of equal length. Since the primary and secondary ampere-turns are approximately equal in magnitude, and since the currents flow in opposite directions around the core, the field between the two winding layers is very nearly equal to that within a solenoid having the same number of ampere-turns. Since the length of the coil is usually large in comparison with the distance between layers, the solenoid may be considered infinite in length, and practically all of the energy in its magnetic field may be considered to be inside the solenoid. Such a solenoid produces the interlayer field distribution shown in Fig. 12·9b, since $\mu = 1$ both in and between the winding layers.

Actually, the current density is not uniform across the layer thickness. Two extreme conditions of current distribution in the wire that might be

used for purposes of computation are (1) the condition where the current is concentrated in two very thin layers, one at the outside of the inside winding layer, and the other at the inside of the outside winding layer,
and (2) the condition where the current is concentrated in a very thin layer at the center of each winding layer. The first extreme gives a factor of 0 in the last term of Eq. 12·1, and the second a factor of $\frac{1}{2}$, instead of the factor of $\frac{1}{3}$ obtained in the following discussion in which a uniform distribution is assumed. Since the conditions usually encountered in pulse transformers lie between these two extremes, and since the layer thickness is usually much smaller than the distance between layers, the assumption of uniform distribution does not produce much error.

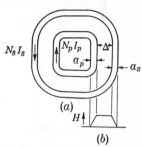

Fig. 12·9.—Distributions of the magnetic field between the primary and secondary winding layers for a simple winding.

The magnitude of H in oersteds (and therefore of B in gauss) is given by the following expressions:

In the primary: $H_1 = \dfrac{4\pi N_p I_p}{\mathcal{L}} \dfrac{x_p}{a_p} = \dfrac{4\pi N_s I_s}{\mathcal{L}} \dfrac{x_p}{a_p}$ oersteds, where x_p is measured from the side of the primary next to the core; a_p is the thickness of the primary layer in cm; N_p is the number of turns on the primary, N_s on the secondary; I_p is the primary current in abamperes, I_s is the secondary current; $\mathcal{L}$ is the winding length in cm.

Between layers: $H_2 = \dfrac{4\pi N_s I_s}{\mathcal{L}}.$

In the secondary: $H_3 = \dfrac{4\pi N_s I_s}{\mathcal{L}}\left(1 - \dfrac{x_s}{a_s}\right),$ where x_s is measured from the inside of the secondary.

The energy in a magnetic field in air ($\mu = 1$) is given by

$$W = \frac{H^2}{8\pi} \text{ ergs/cm}^3,$$

where H is in oersteds. Therefore, the energy stored in the leakage field is given by

$$W = \frac{\mathfrak{u}\mathcal{L}}{8\pi}\left(\int_0^{a_p} H_1^2\, dx_p + H_2^2\Delta + \int_0^{a_s} H_3^2\, dx_s\right)$$

$$= \frac{\mathfrak{u}\mathcal{L}}{8\pi}\left(\frac{4\pi N_s I_s}{\mathcal{L}}\right)^2\left[\int_0^{a_p}\frac{x_p^2}{a_p^2}\, dx_p + \Delta + \int_0^{a_s}\left(1 - \frac{x_s}{a_s}\right)^2 dx_s\right]$$

$$= \frac{2\pi N_s^2 I_s^2 \mathfrak{u}}{\mathcal{L}}\left(\Delta + \frac{\Sigma a}{3}\right),$$

where $\mathfrak{u}$ is the average circumference of the layers in centimeters, Δ is the distance between layers in centimeters, and Σa is the sum of the thicknesses of the layers. Since the energy stored in an inductance is given by $W = \frac{1}{2}LI^2$, the following equation may be solved for the leakage inductance, referred to the secondary:

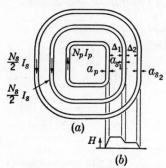

$$\frac{1}{2}L_L I_s^2 = \frac{2\pi N_s^2 I_s^2 \mathfrak{u}}{\mathfrak{L}}\left(\Delta + \frac{\Sigma a}{3}\right).$$

From this equation,

$$L_L = \frac{4\pi N_s^2 \mathfrak{u}}{\mathfrak{L}}\left(\Delta + \frac{\Sigma a}{3}\right) \qquad \text{abhenrys.} \quad (1)$$

Fig. 12·10.—Distribution of the magnetic field for a coil with a single-layer primary and a double-layer secondary winding.

The second example to be considered is a transformer with a one-layer primary and a secondary composed of two equal layers, as shown in Fig. 12·10. The flux distribution is shown in Fig. 12·10b, and the magnitude of H is given by the following expressions:

In primary: $H_1 = \dfrac{4\pi N_p I_p}{\mathfrak{L}}\dfrac{x_p}{a_p} = \dfrac{4\pi N_s I_s}{\mathfrak{L}}\dfrac{x_p}{a_p}.$

In first interlayer space: $H_2 = \dfrac{4\pi N_s I_s}{\mathfrak{L}}.$

In first secondary layer: $H_3 = \dfrac{4\pi N_s I_s}{2\mathfrak{L}}\left(2 - \dfrac{x_{s_1}}{a_{s_1}}\right).$

In second interlayer space: $H_4 = \dfrac{4\pi N_s I_s}{2\mathfrak{L}}.$

In second secondary layer: $H_5 = \dfrac{4\pi N_s I_s}{2\mathfrak{L}}\left(1 - \dfrac{x_{s_2}}{a_{s_2}}\right).$

In these expressions x_p, x_{s_1}, x_{s_2} are measured from the inside of the primary, and of the first secondary and second secondary layers, respectively.

The energy in the field is given by

$$W = \frac{\mathfrak{u}\mathfrak{L}}{8\pi}\left(\int_0^{a_p} H_1^2\,dx_p + H_2^2\Delta_1 + \int_0^{a_{s_1}} H_3^2\,dx_{s_1} + H_4^2\Delta_2 + \int_0^{a_{s_2}} H_5^2\,dx_{s_2}\right)$$

$$= \frac{2\pi N_s^2 I_s^2 \mathfrak{u}}{\mathfrak{L}}\left(\frac{a_p}{3} + \Delta_1 + \frac{7a_{s_1}}{12} + \frac{\Delta_2}{4} + \frac{a_{s_2}}{12}\right)$$

$$= \frac{2\pi N_s^2 I_s^2 \mathfrak{u}}{\mathfrak{L}}\left(\Delta_1 + \frac{\Delta_2}{4} + \frac{\Sigma a}{3}\right),$$

if $a_{s_1} = a_{s_2}$, and

$$L_L = \frac{4\pi N_s^2 \mathfrak{u}}{\mathfrak{L}}\left(\Delta_1 + \frac{\Delta_2}{4} + \frac{\Sigma a}{3}\right) \qquad \text{abhenrys.} \quad (2)$$

The third example to be considered is a transformer with a single-layer primary interleaved between two equal layers of a secondary, as shown in Fig. 12·11. From the flux-density distribution across the coil (indicated in Fig. 12·11b) it may be seen that the transformer can be divided into two equal parts by a line drawn through the center of the primary and each part treated as a simple two-layer transformer. The total energy stored is the sum of the energies in the two parts, and the leakage inductance is given by

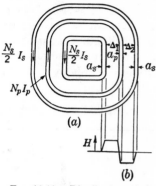

$$L_L = \frac{4\pi N_s^2 \mathfrak{U}}{\mathfrak{L}} \left[\left(\frac{a_{s_1}}{12} + \frac{\Delta_1}{4} + \frac{a_p}{24} \right) \right.$$
$$\left. + \left(\frac{a_p}{24} + \frac{\Delta_2}{4} + \frac{a_{s_2}}{12} \right) \right]$$
$$= \frac{4\pi N_s^2 \mathfrak{U}}{\mathfrak{L}} \frac{1}{4} \left(\Delta_1 + \Delta_2 + \frac{\Sigma a}{3} \right)$$

abhenrys. (3)

FIG. 12·11.—Distribution of the magnetic field for a primary winding interleaved between two secondary-windings.

If a simple two-layer transformer is connected as an autotransformer, the number of turns in the outer layer is $N_s \, (n-1)/n$, where n is the stepup ratio, and the number of ampere-turns is $N_s I_s \, (n-1)/n$. The current in the inner layer is $I_p(n-1)/n$, and the number of ampere-turns is $N_p I_p(n-1)/n$, which is equal to $N_s I_s(n-1)/n$. Therefore, the field between the windings is reduced from that in the iso type by the factor $(n-1)/n$, and the energy by the factor $[(n-1)/n]^2$. Thus,

$$L_L = \frac{4\pi N_s^2 \mathfrak{U}}{\mathfrak{L}} \left(\frac{n-1}{n} \right)^2 \left(\Delta + \frac{\Sigma a}{3} \right). \tag{4}$$

The expressions for the leakage inductance of the auto versions of more complicated types of winding arrangement are the expressions for the iso versions multiplied by this factor $[(n-1)/n]^2$.

These equations have been applied to the specific types of windings diagramed in Figs. 12·12 and 12·13, and the values of the leakage inductance recorded in Table 12·1.

Measurement of leakage inductance can be performed by either a pulse method or a steady-stage method. The circuit that is shown in Fig. 12·14a and by which the increase of current through a standard adjustable calibrated inductance L_s is compared and adjusted to coincide with the increase of current through L_L produces a synchroscope trace of the type shown in Fig. 12·14b. The value of L_L is then determined by the setting of the standard inductance.

If leads can be brought out from both vertical deflecting plates of the synchroscope, the alternate circuit shown in Fig. 12·14c may be used, and L_S adjusted to give a null trace of the type shown in Fig. 12·14d.

It is possible to measure leakage inductance (and also to calibrate the standard adjustable inductor of Fig. 12·14) at a frequency of approximately 1 Mc/sec by means of a Q-meter if suitable corrections are made for the distributed capacitances of the circuit. It is also possible to make an accurate measurement of the leakage inductance of a pulse transformer on a Maxwell bridge.

TABLE 12·1.—RELATIVE VALUES (IN ARBITRARY UNITS) OF L_L, C_D, AND L_LC_D
CALCULATED FOR THE VARIOUS WINDING ARRANGEMENTS SHOWN IN
FIGS. 12·12 AND 12·13

Winding type	Constant length		Constant secondary-wire size		L_LC_D
	L_L	C_D	L_L	C_D	
Windings of Fig. 12·12					
a	12.00	16.0	12.00	16.0	192
b	6.75	21.3	9.00	16.0	144
c	6.00	32.0	12.00	16.0	192
d	4.22	34.7	11.25	13.0	146
e	4.30	37.3	12.89	12.4	161
f	3.50	40.0	14.00	10.0	140
g	4.00	37.3	8.00	18.7	149
h	2.53	58.6	6.75	22.0	149
Windings of Fig. 12·13					
a	4.50	36.0	9.00	18.0	162
b	2.81	48.3	7.50	18.1	136
c	6.00	32.0	6.00	32.0	192
d	3.38	42.7	4.50	32.0	144
e	4.00	37.3	8.00	18.7	149
f	2.53	51.0	6.75	19.1	129
g	3.00	64.0	6.00	32.0	192
h	2.11	69.3	5.63	26.0	146

Distributed Capacitance.—Like leakage inductance, the effective distributed capacitance of various types of windings can be calculated from general formulas to be found in many different texts and handbooks. The considerations in this section are confined to the calculation of effective distributed capacitance for the various types of power-output pulse-transformer windings that have been developed.

The calculation of distributed capacitance as a lumped parameter

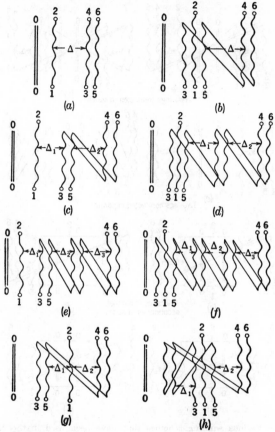

FIG. 12·12.—Various winding schemes that have been used in the construction of pulse transformers for magnetrons:

(a) $L_L = \dfrac{4\pi N_s^2 \mathfrak{U}}{d}\left(\Delta + \dfrac{\Sigma a}{3}\right)$; (b) $L_L = \dfrac{4\pi N_s^2 \mathfrak{U}}{d}\left(\dfrac{n-1}{n}\right)^2\left(\Delta + \dfrac{\Sigma a}{3}\right)$;

(c) $L_L = \dfrac{4\pi N_s^2 \mathfrak{U}}{d}\left(\Delta_1 + \dfrac{\Delta_2}{4} + \dfrac{\Sigma a}{3}\right)$; (d) $L_L = \dfrac{4\pi N_s^2 \mathfrak{U}}{d}\left(\dfrac{n-1}{n}\right)^2\left(\Delta_1 + \dfrac{\Delta_2}{4} + \dfrac{\Sigma a}{3}\right)$;

(e) $L_L = \dfrac{4\pi N_s^2 \mathfrak{U}}{d}\left(\Delta_1 + \dfrac{4\Delta_2}{9} + \dfrac{\Delta_3}{9} + \dfrac{\Sigma a}{3}\right)$;

(f) $L_L = \dfrac{4\pi N_s^2 \mathfrak{U}}{d}\left(\dfrac{n-1}{n}\right)^2\left(\Delta_1 + \dfrac{4\Delta_2}{9} + \dfrac{\Delta_3}{9} + \dfrac{\Sigma a}{3}\right)$;

(g) $L_L = \dfrac{4\pi N_s^2 \mathfrak{U}}{d}\dfrac{1}{4}\left(\Delta_1 + \Delta_2 + \dfrac{\Sigma a}{3}\right)$; (h) $L_L = \dfrac{4\pi N_s^2 \mathfrak{U}}{d}\dfrac{1}{4}\left(\Delta_1 + \Delta_2 + \dfrac{\Sigma a}{3}\right)$:

follows the process of reasoning wherein a given voltage V is placed across one winding of the transformer and the total energy W stored in the electrostatic field is equated to $\frac{1}{2}C_D V^2$, where C_D is defined as the effective distributed capacitance.

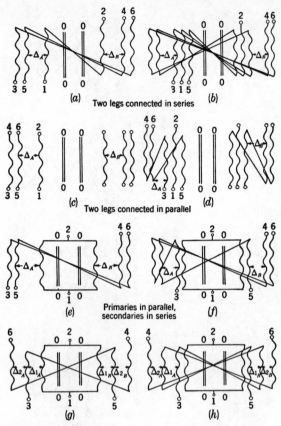

FIG. 12·13.—Various winding schemes that have been used in the construction of pulse transformers for magnetrons:

(a) $L_L = \dfrac{4\pi N_s{}^2 \mathfrak{U}}{\mathfrak{L}} \dfrac{1}{4}\left(\Delta_A + \Delta_B + \dfrac{\Sigma a}{3}\right)$; (b) $L_L = \dfrac{4\pi N_s{}^2 \mathfrak{U}}{\mathfrak{L}} \dfrac{1}{4}\left(\dfrac{n-1}{n}\right)^2\left(\Sigma\Delta + \dfrac{\Sigma a}{3}\right)$;

(c) $L_L = \dfrac{4\pi N_s{}^2 \mathfrak{U}}{\mathfrak{L}} \dfrac{1}{4}\left(\Delta_A + \Delta_B + \dfrac{\Sigma a}{3}\right)$; (d) $L_L = \dfrac{4\pi N_s{}^2 \mathfrak{U}}{\mathfrak{L}} \dfrac{1}{4}\left(\dfrac{n-1}{n}\right)^2\left(\Sigma\Delta + \dfrac{\Sigma a}{3}\right)$;

(e) $L_L = \dfrac{4\pi N_s{}^2 \mathfrak{U}}{\mathfrak{L}} \dfrac{1}{4}\left(\Delta_A + \Delta_B + \dfrac{\Sigma a}{3}\right)$; (f) $L_L = \dfrac{4\pi N_s{}^2 \mathfrak{U}}{\mathfrak{L}} \dfrac{1}{4}\left(\dfrac{n-1}{n}\right)^2\left(\Sigma\Delta + \dfrac{\Sigma a}{3}\right)$;

(g) $L_L = \dfrac{4\pi N_s{}^2 \mathfrak{U}}{\mathfrak{L}} \dfrac{1}{4}\left(\Sigma\Delta_1 + \dfrac{\Sigma\Delta_2}{4} + \dfrac{\Sigma a}{3}\right)$;

(h) $L_L = \dfrac{4\pi N_s{}^2 \mathfrak{U}}{\mathfrak{L}} \dfrac{1}{4}\left(\dfrac{n-1}{n}\right)^2\left(\Sigma\Delta_1 + \dfrac{\Sigma\Delta_2}{4} + \dfrac{\Sigma a}{3}\right).$

The capacitance of a parallel plate capacitor, each of whose electrodes is an equipotential surface, is given by the relation

$$C_o = 0.0885\,\frac{\epsilon A \cdot 10^{-12}}{\Delta} \qquad \text{farads,} \tag{5}$$

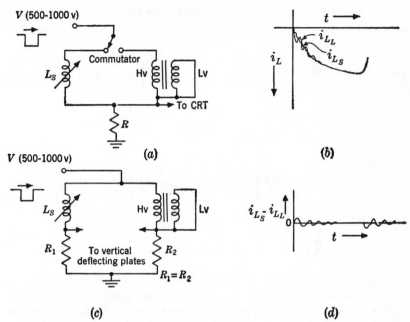

FIG. 12·14.—Method of measurement of leakage inductance.   (Note: L_S should be wound so that it has a low distributed self-capacitance and a low stray capacitance to ground.)

which can be found in most handbooks of electrical engineering, and the energy stored in a capacitance is given by

$$W = \tfrac{1}{2} C_o V^2 \qquad \text{joules.}$$

A pulse transformer with two adjacent winding layers of circumference $\mathfrak{U}$ and length $\mathfrak{L}$ may be considered as a condenser composed of two plates of area $\mathfrak{U}\mathfrak{L}$ cm^2 and separation Δ cm.   Because of the pulse voltages developed across the windings, the plates of this condenser can no longer be considered as equipotential surfaces, and the voltage distribution along the windings must be taken into consideration in the computation of the effective distributed capacitance.   The energy stored in a section of width $\mathfrak{U}$ and height dx (see Fig. 12·15) is given by

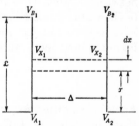

FIG.   12·15.—Voltage at various points on a two-layer coil.

$$dW = \frac{1}{2}\left(0.0885 \frac{\epsilon \mathfrak{U}}{\Delta}\, dx\right)(\delta V_x)^2 \cdot 10^{-12} \qquad \text{joules,}$$

where ϵ is the dielectric constant of the material between the plates.

The quantity δV_x is the voltage difference between the plates at a height x from the lower end of the coil.   For a linear distribution of voltage along the windings,

$$\delta V_x = V_{x_2} - V_{x_1} = \left[V_{A_2} + (V_{B_2} - V_{A_2}) \frac{x}{\mathcal{L}} \right] - \left[V_{A_1} + (V_{B_1} - V_{A_1}) \frac{x}{\mathcal{L}} \right]$$

$$= V_{A_2} - V_{A_1} + \left[(V_{B_2} - V_{B_1}) - (V_{A_2} - V_{A_1}) \right] \frac{x}{\mathcal{L}}$$

$$= \delta V_A + (\delta V_B - \delta V_A) \frac{x}{\mathcal{L}}.$$

Therefore,

$$dW = \frac{0.0885 \epsilon \mathcal{U}}{2\Delta} \left[\delta V_A + (\delta V_B - \delta V_A) \frac{x}{\mathcal{L}} \right]^2 dx \cdot 10^{-12}.$$

Integration over the range from 0 to $\mathcal{L}$ yields

$$W = \frac{0.0885 \epsilon \mathcal{U}}{2\Delta} \frac{\mathcal{L}}{3} \left[(\delta V_A)^2 + \delta V_A \cdot \delta V_B + (\delta V_B)^2 \right] \cdot 10^{-12} \qquad \text{joules.} \quad (6)$$

This equation is used in calculating the energy stored between the core and the first layer, between the first and second layer, and so on.   The equivalent capacitance, referred to the secondary, is obtained by solving the equation $\sum W = \frac{1}{2} C_D V_{\underline{z}}^2$, that is,

$$C_D = \frac{2 \sum W}{V_2^2} \cdot 10^{12} \qquad \text{farads,} \quad (7)$$

where V_2 is the pulse voltage developed across the secondary winding.

By a rough calculation made with the equation for the capacitance between parallel wires of infinite length, the interturn capacitance can be shown to be negligible in comparison with the interlayer capacitance.

It is shown in Sec. 13·1 that, if $L_L C_D$ equals a constant, one condition for minimum energy stored in the coil is that the load impedance

$$R_l = \sqrt{\frac{L_L}{C_D}}.$$

Another condition for minimum energy stored in the coil, obviously, is that the value of $L_L C_D$ be a minimum.   The winding arrangement that gives the lowest values of $L_L C_D$ should therefore be chosen for the transformer.

The leakage inductance and effective distributed capacitance of the various types of pulse-transformer windings shown in Figs. 12·12 and 12·13 have been calculated for $n = 4$, with each of the following sets of assumptions:

1. The thickness of each insulating pad is proportional to the maximum voltage applied across it, and the coil length is the same for all types, but the wire size is variable.
2. The thickness of each insulating pad is proportional to the maximum voltage applied across it, and the secondary wire size is the same for all types, but the coil length is variable.

Values of L_L and C_D (in arbitrary units) calculated with each of the above sets of assumptions and values of the product $L_L C_D$ are given in Table 12·1. Since the product $L_L C_D$ is independent of the length of the winding for a given type, it is the same for both sets of assumptions. The thickness of the winding layers is assumed to be small in comparison with the thickness of the insulation between layers, and is therefore neglected in these calculations.

The results given in Table 12·1 show that all of the auto types have lower values of the product $L_L C_D$ than do any of the iso types, although the value for the highest auto type is identical with that for the lowest iso type. The lowest and highest values for the auto types differ by only about 15 per cent. [Note: If the thickness of insulation between inner winding and core is doubled, the iso types are improved somewhat in comparison with the auto types; also type (h), Fig. 12·12, is improved relative to the other auto types, whereas type (f) becomes relatively poor. Types (f) and (b), Fig. 12·13, still appear to be the best.]

The insertion of an electrostatic shield between the primary and the secondary results in an appreciable increase in $L_L C_D$, and is therefore recommended only where it is absolutely necessary that the direct capacitive coupling between primary and secondary be eliminated.

The preferred method of measuring the effective distributed capacitance of pulse-transformer coils depends upon the type of winding. For transformers with simple one-layer windings, the value of the distributed capacitance may be obtained by measuring the capacitance between windings at 60 or 1000 cycles/sec and applying a factor that depends upon the distribution of voltage on the windings during the pulse.[1]

The self-capacitance of an individual duo-lateral winding can be obtained by measurement, by standard methods, at frequencies approximately equal to the highest important frequencies contained in the pulse. For transformers that employ special interleaving or interconnecting to minimize the product of leakage inductance and distributed capacitance, the circuit of Fig. 12·16 may be used to compare the capacitance current in the lower-voltage winding with the capacitance current in the adjustable equivalent circuit. The inductor L_e' and the resistor R_e' are inserted

---

[1] See Sec. 14·2 for a discussion of the calculation of this factor for regenerative pulse generators.

to simulate the magnetizing current in the transformer and are adjusted first to give a trace which coincides with that of the transformer after the capacitance currents have subsided (that is, toward the latter part of the pulse). The values of L'_L and C'_D are then adjusted to give a capacitance-current spike which coincides with that of the transformer at the beginning of the pulse. The value of C_D may then be read from the setting of C'_D, and the value of L_L from the setting of L'_L. This value of L_L is referred to the lower-voltage winding; the previously described method of measuring L_L gives greater precision since in that method the measured value is referred to the higher-voltage winding and is therefore numerically larger.

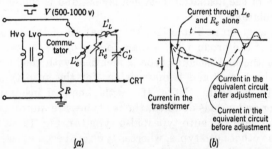

(a)   (b)

Fig. 12·16.—Method of measurement of distributed capacitance. (Note: L_L' should be wound so that its effective distributed capacitance is low.)

The effective distributed capacitance of a pulse-transformer winding can also be measured by means of an r-f bridge.[1]

Characteristic Impedance of a Pulse Transformer.—It is shown in Sec. 13·1 that $\sqrt{L_L/C_D}$ may be thought of as a characteristic impedance of a winding for a transformer that may be represented by the equivalent circuit of Fig. 12·7. For a simple coil with a one-layer primary and a one-layer secondary winding of equal length, and with negligible winding-layer thickness,

$$L_L = \frac{4\pi N_s^2 \Delta \mathfrak{U}}{\mathcal{L}} \times 10^{-9} \qquad \text{henrys,} \qquad (8)$$

and

$$C_D = f_1 C_o = \frac{0.0885 \epsilon \mathfrak{U} \mathcal{L} f_1}{\Delta} \times 10^{-12} \qquad \text{farads,} \qquad (9)$$

where C_o is calculated by the use of Eq. (5), and f_1 is a fraction depending upon the voltage distribution between the primary and the secondary.

[1] For example, see P. R. Gillette, "Pulse Transformer Committee, Proposed Basic Specifications for Pulse Transformers," RL Report No. 881, Nov. 8, 1945.

Then the characteristic impedance is

$$Z_T = \sqrt{\frac{L_L}{C_D}} = \frac{377 N_s \Delta}{\mathcal{L} \sqrt{\epsilon f_1}} \qquad \text{ohms.} \qquad (10)$$

The concept of characteristic impedance is, however, more meaningful when applied to circuits with distributed rather than lumped parameters. A simple example of a circuit having distributed inductance and capacitance and a characteristic impedance Z_0 is one composed of two long parallel strips of conducting material, 1 meter wide and 1 meter apart, which are part of two conducting sheets infinite in extent.[1] If the permeability and dielectric constant of the material between the sheets are respectively μ_1 and ϵ_1 in mks units, it can be shown that, for a plane electromagnetic wave propagated between the two strips,

$$Z_0 = \frac{E}{H} = \sqrt{\frac{\mu_1}{\epsilon_1}} = \sqrt{\frac{\mu}{\epsilon}} \sqrt{\frac{\mu_0}{\epsilon_0}} = \sqrt{\frac{\mu}{\epsilon}}\, 377 \qquad \text{ohms}$$

where μ_0 and ϵ_0 are, respectively, the permability and the dielectric constant of free space in mks units, and 377 ohms is the characteristic impedance of free space.

If the spacing between the strips is reduced to Δ meters and the width of the strips becomes $\mathcal{L}$ meters, and $\mu = 1$,

$$Z_0 = \frac{\Delta}{\mathcal{L} \sqrt{\epsilon}}\, 377 \qquad \text{ohms,}$$

and $\mathcal{L}$ and Δ may be measured in cm or meters.

If these parallel strips are now wrapped into two concentric cylinders whose circumferences are large compared with the distance Δ between the cylinders, and whose length is $\mathcal{L}$, the characteristic impedance for a plane electromagnetic wave traveling circumferentially in the space between the two cylinders is still equal to $(\Delta / \mathcal{L} \sqrt{\epsilon})$ 377 ohms.

If the outer and inner cylinders are now slit helically so that they become coils of N_s and N_p turns respectively, and the electromagnetic wave is ushered in at one end of the coil and out at the other end, the inductance per unit length of circumference is greater by a factor of N_s^2 (for the secondary) than it is for the unslit cylinders. The capacitance per unit length of circumference is different by a factor of f_1, depending upon the particular type of voltage distribution that is set up between the primary and secondary. Therefore, the characteristic impedance of the secondary winding may be expressed by

$$Z_T = \frac{N_s \Delta}{\mathcal{L} \sqrt{\epsilon f_1}}\, 377 \qquad \text{ohms.}$$

[1] J. C. Slater, *Microwave Transmission*, McGraw-Hill, New York, 1942, p. 98.

The characteristic impedance between the two plus (or the two minus) terminals of primary and secondary of a transformer with a simple wind-

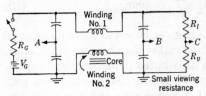

ing, such as that of the above example, whose stepup ratio is unity can be measured by the techniques similar to those used in the impedance measurements of pulse-forming networks (see Sec. 6·6). If pulses are applied between the single-layer primary and the single-layer secondary of a 1/1 transformer, as indicated in Fig. 12·17, the voltage waveforms at points

Fig. 12·17.—Circuit for measuring the characteristic impedance of a pulse-transformer coil with single-layer primary and single-layer secondary of equal length, and with $n = 1$.

A, B, and C are as shown in Fig. 12·18, where δ is the time taken for an impulse to travel along the wires from one end of the coil to the

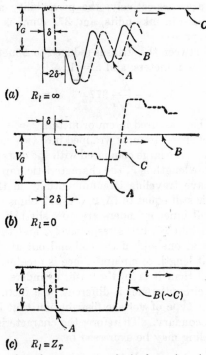

(a) $R_l = \infty$

(b) $R_l = 0$

(c) $R_l = Z_T$

Fig. 12·18.—Drawings of synchroscope traces obtained at points A, B, and C in the circuit of Fig. 12·17 for three different values of R_l.

other. When the value of R_l is so adjusted that the trace of Fig. 12·18c is obtained, the value of R_l is equal to the value of the characteristic impedance Z_T.   For a transformer of this type the values of Z_T obtained by this method of measurement and by the method of calculation previously described agree within a few per cent.

The small oscillations appearing at the very beginning of the pulse on traces B and C, Fig. 12·18, are the result of turn-to-turn transmission of the impulse.   The impulse thus transmitted travels from one end of the coil to the other much more rapidly than the impulse which must travel along the wires.

If a 1/1 transformer is wound symmetrically on two legs of the core, small oscillations appear in the middle of the steps.   These oscillations are the result of small reflections that occur where the two coils are connected.

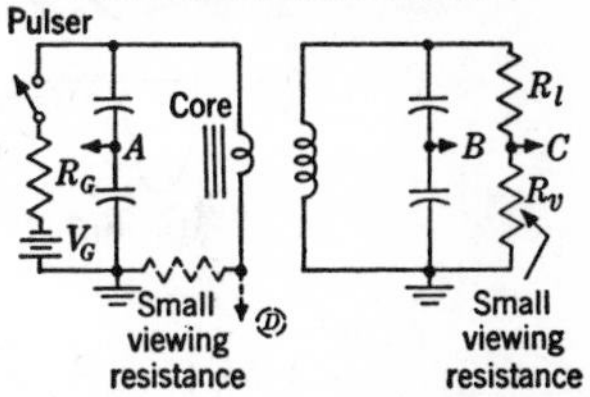

For windings of a more complicated nature the characteristic impedance of part of the winding may be different from that of another part of the winding.   Also, if $n > 1$, the measurement of impedance becomes much more difficult to perform.   Figure 12·20 shows some drawings of synchroscope traces obtained at various points in the circuit of Fig. 12·19, in which a transformer with $n = 1$ and a transformer with $n = 3$, constructed to have the same Z_T (1200 ohms) for the secondary (high-voltage) winding, were pulsed in turn with various loads attached.

FIG. 12·19.—Circuit used for pulsing two transformers, one with $n = 1$, the other with $n = 3$, to obtain the traces shown in Fig. 12·20.

It can be seen from these traces that the general character of the transmission delay of the transformer with $n = 1$ is retained by the transformer with $n = 3$, but that the tops of the steps of the latter are slanting instead of horizontal and that oscillations whose period is either $\frac{1}{3}\delta$ or $\frac{1}{6}\delta$ often appear on these slanting tops.   A simplified explanation is that the sloping tops of the steps are the result of charging an effective distributed capacitance through the characteristic impedance Z_T of the transformer winding.

It is interesting to note the nature of the approximation wherein the effect of distributed inductance per unit length of the wire is replaced by a lumped-parameter leakage inductance in the equivalent circuit.   For $R_l = 0$ and for R_G almost equal to 0, the slope of the average of trace D shown in Fig. 12·20d is $V_G/\delta Z_T$, where δ is the time necessary for an electromagnetic impulse to travel along the secondary winding from one end of the coil to the other.   If S is the total length of the wire, and if L and C are respectively the inductance and capacitance per unit length of the winding,

$$\delta = S\sqrt{LC},$$

$$Z_T = \sqrt{\frac{L}{C}},$$

and the slope of the average of trace D (Fig. 12·20d) is $V_G/LS = V_G/L_L$ where $L_L = LS$.   This slope V_G/L_L is simply the rate at which current increases when it is limited by the lumped-parameter leakage inductance.

For multilayer-winding and duolaterally wound transformers the concept of characteristic impedance from the point of view of distributed parameters becomes more and more strained.   The characteristic imped-

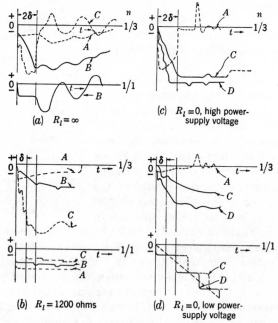

(a) $R_l = \infty$

(c) $R_l = 0$, high power-supply voltage

(b) $R_l = 1200$ ohms

(d) $R_l = 0$, low power-supply voltage

Fig. 12·20.—Drawings of oscilloscope traces obtained at the various points of the circuit shown in Fig. 12·19 for transformers with $n = 1$ and $n = 3$, (a) with $R_l = \infty$, (b) with $R_l = 1200$ ohms, which, for the secondaries of both transformers, is equal to the value of Z_T calculated from $Z_T = \dfrac{N\Delta}{d\sqrt{\epsilon f}}$ 377 ohms, and (c) and (d) with $R_l = 0$.

ances can then be best thought of as equal to $\sqrt{L_L/C_D}$, where L_L and C_D are lumped parameters.

Charging Inductance.—When a pulse transformer is operated into a load of low dynamic impedance (for example, a magnetron), oscillations whose period is usually considerably less than $2\pi\sqrt{L_LC_D}$ often appear on the top of the current pulse.   These oscillations may be considered to be the result of the transmission and reflection in the coil of disturbances that are probably initiated at the end of the secondary to which the oscillator is attached.   The impedance of the secondary winding to the transmission of such disturbances is

$$\frac{N_s \Delta}{\mathcal{L} \sqrt{\epsilon f_1}} \ 377 \text{ ohms.}$$

The time taken for the disturbance to travel along a length of secondary wire of N'_s turns to the first discontinuity in the impedance is

$$\delta = \frac{N'_s \mathfrak{u}}{c} \sqrt{\epsilon} \text{ sec,}$$

where $\mathfrak{u}$ is the mean length of turns of the secondary winding in centimeters, c is the velocity of light in centimeters per second, and N'_s is the number of turns on the secondary winding between the high-voltage end and the first sharp discontinuity in impedance (μ, of course, is equal to unity for the space between the coils). The time transpired before this disturbance is reflected back to the source is 2δ, and when, upon successive reflections that set up shock-excited standing waves, the fluctuations of voltage and current at the source take on the approximate semblance of a sine wave, the period T of the fundamental of these oscillations is either 2δ or 4δ, depending upon the nature of the discontinuity in impedance. The effect is somewhat analogous to the two different fundamental periods of oscillation that are set up in closed and open organ pipes.

Figures 12·18 and 12·20a show examples of such sine-wave oscillations occurring in the operation of the circuits of Figs. 12·17 and 12·19 respectively.

Figures 2·44 and 2·45 show such sine-wave oscillations appearing on the current pulse in a magnetron. The fundamental period of these oscillations is usually

$$T = 2\delta = \frac{2N'_s \mathfrak{u} \sqrt{\epsilon}}{c},$$

and the periods of various harmonics are integral divisions of this period. The periods thus calculated agree with the periods of oscillation observed if there are no interfering effects resulting from capacitance across the primary winding. For each discontinuity in impedance along the coil there is observed among the oscillations sine-wave components of a fundamental period corresponding to each of the resulting reflections.

In the equivalent circuit for a pulse transformer and a biased-diode or magnetron load (Fig. 12·7) the effect of these reflections can, to a crude approximation, be taken into account by inserting in series with C_D an inductance L_D such that

$$T = 2\pi \sqrt{L_D C_D} = \frac{2N'_s \mathfrak{u} \sqrt{\epsilon}}{c}$$

or

$$L_D = \frac{N_s^2 \mathfrak{U}^2 \epsilon}{\pi^2 c^2 C_D}.$$

If the coil is assumed to be constructed with a single-layer primary winding and a single-layer secondary winding of equal length,

$$C_D = \frac{0.0885 \cdot \mathfrak{U} \mathfrak{L} \epsilon f_1 \cdot 10^{-12}}{\Delta} \qquad \text{farads,}$$

where f_1 is a factor depending upon the stepup ratio. Then

$$L_D = \frac{1}{\pi^2 \cdot 9 \cdot 10^{20} \cdot 0.0885 \cdot 10^{-12}} \cdot \frac{N_s^2 \mathfrak{U}^2 \epsilon \Delta}{\mathfrak{U} \mathfrak{L} \epsilon f_1},$$

and

$$\frac{L_D}{L_L} = \frac{1}{\pi^2 \cdot 9 \cdot 10^8 \cdot 0.0885} \cdot \frac{N^2 \mathfrak{U} \Delta}{f_1 \mathfrak{L}} \cdot \frac{\mathfrak{L} \cdot 10^9}{4\pi N^2 \mathfrak{U} \Delta} = \frac{0.1}{f_1}.$$

If, for example, the stepup ratio n is very high, and if $\delta V_B \approx V_2$ and $\delta V_A = 0$ in Eq. (6), then Eq. (7) yields a value of C_D equal to $\frac{1}{3}$ of the total capacitance between primary and secondary, and f_1 is equal to $\frac{1}{3}$. Thus, for this simple coil where f_1 is taken to be $\frac{1}{3}$, $L_D/L_L = 0.3$.

For transformers of the type usually employed with magnetrons, the value of L_D that is obtained from measuring the period of oscillation on the current pulse and using the expression $T = 2\pi \sqrt{L_D C_D}$ is such that

$$\frac{L_D}{L_L} \approx 0.25.$$

P. D. Crout assumes that certain so-called "current modes" in the transformer are associated with generalized coordinates.[1] The result is a set of equations, one for each mode, which duplicate the mesh equations of a lumped network.

The particular current mode which is of interest at this point in the discussion of pulse transformers is that associated with the charging of distributed capacitance (that is, Crout's modes B, C, and D). In illustrating the delineation of the simplest of such current modes (that is, mode B) the voltage distribution between the primary winding and the grounded core shown in Fig. 12·21, where $\mathfrak{L}$ is the length of the winding, should be considered first.

The charge per unit axial length of primary may be denoted by kx, and the total charge that has passed point x toward the right is equal to

$$\int_x^{\mathfrak{L}} kx \, dx = \frac{k}{2} (\mathfrak{L}^2 - x^2).$$

---

[1] P. D. Crout, "A Method of Virtual Displacements for Electrical Systems with Applications to Pulse Transformers," RL Report No. 618, Oct. 6, 1944.

In order that the mode may produce no net mmf on the core, it is required that there flow in the opposite direction in the primary winding a current which is constant along the primary and whose mmf cancels that of the current flowing toward the right.   Since the number of turns per unit length is constant along the primary, the desired average current flowing toward the left is $k\mathcal{L}^2/3$.

Then, if the primary current outside the winding is denoted by dq_B/dt (see Fig. 12·21b), $k = q_B$, and the primary current in the winding (positive for flow to the left) is

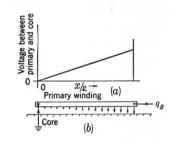

Voltage between primary and core

$x/\mathcal{L} \longrightarrow$

0

Primary winding   (a)

q_B

Core   (b)

$$\frac{dq_B}{dt} - \frac{3}{2\mathcal{L}^2}\,(\mathcal{L}^2 - x^2)\,\frac{dq_B}{dt}$$

$$= \frac{1}{2}\frac{dq_B}{dt}\left(\frac{3x^2}{\mathcal{L}^2} - 1\right).$$

The displacement current from primary to core per unit length of winding is $3x/\mathcal{L}^2\,dq_B/dt$.

As q_B is varied it is evident that this so-called "mode B" has the following properties:

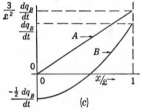

$\frac{3}{\mathcal{L}^2}\dfrac{dq_B}{dt}$

$\dfrac{dq_B}{dt}$

$A \longrightarrow$

$B \longrightarrow$

0

0          $x/\mathcal{L} \longrightarrow$ 1

$-\frac{1}{2}\dfrac{dq_B}{dt}$ (c)

1. No mmf acts upon the core.
2. The primary winding behaves as an autotransformer to charge the primary-to-core distributed capacitance with a linear voltage distribution.

FIG. 12·21.—(a) Voltage distribution between primary and core for a pulse transformer.

(b) Displacement current flowing between primary and core.

(c) Plots of displacement and net primary currents.   Curve A is the displacement current from primary to core per unit length of winding, Curve B is the net primary current.

The displacement current per unit length of winding and the net primary current are plotted in Fig. 12·21c.   It is evident that at all points except one along the length of the coil the net primary current is different from zero (although the net mmf on the core is zero).   The energy stored in the magnetic field associated with this primary current may be represented to a first approximation by an inductance in series with the effective distributed capacitance in the equivalent circuit (whence L_c in Fig. 12·6).

By the same process of delineation of current modes it may be shown that, to a first approximation, an equivalent inductance L_D may be placed in series with the effective distributed capacitance C_D existing between the primary and the secondary (see Fig. 12·6).

Thus, where there is a voltage distribution that increases along the length of the coil between primary and core, or between secondary and primary, there are capacitance currents that flow in such a way that magnetic fields ("squirted" flux) are created outside the coil as well as inside. These fields, obtained with a combination of a transformer with $n = 3$ and the circuit of Fig. 12·19—a combination that is pulsed at a time $t = 0$ for a duration $\gg \delta$—and observed in the axial direction of the coil with a magnetic probe and a synchroscope, are shown for various positions along the coil in Fig. 12·22a. It is obvious from the traces that both fundamentals and harmonics exist in the time variation of the magnetic fields associated with charging currents. A plot of values of these fields for the first and second harmonics has been constructed in Fig. 12·22b, and a rough schematic pattern of these fields about the coil

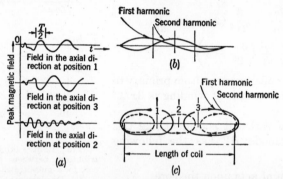

FIG. 12·22.—(a) Drawings of synchroscope traces showing the intensity of the magnetic field in the axial direction obtained with a magnetic probe at various points along the coil.

(b) Plot of the distribution along the coil of the peak magnetic fields of the first and second harmonics that occur in the time variation of the squirted flux.

(c) Rough schematic plot of the field patterns for the first and second harmonics.

for the first and second harmonics has been drawn in Fig. 12·22c. The charging inductance L_D (or several L_D's, one for each harmonic) may be introduced into the equivalent circuit to take into account the energy that is stored in these magnetic fields when charging currents flow in the transformer coil.

There is no contradiction between the concepts of transmission-reflection and squirted flux, as they are merely different aspects of the same phenomenon, a phenomenon which is similar to the oscillations that occur in an organ pipe or along a vibrating string. In all of these phenomena the reflection of traveling waves sets up sinusoidal displacements in the form of standing waves. The difference between the two concepts is that, with a transformer coil in which the voltage distribution is such that the voltage difference increases along the coil, the squirted-flux theory predicts external magnetic fields of the type shown in Fig. 12·22, whereas the pure reflection theory does not.

Summary.—This chapter has given a brief treatment of general transformer theory, has indicated a workable equivalent circuit for a pulse transformer, has shown how the elements in this equivalent circuit may be calculated and measured, and has introduced and briefly discussed the concepts of characteristic impedance and modes of oscillation of a pulse-transformer winding.

CHAPTER 13

PULSE-TRANSFORMER DESIGN

By W. H. Bostick

In this chapter, Sec. 13·1 discusses the relationship between the elements in the equivalent circuit and the rated load impedance, rated pulse duration, and efficiency of a pulse transformer. Section 13·2 presents methods of achieving a design that meets the requirements of specified load impedance, specified pulse duration, and maximum efficiency. Section 13·3 provides design data for a number of successful pulse transformers covering a wide range of pulse durations and impedance levels.

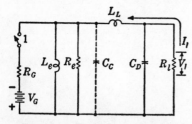

FIG. 13·1.—Equivalent circuit used in the consideration of the optimum relationships among R_l, C_D, L_L, L_e, and R_e for a specified load impedance and pulse duration.

13·1. General Pulse-transformer Design Considerations.—Many successful pulse transformers have been designed without consideration or cognizance of certain relationships between the elements in the equivalent circuit and the transformer rating and efficiency. It is the author's belief, however, that these relationships which are discussed in this section form the most rational general basis for the design of pulse transformers giving maximum transfer of pulse energy to the load.

In developing these relationships, it is helpful to consider the system of Fig. 13·1 where

V_G is a source voltage,

R_G is the source impedance,

L_e is the effective shunt inductance,

R_e is the effective shunt resistance,

R_l is the load impedance (a resistance),

C_C, which represents the capacitance between the low-voltage winding of a transformer and the core (which is grounded), is generally neglected, and

$L_L C_D$ equals a constant (a relationship that is true for a constant mean coil perimeter and a constant number of turns for pulse transformers).

It is desirable to transfer a maximum of energy to R_l in a given interval of time during which switch (1) is closed (that is, the pulse duration τ, which in average design practice is usually considerably greater than $2\pi \sqrt{L_L C_D}$), and hence to transfer a minimum of energy to R_e, L_e (or L_p, see Sec. 12·2), L_L, and C_D. In a treatment of this problem it is helpful to introduce the quantity α;

$$\alpha = \frac{\text{Energy flowing into the core during the pulse}}{\text{Energy transmitted to the load during the pulse}}.$$

Then

$$\alpha = \frac{\int_0^\tau V_l i_m \, dt}{V_l I_l \tau} = \frac{\int_0^\tau \left[\dfrac{V_l^2 t}{L_e} + \dfrac{V_l^2}{R_e} \right] dt}{V_l I_l \tau} = \frac{V_l}{I_l} \left(\frac{\tau}{2L_e} + \frac{1}{R_e} \right),$$

where the core is represented by an equivalent circuit consisting of L_e and R_e in parallel, and i_m is the magnetizing current that builds up in L_e and R_e.

If, as is often true, the laminations are very thin, or if the pulse duration is long compared with the time constant of the lamination (see Sec. 15·1), the core may be approximately represented in the equivalent circuit by L_p, instead of by L_e and R_e.
Then

$$\alpha = \frac{V_l}{I_l} \frac{\tau}{2L_p}.$$

It is also useful to define the quantity β;

$$\beta = \frac{\begin{array}{c}\text{Energy stored in leakage inductance and} \\ \text{distributed capacitance during the pulse}\end{array}}{\text{Energy transmitted to the load during the pulse}}$$

Then

$$\beta = \frac{\frac{1}{2}L_L I_l^2 + \frac{1}{2}C_D V_l^2}{V_l I_l \tau}.$$

For a variable winding length and a variable spacing between the primary and the secondary, $L_L C_D = \text{constant}$ [see Eqs. (12·4), (12·6), and (12·7)]. A maximum amount of pulse energy is transferred to the load (as far as the coil is concerned) if a minimum amount of energy is stored in the coil. Therefore, β is minimized under the condition that $L_L C_D = \text{constant}$.
Thus,

$$\frac{d\beta}{dL_L} = \frac{1}{2V_l I_l \tau} \left(1 - \frac{\text{constant}}{L_L^2} \cdot R_l^2 \right) \left(\frac{V_G}{R_G + R_l} \right)^2 = 0.$$

or

$$\sqrt{\frac{L_L}{C_D}} = R_l, \tag{1}$$

and

$$\frac{1}{2} L_L \left(\frac{V_G}{R_G + R_l} \right)^2 = \frac{1}{2} C_D \left(\frac{V_G R_l}{R_G + R_l} \right)^2.$$

This condition for maximum energy transfer might be obtained by way of a thermodynamical analogy by reasoning that the system would be in its equilibrium state if there were an equipartition of energy between the two degrees of freedom, that is, that

$$\frac{1}{2} L_L I_i^2 = \frac{1}{2} L_L \left(\frac{V_G}{R_G + R_l} \right)^2 = \frac{1}{2} C_D V_i^2 = \frac{1}{2} C_D \left(\frac{V_G R_l}{R_G + R_l} \right)^2.$$

The quantity $\sqrt{L_L/C_D}$, which has the dimensions of impedance, may be thought of as the transient or characteristic impedance of the $L_L C_D$-network. When the impedance of this network is equal to the load impedance, maximum energy transfer to the load is effected.

The resultant value of β for minimum energy stored in the coil is

$$\beta = \frac{L_L I_i^2}{V_l I_l \tau} = \frac{L_L}{R_l \tau} = \frac{\sqrt{L_L C_D}}{\tau}.$$

For transformers in which the voltage stepup ratio $n > 2$ or $n < -1$ (that is, transformers for which the equivalent circuit of Fig. 13·1 applies), and which are operated on a resistance load, observation and calculation (see Fig. 14·12) of pulse shapes show that pulse shape is approximately optimum when the sum $\alpha + \beta$ is a minimum.[1]

For stepup transformers operated on a magnetron load, both calorimetric measurement of efficiency and observation of the shape of the current and voltage pulses show that the efficiency (for fixed R_G and R_l) is maximum and, in general, the pulse shape and performance are optimum when $\alpha + \beta$ is a minimum. The value of the pulse duration τ at which the transformer with a given L_e, R_e (or L_p), and C_D gives a minimum of $\alpha + \beta$ can be determined as follows:

$$\frac{d}{d\tau} (\alpha + \beta) = \frac{d}{d\tau} \left[\sqrt{\frac{L_L}{C_D}} \frac{\tau}{2L_e} + \sqrt{\frac{L_L}{C_D}} \frac{1}{R_e} + \frac{\sqrt{L_L C_D}}{\tau} \right] = 0,$$

$$= \sqrt{\frac{L_L}{C_D}} \frac{1}{2L_e} - \frac{\sqrt{L_L C_D}}{\tau^2} = 0,$$

or

$$\tau_{\text{opt}} = \sqrt{2L_e C_D}. \tag{2}$$

[1] The criteria for optimum pulse shape constitute a very controversial subject. A good pulse shape is the result of a skillful compromise among high rate of rise, low overshoot, small amount of droop, high rate of fall, and low backswing voltage. It is the author's belief that the most suitable compromise among these quantities is obtained by making $\alpha + \beta$ a minimum.

The quantity $\alpha + \beta$ for τ_{opt} is defined as $(\alpha + \beta)_{opt}$, and

$$(\alpha + \beta)_{opt} = \sqrt{\frac{2L_L}{L_e}} + \frac{1}{R_e}\sqrt{\frac{L_L}{C_D}}.$$

If the effect of R_e is neglected,

$$(\alpha + \beta)_{opt} = \sqrt{\frac{2L_L}{L_p}}, \tag{3}$$

$$\tau_{opt} = \sqrt{2L_pC_D},$$

and if

$$\tau = \tau_{opt}$$
$$\alpha = \beta.$$

Then, at any τ such that $\tau/\tau_{opt} = f$,

$$\alpha + \beta = (\alpha + \beta)_{opt}\left(\frac{f}{2} + \frac{1}{2f}\right).$$

Thus, if $f = 2$ or $\frac{1}{2}$,

$$\alpha + \beta = \tfrac{5}{4}(\alpha + \beta)_{opt},$$

if $f = 3$ or $\frac{1}{3}$,

$$\alpha + \beta = \tfrac{5}{3}(\alpha + \beta)_{opt},$$

and if $f = 4$ or $\frac{1}{4}$,

$$\alpha + \beta = \tfrac{17}{8}(\alpha + \beta)_{opt}.$$

It is obvious that, if the transformer is to be operated over a range of pulse durations from τ_{min} to τ_{max}, τ_{opt} should be chosen to be equal to $\sqrt{\tau_{min}\tau_{max}}$.

It is of some interest to relate $(\alpha + \beta)_{opt}$ to the coupling coefficient k. From Fig. 12·4 it is apparent that $2(L_1 - M_1) = L_L$, or

$$M_1 = L_1 - \frac{L_L}{2}.$$

Since

$$k = \frac{M}{\sqrt{L_1L_2}} \approx \frac{M_1}{L_1},$$

$$k = 1 - \frac{1}{2}\frac{L_L}{L_1},$$

or

$$k = 1 - \frac{(\alpha + \beta)^2_{opt}}{4}.$$

If the transformer is a noninverting transformer with a stepup ratio $n = 1$, then $C_D = 0$, and no electrostatic, only magnetic energy is stored in the coil. Minimum energy stored as $\frac{1}{2}L_LI_l^2$ in the coil is then achieved, and the relationship $R_l = \sqrt{L_L/C_D}$ is most nearly approximated when L_L is a minimum.

The capacitance C_C of the low-voltage winding to core is, of course, always present, and energy is stored in C_C. However, C_C does not bear the close relationship to L_L that C_D does, and C_C may be kept small merely by using adequate winding-to-core insulation. In properly designed pulse transformers, C_C is always negligible compared with C_D when $n > 2$ or < -1. Therefore, the value of C_C is of little significance in design considerations, except for the fact that it is usually kept negligibly small.

In addition to C_D there is the input capacitance C_l of the load, which is usually smaller than C_D. For a system using one transformer, the energy stored as $\frac{1}{2}C_D V_l^2 + \frac{1}{2}L_L I_l^2$ for a constant product $L_L C_D$ is a minimum when $R_l = \sqrt{L_L/C_D}$, but the pulse shape is usually optimum (for a voltage-stepup transformer) when $R_l = \sqrt{L_L/(C_D + C_l)}$ (see Sec. 14·1). In a system using stepdown and stepup transformers separated by a cable whose transit time is less than $\sqrt{L_L C_D}$,[1] the energy stored as $\Sigma\frac{1}{2}C_D V_l^2 + \Sigma\frac{1}{2}L_L I_l^2$ for a constant product $L_L C_D$ is a minimum when $R_l = \sqrt{\Sigma L_L/\Sigma C_D}$, but the pulse shape is optimum when $R_l = \sqrt{\Sigma L_L/(C_D - C_l)}$ (see Sec. 14·1), where C_D is the effective primary-to-secondary capacitance of the stepup transformer. Therefore, a compromise must be struck between maximum efficiency of the transformer or transformers and optimum pulse shape. Because the assumption that $\sqrt{L_L/C_D}$ should be equal to R_l generally gives good results and leads to simpler relationships, this assumption is employed in the design methods discussed in Sec. 13·2.

In summary, it is evident that, in order to design a good pulse transformer (that is, one which effects maximum transfer of pulse energy) for a given τ and R_l, the following conditions should be fulfilled:

$$Z_T \equiv \sqrt{\frac{L_L}{C_D}} = R_l, \quad \text{or} \quad \frac{1}{2}L_L I_l^2 = \frac{1}{2}C_D V_l^2. \tag{4}$$

$$\alpha = \beta, \quad \text{or} \quad \sqrt{2L_p C_D} \approx \sqrt{2L_e C_D} \equiv \tau_{\text{opt}} = \tau. \tag{5}$$

$$(\alpha + \beta)_{\text{opt}} \equiv \sqrt{\frac{2L_L}{L_e}} + \frac{1}{R_e}\sqrt{\frac{L_L}{C_D}} \approx \sqrt{\frac{2L_L}{L_p}} = \text{a minimum.} \tag{6}$$

13·2. Design Methods.—In the early history of pulse transformers it was customary to use the following design procedure: the magnetizing current I_m at the end of the pulse was permitted to be equal to 0.1 of the load current I_l. Then, from the relationships (see Sec. 15·1)

$$\Delta\bar{B} = \frac{10^8 V\tau}{NA},$$

$$H = \frac{4\pi N I_m}{10l},$$

---

[1] When the transit time of the cable is appreciably greater than $\sqrt{L_L C_D}$, the considerations are the same as those for a line-type pulser.

and
$$\Delta \bar{B} = \mu_e H,$$

the core volume was computed to be
$$Al = \frac{4\pi \cdot 10^7 \mu_e V \tau I_m}{(\Delta \bar{B})^2} = \frac{4\pi \cdot 10^6 \mu_e V \tau I_l}{(\Delta \bar{B})^2}$$
where

$\Delta \bar{B}$ is the increment in gauss (at the end of the pulse) of the average
    flux density of the core above the remanent value of B,

H is the magnetic field in oersteds created by I_m,

A is the cross-sectional area of the core in square centimeters,

l is the mean magnetic-path length of the core in centimeters,

μ_e is the effective permeability of the core,

V is the pulse voltage, and

N is the number of turns on the winding to which is applied the pulse
    voltage V.

A guess was made as to a suitable value of $\Delta \bar{B}$, the core volume Al
was computed, and a core having this product, for which the factors A
and l were suitably estimated, was then chosen. The value of N was
computed, and a simple winding scheme selected. The insulation thickness Δ was chosen so that it would be sufficient to withstand the voltage
puncture stress, and sufficient coil margins were left to withstand the
voltage creep stress.

Formerly, an operational requirement frequently placed on a pulse
transformer was the specification of $t_{r\max}$, the maximum allowable time
taken for the pulse to rise to 0.9 of the full amplitude of the output of the
pulse transformer on a resistance load R_l. For the transformer and load,
the resultant time of rise t_r, usually computed without a consideration of
the effective distributed capacitance, was obtained from the expression

$$0.9 = 1 - e^{-\frac{R_l}{L_L} t_r},$$
or
$$t_r = -\frac{L_L}{R_l} \ln 0.1 = \frac{L_L}{R_l} \ln 10.$$

If the computed t_r exceeded the specified $t_{r\max}$, L_L had to be reduced by
reducing N or A, thereby increasing $\Delta \bar{B}$, or by reducing Δ. If the computed t_r was less than $t_{r\max}$, the design was considered satisfactory.

In more careful designs where the distributed capacitance was taken
into account, the time of rise was calculated on the basis of Eqs. (14·1)
and (14·2), and an effort was made to choose a design which had a value of
σ (see Sec. 14·1) of about 0.5. Except for this occasional effort, which
satisfies the criterion of Eq. (4), early design procedure involved no con-
scious attempt to satisfy the criteria of Eqs. (4), (5), and (6). To take

full cognizance of these criteria constitutes a more rational and direct approach to the problem of pulse-transformer design. This direct approach, or an approximation thereto, should be used whenever the conditions of design call for maximum transfer of pulse energy.

It is possible, for a given type of winding, to express α and β as functions of the number of turns, maximum allowable creep stress, the voltage on the high-voltage winding, the wire diameter, etc., and to minimize $(\alpha + \beta)_{opt}$ under the constraining conditions of Eqs. (4), (5), and (6). This method is straightforward and leads to the optimum design. The algebraic equation resulting from this procedure is, however, of such high degree that its numerical solution for each new transformer design is prohibitively laborious. An alternative, but nevertheless equivalent, procedure is to approach the optimum design by a series of approximating designs. It is possible to use the criteria of Eqs. (4) and (5) as constraints on the design, and then to make an estimate as to the optimum flux density, the number of turns, or the core volume. Although the resultant transformer satisfies Eqs. (4) and (5), but not necessarily Eq. (6), its design may be sufficiently good for the intended purpose. If, however, the best possible performance is desired in this transformer, it is necessary to make several estimates of flux density, number of turns, or core volume, and either to calculate or measure $(\alpha + \beta)_{opt}$ for these designs. When the design possibilities have been thoroughly explored and the design has been found which satisfies, by measurement as well as calculation, the criteria of Eq. (6) as well as those of Eqs. (4) and (5), and which operates satisfactorily in the intended circuit, the design may be considered to be completed.

There are, of course, complicating factors such as the saturation characteristics of the core, the range of pulse durations that must be passed, and the magnitude of the backswing voltage that can be tolerated. A compromise must often be struck between these circumstances and adherence to the criteria of Eqs. (4), (5), and (6). Also, except under unusual circumstances, an approximate core size must be used because, for economic reasons, cores are manufactured in a set of standard sizes, finite in number.

This process of design wherein it is attempted to satisfy the criteria of Eqs. (4), (5), and (6) has been carried out at the Radiation Laboratory for a number of power-output pulse transformers for magnetrons. Some of these designs for various power ranges and pulse durations are recorded in Sec. 13·3. These designs are useful in the design of new transformers because they provide a good starting point in the initial estimates of the number of turns, flux density, or core size to be used.

Given also in Sec. 13·3 are the designs of several interstage and regenerative-pulse-generator low-power pulse transformers in which the criteria of Eqs. (4) and (5) were approximately satisfied, but in which no particular exploratory effort was made to satisfy the criterion of Eq. (6).

With the use of Eqs. (4), (5), and (6), analytical expressions, which are algebraically simple, are now developed to show the general dependence of optimum flux density, optimum number of turns, and optimum core volume on the effective permeability of the core, the dielectric constant of the insulation, the winding arrangement, wire size, output voltage, load impedance, and pulse duration. These relationships prove especially useful in providing a means of extrapolating from a successful design to a new design of the same winding type, but perhaps different voltage, impedance, pulse duration, wire size, dielectric constant of insulation, and effective permeability of core.

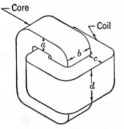

FIG. 13·2.—Idealized core and coil used in the thermodynamical considerations of the energy stored in the transformer.

It is helpful at the outset to express the second law of thermodynamics in the following way: the equilibrium or most probable state of an unisolated system is usually achieved when the energy of that system has become a minimum. In a corollary of the second law of thermodynamics (see Sec. 12·1), the law of equipartition, it may be stated that the energy of the system tends to be distributed equally to each degree of freedom that enters quadratically into the expression of the energy of the entire system.

In the pulse transformer (shown in Fig. 13·2), the total volume of the coil is assumed to be equal to the space between the primary and secondary windings, and the total volume of the transformer in which energy is stored is assumed to be equal to the sum of the volumes of the core and coil. If this transformer is to be used to transform and transfer a pulse of electromagnetic energy, it is obviously desirable to have a minimum of energy in the transformer at the end of the pulse, that is, to leave the transformer in a minimum-energy state. If the energies stored in the core and coil are considered, by way of a thermodynamical analogue, to constitute two degrees of freedom for the transformer, the equilibrium or minimum energy state of the transformer is that wherein $\alpha = \beta$ (which, as has been proved in Sec. 13·1 also, gives a minimum for $\alpha + \beta$ when $\tau = \tau_{opt}$). Furthermore, according to the second law of thermodynamics, the equilibrium (and hence the minimum-energy) state of the transformer is (among other things) that in which the "electromagnetic temperature"[1] is constant throughout the transformer, and

[1] Here electromagnetic temperature may be thought of as analogous to ordinary temperature which, in a gas for example, is proportional to the average kinetic-energy density.

hence that in which the energy densities of core and coil are equal. This latter condition effects a minimum of $(\alpha + \beta)_{\text{opt}}$, and, coupled with the condition that $\alpha = \beta$, lays down the additional condition that the volumes of the core and coil should be equal.[1]

If the core and coil are of rectangular cross section $a \times b$ and $c \times d$ respectively (Fig. 13·2), and if each completely fills up the rectangular hole in the other, as each should if the transformer volume is to be kept to a minimum,

$$\text{Core volume} = ab(2d + 2c + 4a) = 4a^2b + 2abd + 2abc,$$

and

$$\text{Coil volume} = cd(2b + 2a + 4c) = 4c^2d + 2cdb + 2cda.$$

Since the core volume should equal the coil volume,

$$4a^2b + 2abd + 2abc = 4c^2d + 2cdb + 2cda. \tag{7}$$

Equation (7) can hold for any arbitrarily chosen a and b only if $a = c$ and $b = d$. Therefore the mean perimeter of coil should be equal to the mean magnetic-path length of core.

Because in practice there are complicating factors such as the length of the coil margin, the necessary spacing between the high-voltage winding and the core, the volume taken up by the copper, and complicated windings, it is desirable to change the equalities of energy density, volume, and perimeter of the core and coil to approximations and, in some cases, to proportionalities.

Of the criteria of Eqs. (4), (5), and (6) for optimum pulse-transformer design the last is then achieved by designing a transformer such that

$$\text{The energy density of core} \approx \text{the energy density of coil,} \tag{8}$$

and

$$\text{The mean perimeter } \mathfrak{U} \text{ of coil} \approx \text{the mean magnetic-path length } l \text{ of core.} \tag{9}$$

---

[1] The foregoing procedure bears some formal resemblance to general practice in the design of power transformers. In power transformers operating at a constant frequency, the energy stored in the coil and core is, for the most part, not lost but returned to the circuit. It is the sum of the average power dissipated in the iron of the core and the copper of the coil that is of primary importance. It might be said by way of thermodynamical analogue that a power transformer will remain in its lowest or equilibrium energy state if the rate of dissipation of energy per unit volume is approximately constant throughout its whole volume. Minimum total power will then be dissipated in the transformer when the transformer volume is a minimum (consistent, of course, with the saturation properties of the core and maximum temperature characteristics of the insulation). The transformer volume will be a minimum when the perimeters and volumes of core and coil are approximately equal. The resultant power transformer will thus have total iron losses and copper losses that are approximately equal.

The average energy density of the coil (that is, of the space between the primary and the secondary) is

$$\frac{\epsilon f_1 V^2}{9 \cdot 10^4 \cdot 8\pi\Delta^2} + \frac{H^2}{8\pi} \qquad \text{ergs/cm}^3,$$

where

   ϵ is the dielectric constant of the insulation,
   V is the pulse potential of the high-voltage winding in volts,
   Δ is the spacing between the primary and secondary in cm,
   f_1 is a constant depending upon the voltage distribution between the windings that results from a given winding configuration and stepup ratio,
   $H = 4\pi NI/10\mathscr{L}$ oersteds,
   $N =$ the number of turns on the high-voltage winding,
   $I =$ the load current in that winding in amperes,
   $\mathscr{L} =$ the length of the windings in cm (the primary and secondary windings are equal in length).

Because of Eq. (12·10) and relationship (4)

$$Z_T = \frac{377N\Delta\sqrt{f_2}}{\mathscr{L}\sqrt{\epsilon f_1}} = R_l, \tag{10}$$

where f_2 is a factor relating L_L to the winding arrangement, and also

$$\frac{\epsilon f_1 V^2}{9 \cdot 10^4 \cdot 8\pi\Delta^2} = \frac{H^2}{8\pi}.$$

If the average energy density in the coil is now made proportional to the energy density in the core at the end of the pulse,

$$\frac{\epsilon f_1 V^2}{9 \cdot 10^4 \cdot 4\pi\Delta^2} = \frac{f_3(\Delta\bar{B})^2}{8\pi\mu_e} = \frac{f_3}{8\pi\mu_e}\left(\frac{V\tau 10^8}{NA}\right)^2, \tag{11}$$

where f_3 is a factor of proportionality. If the average energy densities of core and coil are made equal, $f_3 = 1$. The actual value of f_3 used in practice is usually 1 ± 0.5.

Relationships (5) and (11) yield

$$\mathfrak{u}\Delta\mathscr{L} = \frac{1}{f_3} Al. \tag{12}$$

Also,

$$\mathscr{L} = f_4 N d_2, \tag{13}$$

where d_2 is the wire diameter of the high-voltage winding, and f_4 is a constant of proportionality, depending upon the winding configuration and stepup ratio. For a winding with a single-layer secondary, for example, $f_4 = 1$. Equations (12) and (13) then yield

$$\Delta = \frac{A}{f_3 f_4 N d_2},\tag{14}$$

where, because of Eq. (9), $\mathfrak{u}$ and l are assumed to be proportional and their factor of proportionality, which is close to unity, has been absorbed in $f_3 f_4$. Equation (11) becomes

$$\frac{\epsilon f_1 V^2}{9 \cdot 10^4 \cdot A^2}(f_3 f_4 N d_2)^2 = \frac{f_3}{2\mu_e}\left(\frac{V\tau 10^8}{NA}\right)^2,$$

or

$$N_{\text{opt}}^4 = \frac{9 \cdot 10^{20}\tau^2}{2\mu_e \epsilon f_1 f_3 (f_4 d_2)^2},$$

or

$$N_{\text{opt}} = \frac{9^{1/4} 10^5 \tau^{1/2}}{2^{1/4}(\mu_e \epsilon f_1 f_3)^{1/4}(f_4 d_2)^{1/2}}$$
$$= k_N \frac{\tau^{1/2}}{(\mu_e \epsilon f_1 f_3)^{1/4}(f_4 d_2)^{1/2}}.\tag{15}$$

Equations (10) and (14) yield

$$R_l = \frac{377 NA \sqrt{f_2}}{\sqrt{\epsilon f_1} f_3 f_4 N d_2 f_4 N d_2} = \frac{377 A \sqrt{f_2}}{\sqrt{\epsilon f_1} f_3 N(f_4 d_2)^2},$$

or

$$A = \frac{R_l \sqrt{\epsilon f_1} f_3 N(f_4 d_2)^2}{377 \sqrt{f_2}}.\tag{16}$$

Then

$$(\Delta\bar{B})_{\text{opt}} = \frac{V\tau 10^8}{N_{\text{opt}} A} = \frac{V\tau 10^8 \cdot 2^{1/2}(\mu_e \epsilon f_1 f_3)^{1/2}(f_4 d_2) 377 f_2^{1/2}}{10^8 \tau R_l (\epsilon f_1)^{1/2} f_3 (f_4 d_2)^2 \cdot 9^{1/2} \cdot 10^2},$$

or

$$(\Delta\bar{B})_{\text{opt}} = \frac{2^{1/2} \cdot 377 f_2^{1/2} V \mu_e^{1/2}}{3 \cdot 10^2 \cdot f_3^{1/2} f_4 d_2 R_l},$$

or

$$(\Delta\bar{B})_{\text{opt}} = \frac{k_B f_2^{1/2}}{f_3^{1/2} f_4} \frac{V \mu_e^{1/2}}{d_2 R_l}.\tag{17}$$

On the basis of Eqs. (15) and (16), the volume of the transformer core can be calculated under the condition that $A = 2a^2$ (see Fig. 13·2). The volume of the transformer is dependent upon b/a, and, to minimize the volume with respect to b/a, a value of $b/a \approx 2$ is suitable. Hence the value of

$$A = ab = 2a^2\tag{18}$$

is chosen.

If the cross section of the coil is assumed to be approximately equal to that of the core, l will be approximately equal to $10a$.

Then,

$$\text{core volume} \approx 20a^3 = \frac{20 \cdot 10^6 \cdot 9^{3/8} \cdot 10^{3/2}}{2^{15/8}377^{3/2}} \cdot \frac{R_l^{3/2}(\epsilon f_1)^{3/8}f_3^{3/8}(f_4 d_2)^{3/4}\tau^{3/4}}{f_2^{3/4}\mu_e^{3/8}}$$

$$= k_{\text{vol}} \cdot \frac{R_l^{3/2}(\epsilon f_1)^{3/8}f_3^{3/8}(f_4 d_2)^{3/4}\tau^{3/4}}{f_2^{3/4}\mu_e^{3/8}} \text{ cm}^3. \tag{19}$$

Also,

$$(\alpha + \beta)_{\text{opt}} = \frac{(\Delta \bar{B})_{\text{opt}}^2}{4\pi\mu_e} \cdot \text{core volume} \cdot \frac{1}{\dfrac{V^2\tau}{R_l}}$$

$$= \frac{2^{1/8}377^{1/2}10^7}{4\pi \cdot 9^{5/8}10^{5/2}} \cdot \frac{(\epsilon f_1)^{3/8}f_2^{1/4}f_3^{1/8}(f_4 d_2)^{1/4}R_l^{1/2}}{\mu_e^{3/8}\tau^{1/4}}$$

$$= k_{(\alpha+\beta)_{\text{opt}}} \frac{(\epsilon f_1)^{3/8}f_2^{1/4}f_3^{1/8}(f_4 d_2)^{1/4}R_l^{1/2}}{\mu_e^{3/8}\tau^{1/4}}. \tag{20}$$

Equations (15), (17), (19), and (20) are valuable in that they express the general dependence of N_{opt}, $(\Delta \bar{B})_{\text{opt}}$, $(\alpha + \beta)_{\text{opt}}$, and core volume on the quantities μ_e and ϵ, the properties of the materials a designer has at his disposal, and on R_l, τ, V, and d_2, the requirements which must be met in the design. When a transformer of a certain winding type has proved successful (that is, $\sqrt{L_L/C_D} = R_l$, $\tau_{\text{opt}} \equiv \sqrt{2L_p C_D} = \tau$, and $(\alpha + \beta)_{\text{opt}}$ is low) these equations are of further value in that they can be used to extrapolate (or scale) from this design to designs of the same winding type but for different values of R_l, V, and τ. This procedure of extrapolation essentially determines the constants k_N, k_B, k_{vol}, and $k_{(\alpha+\beta)_{\text{opt}}}$ on the basis of previous design experience. It is also possible to compute the values of these constants. These computed values are, however, less satisfactory because they do not take into consideration the margin length, the insulation between the primary and the core, etc.

It is to be noted that in Eq. (20) d_2 appears explicitly. If $(\alpha + \beta)_{\text{opt}}$ should be expressed with d_2 given implicitly in terms of V and R_l, as it occasionally can be, the $R_l^{1/2}$ term is altered in the equation.

It is interesting to note that the manner of dependence of $(\Delta \bar{B})_{\text{opt}}$ on V and R_l corresponds roughly with existing practice in the design of audio transformers: for example, when the power handled is low the transformer is designed to operate at low flux densities; when the power is high, the transformer is designed to operate at high flux densities.

It may prove instructive to illustrate an attempt at meeting the criteria of Eqs. (4), (5), and (6) with a design of a regenerative-pulse-generator transformer and a power-output pulse transformer for a magnetron.

Design of a Regenerative-pulse-generator or Blocking-oscillator Transformer.—It is assumed that the regenerative-pulse-generator transformer that is used as an example operates in a circuit with an effective series impedance in the grid loop of about 500 ohms and a tube whose r_p is about 500 ohms. It is also assumed for simplicity that this transformer has only two windings and that practically no power is delivered to an external circuit during the pulse. The characteristic impedance Z_T of the grid winding of the transformer is chosen to be approximately 500 ohms. The pulse duration is specified to be 1.0 μsec, the stepup ratio is $n = -1$, and the voltage to be applied to the plate winding of the transformer is not more than 500 volts.

In this example the core selected is a 0.002-in., type C Hipersil core whose μ_e for this type of application, as experience has shown, is about 400. The dielectric constant ϵ, for the insulation chosen is 3.5.

The effective distributed capacitance of this transformer, which, it is hoped, will have a simple single-layer primary winding and a single-layer secondary winding, is equal to the total capacitance between primary and secondary, that is,

$$C_D = \frac{0.0885\epsilon\mathcal{U}\mathcal{L} \cdot 10^{-12}}{\Delta} \qquad \text{farads,} \qquad (12·5)$$

and $f_1 = 1$ [see Eq. 12·9], where $\mathcal{U}$ is the mean perimeter of the coil, ϵ is the dielectric constant of the insulation, and $\mathcal{L}$ is the winding length. The leakage inductance

$$L_L = \frac{4\pi N^2 \Delta \mathcal{U}}{10^9 \mathcal{L}} \qquad \text{henrys,} \qquad (12·8)$$

and hence $f_2 = 1$ [see Eq. (13·10)]. Also,

$$L_p = \frac{4\pi N^2 A \mu_e}{10^9 l} \qquad \text{henrys.} \qquad (15·8)$$

By satisfying the criterion of Eq. (4), that is, $\sqrt{L_L/C_D} = R_l$, the relationship

$$\Delta = \frac{R_l \mathcal{L} \sqrt{\epsilon}}{377N} \qquad (21)$$

is obtained. Equation (5), that is, $\tau_{\text{opt}} \equiv \sqrt{2L_pC_D} = \tau$, gives the relationship

$$\begin{aligned}
\tau^2 &= \frac{8\pi N^2 A \mu_e}{10^9 l} \cdot \frac{0.0885\epsilon\mathcal{U}\mathcal{L} \cdot 10^{-12}}{\Delta} = \frac{8\pi N^2 A \mu_e}{10^9 l} \cdot \frac{0.0885\epsilon\mathcal{U} \cdot 10^{-12} \cdot 377N}{R_l \sqrt{\epsilon}} \\
&= \frac{8\pi \cdot 0.0885 \cdot 10^{-21} \cdot 377\mu_e \sqrt{\epsilon} \, N^3}{R_l} \cdot \frac{A\mathcal{U}}{l} \\
&= \frac{84 \times 10^{-20}}{R_l} \mu_e \sqrt{\epsilon} \, N^3 \frac{A\mathcal{U}}{l}.
\end{aligned} \qquad (22)$$

If a core is designed with complete latitude in the choice of dimensions, the dimensions should be chosen approximately in accord with the principles set forth in Eqs. (5), (8), (9), and (18). The type C Hipersil cores are manufactured in a set of more or less "quantized" sizes that have been wisely chosen and that are approximately in accord with the principles set forth in Eqs. (5), (8), (9), and (18). From the relationships given by Eqs. (15), (17), and (19), a knowledge of the approximate wire size required, and from past experience with transformers operating under the specified conditions, it is evident that two suitable candidate sizes of the Hipersil cores available are:

Core No. 1: window $\frac{1}{2}$ in. by $\frac{1}{4}$ in., strip width $\frac{1}{4}$ in., build $\frac{1}{8}$ in.; $A = 0.2$ cm^2, $l = 5.4$ cm, $Al = 1.1$ cm^3.

Core No. 2: window 1 in. by $\frac{5}{16}$ in., strip width $\frac{3}{8}$ in., build $\frac{1}{4}$ in.; $A = 0.6$ cm^2, $l = 9.4$ cm, $Al = 5.6$ cm^3.

For any transformer whose core dimensions are thus established, $A\mathfrak{U}/l$ may be expressed in terms of a (see Fig. 13·2). For example, for core No. 2, which is a well-proportioned core (except that l is slightly large and b/a is a little too low), $l = 15.7a$, $A = 1.67a^2$, $\mathfrak{U} \approx 9a$, and

$$\frac{A\mathfrak{U}}{l} = \frac{9 \cdot 1.67a^2}{15 \cdot 7} = 0.95a^2.$$

Then for Core No. 2, Eq. (22) yields

$$N^3a^2 = \frac{R_l \cdot 10^{20}\tau^2}{0.95 \cdot 84\mu_e\sqrt{\epsilon}} = \frac{500 \cdot 10^{20} \cdot 10^{-12}}{0.95 \cdot 84 \cdot 400\sqrt{3.5}}$$
$$= 0.83 \times 10^{-6}.$$

Since, for core No. 2, $a = 0.6$ cm

$$N^3 = \frac{0.83}{0.36} \times 10^6 = 2.3 \times 10^6,$$

or

$$N = 132.$$

In such transformers the average power dissipated in the winding, even if the wire diameter is very small, is usually negligibly small as far as permissible temperature rise is concerned. The wire size is consequently chosen on the basis of ease of winding and window size of the core, and on keeping the winding resistance negligible in comparison with the load resistance.

If size No. 38 heavy Formex wire (diameter = 0.0048 in. = 0.0122 cm) is used,

$$\pounds \approx 1.65 \text{ cm}.$$

Then

$$\Delta = \frac{R_l \mathcal{L} \sqrt{\epsilon}}{377N} = \frac{500 \cdot 1.65 \cdot 1.87}{377 \cdot 132} = 0.031 \text{ cm} = 0.012 \text{ in.},$$

and

$$C_D = \frac{0.0885 \cdot 3.5 \cdot 5.4 \cdot 1.65 \cdot 10^{-12}}{0.031} = 89 \times 10^{-12} \text{ farads},$$

$$L_L = \frac{4\pi \cdot 132^2 \cdot 0.031 \cdot 5.4}{10^9 \cdot 1.65} = 22.2 \times 10^{-6} \text{ henrys},$$

and

$$L_p = \frac{4\pi \cdot 132^2 \cdot 0.6 \cdot 400}{10^9 \cdot 9.4} = 5 \cdot 6 \times 10^{-3} \text{ henrys}.$$

The quality of the design may then be assayed by computing

$$(\alpha + \beta)_{\text{opt}}$$

for this transformer as follows:

$$(\alpha + \beta)_{\text{opt}} = \sqrt{\frac{2L_L}{L_p}} = \sqrt{\frac{2 \cdot 22.2 \times 10^{-6}}{5.6 \times 10^{-3}}} = \sqrt{7.94 \times 10^{-4}}$$
$$= 0.0282 \approx 0.03.$$

This value of $(\alpha + \beta)_{\text{opt}}$ corresponds to an efficiency of approximately 97 per cent, which is creditably high for a pulse transformer. The designer should, however, not take all the credit for himself; this low value of $(\alpha + \beta)_{\text{opt}}$ is possible because of the low value of impedance (see Eq. (20)) for which the transformer is designed, and also because the current-carrying requirements on the wire are such as to permit the choice of a small-diameter wire.

Perhaps the value of $(\alpha + \beta)_{\text{opt}}$ for this transformer could, if necessary, be reduced by choosing a better proportioned core, that is, one with a lower value of l. For example, the transformer may be constructed on two loops of core No. 1, for which $a = 0.32$, $l = 16.9a$, $A = 3.92a^2$, $\mathfrak{U} \approx 15.5a$.
Then

$$\frac{A\mathfrak{U}}{l} = \frac{3.92a^2 \cdot 15.5}{16.9} = 3.58a^2,$$

and

$$N^3 a^2 = \frac{500 \cdot 10^{20} \cdot 10^{-12}}{3.58 \cdot 84 \cdot 400 \cdot 1.87} = 0.222 \times 10^{-6},$$

and

$$N^3 = \frac{0.222 \times 10^6}{0.102} = 2.18 \times 10^6,$$

and

$$N = 130.$$

This transformer is then constructed on two loops (side by side) of core No. 1 by putting two single-layer windings each of 65 turns and of No. 38HF wire on each leg of the core.   The total winding length is then

$$\mathfrak{L} = 0.8 \cdot 2 = 1.6 \text{ cm.}$$

Then

$$\Delta = \frac{500 \cdot 1.6 \cdot 1.87}{377 \cdot 130} = 0.0305 \text{ cm} = 0.012 \text{ in.}$$

Thus, this transformer on two loops of core No. 1 has practically the same values of N, $\mathfrak{L}$, $\mathfrak{U}$, A/l, and Δ, and therefore has very nearly the same values of C_D, L_L, L_p, and $(\alpha + \beta)_{opt}$ as the transformer on core No. 2. The transformer constructed on two loops of core No. 1 has a lower mean magnetic-path length, but is less favorably proportioned with regard to a low value of $\mathfrak{U}$ than the transformer on core No. 2.   The two cores are therefore equally suitable.   If only one loop of core No. 1 were employed, it would prove necessary to increase the number of turns and hence to use very fine wire, which is difficult to handle and whose resistance may become an appreciable fraction of 500 ohms.   In fact, the winding resistance of each of these two transformers wound with No. 38 is about 16 ohms, which is three per cent of 500 ohms and therefore dissipates 3 per cent of the output power, thereby cutting the over-all efficiency of the transformer from 97 per cent to 94 per cent.   This efficiency may be improved 1 to 2 per cent by the use of core No. 2 which permits a longer winding length and hence an increase in wire size.   If the impedance of the load were higher, it would be possible to use wire with a smaller diameter.

Design of a Power-output Pulse Transformer for a Magnetron.—It is assumed that the power-output pulse transformer that is used as an example is one which is intended for use on small lightweight airborne equipment and which must meet the following requirements:

Voltage out/voltage in: 12.5 kv/2.5kv; $n = 5$,
Impedance out/impedance in: 1250/50,
Pulse durations: 0.5, 1.0, and 2.0 μsec,
Pulse recurrence frequencies: 2000, 1000, and 500 pps,
Filament current supplied to the magnetron: 1.0 amp.

The lower limit to the wire sizes in this transformer is fixed not by the value of the load impedance (as it is in the previous example) but by the permissible temperature rise of the windings, which is the result of the "effective currents" in the primary and secondary windings.   The effective current is the effective sum (as far as energy dissipation in the wire is concerned) of the filament current and the pulse current, with skin effect and proximity effect taken into consideration.   In the primary winding there is, of course, no filament current.   In order to keep the operating temperature of the winding at a safe value, it is, in general, desirable to limit the effective current density to a value of about 5000 amp/in.[2] The current density for a filament current of 1.0 amp in several wire sizes is given as follows: No. 24, 3170 amp/in.[2]; No. 25, 4000 amp/in.[2]; No. 26, 5000 amp/in.[2]

It should be remembered that this pulse transformer is required to perform satisfactorily at a pulse duration of 0.5 μsec as well as at 1.0 and 2.0 μsec. To achieve a favorable value of $\alpha + \beta$ over this range of pulse durations and to keep the transformer small and light, the wire diameter must be kept to a minimum. Since this transformer is to be insulated with oil and hence oil-cooled, it is possible to use No. 25 or even No. 26 wire for the secondary, even though the filament current densities therein approach 5000 amp/in.[2]

A rough calculation should be made to ascertain how much effective pulse current, in addition to the filament current, will dissipate power in the secondary winding. The load current in the secondary is about 10 amp, and since there are two wires of No. 26 in parallel to carry this current, the pulse current per wire is 5 amp. The duty ratio is 0.001. The skin depth for a 0.5-μsec pulse may be computed to be

$$\Delta_p \approx \sqrt{0.5} \cdot 10^{-2} \text{ cm} = 0.007 \text{ cm} = 0.0028 \text{ in.}$$

(see Sec. 15·3). Since the bare-copper diameter of No. 26 wire is 0.0159 in., the skin-effect factor is approximately

$$\frac{d}{4\Delta_p} = \frac{0.0159}{4 \cdot 0.0028} \approx 1.5.$$

The proximity factor is $2 \cdot 1.4 = 2.8$ (see Sec. 15·3). The effective pulse power dissipated in the winding is then

$$0.001 \cdot I_{\text{pulse}}^2 R \cdot 1.5 \cdot 2.8 = 0.0042 I_{\text{pulse}}^2 R,$$

where R is the resistance of the winding and I_{pulse} is the pulse current. The total effective current I_{eff} may then be calculated by the equation

$$I_{\text{eff}}^2 R = I_{\text{fil}}^2 R + 0.0042 I_{\text{pulse}}^2 R,$$

or

$$I_{\text{eff}} = \sqrt{1.0^2 + 0.0042 \cdot 25} = \sqrt{1.0 + 0.10}$$
$$= 1.05 \approx 1 \text{ amp.}$$

It is therefore obvious that practically all of the power dissipated in the secondary winding is the result of filament current and that the effective current density in this winding for both pulse and filament current is about 5000 amp/sq. in. for No. 26 wire.

With winding arrangement (*f*) in Fig. 12·13 it is often advantageous to use the same wire size in the primary as in the secondary. If No. 26 wire (one wire on each leg of the core) is also used in the primary, the effective current therein is $I_{\text{eff}} \approx 25 \cdot \sqrt{0.0042} \approx 1.6$ amp if the proximity factor of 2.8 is used in the calculations. This value of I_{eff} means an effective current density in the primary wire of about 8000 amp/in.[2] The actual value of I_{eff} will be somewhat less than 1.6 amp because the proximity factor for the primary is actually less than 2.8. The effective current density in the primary will, at any rate, be greater than 5000 amp/in.[2] However, because the weight, space, and pulse-performance requirements placed upon the transformer are rigorous, it is justifiable to use No. 26 wire on the primary, notwithstanding the high effective current density.

For this type of transformer (as has been shown in Sec. 12·2) the winding arrangement (*f*) in Fig. 12·13 (the Lord-type winding) has the lowest $L_L C_D$-product and therefore represents a transformer whose coil stores less pulse energy than the coil of any other type of winding that could be chosen. Therefore winding arrangement (*f*) is the most suitable one for this transformer. Now, from the equation for L_L for winding (*f*), the total leakage inductance for the coils on both legs is

$$L_L = \frac{4\pi N_s^2 \mathfrak{u}}{\mathfrak{L}} \frac{1}{4}\left(\frac{n-1}{n}\right)^2 \left(\Delta_1 + \Delta_2 + \frac{\Sigma a}{3}\right), \tag{23}$$

where $n = 5$, and $\Sigma a/3$ is, for the purposes of simplification, to be neglected.

The total distributed capacitance between primary and secondary for the coils on both legs, according to Eq. (12·5) and (12·6), is

$$C_D = \frac{2\Sigma W}{V_s^2} = \frac{0.0885\epsilon\mathfrak{u}}{V_s^2}\frac{\mathfrak{L}}{3}\left[\frac{(\delta V_1)^2 + \delta V_1 \cdot \delta V_2 + (\delta V_2)^2}{\Delta_1}\right.$$
$$+ \left.\frac{(\delta V_1)^2 + \delta V_1 \cdot \delta V_2 + (\delta V_2)^2}{\Delta_2}\right] = \frac{0.0885\epsilon\mathfrak{u}}{25}\cdot\frac{\mathfrak{L}}{3}\left(\frac{1^2 + 1\cdot 2 + 2^2}{\Delta_1}\right.$$
$$+ \left.\frac{3^2 + 3\cdot 4 + 4^2}{\Delta_2}\right), = \frac{0.0885\epsilon\mathfrak{u}}{25}\frac{\mathfrak{L}}{3}\left(\frac{7}{\Delta_1} + \frac{37}{\Delta_2}\right). \tag{24}$$

It is desirable to keep the characteristic impedances of the first and second legs of the transformer approximately equal. The characteristic impedance Z_1 of leg No. 1 is proportional to $\sqrt{7\Delta_1^2}$. The characteristic impedance Z_2 of leg No. 2 is proportional to $\sqrt{37\Delta_2^2}$. If $Z_1 = Z_2$,

$$\frac{\Delta_1}{\Delta_2} = \sqrt{\frac{37}{7}} = 2.3 \approx 2.$$

Also, in order to make the voltage stress on the insulation pads 1 and 2 the same, Δ_1/Δ_2 should equal 2. If

$$\Delta_{av} = \frac{\Delta_1 + \Delta_2}{2} \approx \sqrt{\Delta_1\Delta_2},$$
$$\Delta_{av} = \tfrac{3}{2}\Delta_1 = \tfrac{3}{4}\Delta_2.$$

Then Eqs. (23) and (24) become, respectively,

$$L_L = \frac{4\pi N_s^2 \mathcal{U}}{\mathcal{L}}\frac{1}{4}\left(\frac{n-1}{n}\right)^2 \cdot 2\Delta_{av} = \frac{4\pi N_s^2 \mathcal{U}\Delta_{av}}{2\mathcal{L}}f_2,$$

where

$$f_2 = \left(\frac{n-1}{n}\right)^2,$$

and

$$C_D \approx \frac{0.0885\epsilon\mathcal{U}\mathcal{L}}{25 \cdot 3}\frac{1}{\Delta_{av}}\left(7 \cdot \frac{3}{2} + 37 \cdot \frac{3}{4}\right)$$
$$= \frac{0.0885\epsilon\mathcal{U}\mathcal{L}}{3 \cdot 25}\frac{1}{\Delta_{av}} \cdot \frac{153}{4}$$
$$= \frac{2 \cdot 0.0885\epsilon\mathcal{U}\mathcal{L}}{2 \cdot 3} \cdot \frac{1.53}{\Delta_{av}} = \frac{2 \cdot 0.0885\epsilon\mathcal{U}\mathcal{L}}{\Delta_{av}}f_1,$$

where

$$f_1 = \frac{1\,53}{2 \cdot 3} = 0.255.$$

Also, it should be remembered that

$$L_p = \frac{4\pi N_s^2 A\mu_e}{10^9 l} \quad \text{henrys,}$$
$$L_L = \frac{4\pi N_s^2 \mathcal{U}\Delta_{av}}{10^9 2\mathcal{L}}f_2 \quad \text{henrys,}$$
$$C_D = \frac{2 \cdot 0.0885\epsilon\mathcal{U}\mathcal{L}}{\Delta_{av}}f_1 \times 10^{-12} \quad \text{farads,}$$

and

$$R_l = \frac{377 N_s \Delta_{av}\sqrt{f_2}}{2 \cdot \mathcal{L}\sqrt{\epsilon f_1}} \quad \text{ohms.}$$

Then

$$\Delta_{av} = \frac{2 \cdot R_l\mathcal{L}\sqrt{\epsilon f_1}}{377 N_s\sqrt{f_2}} \quad \text{cm,}$$

and

$$\tau_{opt}^2 = 2C_D L_p = \frac{4 \cdot 0.0885\epsilon\mathcal{U}\mathcal{L} \cdot 10^{-12}}{\Delta_{av}} \cdot f_1 \cdot \frac{4\pi N_s^2 A\mu_e}{10^9 l} \quad \text{sec}^2,$$
$$= \frac{16\pi \cdot 0.0885 \cdot 10^{-12}}{10^9}\mu_e\epsilon f_1 N_s^2 \cdot \frac{\mathcal{L}A\mathcal{U}}{l} \cdot \frac{377 N_s\sqrt{f_2}}{2R_l\mathcal{L}\sqrt{\epsilon f_1}}$$
$$= \frac{8\pi \cdot 377}{10^9} \cdot 0.0885 \cdot 10^{-12}\mu_e\sqrt{\epsilon f_1 f_2}\frac{N_s^3}{R_l}\frac{A\mathcal{U}}{l},$$

or

$$\tau_{\text{opt}}^2 = 84.0 \times 10^{-20} \frac{\mu_e \sqrt{\epsilon f_1 f_2} \, N_s^3}{R_l} \frac{A\mathfrak{u}}{l}.$$

Then

$$N_s^3 \frac{A\mathfrak{u}}{l} = \frac{\tau_{\text{opt}}^2 \cdot R_l}{84 \times 10^{-20} \mu_e \sqrt{\epsilon f_1 f_2}} = 1.19 \times 10^{18} \tau_{\text{opt}}^2 \frac{R_l}{\mu_e \sqrt{\epsilon f_1 f_2}}$$

$$= 1.19 \times 10^6 \tau_{\text{opt}}'^2 \frac{R_l}{\mu_e \sqrt{\epsilon f_1 f_2}},$$

where τ_{opt}' is given in μsec.

A core which may be tried is a 0.002 in. Hipersil core: window, $1\frac{1}{8}$ in. by $\frac{1}{2}$ in.; strip width, 1 in.; build, $\frac{7}{16}$ in. For this core

$$a = 1.1 \text{ cm},$$
$$A = 2.82 \text{ cm}^2 = 2.31 a^2,$$
$$l = 13.2 \text{ cm} = 12a,$$

and

$$\mathfrak{u} \approx 11.2 \text{ cm} = 10.2a.$$

Then

$$\frac{\mathfrak{u} A}{l} = \frac{10.2a \cdot 2.31 a^2}{12a} = 1.96 a^2 = 2.38 \text{ cm}^2.$$

Also, μ_e for this core material in this type of application is about 600, $\epsilon = 3.5$, and as has been seen, $\sqrt{f_1} = 0.505$, and $\sqrt{f_2} = \frac{4}{5}$. Then

$$N_s^3 = \frac{1.19 \times 10^6 \cdot 1250}{2.38 \cdot 1.87 \cdot 0.505 \cdot 0.8 \cdot 600} = 1.38 \times 10^6$$

or

$$N_s \approx 111.$$

This transformer, with $N_s = 110$ turns, the appropriate Δ_1 and Δ_2, and approximately adequate creep distances, can be wound according to winding scheme (f), Fig. 12·13, with No. 25 heavy Formex wire on the secondary.

It is customary to try a new pulse-transformer design in the circuit for which it is intended before the design is considered satisfactory. It is intended that this particular transformer be used with both hard-tube and line-type pulsers. Therefore a pair of such transformers is constructed and operated in tandem with a hard-tube pulse generator and magnetron. Unfortunately, it is found that the backswing voltage on the pulser switch tube is excessive on the 2-μsec pulse operation. (A discussion of backswing voltage is given in Sec. 14·1.) From Eq. (14·13) it can be shown that the backswing voltage can be reduced by increasing L_p. A compromise transformer is therefore designed on this same core with $N_s = 125$ with No. 26 wire on the secondary in an attempt to satisfy this backswing requirement. Thus, some sacrifice is made in the accuracy with which Eq. (5) (that is, $\tau_{\text{opt}} = \sqrt{2C_DL_p}$) is satisfied. Equation (4) (that is, $\sqrt{L_L/C_D} = R_l$) may be satisfied by choosing Δ_{av} according to the equation

$$\Delta_{\text{av}} = \frac{R_l \cdot 2\mathcal{L} \sqrt{\epsilon f_1}}{377 N_s \sqrt{f_2}} = \frac{1250 \cdot 2 \cdot 2.38 \cdot 1.87 \cdot 0.505}{377 \cdot 125 \cdot 0.8} = 0.149 \text{ cm}$$
$$= 0.058 \text{ in.,}$$

where

$$\mathcal{L} \approx 50 \cdot 0.0178 \text{ in.} \approx 0.9 \text{ in.} = 2.38 \text{ cm.}$$

The transformer is then constructed with $\Delta_1 = \frac{2}{3} \Delta_{\text{av}}$ and $\Delta_2 = \frac{4}{3}\Delta_{\text{av}}$. Its C_D and L_L are measured, and the nominal pad thicknesses Δ_1 and Δ_2 further adjusted to make $\sqrt{L_L/C_D} \approx R_l$, with the thought in mind that the insulation must be fitted into the window and that the puncture stress of the insulation must be kept at a safe value.

The parameters of the new transformer are measured and the following values (referred to the secondary) are obtained: $L_L = 54 \times 10^{-6}$ henry, $C_D = 50 \times 10^{-12}$ farad, and $L_p = 24 \times 10^{-3}$ henry. From these values it can be calculated that

$$Z_T = \sqrt{\frac{L_L}{C_D}} = 1040 \text{ ohms,}$$
$$\tau_{\text{opt}} = \sqrt{2L_pC_D} = 1.5 \text{ } \mu\text{sec,}$$
$$(\alpha + \beta)_{\text{opt}} = 0.067,$$

and that the efficiency at 1.5 μsec is

$$\eta = 100[1 - (\alpha + \beta)_{\text{opt}}] = 93.3 \text{ per cent.}$$

This value of $Z_T = 1040$ ohms, though not exactly equal to the load impedance R_l (1250 ohms), is considered to be satisfactorily near to this value. Furthermore, optimum pulse shape on a magnetron load is obtained with a hard-tube pulser when

$$\sqrt{\frac{2L_L}{C_D + C_l}} = R_l,$$

and with a line-type pulser when

$$\sqrt{\frac{L_L}{C_D + C_l}} = R_l,$$

where $C_l (\approx 15 \text{ } \mu\mu f)$ is the load capacitance (see Sec. 14·1). For a pair of these transformers used with a hard-tube pulser,

$$\sqrt{\frac{2L_L}{C_D + C_l}} = 1270 \text{ ohms.}$$

For one of these transformers used with a line-type pulser,

$$\sqrt{\frac{L_L}{C_D + C_l}} = 910 \text{ ohms.}$$

Since the most important use for this transformer is in a radar system employing a hard-tube pulser, the value of Z_T for the transformer is considered to be satisfactory from the point of view of pulse shape as well as from that of maximum energy transfer. The value of $\tau_{opt} = 1.5$ μsec, though greater than $\sqrt{\frac{1}{2} \mu\text{sec} \cdot 2 \mu\text{sec}}$, is considered to be satisfactory; it is impossible to have $\tau_{opt} = 1$ μsec because of the maximum allowable backswing voltage. The value of the efficiency is considered to be sufficiently high to make unnecessary the trial of any other core sizes in the design.

The measured values of L_L, C_D, and L_p are usually more accurate than the calculated values because it is very difficult to control the coil dimensions with great accuracy and to have exact knowledge of the effective permeability of the core under the particular conditions of operation.

The resultant design is that of transformer 232BW2 given in Tables 13·1 and 13·2. Two such transformers are built, operated in tandem on a magnetron, and are found to hold the backswing voltage on the pulse-generator switch tube to an acceptably low value. Transformer 232AW2, somewhat similar, but a simon-pure autotransformer, is then designed to be used in the stepdown position.

Calorimetric measurements are then performed on transformer 232BW2 (as a cased unit) under operating conditions, and its calorimetric efficiency (exclusive of power dissipated by the filament current) is found to be 93 per cent at 1 μsec. This value of efficiency agrees within 1 per cent with $(\alpha + \beta)_{opt}$ calculated from the measured values of L_p and L_L.

It is not clear, however, that all the difficulties have been overcome. The creep stress of the high-voltage end of the secondary to ground is about 100 volts/mil, and therefore it is doubtful that the transformer will stand the voltage of 12 kv for any length of time. With No. 26 wire the effective current density in the primary winding is very high. If there is any doubt that oil and paper insulation will withstand the high ambient temperatures encountered by these transformers (which are assumed to be used, for example, on equipment for carrier-based aircraft in the Pacific), a life test under operating conditions should be performed with the stepup transformer in a simulated ambient temperature of 85°C.

Successful operation after 2000 hours of this life test is sufficient to justify the recommendation that this transformer be used in the equipment.

A photograph of the core-and-coil assembly of transformer 232BW2 is shown in Fig. 13·3, together with the core-and-coil assembly of a 600-kw pulse transformer (transformer 410AW2 in Tables 13·1 and 13·2).

Departures from Customary Design Practice.—It is desirable, in general, to try to meet criteria of Eqs. (4), (5), and (6) in the design of a pulse transformer. Often, however, it may prove advantageous to depart from the practice of using single-layer primary and single-layer secondary windings of the same length. For example, if the pulse duration is long, and if the effective impedance of the load is very high (as it is in a trans-

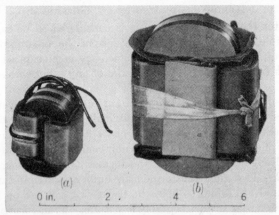

Fig. 13·3.—Core-and-coil assemblies of oil-filled pulse transformers (a) 120 kw (232BW2), 0.5 to 2.0 μsec. (b) 600 kw (410AW2) 0.5 to 2.0 μsec.

former used in the triggering of series gaps), the high-voltage winding may be composed of several layers. The consequent increase in L_L is acceptable since it is desirable to make

$$\tau_{\mathrm{opt}} = \sqrt{2L_pC_D} = \frac{\sqrt{2L_pL_L}}{R_l}$$

and

$$\sqrt{\frac{L_L}{C_D}} = R_l,$$

where R_l and τ_{opt} are both large.

Where pulse transformers must operate into loads of very high resistance and/or low capacitance it is frequently desirable to use a duolaterally wound coil. This duolaterally wound coil facilitates winding with small wire sizes and has, in general, low effective distributed capacitance. The higher leakage inductance associated with duolaterally wound coils can be tolerated because of the high load resistance for which these transformers are designed. There are many possible arrangements of duolateral "pies" and layers, and the designer should choose the arrangement which, for his purpose, stores a minimum amount of energy in the transformer coil. Such duolaterally wound transformers are suitable for use at both low- and high-voltage levels. Duolaterally wound transformers for operation at high-voltage levels are particularly suitable for use as trigger transformers.

According to customary design practice, pulse transformers that are to operate at very high voltages require a core of very large l since the margins of the coil must be made long enough to withstand the high creep stress. If the load impedance for such a transformer is high (as it usually is), this difficulty can be obviated by a design of the type shown in Fig. 13·4. This particular transformer design employs a toroidal core, Teflon insulation (to reduce C_D and withstand the voltage stress) impregnated with oil, and primary and secondary windings of unequal length. This transformer is capable of supplying current to the filament whose cathode it pulses. The insulation and wire for this transformer must, of course, be wound on the core with a bobbin. Pulse transformers with a winding

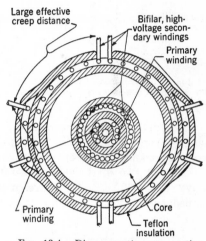

Fig. 13·4.—Diagrammatic cross section showing a way of placing windings on a toroidal core for a transformer to be operated at very high voltages and into a high load impedance. This transformer has a bifilar secondary winding and the core is allowed to "float" electrically.

of this type have operated successfully at an output voltage of 100 kv on a load impedance of about 20,000 ohms, at 0.5 μsec pulses, with a stepup ratio $n = 5.5$.

When special requirements such as the maximum amount of overshoot, droop, or backswing are placed upon the pulse-transformer design, it is necessary to consider the effect of the various individual elements in the equivalent circuit on pulse shape, a discussion of which is given in Sec. 14·1. Even when satisfying such special requirements, it frequently proves effective to make the preliminary or trial design on the basis of the criteria of Eqs. (4), (5), and (6).

13·3. Typical Pulse-transformer Designs.—A number of successful pulse-transformer designs were developed by the Radiation Laboratory

for various applications in radar systems. These designs were usually
achieved by the process of a series of successive approximations in design
outlined in Sec. 13·2. Diagrammatic winding specifications and ratings
for some of the more widely used of these designs are included in this
section. The designs are divided into two groups, regenerative-pulse-
generator transformers and pulse-generator-output transformers.

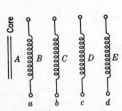

FIG. 13·5.—Schematic winding diagram
for a typical regenerative-pulse-generator
transformer.

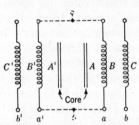

FIG. 13·6.—Schematic winding diagram
for a typical stepup low-power output
transformer.

Regenerative-pulse-generator transformers, which have three or four
single-layer windings with turns ratios near unity may also be used as
coupling transformers between amplifier stages.

All but two of the pulse-generator-output transformers (Nos. 148-
CW2 and 232AW2) were designed to drive magnetrons from low-
impedance pulse-cable or line-type pulsers. They have windings of a

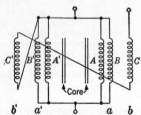

FIG. 13·7.—Schematic winding diagram for
a typical stepdown autotransformer.

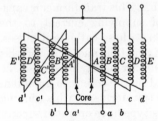

FIG. 13·8.—Schematic winding diagram
for a typical stepup high-power output
transformer.

type [winding arrangement (*f*), Fig. 12·13] designed to minimize
the product of leakage inductance and distributed capacitance, and
bifilar secondaries to permit the supply of cathode-heater power
to magnetrons from low-voltage-insulated filament transformers.
One example of a stepdown transformer, No. 232AW2, is included
to indicate, by comparison with the corresponding stepup design
(No. 232BW2), how the other designs in this group may be modified
for use as stepdown transformers to be employed between hard-

tube pulsers and low-impedance cable.   All of these transformers, except
No. 148 CW2 and 148 DW2, have values of n between 3 and 5.

The values of pulse duration and load impedance given in Table 13·1
for these transformers are, in general, those determined from the values of
shunt inductance, leakage inductance, and distributed capacitance by

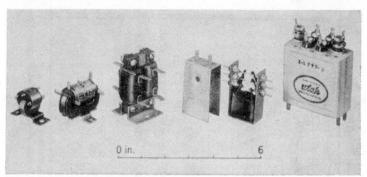

FIG. 13·9.—Some examples of low-power regenerative-pulse-generator pulse transformers.

the method outlined in Sec. 13·1.   The voltages given are determined
from insulation thicknesses and from a stress factor of 250 volts per mil
for oil-impregnated units, or 100 volts per mil for small dry-type units.

In Figs. 13·5 to 13·8 a single coiled line represents a single winding
layer, which is, in general, to be centered on the coil form.   In general

FIG. 13·10.—Three pulse transformers designed for operation at 120 kv, 0.5, 1.0, and
2.0 μsec.   (a) Core-and-coil assembly of an oil-filled pulse transformer (232-BW2) on a
0.002-in. Hipersil core.   (b) G. E. pulse transformer with Permafil insulation on a 0.003-in.
Monemax core.   (c) Westinghouse pulse transformer with Fosterite insulation on a
0.002-in. Hipersil core.

all windings on one leg of the core are wound in the same direction.   In
these figures, however, the windings on one leg are wound in the opposite
direction from the windings on the other leg.   Connections between winding layers are indicated by straight lines.   The wire size and the number

TABLE 13·1.—Operating Data for Typical Pulse Transformers

Design	132 AW2	145 CW2	224 AW2	148 CW2	232 AW2	232 BW2	232 FW2	285 DW2	311 IW2	355 BW2	377 BW2	410 AW2
Pulse voltage, kv	1/1/1	0.5/0.5/0.5	1/1/0.3	2/0.2(a)* 2/0.4(b) 2/0.4(c)	12.5/2.5	12.5/2.5	16.5/3.3	28/7	36/12	15/3.3	54/24	22/5.5
Pulse duration, μsec	0.3–1.5	1–5	0.1–0.5	0.6–3(a)† 0.25–2.5(b) 0.5–2.5(c)	0.5–2.5	0.5–2.5	0.25–1.25	1–2	1.5–2.5	1–5	1	0.5–2.5
Maximum duty ratio	0.002	0.002	0.002	0.002	0.001	0.001	0.001	0.0006	0.0006	0.001	0.0005	0.001
Load impedance, ohms	250	500	1000	1600(a) 1000(b) 2000(c)	50 step-down	1250	1250	400	450	1000	250	800
Noninduced voltages, volts	1	0.5	1	....	....	....	....	....	....	....	....	....

* (a), (b), and (c) refer to the voltage ratios obtained with the various ways of connecting the transformer.
† (a), (b), and (c) refer to the various pulse durations that can be obtained at rated voltage with the various connections which give rise to voltage ratio (a), (b), and (c).

of turns are given in Table 13·2.   The total thicknesses of the insulating pads between the winding layers and between the inner winding and the core are given in mils.   Pads between windings that are 15 mils thick or greater are usually wound with 5-mil unsized Kraft paper; those of less thickness are wound with 2-mil Kraft paper.   A part of the thickness of the pads between inner windings and cores may consist of a fiber coil form; this form should fit closely around the core in order to make the mean perimeter of the coil a minimum.   Vacuum (less than 1 mm of mercury) impregnation with a good grade of transformer oil is recommended for all units rated at greater than 6 kv.   Any of the varnishes of

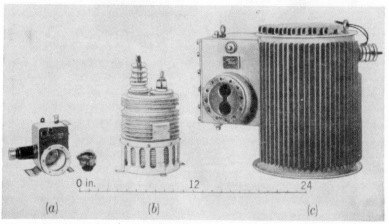

Fig. 13·11.—Three pulse transformers designed for operation at different power levels. (a) 120 kw (232 BW2) with well for magnetron (Westinghouse).   (b) 2 Mw (GE) (c) 10 Mw (377 BW2) with form-fitting well for magnetron (GE).

the solventless type, which harden without leaving voids, may be used for the dry-type units (which are rated at less than 6 kv).   Good solvent-type varnishes may also be used for units rated at less than 2 kv.   Standard sizes of Westinghouse 0.002-in. oriented Hipersil cores are specified throughout, except in some cases where two standard loops may be placed side by side to make up the specified strip width.

Figure 13·9 shows several examples of low-power regenerative-pulse-generator transformers that have been developed; Fig. 13·10 shows three 120-kw pulse transformers; and Fig. 13·11 shows three pulse transformers of pulse powers of 120 kw, 2 Mw, and 10 Mw.   Two of these latter transformers have wells into which the magnetron may be plugged.   The well of the 10-Mw transformer is form-fitting and is greased with Dow-Corning Compound to exclude air when the magnetron is plugged in. Figure 13·12 shows pulse transformers employing permalloy cores and

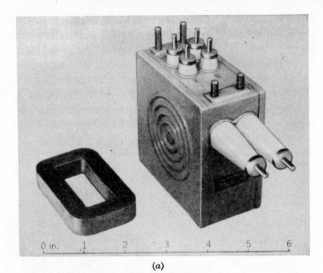

FIG. 13·12.—Three pulse transformers constructed with continuously wound permalloy cores (Western Electric Company). (a) Rectangular core of 1-mil 4-79 molybdenum permalloy and pulse transformer in which it is used. Pulse power: 100 kw. (b) 3-lb. rectangular core of 2-mil 45 permalloy and $\frac{1}{4}$-lb. core of 1-mil 4-79 molybdenum permalloy with the pulse transformers in which they are used.

TABLE 13·2.—DESIGN SPECIFICATIONS FOR TYPICAL PULSE TRANSFORMERS

Design	132 AW2	145 CW2	224 AW2	148 CW2	232 AW2	232 BW2	232 FW2	285 DW2	311 IW2	355 BW2	377 BW2	410 AW2
Core window, in.²	1 × 5/16	1 × 3/8	3/4 × 1/4	1 × 3/8	1 1/8 × 1/2	1 1/8 × 1/2	1 1/8 × 1/2	2 1/4 × 7/8	3 × 1 1/4	1 1/16 × 5/8	4 11/16 × 1 1/4	2 1/4 × 11/16
Strip, in.	3/8	9/16	1/4	9/16	1/2	1/2	1/2	2	2	1	3 1/4	1
Build, in.	37	37	1/4	37	1/16	1/16	1/16	1 1/4	1 1/4	5/8	1 1/2	7/8
Assembly wire	Fig. 13·5	Fig. 13·5	Fig. 13·5	Fig. 13·6 HF	Fig. 13·7 HF	Fig. 13·8 HF	Fig. 13·8 HF	Fig. 13·8 QF	Fig. 13·8 QF	Fig. 13·8 HF	Fig. 13·8 QF	Fig. 13·8 QF
A, in.	0.015	0.020	0.020	0.020	0.025	0.020	0.025	0.050	0.090	0.030	0.200	0.045
a	32-#30	125-#36	35-#32	25-#35 5 in.//	25-#26 2 in.//	25-#26 2 in.//	14-#23 2 in.//	16-#21 3 in.//	21-#23 3 in.//	34-#23	16-#23 5 in.//†	26-#22 2 in.//
B, in.	0.010	0.005	0.010	0.020	0.050	0	0	0.010	0.010	0.005	0	0.010
b	32-#30	125-#36	35-#32	110-#35	50-#26			16-#21 3 in.//	21-#23 3 in.//	34-#23		26-#22 2 in.//
C, in.	0.010	0.005	0.010	0.020	0.050	0.040	0.100	0.080	0.090	0.050	0.180	0.075
c	32-#30	125-#36	35-#32			50-#26	28-#23	24-#21 2 in.//	21-#23 3 in.//	60-#27	10-#23 8 in.//††	39-#19
D, in.	0.015	0.020	0.010			0.005	0.005	0.010	0.010	0.005	0	0.010
d			10-#21			50-#26	28-#23	24-#21 2 in.//	21-#23 3 in.//	60-#27		39-#19
E, in.			0.020			0.050	0.050	0.070	0.090	0.060	0.200	0.050
A', in.				0.020	0.025	0.020	0.025	0.050	0.090	0.030	0.200	0.045
a'				22-#35 5 in.//	25-#26 2 in.//	25-#26 2 in.//	14-#23 2 in.//	16-#21 3 in.//	21-#23 3 in.//	34-#23	16-#23 5 in.//†	26-#22 2 in.//
B', in.				0.020	0.030	0	0	0.010	0.010	0.005	0	0.010
b'				110-#35	50-#26			16-#21 3 in.//	21-#23 3 in.//	34-#23		26-#22 2 in.//
C', in.				0.020	0.040	0.025	0.050	0.010	0.045	0.025	0.100	0.040
c'						50-#26	28-#23	24-#21 2 in.//	21-#23 3 in.//	60-#27	10-#23 8 in.//††	39-#19
D', in.						0.005	0.005	0.010	0.010	0.005	0	0.010
d'						50-#26	28-#23	24-#21 2 in.//	21-#23 3 in.//	60-#27		39-#19
E', in.						0.040	0.030	0.050	0.050	0.040	0.120	0.040

† 3 wires in primary, 2 in secondary, 2 cords.
†† 3 cotton cords equal in diameter to the wire, wound in parallel with the wire to effect space-winding.

// Parallel.
QF Quadruple formex.
HF Heavy formex.
32-#30 means 32 turns of No. 30 wire.

constructed with diaphragms to accommodate the thermal expansion of the oil.

In these figures are exhibited some of the final results of the designer's effort.

Summary.—Chapter 13 has established relationships between the elements in the equivalent circuit of the pulse transformer and the optimum load impedance, pulse duration, and efficiency. General design methods for achieving these relationships in building the pulse transformer have been advanced, and two examples of the application of these methods are given. The design data on a number of successful pulse transformers are given, and methods for employing these data and the general design methods used in designing new transformers are outlined.

CHAPTER 14

EFFECT OF PULSE-TRANSFORMER PARAMETERS ON CIRCUIT BEHAVIOR

BY W. H. BOSTICK

14.1. The Effect of Pulse-transformer Parameters on Pulse Shapes on Resistance and Biased-diode or Magnetron Loads.—This section treats in turn, the effect of the pulse transformer upon the rise, the top, and the tail of rectangular pulses applied to the primary when resistance and biased-diode loads are connected to the secondary. In this treat-

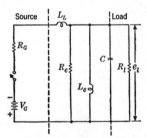

Fig. 14·1.—Equivalent circuit of a pulse generator, a pulse transformer, and a resistance load.

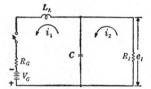

Fig. 14·2.—Equivalent circuit for the computation of the rise of the pulse on a resistance load.

ment the simple equivalent circuit of Fig. 14·1 is, for the most part, employed, and the rectangular pulses are considered to be generated by the closing and opening of the switch shown in the circuit.

The Rise of the Pulse on a Resistance Load.—The rise of the pulse on a resistance load R_l is considered for a transformer in which the effect of R_e is assumed to be negligible compared with that of R_l, and where the time of rise is so short that the effect of L_e is also negligible. The initial energies in L_L, L_e, and C are assumed to be zero. The mesh currents may be chosen as shown in Fig. 14·2. The Laplace transforms of the mesh equations may be written as follows:

$$\left(p^2 + \frac{R_G}{L_L}p + \frac{1}{L_LC}\right)i_1(p) - \frac{1}{L_LC}i_2(p) = \frac{V_G}{L_L}$$

$$-\frac{1}{R_lC}i_1(p) + \left(p + \frac{1}{R_lC}\right)i_2(p) = 0,$$

563

whence

$$e_l(p) = R_l i_2(p) = \frac{V_G}{L_L C} \frac{1}{\left[\left(p^2 + \frac{R_G}{L_L} p + \frac{1}{L_L C}\right)\left(p + \frac{1}{R_l C}\right) - \frac{1}{L_L C} \frac{1}{R_l C}\right]},$$

$$= \frac{V_G}{L_L C} \frac{1}{p\left[p^2 + \left(\frac{R_G}{L_L} + \frac{1}{R_l C}\right)p + \frac{1}{L_L C}\left(1 + \frac{R_G}{R_l}\right)\right]};$$

or

$$R_l i_2(p) = \frac{V_G}{L_L C} \frac{1}{p(p^2 + 2ap + b)}.$$

Then

$$e_l(t) = \frac{V_G R_l}{R_G + R_l}\left[1 - e^{-at}\left(\frac{a}{k}\sinh kt + \cosh kt\right)\right], \tag{1}$$

where

$$2a = \frac{R_G}{L_L} + \frac{1}{CR_l},$$

$$b = \frac{1}{L_L C}\left(1 + \frac{R_G}{R_l}\right),$$

and

$$k^2 = a^2 - b.$$

When

$$b > a^2,$$
$$k = j\omega,$$
$$\omega^2 = b - a^2,$$

and

$$e_l(t) = \frac{V_G R_l}{R_G + R_l}\left[1 - e^{-at}\left(\frac{a}{\omega}\sin \omega t + \cos \omega t\right)\right]. \tag{2}$$

To show how the rise of the pulse is affected by variation in the values of the elements in the equivalent circuit of Fig. 14·2,

$$\frac{e_l}{V_G}\left(1 + \frac{R_G}{R_l}\right)$$

is plotted in Fig. 14·3 against $T = \frac{\sqrt{b}}{2\pi} t$ for different values of the parameter σ, where

$$\sigma \equiv \frac{a}{\sqrt{b}} = \frac{CR_G R_l + L_L}{2\sqrt{R_l L_L C(R_G + R_l)}}.$$

If R_G is so small that $R_G \ll R_l$ and $CR_G \ll L_L/R_l$, as it is in a hard-tube pulse generator, and if $\sqrt{L_L/C}$ is made equal to R_l, as has hitherto been found advisable, $\sigma = 0.5$. If $R_G = R_l$, as it does in a line-type pulse generator, and if $\sqrt{L_L/C}$ is made equal to R_l, $\sigma = 1/\sqrt{2} = 0.71$. From the curves of Fig. 14·3 it may be seen that these two values of σ give reasonably good compromises between maximum rate of rise and minimum overshoot.

Rise of the Pulse on a Magnetron or a Biased-diode Load.—The rise of the pulse on a magnetron or biased-diode load is considered for a transformer in which the effect of R_e is negligible compared with that of R_G, and where the time of rise is so short that the effect of L_e is also negligible.

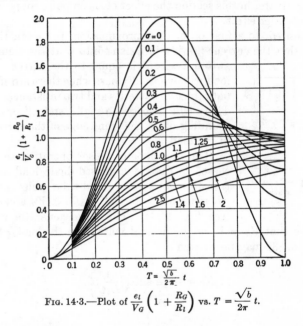

Fig. 14·3.—Plot of $\dfrac{e_l}{V_G}\left(1 + \dfrac{R_G}{R_l}\right)$ vs. $T = \dfrac{\sqrt{b}}{2\pi}\,t$.

Both a magnetron and a biased-grid load exhibit the general load characteristics of a biased diode, which is represented in the equivalent circuit of Fig. 14·4 by a battery, series resistance, and switch that closes when the voltage across the load is equal to or greater than the battery voltage.

If switch 1 closes at $t = 0$ and switch 2 is open,

$$i_1(t) = \frac{V_G}{L_L}\frac{e^{-\frac{R_G}{2L_L}t}}{\sqrt{\dfrac{1}{L_LC} - \left(\dfrac{R_G}{2L_L}\right)^2}}\sin\sqrt{\frac{1}{L_LC} - \left(\frac{R_G}{2L_L}\right)^2}\,t, \qquad (3)$$

and $e_l(t)$ can be obtained from Fig. 14·3 by choosing a curve corresponding to a value of σ obtained by letting $R_l = \infty$ and $R_G = 0$ for the hard-tube pulse generator, or $R_G = \sqrt{L_L/C}$ for the line-type pulse generator.

Although the energy stored in L_D (see Fig. 12·7) has some effect upon the shape of the current and voltage pulses in the load, it is neglected thus far in this computation for two reasons. First, the introduction of L_D in the equivalent circuit represents only approximately the actual conditions existing in a transformer; and second, it is desirable to keep the set of assumptions for the design of a transformer simple, and thus to include only the most important circuit elements. For these reasons also, L_D is neglected in the treatment of pulse-transformer design in Secs. 13·1 and 13·2, and later in this section the effect of L_D on pulse shape is treated as a second-order effect.

It is desired, to a first order of approximation, to design the transformer so that the current flowing in L_L and into C at the time t_1 when

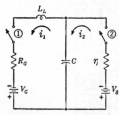

FIG. 14·4.—Circuit for the computation of the rise of a pulse on a biased-diode load.

switch 2 closes is equal to the current that the load will eventually pass when there are effectively only the two batteries and two resistances in series. There will then be no high "spike," or excessive rounding-off of the front edge of the current pulse in the load.

The first type of pulser operation that is discussed is that of a biased-diode load and pulse transformer with a hard-tube pulse generator, where usually $i_1 R_G \ll V_G$, $i_2 R_G \ll V_G$, and $i_2 r_l \ll V_s$ (see Fig. 14·4). The pulse generator is usually designed so that $V_G \approx V_s \approx$ the desired voltage on the load. Since R_G is small, Eq. (3) may be written

$$i_1(t) = \frac{V_G}{\sqrt{\dfrac{L_L}{C}}} \sin \sqrt{\frac{1}{L_L C}}\, t.$$

It may be seen from Fig. 14·3 that, for the curve $\sigma = 0$ (that is, for $R_G = 0, R_l = \infty$),

$$\frac{e_l}{V_G} = 1 \approx \frac{e_l}{V_s}$$

at the moment when

$$\sin \sqrt{\frac{1}{L_L C}}\, t \equiv \sin \sqrt{\frac{1}{L_L C}}\, t_1 = \mathbf{1}.$$

At this moment

$$i_1 = \frac{V_G}{\sqrt{\dfrac{L_L}{C}}}$$

and if $\sqrt{L_L/C}$ is chosen to be equal to R_l, the static impedance of the load at the point at which the tube is to be operated, i_1 has the proper value at the time t_1 when switch 2 closes. Immediately after the time t_1 there is a very brief interval of time during which a small additional rise in e_l requires some of the current which is flowing in L_L to flow into C. For the remainder of the pulse, however, e_l remains at a practically constant value, and all the current flowing in L_L flows through the load r_l.

The value of i_1 as a function of t, reckoned from the time of the closing of the switch 2, is

$$i_1(t) \approx \left(i_0 - \frac{V_G - V_s}{R_G + r_l}\right) e^{-\left(\frac{R_G + r_l}{L_L}\right)t} + \frac{V_G - V_s}{R_G + r_l} \approx i_2(t),$$

where i_0 is the initial current in L_L at the closing of switch 2. If

$$\sqrt{\frac{L_L}{C}} < R_l,$$

i_0 is too large, and there is exhibited on the front edge of the current pulse a spike that decays to the equilibrium value of the current with a time constant approximately equal to $L_L/(R_G + r_l)$.

If $\sqrt{L_L/C} > R_l$, i_0 is too small, and the current pulse has an initial value that is too low. The equilibrium value of the current pulse is approached with the same time constant approximately equal to

$$\frac{L_L}{(R_G + r_l)}.$$

There are, of course, oscillations on the current pulse. These oscillations, to a first order of approximation, may be said to be caused by the shock excitation of the $L_D C_D$-branch of the equivalent circuit of Fig. 12·7. They are, in most cases, of a period shorter than the time constant $L_L/(R_G + r_l)$ and are superimposed upon the general trends that occur with this time constant.

The observed rise of current pulses on a magnetron and calculations according to the foregoing assumptions are in good agreement (see, for example, Figs. 2·44 and 2·45).

The second operation to be discussed is that of a biased-diode load and pulse transformer with a line-type pulse generator, where usually $V_G \approx 2V_s$, $R_G = R_l$ (after the closing of switch 2), and $R_G \gg r_l$ (when all values are referred to the same impedance level). Prior to the closing of switch 2 in Fig. 14·4 it is assumed that R_l is infinite. Then, if

$$\sqrt{\frac{L_L}{C}} = R_G,$$

$\sigma = 0.50$ and

$$\sqrt{\frac{1}{L_L C} - \left(\frac{R_G}{2L_L}\right)^2} = \sqrt{\frac{3}{4L_L C}} = 0.866 \sqrt{\frac{1}{L_L C}}.$$

Eq. (3) then becomes

$$i_1(t) = \frac{V_G}{0.866 R_G} e^{-\frac{R_G}{2L_L}t} \sin 0.866 \sqrt{\frac{1}{L_L C}} \, t.$$

Also

$$\sqrt{b} = \sqrt{\frac{1}{L_L C}},$$

and

$$T = \frac{\sqrt{b}}{2\pi} t = \sqrt{\frac{1}{L_L C}} \frac{1}{2\pi} t.$$

In Fig. 14·3, for the curve corresponding to $\sigma = 0.5$,

$$\frac{e_l}{V_G} = \frac{1}{2} \left(\approx \frac{V_s}{V_G} \right) \qquad \text{at } T = 0.207.$$

Then

$$e^{-\frac{R_G t}{2 L L}} = e^{-0.207 \cdot \pi} = e^{-0.650} = 0.52.$$

Also,

$$\sin 0.866 \sqrt{\frac{1}{L_L C}} \, t = \sin 0.866 \cdot 2\pi \cdot 0.207 = \sin 65° = 0.903.$$

Thus

$$i_1 = \frac{V_G}{R_G} \frac{0.52 \cdot 0.903}{0.866} = 0.54 \frac{V_G}{R_G} \approx \frac{V_G}{2R_G} = \frac{V_G}{R_G + R_l}.$$

Thus, in a line-type pulser, if $\sqrt{L_L/C} = R_l$, the current flowing in L_L at the time when switch 2 closes is equal, to a reasonable approximation, to the equilibrium current (that is, the current that flows when V_G, V_s, R_G, and r_l are connected in a series circuit). If $\sqrt{L_L/C} \neq R_l$, the

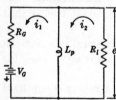

FIG. 14·5.—Equivalent circuit for computing the droop on the top of the pulse on a resistance load.

same exponential approach to the equilibrium value of the load current occurs, but in this case the time constant $L_L/(R_G + r_l)$ is much shorter.

The Top of the Pulse on a Resistance Load. The beginning of the top of the pulse on a resistance load is influenced by L_L and C, as may be seen from Fig. 14·3. There is also a droop in the pulse when $R_G > 0$, because of the fact that current builds up in L_p. Since the effects of L_L and C_D usually are relatively unimportant as far as this droop is concerned, the equivalent circuit of Fig. 14·5 may be used in the computation of this droop. The initial current in L_p is assumed to be zero, and t is reckoned from the beginning of the top of the pulse. Then

$$e_l(t) = \frac{V_G R_l}{R_G + R_l} e^{-\frac{1}{L_p} \cdot \frac{R_G R_l}{R_G + R_l} t}.$$

When, as in most line-type pulse generators, $R_G = R_l$,

$$e_l(t) = \frac{V_G}{2} e^{-\frac{R_l}{2L_p}t}.$$

The Top of the Pulse on a Magnetron or a Biased-diode Load.—The beginning of the top of the pulse on a magnetron or biased-diode load has oscillations which, as already shown, may be considered to be caused by the shock excitation of the $L_D C_D$-circuit in Fig. 12·6, and may also have a spike or an upward slope depending upon the value of $\sqrt{L_L/C}$ relative to R_l. When $R_G > 0$, there is a general droop on the pulse, and this droop may be calculated approximately from a consideration of the equivalent circuit of Fig. 14·6, whence

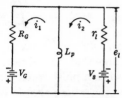

FIG. 14·6.—Equivalent circuit for computing the droop of the current pulse on a biased-diode load.

$$i_2(t) = \left[\left(\frac{V_G - V_s}{R_G + r_l} + \frac{V_s}{r_l} \right) e^{-\frac{1}{L_p} \cdot \frac{R_G r_l}{R_G + r_l} t} - \frac{V_s}{r_l} \right]$$

and

$$e_l = V_s + i_2 r_l.$$

(When e_l becomes equal to or less than V_s, the i_2-branch of the circuit must, of course, be considered to be open-circuited and the above expression for i_2 does not hold thereafter.)

Thus the top of the current pulse i_2 on a biased-diode load suffers much more droop than the top of the corresponding voltage pulse, or than the top of the pulse on a resistance load. For the same reason any voltage oscillations caused by the transformer produce much larger fluctuations in the current pulse because these voltage oscillations produce current flow through the relatively small resistance r_l instead of through the higher resistance R_l. Calculations and measurements of the droop of the pulse on resistance and magnetron loads agree within the experimental error.

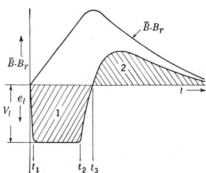

FIG. 14·7.—Typical pulse and backswing produced by a pulse transformer.

General Backswing on the Tail of the Pulse.—Figure 14·7 shows a pulse with the characteristic backswing produced by the pulse transformer.

Since the flux density must return to the same remanent point B_r before the beginning of each pulse [see Fig. 15·2 and Eq. (15·10)],

$$\text{area (1)} = \int_0^{t_3} e_l \, dt = \frac{-NA}{10^8} \int_{B_r}^{\bar{B}_{\max}} d\bar{B} = \frac{-NA}{10^8} (\bar{B}_{\max} - B_r),$$

and

$$\text{area (2)} = \int_{t_3}^{t_4} e_l \, dt = \frac{-NA}{10^8} \int_{\bar{B}_{\max}}^{B_r} d\bar{B} = \frac{-NA}{10^8} (B_r - \bar{B}_{\max}),$$

area (2) = −area (1). The interval of time $t_4 - t_3$ is chosen to be so large that, for all practical purposes, e_l has become equal to zero. Thus, when a pulse transformer is used, there is always a general voltage backswing whose area is equal to that of the pulse itself, but whose shape is determined by the values of R_e, C, L_e, and R_l if a resistance load is still connected, and by the charge on C and the current in L_p at t_2. When R_l becomes infinite, at a time very shortly after t_2, there are oscillations of a higher frequency superimposed upon the general backswing because of energy stored in L_L.

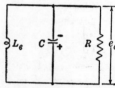

The shape of the general backswing may be calculated by assuming that the constant-voltage generator V_G is disconnected from the circuit at the time t_2 (see Fig. 14·7). The equivalent circuit is then that of Fig. 14·8 where, to a good approximation, the initial current in L_e is $V_l t_2 / L_e$ and the initial voltage on C is V_l.

Fig. 14·8.—Equivalent for the computation of the pulse tail.

Then, if $t = 0$ at the time t_2,

$$e_C(t) = V_l e^{-at} \left(\cosh kt - \frac{\dfrac{t_2}{L_e C} + a}{k} \sinh kt \right)$$

for the nonoscillatory condition, and

$$e_C(t) = V_l e^{-at} \left(\cos \omega t - \frac{\dfrac{t_2}{L_e C} + a}{\omega} \sin \omega t \right)$$

for the oscillatory condition, where

$$a \equiv \frac{1}{2RC},$$

$$\omega \equiv \sqrt{\frac{1}{L_e C} - \left(\frac{1}{2RC} \right)^2},$$

and

$$k \equiv -j\omega.$$

When a pulse transformer is used on a resistance load, $R = R_l$, and the pulse tail is usually "well damped" (see Fig. 14·9). When a pulse transformer is used on a biased-diode or magnetron load, the load is disconnected very shortly after t_2 and R is essentially equal to R_e (if no artificial diode or resistance damping is used in the circuit). A typical backswing (without the superimposed oscillations) for this latter case is also shown in Fig. 14·9.

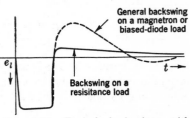

When a pulse transformer is used with a line-type pulse generator, the effective value of C in Fig. 14·8 is equal to the sum of the distributed capacitance of the pulse transformer and the capacitance of the load. When a hard-tube pulse generator is employed with stepdown and stepup

FIG. 14·9.—Typical backswings with resistance and biased-diode loads.

transformers, the effective values of R and L are respectively equal to $R_e/2$ and $L_e/2$, and the effective value of C is equal to the sum of the effective distributed capacitance of the two transformers, the load, and the pulse generator. Calculations and measurements of the general shape of the tail of the pulse obtained with hard-tube and line-type pulsers employing pulse transformers and either resistance or magnetron loads agree within the experimental error.

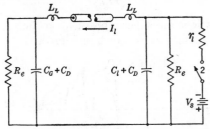

FIG. 14·10.—Equivalent circuit for the computation of oscillations appearing on the pulse tail with a hard-tube pulse generator and a biased-diode load.

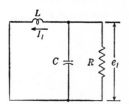

FIG. 14·11.—Circuit approximately equivalent to the circuit of Fig. 14·10.

Oscillations on the Pulse Tail.—The tail of the voltage pulse from a transformer on a resistance load usually exhibits no oscillations superimposed on the general backswing (that is, the energy stored in L_L has very little influence on the voltage-pulse tail).

However, on a biased-diode or magnetron load, oscillations usually appear which are superimposed on the general voltage backswing. In the analysis of these oscillations the example of the hard-tube pulse generator with two pulse transformers, the effective equivalent circuit of which is shown in Fig. 14·10, is considered first.   The load current I_l flowing in L_L at the end of the pulse is suddenly interrupted by the opening of switch 2, and the pulse-generator voltage source has been disconnected.   To a good approximation, the circuit of Fig. 14·10 may be replaced by that of Fig. 14·11, where

$$L = 2L_L,$$
$$\frac{1}{C} = \frac{1}{C_G + C_D} + \frac{1}{C_D + C_l},$$
$$R = 2R_e.$$

The initial current in L is I_l, and, for the purpose of calculating the oscillations occurring on the backswing, the effective initial charge on C is zero.   The voltage e_l is then given by

$$e_l(t) = \frac{I_l}{C} \frac{e^{-\frac{1}{2RC}t} \sin \sqrt{\frac{1}{LC} - \left(\frac{1}{2RC}\right)^2} \, t}{\sqrt{\frac{1}{LC} - \left(\frac{1}{2RC}\right)^2}}.$$

If, as is usually the case,

$$\frac{1}{LC} \gg \left(\frac{1}{2RC}\right)^2,$$

then

$$e_l(t) = \sqrt{\frac{L}{C}} I_l e^{-\frac{1}{2RC}t} \sin \frac{t}{\sqrt{LC}}.$$

These high-frequency oscillations are superimposed upon the general backswing to produce a pulse tail such as is shown in Fig. 14·12a.   If a

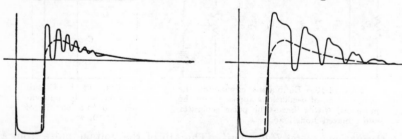

(a) With a hard-tube pulse generator.   (b) With a line-type pulse generator.
Fig. 14·12.—Typical voltage-pulse tails on a magnetron load.

cable is used between the stepdown-stepup pulse transformers, the period of oscillation $2\pi \sqrt{LC}$ is increased by twice the transit time of the cable.

There is good agreement between the calculated and the observed pulse tails obtained with a hard-tube pulser, pulse transformers, and magnetron load.

In a line-type pulse generator with a magnetron load there is a mismatch in impedance at the magnetron when the pulse voltage drops at the end of the pulse. As a result, a small portion of the energy is left in the circuit in the form of a negative voltage spike that is propagated down the pulse-forming network, reflected at the open end, and propagated back to the pulse transformer, where it appears as a negative spike on

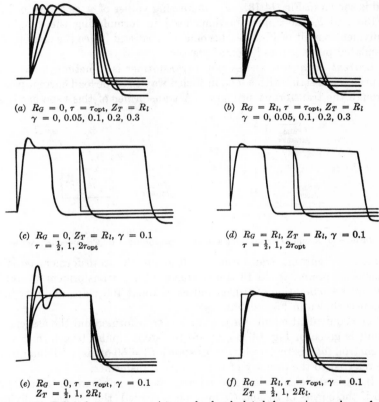

(a) $R_G = 0$, $\tau = \tau_{\text{opt}}$, $Z_T = R_l$
    $\gamma = 0, 0.05, 0.1, 0.2, 0.3$

(b) $R_G = R_l$, $\tau = \tau_{\text{opt}}$, $Z_T = R_l$
    $\gamma = 0, 0.05, 0.1, 0.2, 0.3$

(c) $R_G = 0$, $Z_T = R_l$, $\gamma = 0.1$
    $\tau = \tfrac{1}{2}, 1, 2\tau_{\text{opt}}$

(d) $R_G = R_l$, $Z_T = R_l$, $\gamma = 0.1$
    $\tau = \tfrac{1}{2}, 1, 2\tau_{\text{opt}}$

(e) $R_G = 0$, $\tau = \tau_{\text{opt}}$, $\gamma = 0.1$
    $Z_T = \tfrac{1}{2}, 1, 2R_l$

(f) $R_G = R_l$, $\tau = \tau_{\text{opt}}$, $\gamma = 0.1$
    $Z_T = \tfrac{1}{2}, 1, 2R_l$.

FIG. 14·13.—Pulse shapes on a resistance load calculated for various values of the parameters. $(\alpha + \beta)_{\text{opt}} = \gamma;\ \dfrac{Z_T}{R_l} = \dfrac{1}{R_l}\sqrt{\dfrac{L_L}{C_D}};\ \dfrac{\tau}{\sqrt{2L_LC_D}} = \dfrac{\tau}{\tau_{\text{opt}}};\ \dfrac{R_G}{R_l}.$

the tail of the voltage pulse. Such a series of spikes, drawn from a synchroscope trace obtained with a line-type pulse generator having a rotary spark gap as the switch, is shown in Fig. 14·12b.

The General Pulse Shape on a Resistance Load.—With the assumption of a resistance load having no appreciable capacitance, the effect on pulse shape of varying the values of the parameters

$$(\alpha + \beta)_{\text{opt}} = \gamma,$$

$$\frac{Z_T}{R_l} = \frac{1}{R_l}\sqrt{\frac{L_L}{C_D}},$$

$$\frac{\tau}{\sqrt{2L_L C_D}} = \frac{\tau}{\tau_{\text{opt}}},$$

and R_G/R_l is calculated on the basis of the equivalent circuit of Fig. 13·1, and is shown in Fig. 14·13. For increasing values of γ, as shown in Fig. 14·13a and b, the approximations used in formulating the simplified equivalent circuit of Fig. 13·1 become greater, and hence the error in the calculated pulse shapes becomes greater.

Current Transformers.—A pulse transformer is sometimes used with its primary in series with a load in such a way that the load current passes through the transformer primary. A transformer of this type has been

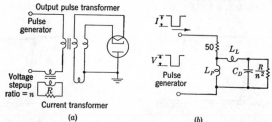

FIG. 14·14.—(a) A typical circuit using a current transformer. (b) Circuit equivalent to (a).

termed a "current transformer" although the transformer actually transforms power, as do all transformers. Such transformers are often used in the generation of trigger pulses of about 100 volts, and a typical circuit is shown in Fig. 14·14a.

The equivalent circuit for the current transformer and the associated circuit is given in Fig. 14·14b, where the stepup pulse transformer with magnetron load is replaced by a resistance $R_l = 50$ ohms. All quantities are referred to the primary of the current transformer.

If L_p is sufficiently large to be neglected in comparison with R/n^2, and if the effects of L_L and C_D may be neglected, the voltage V divides between R_l and R/n^2 in such a way that the voltage across the primary of the current transformer is

$$\frac{V\dfrac{R}{n^2}}{R_l + \dfrac{R}{n^2}} \approx \frac{VR}{R_l n^2}.$$

The voltage across the secondary of the current transformer is then $VR/R_l n$. It is thus seen that, for a given value of R, the voltage across the secondary of the current transformer increases if n is decreased, provided that the current in L_p remains small compared with that in R/n^2.

Obviously, it is desirable to have only a small fraction of V across the primary of the current transformer, and it is therefore desirable to choose values of R and n such that the proper output voltage is obtained, parasitic oscillations (from L_L and C_D) are sufficiently damped, and a sufficiently small voltage is applied at the primary.

Current transformers of this type may be used to view the current pulse in a magnetron or other load. Under these circumstances the "primary winding" may be the lead (or leads) carrying the load current, and in most instances this lead need only be passed through the core window to produce sufficient output voltage at the secondary terminals.

14·2. The Effect of Pulse-transformer Parameters on the Behavior of Regenerative Pulse Generators.—The general criteria of Eqs. (13·4), (13·5), and (13·6) hold for regenerative-pulse-generator (blocking-oscillator) transformers as they do for most pulse transformers. Thus, for a regenerative-pulse-generator transformer the optimum pulse duration is equal to $\sqrt{2L_pC_D}$, and the excellence of the transformer is judged by the value of $(\alpha + \beta)_{\text{opt}}$. For a regenerative pulse generator that supplies no appreciable power to an external circuit, the secondary-winding impedance $\sqrt{L_L/C_D}$ should be chosen approximately equal to the effective impedance of r_g (the grid-to-cathode resistance)

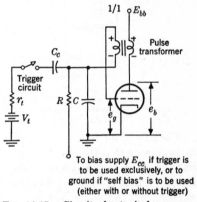

To bias supply E_{cc} if trigger is to be used exclusively, or to ground if "self bias" is to be used (either with or without trigger)

FIG. 14·15.—Circuit of a typical regenerative pulse generator.

and C in series, or of r_g and the impedance of the line in series if a lumped-parameter line is used instead of C (see Fig. 14·15).

There are several variations on the general scheme of regenerative pulse generators or blocking oscillators. These circuits, however, are all essentially the same in their mode of operation, and a general physical description of their operating mechanism is given in Sec. 4·2. As an example of a regenerative pulse generator, the circuit shown in Fig. 14·15 is used to show the effect of pulse-transformer parameters on circuit behavior. The voltage stepup ratio of the pulse transformer in this example is chosen, for purposes of simplification, to be $n = -1$, that is, the windings of the transformer, although wound in the same direction, are connected so that the pulse to the grid is inverted. It may prove advantageous in practice to select different values of n for different tube and load characteristics.

There are various stray capacitances in this circuit and the pulse transformer has a certain amount of leakage inductance; in order to avoid the difficulties involved in the analysis of such a complicated circuit, it is profitable to start first with the most simplified of equivalent circuits and then to proceed to the more complicated circuits that take into consideration more of the actual circuit elements. The analysis of the pulse-making operation is treated by considering first the leading edge or rise of the pulse, second the top of the pulse, and third the tail of the pulse.

In order that linear analysis may be employed, the plate resistance r_p and amplification factor μ of the tube are considered constant for the period of time under immediate consideration.

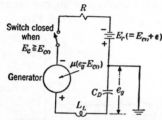

FIG. 14·16.—Simplified equivalent circuit for a regenerative pulse generator in which the effects of C, C_{gp}, r_p, L_p (and L_L) are neglected.

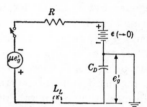

FIG. 14·17.—Circuit of Fig. 14·16 further simplified by setting $e_g{}' = |e_g - E_{co}|$.

The Rise of the Pulse.—For purposes of simplification, it is assumed in the beginning that the effect of the trigger circuit is negligible, that $r_p = 0$, that the effect of the leakage inductance is negligible in comparison with that of R, that $C = 0$ (see Fig. 14·15), and that the plate-to-grid capacitance C_{gp} of the tube is negligible. The equivalent circuit is then that of Fig. 14·16, where C_D and L_L are, respectively, the effective distributed capacitance and leakage inductance of the transformer. It is assumed that the bias voltage

$$E_c = E_{co} + \epsilon,$$

where ϵ is a positive voltage which can be vanishingly small, but which, nevertheless, can instigate the process of regeneration. It is readily shown that this circuit can be simplified to that of Fig. 14·17, where $e_g' = |e_g - E_{co}|$.

Kirchhoff's voltage-law equation for the circuit yields the following differential equation, where the initial voltage on C_D is equal to zero:

$$\frac{1}{C_D} \int i \, dt + Ri = \mu e_g' + \epsilon.$$

The Laplace transform of this equation is

$$\left(\frac{1}{C_D p} + R\right)i(p) = \mu e_g'(p) + \frac{\epsilon}{p} = \frac{\mu i(p)}{C_D p} + \frac{\epsilon}{p},$$

since

$$e_g' = \frac{1}{C_D}\int i \, dt,$$

and therefore

$$\mu e_g'(p) = \frac{\mu i(p)}{C_D p}.$$

Then

$$e_g'(p) = \frac{\epsilon}{p C_D R\left(p + \dfrac{1-\mu}{C_D R}\right)}.$$

The change in plate voltage on the tube is given by $e_b = -\mu e_g'$, since r_p has been assumed to be equal to zero.   Then

$$e_b = \frac{-\mu e(e^{\frac{\mu-1}{C_D R}t} - 1)}{\mu - 1}. \tag{4}$$

If μ is greater than one, the exponent is positive and regeneration takes place in such a way that $|e_b|$ increases until $|e_b| = E_{bb}$.   Throughout this section it is assumed that when the generator output voltage (which in this example is $-e_b$) is equal to E_{bb}, the amplification factor μ of the tube is less than one, and that regeneration therefore stops.   If it is assumed that, during the rise of the pulse until the generator output equals E_{bb}, the average value of μ is given by $\mu|E_{co}| = E_{bb}$, μ must be assumed to become suddenly less than 1 at the moment when e_g' becomes equal to or greater than $|E_{co}|$.   The voltage e_g passes through zero and grid-to-cathode current begins to flow at this moment.   Although the equivalent circuit must be modified at this instant to account for the grid-to-cathode current, this modification can be made with relative ease because the generator output attains its peak value E_{bb} at this moment and remains constant as long as $e_g \geqq 0$.   For purposes of simplifying the analysis the assumption that $\mu = |E_{bb}/E_{co}|$ is, therefore, used throughout this treatment of the regenerative pulse generator.   This simplification is desirable because the aim of this treatment is to show analytically, rather than numerically, how the elements in the equivalent circuit of a pulse transformer affect the pulse shape produced by a regenerative pulse generator.

Perhaps a more appropriate assumption with regard to the average value of μ during the rise of the pulse is to let

$$\mu(|E_{co}| + e_g'') = E_{bb},$$

where e_g'' is a positive grid voltage at which μ begins to change abruptly from a value greater than one to a value much less than one (see Fig. 14·26). In computing the rise of the pulse under this assumption it is necessary to make the circuit modification (with appropriate boundary conditions) at the moment e_g passes through zero while the generator output is still rising. It is assumed that the generator output continues to rise until $e_g = e_g''$, at which time μ is assumed to become $\ll 1$, and the generator voltage is assumed to remain constant at E_{bb} as long as $e_g \gtreqqless e_g''$. A linear solution of the rise of the pulse under these circumstances could almost never be given in an analytical form, and therefore is of little general value to the pulse-transformer designer.

If, in the simple example under consideration, it is now assumed that the leakage inductance L_L is finite, L_L may be inserted in series between the generator and C_D in Fig. 14·17. The Laplace transform of Kirchhoff's voltage-law equation for this circuit then becomes

$$\left(L_L p + \frac{1}{C_D p} + R\right) i(p) = \frac{\mu i(p)}{C_D p} + \frac{\epsilon}{p},$$

whence

$$i(p) = \frac{\epsilon}{L_L \left[p^2 + \dfrac{R}{L_L} p + \dfrac{1}{L_L} \left(\dfrac{1-\mu}{C_D} \right) \right]},$$

$$e_g'(p) = \frac{\epsilon}{L_L C_D p \left\{ p + \dfrac{R}{2L_L} - \left[\left(\dfrac{R}{2L_L} \right)^2 - \dfrac{1-\mu}{L_L C_D} \right]^{\frac12} \right\}}.$$
$$\left\{ p + \dfrac{R}{2L_L} + \left[\left(\dfrac{R}{2L_L} \right)^2 - \dfrac{1-\mu}{L_L C_D} \right]^{\frac12} \right\}$$

The change in plate voltage on the tube is again given by $e_b = -\mu e_g'$, since r_p has been assumed to be equal to zero. The solution is of the form

$$e_b(p) = \frac{a_0}{(p+\alpha)(p+\gamma)p}, \tag{5}$$

whose inverse Laplace transform is

$$e_b(t) = -a_0 \left[\frac{1}{\alpha\gamma} + \frac{\gamma e^{-\alpha t} - \alpha e^{-\gamma t}}{\alpha\gamma(\alpha-\gamma)} \right], \tag{6}$$

where

$$a_0 = \frac{\mu\epsilon}{L_L C_D},$$

$$\alpha = \frac{R}{2L_L} - \left[\left(\frac{R}{2L_L} \right)^2 - \frac{1-\mu}{L_L C_D} \right]^{\frac12},$$

and

$$\gamma = \frac{R}{2L_L} + \left[\left(\frac{R}{2L_L}\right)^2 - \frac{1-\mu}{L_L C_D}\right]^{\frac{1}{2}}.$$

If

$$\alpha = \frac{R}{2L_L} - \left[\left(\frac{R}{2L_L}\right)^2 - \frac{1-\mu}{L_L C_D}\right]^{\frac{1}{2}} < 0,$$

that is, if $\mu > 1$, the first exponential term contains a positive exponential, and regeneration occurs.

The solution (6) may be put in the following form:

$$e_b(t) = \frac{\mu\epsilon}{\mu-1}\left[1 - \frac{e^{-\frac{Rt}{2L_L}}\left\{\frac{R}{2L_L}\sinh\left[\left(\frac{R}{2L_L}\right)^2 - \frac{1-\mu}{L_L C_D}\right]^{\frac{1}{2}}t \\ + \left[\left(\frac{R}{2L_L}\right)^2 - \frac{1-\mu}{L_L C_D}\right]^{\frac{1}{2}}\cosh\left[\left(\frac{R}{2L_L}\right) - \frac{1-\mu}{L_L C_D}\right]^{\frac{1}{2}}t\right\}}{\left[\left(\frac{R}{2L_L}\right)^2 - \frac{1-\mu}{L_L C_D}\right]^{\frac{1}{2}}}\right]. \quad (7)$$

If μ is large enough and R small enough to make

$$\frac{\mu-1}{L_L C_D} \gg \left(\frac{R}{2L_L}\right)^2,$$

$\alpha \approx -\gamma$, and Eq. (6) becomes

$$e_b(t) \approx \epsilon\left[1 - \cosh\left(\frac{\mu}{L_L C_D}\right)^{\frac{1}{2}}t\right]. \quad (8)$$

The output $|e_b|$ of the generator in Fig. 14·17 continues to increase according to the expression given in Eq. (7) [or that in Eq. (8), if the

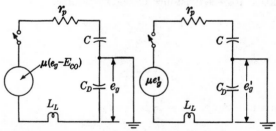

FIG. 14·18.—Equivalent circuit for a regenerative pulse generator where the effect of R and C_{gp} may be neglected. (a) Initial voltage on C equal to $E_{co} + \epsilon$. (b) Initial voltage on C equal to ϵ.

approximation is valid] until $|e_b| = E_{bb}$, at which time μ is assumed to become suddenly much less than one and the voltage $|e_b|$ levels off, thereby forming the top of the pulse.

The next example to be considered is one where $C \neq 0$ and R is so large that its effect is negligible compared with that of C, and where the effect of r_p is taken into account. The equivalent circuit is then that of Fig. 14·18a, which can be replaced by that of Fig. 14·18b for which

$$\left[L_L p + r_p + \frac{1}{p}\left(\frac{1}{C} + \frac{1}{C_D} \right) \right] i(p) = \mu e_g'(p) + \frac{\epsilon}{p} = \frac{\mu i(p)}{C_D p} + \frac{\epsilon}{p}.$$

Then

$$\mu e_g'(p) = \cfrac{\mu \epsilon}{L_L C_D p \left[p^2 + \dfrac{r_p}{L_L} p + \dfrac{1}{L_L}\left(\dfrac{1}{C} + \dfrac{1-\mu}{C_D} \right) \right]}$$

$$= \cfrac{\mu \epsilon}{L_L C_D p \left\{ p + \dfrac{r_p}{2L_L} - \left[\left(\dfrac{r_p}{2L_L} \right)^2 - \dfrac{1}{L_L}\left(\dfrac{1}{C} + \dfrac{1-\mu}{C_D} \right) \right]^{1/2} \right\}} \cdot \\ \left\{ p + \dfrac{r_p}{2L_L} + \left[\left(\dfrac{r_p}{2L_L} \right)^2 - \dfrac{1}{L_L}\left(\dfrac{1}{C} + \dfrac{1-\mu}{C_D} \right) \right]^{1/2} \right\}$$

This equation and its inverse Laplace transform are of the same form, respectively, as Eqs. (5) and (6), where now

$$a_0 = -\frac{\mu \epsilon}{L_L C_D}.$$

$$\alpha = \frac{r_p}{2L_L} - \left[\left(\frac{r_p}{2L_L} \right)^2 - \frac{1}{L_L}\left(\frac{1}{C} + \frac{1-\mu}{C_D} \right) \right]^{1/2},$$

and

$$\gamma = \frac{r_p}{2L_L} + \left[\left(\frac{r_p}{2L_L} \right)^2 - \frac{1}{L_L}\left(\frac{1}{C} + \frac{1-\mu}{C_D} \right) \right]^{1/2}.$$

The condition for the existence of regeneration is that

$$\frac{1}{C} + \frac{1-\mu}{C_D} < 0,$$

or

$$\mu > \frac{C_D}{C} + 1.$$

In the present example $e_b = -\mu e_g' + i r_p$, whence

$$e_b(p) = -\mu e_g'(p) + r_p i(p)$$

$$= \frac{a_0}{p(p+\alpha)(p+\gamma)} + \frac{a_1}{(p+\alpha)(p+\gamma)},$$

where

$$a_1 = \frac{r_p \epsilon}{L_L},$$

and the inverse Laplace transform of the second term is

$$a_1 \left(\frac{e^{-\alpha t} - e^{-\gamma t}}{\gamma - \alpha} \right).$$

The complete solution for this example is then

$$e_b(t) = a_0 \left[\frac{1}{\alpha \gamma} + \frac{\gamma e^{-\alpha t} - \alpha e^{-\gamma t}}{\alpha \gamma (\alpha - \gamma)} \right] + a_1 \left[\frac{e^{-\alpha t} - e^{-\gamma t}}{\gamma - \alpha} \right]. \tag{9}$$

There are two special cases of this general solution that are of interest:

Case 1. Where the time constant α is determined primarily by r_p and C_D (that is, L_L is negligibly small as far as its effect on i is concerned). For this case the Laplace transform of Kirchhoff's voltage-law equation is

$$\left[\left(\frac{1}{C} + \frac{1}{C_D} \right) \frac{1}{p} + r_p \right] i(p) = \frac{\mu i(p)}{C_D p} + \frac{\epsilon}{p},$$

whence

$$e_g'(p) = \frac{\epsilon}{r_p C_D} \frac{1}{p \left[p + \frac{1}{r_p} \left(\frac{1}{C} + \frac{1 - \mu}{C_D} \right) \right]},$$

and

$$e_g'(t) = \frac{\epsilon C}{C_D + C(1 - \mu)} \left[1 - e^{-\frac{1}{r_p} \left(\frac{1}{C} + \frac{1-\mu}{C_D} \right) t} \right],$$

$$e_b(p) = -\mu e_g'(p) + r_p i(p) = -\mu e_g'(p) + \frac{\epsilon}{p + \frac{1}{r_p} \left(\frac{1}{C} + \frac{1 - \mu}{C_D} \right)},$$

and

$$r_p i(t) = \epsilon e^{-\frac{1}{r_p} \left(\frac{1}{C} + \frac{1-\mu}{C_D} \right) t}.$$

Then

$$e_b(t) = \epsilon \left[\frac{-\mu C}{C(\mu - 1) - C_D} + 1 \right] e^{-\frac{1}{r_p} \left(\frac{1}{C} + \frac{1-\mu}{C_D} \right) t} + \frac{\mu \epsilon C}{C(\mu - 1) - C_D}. \tag{10}$$

Case 2. Where the time constant α is determined primarily by L_L and C_D (that is, r_p is negligibly small as far as its effect upon i is concerned). In this case $\alpha = -\gamma$ and Eq. (9) may be simplified to give

$$e_b(t) = -a_0 \left(\frac{1}{\gamma^2} - \frac{1}{\gamma^2} \cosh \gamma t \right) + \frac{a_1}{\gamma} \sinh \gamma t$$

$$= \epsilon \left(\frac{\mu C}{C(\mu - 1) - C_D} \left\{ 1 - \cosh \left[-\frac{1}{L_L} \left(\frac{1}{C} + \frac{1 - \mu}{C_D} \right) \right]^{\frac{1}{2}} t \right\} \right.$$

$$+ \frac{r_p (L_L C_D)^{\frac{1}{2}}}{L_L} \left[\frac{C}{C(\mu - 1) - C_D} \right]^{\frac{1}{2}} \left\{ \sinh \left[-\frac{1}{L_L} \left(\frac{1}{C} + \frac{1 - \mu}{C_D} \right) \right]^{\frac{1}{2}} t \right\} \right). \tag{11}$$

If $C \gg C_D$ and $ir_p \ll |\mu e_g'|$, Eq. (11) can be further simplified to become Eq. (8).

From the expression for e_b in Eq. (8) it is possible to make a calculation of the time of rise of the pulse when this time of rise is governed only by the transformer characteristics. Effects that are due to r_p, C, and the grid-to-plate capacitance C_{gp}, of course, actually increase this time of rise.

If it is assumed that ϵ is 1 volt at $t = 0$ and if the interval of time $t_1 > t > 0$ elapsing until e_b is -1 volt is computed,

$$-1 = 1 \left[1 - \cosh \left(\frac{\mu}{L_L C_D} \right)^{\frac{1}{2}} t_1 \right],$$

$$\cosh \left(\frac{\mu}{L_L C_D} \right)^{\frac{1}{2}} t_1 = 2,$$

or

$$\left(\frac{\mu}{L_L C_D} \right)^{\frac{1}{2}} t_1 = 1.32,$$

and if

$$\left(\frac{\mu}{L_L C_D} \right)^{\frac{1}{2}}$$

is known, t_1 may be computed. If $t_2 > t > 0$ is the interval of time until $e_b = -10$ volts,

$$\cosh \left(\frac{\mu}{L_L C_D} \right)^{\frac{1}{2}} t_2 = 11,$$

or

$$\left(\frac{\mu}{L_L C_D} \right)^{\frac{1}{2}} t_2 = 3.1.$$

If $t_3 > t > 0$ is the interval of time until $e_b = -300$ volts,

$$\cosh \left(\frac{\mu}{L_L C_D} \right)^{\frac{1}{2}} t_3 = 301$$

and

$$\left(\frac{\mu}{L_L C_D} \right)^{\frac{1}{2}} t_3 = 7.2.$$

A reasonable definition for the time of rise of a pulse from a regenerative pulse generator would be $t_3 - t_2 = \Delta t$; then

$$\left(\frac{\mu}{L_L C_D} \right)^{\frac{1}{2}} \Delta t = 4.1.$$

For a numerical example, when $L_L = 20 \times 10^{-6}$ henry, $C_D = 20 \times 10^{-12}$ farad, and $\mu = 20$,

$$\Delta t = \frac{4.1}{\left(\dfrac{20}{20 \cdot 20 \times 10^{-18}}\right)^{1/2}} = 0.018 \ \mu\text{sec.}$$

A simple example is now considered where the effect of a trigger circuit of source voltage V_t and internal resistance r_t (see Fig. 14·15) are taken into account, where the effects of C_{gp}, R, and r_p are neglected, and where C is finite. The equivalent circuit for this example is given in Fig. 14·19 where the initial charges on C and C_D are assumed to be equal to zero. This assumption is equivalent to the hypothesis that the initial voltage on C is actually E_{co} when the generator output is equal to $\mu(e_g - E_{co})$ and the voltage across C_D is e_g. It is assumed that the coupling capacitance between the trigger circuit

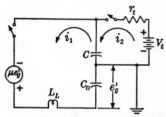

FIG. 14·19.—Equivalent circuit for a regenerative pulse generator where the effect of the trigger circuit is taken into account and where the effects of C_{gp}, R and r_p are neglected.

and the rest of the circuit is so large that its effect is negligible. The Laplace transforms of the two mesh equations are then

$$\left[p^2 + \frac{1}{L_L}\left(\frac{1}{C} + \frac{1-\mu}{C_D}\right)\right] i_1(p) - \frac{1}{L_L C} i_2(p) = 0,$$

and

$$-\frac{1}{r_t C} i_1(p) + \left(\frac{1}{r_t C} + p\right) i_2(p) = \frac{V_t}{r_t}.$$

Then

$$i_1(p) = \frac{\begin{vmatrix} 0 & -\dfrac{1}{L_L C} \\ \dfrac{V_t}{r_t} & \left(\dfrac{1}{r_t C} + p\right) \end{vmatrix}}{\begin{vmatrix} p^2 + \dfrac{1}{L_L}\left(\dfrac{1}{C} + \dfrac{1-\mu}{C_D}\right) & -\dfrac{1}{L_L C} \\ -\dfrac{1}{r_t C} & p + \dfrac{1}{r_t C} \end{vmatrix}}$$

or

$$i_1(p) = \frac{\dfrac{V_t}{r_t L_L C}}{\left[p^2 + \dfrac{1}{L_L}\left(\dfrac{1}{C} - \dfrac{1-\mu}{C_D}\right)\right]\left[p + \dfrac{1}{r_t C}\right] - \dfrac{1}{r_t L_L C^2}}, \tag{12}$$

and

$$e'_g(p) = \frac{i_1(p)}{C_D p}. \tag{13}$$

It is usually impossible to express i_1 or e'_g analytically because the Laplace

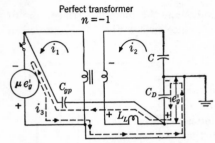

Perfect transformer
$n = -1$

FIG. 14·20.—Equivalent circuit for a regenerative pulse generator where the effect of C_{gp} is taken into account and where the effects of R and r_p have been neglected.

transform involves the solution of a cubic equation in p. Nevertheless, Eq. (13) can be readily solved numerically for a given set of constants, and the rise of the pulse for the circuit of Fig. 14·19 may be calculated.

A simple example is now treated where the effect of C_{gp} is taken into account but the effects of r_p and R are neglected, and it is assumed that there is an initial voltage $\epsilon (E_{co} + \epsilon$ in the actual circuit) on the capacitance C. The equivalent circuit is given in Fig. 14·20.

Since the transformer in the circuit of Fig. 14·20 is perfect, $i_1 = i_2$ and the Laplace transforms of the mesh equations yield

$$\left[L_L p + \frac{1}{p}\left(\frac{1}{C} + \frac{1-\mu}{C_D} \right) \right] i_2(p) - \frac{1-\mu}{pC_D} i_3(p) = \frac{\epsilon}{p}$$

and

$$-\left(\frac{1+\mu}{pC_D} \right) i_2(p) + \frac{1}{p}\left(\frac{1}{C_{gp}} + \frac{1+\mu}{C_D} \right) i_3(p) = 0,$$

whence

$$i_2(p) = \frac{\epsilon \left(\dfrac{1}{C_{gp}} + \dfrac{1+\mu}{C_D} \right)}{L_L \left\{ \left[p^2 + \dfrac{1}{L_L}\left(\dfrac{1}{C} + \dfrac{1-\mu}{C_D} \right) \right]\left[\dfrac{1}{C_{gp}} + \dfrac{1+\mu}{C_D} \right] - \dfrac{(1-\mu^2)}{L_L C_D{}^2} \right\}},$$

$$i_3(p) = \frac{\dfrac{\epsilon(1+\mu)}{C_D}}{L_L \left\{ \left[p^2 + \dfrac{1}{L_L}\left(\dfrac{1}{C} + \dfrac{1-\mu}{C_D} \right) \right]\left[\dfrac{1}{C_{gp}} + \dfrac{1+\mu}{C_D} \right] - \dfrac{(1-\mu^2)}{L_L C_D{}^2} \right\}},$$

and

$$\mu e'_g(p) = \frac{\mu}{pC_D} [i_2(p) - i_3(p)].$$

The condition for regeneration is that

$$\frac{1}{L_L}\left(\frac{1}{C} + \frac{1-\mu}{L_L C_D}\right) - \frac{1-\mu^2}{L_L C_D} \cdot \frac{C_{gp}}{C_D + C_{gp}(1+\mu)} < 0.$$

If the value of C is so large that its effect may be neglected,

$$\mu e_g'(p) = \frac{\dfrac{\mu \epsilon C_D}{C_D + C_{gp}(1+\mu)}}{L_L C_D \left\{ p^2 - \dfrac{\mu - 1}{L_L[C_D + C_{gp}(1+\mu)]} \right\} p}.$$

Then

$$\mu e_g'(t) = -\frac{\mu \epsilon}{\mu - 1}\left(1 - \cosh\left\{\frac{\mu - 1}{L_L[C_D + C_{gp}(1+\mu)]}\right\}^{\frac{1}{2}} t\right),$$

or

$$\mu e_g'(t) = \frac{\mu \epsilon}{\mu - 1}\left(\cosh\left\{\frac{\mu - 1}{L_L[C_D + C_{gp}(1+\mu)]}\right\}^{\frac{1}{2}} t - 1\right).$$

It is thus obvious that the effect of C_{gp} on the rise of the pulse is to increase the effective capacitance of the pulse transformer by the additive quantity $C_{gp}(1 + \mu)$.

It is possible by the foregoing procedures to calculate the rise of the pulse both when a trigger is used and when the effects of C_{gp}, r_p, and C are taken into account, except that the solutions for e_b involve solutions of algebraic equations of degree of three or higher, and therefore each solution must be a numerical one. Nevertheless, the task may be accomplished in a straightforward manner.

The effective distributed capacitance C_D between the plate winding and the grid winding is equal to the total capacitance between the two single-layer windings for a transformer of voltage-stepup ratio $n = -1$. This fact is illustrated in Fig. 14·21 for two cases, one where C is very large, and one where C is very small. The voltage distributions along the winding before and during the pulse show that the amount of electrostatic energy stored when a voltage pulse e_b is applied across one winding is the same as that stored when a constant voltage e_g is applied between the windings.

When a transformer has a stepup ratio $n \neq -1$, it is possible to calculate C_D by the application of the principles set forth in Sec. 12·2.

If there is a third winding on the transformer, the effective distributed capacitance, leakage inductance, and load of this winding must be taken into account in the analysis of circuit behavior.

The regenerative pulse generator frequently employs a lumped-constant line, or network, instead of the capacitance C. For these circumstances, the rise of the pulse may be computed by substituting for

C in the equivalent circuit a resistance equal to the characteristic impedance of the line.

If there are to be only two windings on the transformer and no appreciable amount of power is to be delivered to an external circuit, it is
desirable in the design of a regenerative pulse generator to choose the

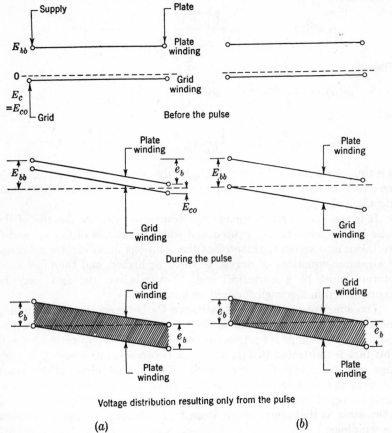

Voltage distribution resulting only from the pulse

(a)   (b)

FIG. 14·21.—Voltage distributions along the windings of a transformer used in a regenerative pulse generator with $n = -1$.   (a) When C is large.   (b) When C is small.

impedance of the line, which in most cases may be considered as the load,
approximately equal to r_p, the impedance of the source.   The value of n
for the grid winding should be chosen on the basis of the tube characteristics.   If a third winding is to be used, the value of n for this winding
should be chosen on the basis of the tube characteristics and the load for
this winding.

The Top of the Pulse.—The interval of time during which the pulse is more or less flat is usually called the "top" of the pulse. The behavior of the circuit during this interval is now described. When the output of the generator $\mu e_g'$ is equal to E_{bb}, $e_g \geqq 0$, μ is assumed to become less than one, and the output of the generator is assumed to remain equal to E_{bb} until the grid voltage e_g, which is now positive, falls to zero or lower. The equivalent circuit is then that of Fig. 14·22 in which r_g is the grid-to-cathode resistance. The switch remains closed when the voltage e_g across C_D is greater than zero. The effect of the trigger circuit in this instance is neglected.

It is possible to give a straightforward solution for e_g with initial currents in L_L and L_p and an initial voltage on C calculated from the rise of the pulse. For the purpose of simplification, however, it is assumed that the initial voltage across C, which was E_{co} at the beginning of the rise of the pulse, has not changed appreciably during this rise, and that no appreciable current has built up in L_p, the shunt inductance of the transformer, during the rise of the pulse. Furthermore, the effect of L_L is neglected.

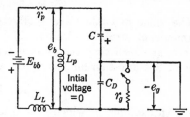

Fig. 14·22.—Equivalent circuit for the operation of a regenerative pulse generator during the top of the pulse. Initial voltage on $C \approx -E_{co}$ if $C \gg C_D$.

This simplified example may be broken down into two extreme cases that are even more simplified.

Case 1. Where C is so large that the pulse is terminated by the effect of L_p alone. If the current in r_g is neglected,

$$e_b = -E_{bb}e^{-\frac{r_p}{L_p}t}.$$

Since there is no appreciable voltage developed across C other than its initial voltage E_{co},

$$-e_g = e_b - E_{co}.$$

It is assumed that the energy stored in C_D has little effect upon the duration of the pulse. When $e_g = 0$ (and hence $e_b = E_{co}$), μ becomes $\geqq 1$, regeneration in the "off" direction takes place, and the pulse is terminated. This maximum pulse duration τ_{max} that the circuit having a pulse transformer can produce is then given by

$$|E_{co}| = E_{bb}e^{-\frac{r_p}{L_p}\tau_{max}}$$

or

$$\tau_{max} = \frac{L_p}{r_p}\ln\frac{E_{bb}}{|E_{co}|} = \frac{L_p}{r_p}\ln\mu.$$

Because of the simplifying assumptions that have been made, the value of τ_{max} thus calculated is somewhat greater than the maximum pulse duration that can actually be achieved.

Case 2. Where L_p is large, and C is so small that the pulse duration is determined primarily by the value of C, yet large enough to keep its initial voltage at the beginning of the top of the pulse equal to E_{co}. Under these circumstances, if the effect of C_D may be neglected during the time when $e_g > 0$ and the switch is closed (Fig. 14·22),

$$e_g = \frac{(E_{bb} - |E_{co}|)r_g e^{-\frac{t}{(r_g + r_p)C}}}{r_p + r_g}.$$

The value of e_g thus eventually comes very close to zero, and a small amount of current buildup in L_p is sufficient to make e_g go completely to zero, at which time the pulse is terminated. An approximate value for the pulse duration limited by the value of C is

$$\tau_{max} = (r_p + r_g)C.$$

An example in which $C = 0$ and in which any grid current that is drawn must flow through R is represented in Fig. 14·23 where, at the

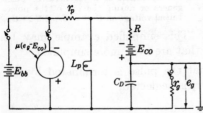

FIG. 14·23.—Equivalent circuit for the operation of a regenerative pulse generator during the top and tail of the pulse where $C = 0$.

beginning of the top of the pulse, the battery is substituted for the generator in the circuit. The value of R is usually much larger than r_g and e_g never gets very far above zero. In fact e_g usually becomes less than zero immediately after the peak of the rise of the pulse, and the generator is again switched into the circuit. In this particular example the pulse has no "flat" top, and the pulse "tail" starts as soon as the rise is finished. The shape of the pulse tail is then determined by the time constants RC_D and/or $\sqrt{L_pC_D}$, by μ, and by the initial energies in L_p and C_D. This example is not treated in detail since it is not of so much practical interest as others.

The Tail of the Pulse.—The pulse tail is now calculated for the case where C is finite and where the circuit is considered to have arrived at the condition where again $e_g = 0$. When e_g falls to $\leqq 0$, μ again becomes greater than one and the circuit regenerates "off," much as it regenerated "on." The order of magnitude of the regeneration time is, as was shown for a simple case, $\approx \sqrt{L_LC_D/\mu}$, which is short compared with the time $\sqrt{L_pC_D}$. Therefore, it is assumed that the circuit has regenerated "off," that the generator is therefore disconnected from the circuit, and that $e_g = E_{co}$ at the time $t = 0$. The equivalent circuit is then that of Fig. 14·24 where R_e represents the effect of losses in the core and any damping resistance that may be connected.

The behavior of the circuit may then be considered in two parts. The first part involves the change in e_b from the moment that $e_g = E_{co}$. The variation of e_b depends upon the values of L_p, R_e, and C_D, and upon the current in L_p and the charge on C_D (both of which can be determined for a given circuit condition) at the moment when $e_g = E_{co}$. The equations for the variation of e_b are identical in form with those given in Sec. 14·1 for the tail of the voltage pulse on a magnetron.

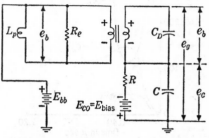

The second part of the circuit behavior involves the discharge of C through R until the voltage across C is equal to E_c (which, for all the cases thus far considered, is equal to E_{co}). The initial

Fig. 14·24.—Equivalent circuit for the operation of a regenerative pulse generator during the tail of the pulse.

charge on C depends, of course, on the operation up to the time when $e_g = E_{co}$. If the voltage across C at this time is denoted by V_C (V_C is usually -0.5 to $-0.8E_{bb}$), the voltage e_C is given by

$$e_C = E_{co} - (V_C - E_c)e^{-\frac{t}{RC}},$$

and

$$e_g = e_b + e_C. \tag{14}$$

Comparison of Theory and Experiment.—The foregoing theory, which assumes μ to be equal to E_{bb}/E_{co} and to be constant, and which neglects various circuit elements in the approximate solutions outlined, gives by no means a complete and highly accurate description of the operation of a regenerative pulse generator. A complete and accurate solution of the problem can be achieved only by laborious graphical methods that fail to give the average investigator the comprehensive view provided by analytical solutions. It is the author's belief that this foregoing theory, rough and brief as it is, is of definite value in being able to show in an analytical manner the dependence of the circuit behavior on the various elements.

Figure 14·25 shows typical pulse shapes obtained from a regenerative pulse generator with two different values of C.[1] The general shape of the

[1] H. M. Zeidler, "Analysis of the Blocking Oscillator," Master's Thesis, E. E. Dept., M.I.T., 1943.

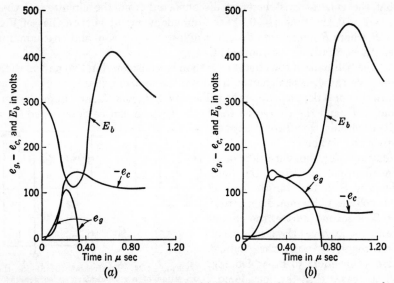

FIG. 14·25.—Typical pulse shapes obtained from a regenerative pulse generator employing a 6SN7 triode, a 132AW2 pulse transformer (see Table 13·2), for which $R = 25,000$ ohms, and $E_{bb} = 300$ volts. (a) $C = 235\mu\mu\text{f}$. (b) $C = 2700\ \mu\mu\text{f}$.

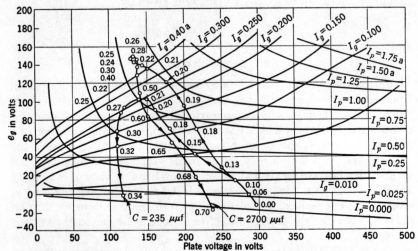

FIG. 14·26.—Operating curves for the two pulses shown in Fig. 14·25 with time intervals indicated in μsec.

rise of each pulse agrees with that given by the theory in Eqs. (8) and
(11).   The effect of the value of C on the pulse duration is illustrated.
The shape of the pulse tail agrees approximately with that given by the
theory in Eq. (14).   Figure 14·26 shows the operating curves or trajec-
tories (with time intervals indicated in microseconds) for the two operations of the circuit.   The inverse slope at any point on a curve of constant
plate current I_p is equal to the value of μ of the tube at this particular

point.   It may be observed that these
operating lines bear out, in a rough way,
the predictions of the foregoing theory:
during the rise of the pulse the circuit
moves rapidly through the region where
μ is approximately constant and greater
than one until it enters the region where
μ abruptly decreases to a value much
less than one.   In this region (giving
rise to the top of the pulse) the circuit
lingers until the grid voltage drops toward zero and into a region where μ
again becomes greater than one.   The

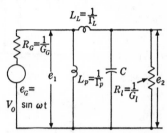

Fig. 14·27.—Equivalent circuit
generator, transformer, and load for
the computation of the frequency
response.

circuit then regenerates off, passing rapidly through the region where μ is
approximately constant and greater than one.   It is obvious from Fig.
14·25 that, from the point of view of accuracy in calculation, μ should be
assumed to equal $E_{bb}/(e_g'' + |E_{co}|)$ when $e_g < e_g''$, rather than to equal
$E_{bb}/|E_{co}|$ when $e_g < 0$.   As has already been stated, however, this former
assumption complicates the problem to the extent that the solutions lose
their analytical character and hence much of their usefulness.

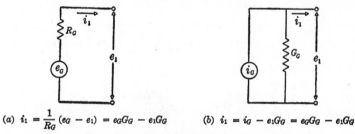

(a) $i_1 = \dfrac{1}{R_G} (e_G - e_1) = e_G G_G - e_1 G_G$ (b) $i_1 = i_G - e_1 G_G = e_G G_G - e_1 G_G$

Fig. 14·28.—Equivalent voltage and current sources.

**14·3. The Effect of Pulse-transformer Parameters on Frequency
Response.**—The equivalent circuit of Fig. 14·27 may be used to represent
a generator, a stepup or reversing transformer, and a load, where the
capacitance to ground of the transformer-primary winding may be
neglected.

It is more convenient to write the equations on the node rather than on the loop basis.   Therefore, the voltage source in Fig. 14·28a is replaced by the current source of Fig. 14·28b and the equivalent circuit of Fig. 14·29, where $i_G = e_G G_G$, is thereby obtained.   Then

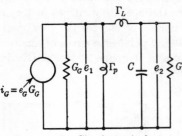

Fig. 14·29.—Circuit equivalent to that of Fig. 14·27, formulated on the node basis.

$$e_1 G_G + \frac{e_1 \Gamma_p}{j\omega} + \frac{(e_1 - e_2)}{j\omega} \Gamma_L = e_G G_G,$$

and

$$e_2 j\omega C + e_2 G_l + \frac{(e_2 - e_1)}{j\omega} \Gamma_L = 0.$$

Or

$$\left[G_G - \frac{j}{\omega}(\Gamma_p + \Gamma_L) \right] e_1 + \frac{j}{\omega} \Gamma_L e_2 = e_G G_G,$$

and

$$\frac{j}{\omega} \Gamma_L e_1 + \left(G_l - \frac{j}{\omega} \Gamma_L + j\omega C \right) e_2 = 0.$$

Then

$$e_2 = \frac{\begin{vmatrix} G_G - \dfrac{j}{\omega}(\Gamma_p + \Gamma_L) & e_G G_G \\[2ex] \dfrac{j}{\omega} \Gamma_L & 0 \end{vmatrix}}{\begin{vmatrix} G_G - \dfrac{j}{\omega}(\Gamma_p + \Gamma_L) & \dfrac{j}{\omega} \Gamma_L \\[2ex] \dfrac{j}{\omega} \Gamma_L & G_l - \dfrac{j}{\omega} \Gamma_L + j\omega C \end{vmatrix}},$$

and

$$\frac{e_2}{e_G} = - \frac{G_G j \Gamma_L}{\omega} \frac{1}{\left[G_G - \dfrac{j}{\omega}(\Gamma_p + \Gamma_L) \right]\left[G_l - \dfrac{j}{\omega} \Gamma_L + j\omega C \right] + \dfrac{\Gamma_L^2}{\omega^2}},$$

$$\frac{e_2}{e_G}$$
$$= \frac{G_G \Gamma_L \omega \{ \omega[G_l(\Gamma_p + \Gamma_L) + G_G(\Gamma_L - \omega^2 C)] - j[\omega^2 G_G G_l + \omega^2 C(\Gamma_p + \Gamma_L) - \Gamma_p \Gamma_L] \}}{[\omega^2 G_G G_l + \omega^2 C(\Gamma_p + \Gamma_L) - \Gamma_p \Gamma_L]^2 + \omega^2 [G_G(\Gamma_L - \omega^2 C) + G_l(\Gamma_p + \Gamma_L)]^2}.$$

Then

$$\left| \frac{e_2}{e_G} \right| = G_G \Gamma_L \omega \{ [\omega^2 G_G G_l + \omega^2 C(\Gamma_p + \Gamma_L) - \Gamma_p \Gamma_L]^2 + \omega^2 [G_G(\Gamma_L - \omega^2 C)$$
$$+ G_l(\Gamma_p + \Gamma_L]^2 \}^{-\frac{1}{2}}$$

and

$$- \tan \varphi = \frac{\omega^2 G_G G_l + \omega^2 C(\Gamma_p + \Gamma_L) - \Gamma_p \Gamma_L}{\omega[G_l(\Gamma_p + \Gamma_L) + G_G(\Gamma_L - \omega^2 C)]}.$$

If all quantities are referred to the impedance level of $1/G_l = 1$ ohm, and if $G_G = G_l$, then

$$\left|\frac{e_2}{e_G}\right| = \Gamma_L\omega\{[\omega^2 + \omega^2 C(\Gamma_p + \Gamma_L) - \Gamma_p\Gamma_L]^2 + \omega^2[2\Gamma_L + \Gamma_p - \omega^2 C]^2\}^{-\frac{1}{2}},$$

and

$$-\tan\varphi = \frac{\omega^2 + \omega^2 C(\Gamma_p + \Gamma_L) - \Gamma_p\Gamma_L}{\omega(\Gamma_p - \omega^2 C + 2\Gamma_L)}.$$

Usually

$$\frac{1}{L_p} \ll \frac{1}{L_L} \quad \text{or} \quad \Gamma_p \ll \Gamma_L.$$

Hence

$$\left|\frac{e_2}{e_G}\right| \approx \Gamma_L\omega\{[\omega^2 + \omega^2 C\Gamma_L - \Gamma_p\Gamma_L]^2 + \omega^2[-\omega^2 C + 2\Gamma_L]^2\}^{-\frac{1}{2}}$$

and

$$-\tan\varphi \approx \frac{\omega^2 + \omega^2 C\Gamma_L - \Gamma_p\Gamma_L}{\omega(2\Gamma_L - \omega^2 C)}.$$

If C is assumed to be approximately equal to C_D, the distributed capacitance of the transformer, the characteristic impedance of the winding may be chosen equal to the load resistance, that is,

$$Z_T = \sqrt{\frac{L_L}{C_D}} = \sqrt{\frac{1}{C\Gamma_L}} = \frac{1}{G_l} = 1 \text{ ohm.} \tag{13·4}$$

Also, since

$$\tau_{\text{opt}} = \sqrt{2L_p C_D}, \tag{13·5}$$

and

$$(\alpha + \beta)_{\text{opt}} \equiv \gamma = \sqrt{\frac{2L_L}{L_p}}, \tag{13·6}$$

$$C_D = L_L = \frac{\gamma\tau_{\text{opt}}}{2},$$

or

$$\Gamma_L = \frac{2}{\tau_{\text{opt}}\gamma},$$

and

$$L_p = \frac{\tau_{\text{opt}}}{\gamma} \quad \text{or} \quad \Gamma_p = \frac{\gamma}{\tau_{\text{opt}}}.$$

Then

$$\left|\frac{e_2}{e_G}\right| \approx \frac{2\omega}{\gamma\tau_{\text{opt}}\left[\left(2\omega^2 - \frac{2}{\tau_{\text{opt}}^2}\right)^2 + \omega^2\left(-\frac{\gamma\omega^2\tau_{\text{opt}}}{2} + \frac{4}{\gamma\tau_{\text{opt}}}\right)^2\right]^{\frac{1}{2}}},$$

and

$$- \tan \varphi = \frac{2\omega^2 - \dfrac{2}{\tau_{\text{opt}}^2}}{\omega \left(\dfrac{4}{\gamma \tau_{\text{opt}}} - \dfrac{\gamma \omega^2 \tau_{\text{opt}}}{2} \right)}.$$

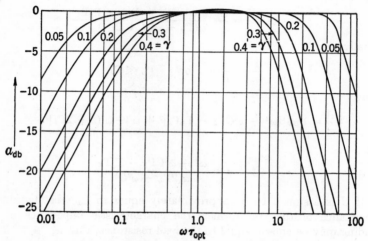

Fig. 14·30.—Plot of the amplitude response, a_{db} vs. $\omega \tau_{\text{opt}}$.

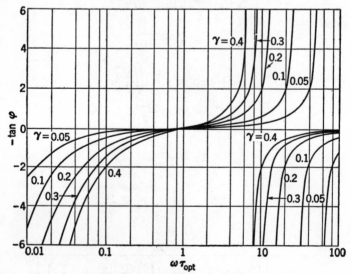

Fig. 14·31.—Plot of $-\tan \varphi$ vs. $\omega \tau_{\text{opt}}$.

The response of the transformer may be expressed as follows:

$$a_{db} = 20 \log_{10} 2 \left| \frac{e_2}{e_G} \right|.$$

In Figs. 14·30, 14·31, and 14·32 are plotted respectively a_{db} vs. $\omega\tau_{opt}$, $-\tan\varphi$ vs. $\omega\tau_{opt}$, and $-\varphi$ vs. $\omega\tau_{opt}$ for several values of $(\alpha + \beta)_{opt} = \gamma$.

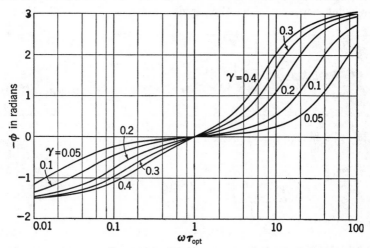

Fig. 14·32.—Plot of $-\varphi$ vs. $\omega\tau_{opt}$.

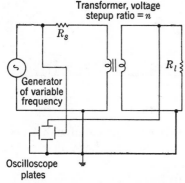

Fig. 14·33.—Circuit for oscilloscope presentation of the frequency-response characteristics of a transformer.

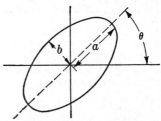

Fig. 14·34.—Appearance of oscilloscope trace with the circuit of Fig. 14·33.

It is to be remembered that the equivalent circuit from which these curves are calculated is valid only when L_L is very small compared with L_p, and hence when γ is small. As γ becomes larger, the error involved in using this equivalent circuit becomes greater. Hence, these curves drawn for $\gamma = 0.3$ and 0.4 involve an appreciable degree of approximation.   It has also been assumed that L_p is constant over the frequency range shown.   This assumption is valid only if the laminations are thin enough and their resistivity and μ so high [see Eqs. (15·30) and (15·31)] that the impedance of R_e is high compared with that of L_e over the frequency range considered.

It is possible to use oscilloscope presentation for the measurement of $|e_2/e_G|$ and $\tan \varphi$ by using the circuit shown in Fig. 14·33, where the

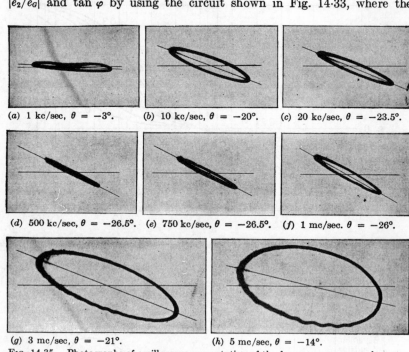

(a) 1 kc/sec, $\theta = -3°$.   (b) 10 kc/sec, $\theta = -20°$.   (c) 20 kc/sec, $\theta = -23.5°$.

(d) 500 kc/sec, $\theta = -26.5°$.   (e) 750 kc/sec, $\theta = -26.5°$.   (f) 1 mc/sec. $\theta = -26°$.

(g) 3 mc/sec, $\theta = -21°$.   (h) 5 mc/sec, $\theta = -14°$.

FIG. 14·35.—Photographs of oscilloscope presentation of the frequency-response characteristics of a pulse transformer with $n = -1$ and $R_l = R_G = 1000$ ohms.

actual generator has an impedance that is small compared with $R_G = R_l$.

The oscilloscope traces are of the general form shown in Fig. 14·34, where

$$\left|\frac{e_2}{e_G}\right| = \frac{\tan \theta}{n},$$

and

$$\tan \frac{\varphi}{2} = \frac{b}{a}.$$

Then

$$a_{\mathrm{db}} = 20 \log_{10} \frac{2 \tan \theta}{n}.$$

In the measurement of frequency response it is often convenient to use two identical transformers, one a stepdown, the other a stepup, in order to make n for the pair equal to one. The slope $\tan \theta$ for the combination may then be obtained and compared with the slope $\tan \theta'$ obtained when no transformer is used in the circuit. Then $|e_2/e_G|$ for the

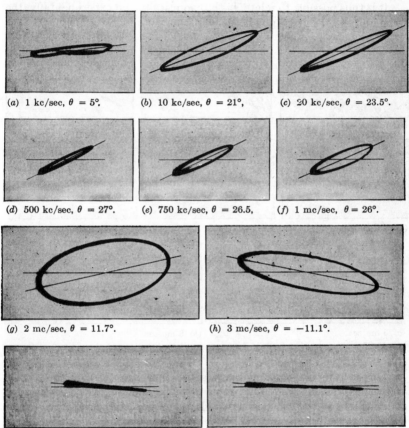

(a) 1 kc/sec, $\theta = 5°$.   (b) 10 kc/sec, $\theta = 21°$,   (c) 20 kc/sec, $\theta = 23.5°$.

(d) 500 kc/sec, $\theta = 27°$.   (e) 750 kc/sec, $\theta = 26.5$,   (f) 1 mc/sec, $\theta = 26°$.

(g) 2 mc/sec, $\theta = 11.7°$.   (h) 3 mc/sec, $\theta = -11.1°$.

(i) 4 mc/sec, $\theta = -6°$.   (j) 5 mc/sec, $\theta = -3.5°$.

FIG. 14·36.—Photographs of oscilloscope presentation of the frequency-response characteristics of two pulse transformers ($n = \frac{1}{5}$ and $n = 5$) with resultant $n = 1$.

transformer pair is equal to $\tan \theta/\tan \theta'$. This method is recommended because it eliminates errors arising from lack of orthogonality of the scope plates.

In Fig. 14·35 are shown photographs of scope traces obtained at various frequencies in the measurement of the frequency response of a transformer that is operated with $n = -1$ and $R_l = 1000$ ohms.

Figure 14·36 shows similar photographs for a combination of transformers (232AW2 and 232BW2, see Tables 13·1 and 13·2) stepdown $n = \frac{1}{5}$ — stepup $n = 5$ operating into a load $R_l = 1000$ ohms.

Figure 14·37 shows the oscilloscope traces obtained when the transformer or transformers are omitted from the circuit.

It is thus possible to relate, both theoretically and experimentally, the pulse and frequency-response characteristics of a transformer.

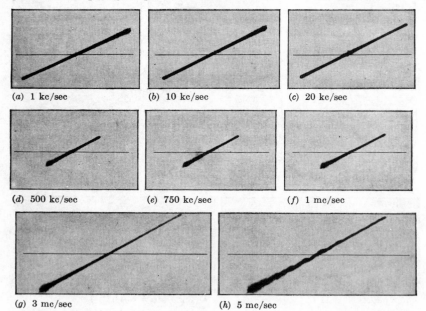

(a) 1 kc/sec   (b) 10 kc/sec   (c) 20 kc/sec

(d) 500 kc/sec   (e) 750 kc/sec   (f) 1 mc/sec

(g) 3 mc/sec   (h) 5 mc/sec

Fig. 14·37.—Photographs of oscilloscope presentation of the trace without the transformer in the circuit, $\theta = 28°$ for all frequencies, $R_l = R_G = 1000$ ohms.

This chapter has treated the effect of pulse-transformer parameters on the pulse shape generated by power pulse generators when resistance and magnetron (or biased-diode) loads are used. The effect of the pulse-transformer parameters on the behavior of a regenerative-pulse-generator circuit has been outlined. The effect of the parameters of stepup and inverting transformers on the frequency response with a resistance load has also been discussed.

CHAPTER 15

MATERIALS AND THEIR USES IN DESIGN

By W. H. Bostick

CORE MATERIAL

15·1. D-c Properties and Test Results.—It has been pointed out in Secs. 12·2 and 13·1 that the primary or shunt inductance L_p of a pulse transformer must be large compared with the leakage inductance L_L if the transformer is to have a high efficiency. To achieve a low value of L_L/L_p it is necessary to make a wise choice of core material and type of core in designing the transformer. It is therefore of importance to investigate the factors that influence L_p (or L_e and R_e).

Required Geometrical and Electrical Properties of the Core.—In general, the core should be made in the form of a closed path with a mean magnetic-path length as small as the coil that it encloses permits. In order that eddy currents may be reduced, the core must be fabricated from thin laminations or strips, and the core material should have as high a resistivity as is consistent with the retention of good magnetic and working properties of the steel. The rolling of the magnetic material into thicknesses in the range of 0.001 to 0.005 in., and the fabrication of this material into the core, must not seriously reduce μ_o, alter the shape of the B-H loop in the vicinity of B_{sat}, or increase the value of H_c (see Fig. 15·2) of the material. Furthermore, it must be possible in one way or another to assemble the coils on the core or vice versa. The interlaminar resistance must be sufficiently high to keep the effect of interlaminar eddy currents negligibly small, and the thickness of the interlaminar insulating layer should be small enough to permit a high space factor (ratio of active volume to total volume) for the completed core.

D-c Properties of the Core Material.—The pulse properties of a core depend to a great extent upon the d-c or low-frequency properties of the core and the core material. The d-c magnetic properties of a core that are relevant to pulse-transformer use will now be discussed.

Usually voltage pulses of only one polarity are applied to the transformer, and under these conditions the core material is operated only in the region to the right or left of the H-axis. If the pulse-transformer core is initially unmagnetized, and rectangular pulses of constant voltage and one polarity are applied, the resultant incremental B-H loops of constant flux swing[1] ΔB will, during a brief transient period, bring the core material to the state where the loop from the remanent point to the B-H curve has a change in flux density equal to ΔB.   The location of

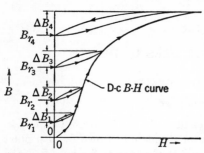

the remanent point depends upon the particular value of ΔB and on the shape of the B-H curve (see Fig. 15·1). If ΔB is large, the remanent flux density at the beginning of each pulse (after the transient period is over) is very nearly equal to B_r, the remanent flux density of the core when the material is driven to saturation.[2]

It is often desirable to have a large ΔB during the pulse in order to keep the number of turns on the coil and the cross-sectional area of the core reasonably small [see Eq. (10)].   With a material of large remanent induction B_r (see Fig. 15·2a) the ΔB over which the core may be operated during the pulse without saturation is small.

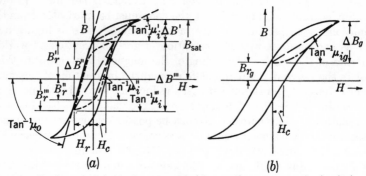

Fig. 15·2.—D-c hysteresis loop of a core with (a) a continuous magnetic circuit (no butt joint), (b) a gap in the magnetic circuit.

From the d-c or low-frequency hysteresis loops of two sample cores, one without butt joints shown in Fig. 15·2a and the other with butt joints,

---

[1] In the discussion of the d-c properties of the core material, ΔB and B are used instead of $\Delta \overline{B}$ and $\overline{B}$, which are used in the discussion of the pulse properties of the core to denote values of flux density averaged throughout the lamination thickness.

[2] In the computation of the optimum gap length in the core and of the values of μ when a reverse current is employed, it is assumed in this section, for purposes of simplification, that ΔB is so large that the resultant remanence always corresponds to the B-H loop of the core material driven to saturation.

(that is, gaps in the magnetic circuit) shown in Fig. 15·2b, it is obvious that B_r may be reduced (and the available ΔB thereby increased) by—

1. The insertion of a gap (a butt joint) in the core (see Fig. 15·2b).
2. A reverse magnetic field H_r (see Fig. 15·2a) produced by a current that flows through the primary in the reverse direction between pulses and leaves the core with a remanence $B = B_r''$ (and $H = 0$) at the beginning of each pulse.
3. A reverse magnetic field H_r produced by a constant reverse current (in either the primary winding or a special winding in the transformer) that leaves the core material at $B = B_r'''$ and $H = -H_r$ at the beginning of each pulse (see Fig. 15·2a).

To achieve a value of B_r that is well below the B-axis (and hence a high available ΔB) by Methods 2 and 3 without requiring an inordinately

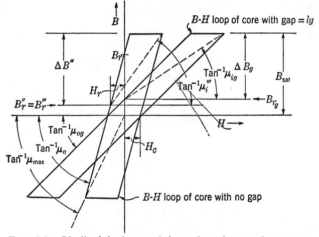

FIG. 15·3.—Idealized d-c hysteresis loop of a pulse-transformer core.

large amount of current to achieve the requisite H_r, and to achieve a high average d-c incremental permeability μ_i, it is obviously desirable to have a very low H_c. To achieve a low B_r by Method 1 without introducing an extremely large gap (which markedly reduces μ_{og} and μ_i) it is also desirable to have a low H_c [see Eq. (4)]. The available ΔB is also dependent upon B_{sat}, the saturation induction of the core material; thus, other things being equal, it is desirable to have a core material with as high a value of B_{sat} as possible in order to obtain a large variation in flux density.

The average incremental d-c permeability μ_i over the range ΔB is, in most cases, a major factor in determining the pulse permeability. It is therefore desirable to have μ_i a maximum.

Optimum Gap Length of the Core.—Most low-power pulse transformers operate with relatively small values of ΔB (less than 1000 gauss), and in many of these transformers no special precautions need be taken to reduce B_r (see Fig. 15·1). With high-power pulse transformers, however, it is often advisable to use a large ΔB. In many high-power applications a gap, rather than reverse current, proves to be the more practical method of reducing B_r.

It is possible to calculate approximately the gap length necessary to produce maximum μ_i over the range ΔB if the hysteresis loops of Fig. 15·2a and b are assumed to become, through a process of idealization, the loops of Fig. 15·3.

It is sometimes desirable to increase the induction during the pulse almost to saturation in order to achieve the maximum ΔB. Therefore, it is assumed that the value of ΔB that is effective during the pulse is

$$\Delta B = B_{sat} - B_{rg},$$

where B_{rg} as defined in Fig. 15·3 is the remanence of a core containing a gap.

The magnetomotive force Hl may be equated to the flux multiplied by the sum of the reluctances of the core material and the gap. Thus,

$$Hl = BA\left(\frac{l}{A\mu_o} + \frac{l_g}{A}\right) = B\left(\frac{l}{\mu_o} + l_g\right).$$

Then

$$\frac{1}{\mu_{og}} \equiv \frac{H}{B} = \frac{1}{\mu_o} + \frac{l_g}{l},$$

or

$$\mu_{og} = \frac{\mu_o}{1 + \mu_o\dfrac{l_g}{l}}, \tag{1}$$

where l is the mean magnetic-path length of the core and is assumed to be essentially equal to the total magnetic-path length of iron and gap, l_g is the gap length, and A is the cross-sectional area of the core. From Fig. 15·3 it is evident that

$$B_r = \mu_o H_c,$$
$$B_{rg} = \mu_{og} H_c,$$

and

$$\mu_{ig} = \frac{B_{sat} - B_{rg}}{\dfrac{B_{sat}}{\mu_{og}} + H_c} = \left(\frac{B_{sat} - \mu_{og}H_c}{B_{sat} + \mu_{og}H_c}\right)\mu_{og}.$$

Since a gap is usually chosen in practice so that $B_{rg} \ll B_{sat}$, the following approximation can be written for this last equation:

$$\mu_{ig} \approx \left(1 - \frac{2\mu_{og}H_c}{B_{sat}}\right)\mu_{og} = \mu_{og} - \frac{2H_c}{B_{sat}}\mu_{og}^2. \qquad (2)$$

It is desired to maximize μ with respect to l_g/l, that is, $d\mu_{ig}/d(l_g/l)$ should be equated to zero. Since

$$\frac{d\mu_{ig}}{d\left(\dfrac{l_g}{l}\right)} = \frac{\partial\mu_{ig}}{\partial\mu_{og}}\frac{d\mu_{og}}{d\left(\dfrac{l_g}{l}\right)},$$

and $d\mu_{og}/d(l_g/l)$ vanishes only for $\mu_o = 0$, and μ_o is always greater than zero in practice, the value of gap length for maximum μ_{ig} may be obtained from the relation

$$\frac{\partial\mu_{ig}}{\partial\mu_{og}} = 1 - \frac{4H_c}{B_{sat}}\mu_{og} = 0,$$

or

$$1 + \mu_o\frac{l_g}{l} - \frac{4H_c}{B_{sat}}\mu_o = 0.$$

From this relationship, the optimum ratio l_g/l for a core that is to be driven almost to B_{sat} is

$$\left(\frac{l_g}{l}\right)_{\text{opt}} = \frac{4H_c}{B_{sat}} - \frac{1}{\mu_o}. \qquad (3)$$

The value of μ_{ig} for this optimum length of gap is given by

$$\mu_{ig} = \frac{B_{sat}}{8H_c}. \qquad (4)$$

If, for a given material with no gap in the core, the remanence $B'_r = fB_{sat}$, where f is some fraction less than 1,

$$\left(\frac{l_g}{l}\right)_{\text{opt}} = \frac{1}{\mu_o}(4f - 1) = \frac{H_c}{B_{sat}}\left(4 - \frac{1}{f}\right).$$

In most core materials used in pulse transformers, $f \approx 0.75$. Then

$$\left(\frac{l_g}{l}\right)_{\text{opt}} \approx \frac{2}{\mu_o}.$$

Thus, the optimum gap length for a Mo permalloy core ($H_c \approx 0.04$ oersteds, $B_{sat} \approx 8500$ gauss) is about one-third the optimum gap length for a Hipersil core ($H_c \approx 0.25$ oersteds, $B_{sat} \approx 17{,}500$ gauss[1]), and the

---

[1] Complete ferric saturation occurs at $B = 20{,}250$ gauss. For purposes of constructing an idealized d-c B-H loop, however, $B_{sat} = 17{,}500$ gauss is a more suitable value for Hipersil.

value of μ_{ig} for the optimum gap length is about three times as great for the Mo permalloy core as for the Hipersil core.

A typical 0.002-in. Hipersil core with $l = 5$ in. is manufactured with a butt joint containing a total gap length of about 0.001 in.   Thus

$$\frac{l_g}{l} = \frac{0.001 \text{ in.}}{5 \text{ in.}} = 2 \times 10^{-4}.$$

The value of μ_o for this material is about 10,000, for which

$$\left(\frac{l_g}{l}\right)_{\text{opt}} \approx \frac{2}{\mu_o} \approx 2 \times 10^{-4}.$$

Thus, the gap used is approximately of optimum length if the core is to be driven almost to B_{sat}.

The value of μ_{ig} calculated from Eq. (4) in terms of μ_o for $l_g/l = (l_g/l)_{\text{opt}}$ is

$$\mu_{ig} = \frac{\mu_o}{8f}.$$

If $f = 0.75$, $\mu_{ig} = \mu_o/6$.

The quantity $\mu_{\max}$ (see Fig. 15·3) is related to μ_o by the following equation:

$$\mu_{\max} = \frac{B_{\text{sat}}}{\dfrac{B_{\text{sat}}}{\mu_o} + H_c} = \left(\frac{B_{\text{sat}}}{B_{\text{sat}} + B_r}\right)\mu_o = \frac{1}{1+f}\mu_o.$$

Hence, when

$$\frac{l_g}{l} = \left(\frac{l_g}{l}\right)_{\text{opt}},$$

$$\mu_{ig} = \frac{\mu_{\max}(1+f)}{8f}.$$

When $f = 0.75$,

$$\mu_{ig} \approx 0.3\mu_{\max}.$$

It is to be remembered that the foregoing values of $\left(\dfrac{l_g}{l}\right)_{\text{opt}}$ and μ_{ig} are calculated for a core that is driven to B_{sat}.   If it is desired to drive the flux density to some value B_m that is less than B_{sat}, but still much greater than B_{rg}, Eq. (2) becomes

$$\mu_{ig} = \mu_{og} - \frac{2H_c}{B_m}\mu_{og}^2,$$

and Eq. (3) becomes

$$\left(\frac{l_g}{l}\right)_{\text{opt}} = \frac{4H_c}{B_m} - \frac{1}{\mu_o}.$$

Effect of Reverse Magnetic Field.—For some applications in which high values of ΔB are required, it is not only practical but advantageous to use a reverse current (usually with an ungapped core structure). The following analysis of the effect of reverse current holds for cores, whether they have a gap or not, as long as their d-c hysteresis loops are approximately representable by the idealized loop of Fig. 15·4.

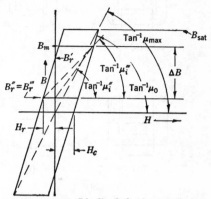

The quantity B_r''' is defined as the induction that results from the application of a d-c reverse field H_r. It is assumed, for simplicity, that the remanent induction B_r'' resulting from the application of a peak reverse field

FIG. 15·4.—Idealized d-c hysteresis loop depicting the operation of a core with either a d-c H_r, or a peak reverse H_r between pulses.

H_r between pulses (which drops to zero just before the beginning of the pulse) is equal to B_r'''. Thus

$$B_r''' = B_r'' = (H_c - H_r)\mu_o.$$

The value of μ_i that results from

$$\Delta B = B_m - B_r'',$$

where H_r is applied as a peak reverse field between pulses and falls to zero at the beginning of the pulses, is

$$\mu_i'' = \frac{B_m - B_r''}{H_c + \dfrac{B_m}{\mu_o}} = \frac{B_m - (H_c - H_r)\mu_o}{H_c + \dfrac{B_m}{\mu_o}}.$$

It is possible, if desired, to express μ_i'' in terms of $\mu_{\max}$ since

$$\mu_{\max} = \frac{B_{\mathrm{sat}}}{H_c + \dfrac{B_{\mathrm{sat}}}{\mu_o}}.$$

Then

$$\mu_o = \frac{B_{\mathrm{sat}}\mu_{\max}}{B_{\mathrm{sat}} - H_c\mu_{\max}}, \tag{5}$$

and

$$\mu_i'' = \frac{B_m - (H_c - H_r)\dfrac{B_{\mathrm{sat}}\mu_{\max}}{B_{\mathrm{sat}} - H_c\mu_{\max}}}{H_c + \dfrac{(B_{\mathrm{sat}} - H_c\mu_{\max})B_m}{B_{\mathrm{sat}}\mu_{\max}}}.$$

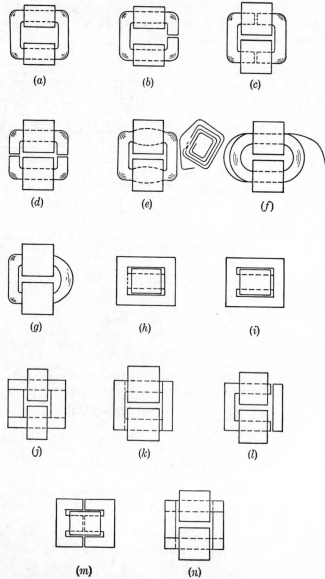

Fig. 15·5.—Diagrams showing various types of pulse transformer cores.
(a) Continuously-wound strip core.
(b) One butt joint sawed in a continuously wound strip core.
(c) Two butt joints sawed in a continuously wound strip core.
(d) Two butt joints sawed in a continuously wound strip core.   Coils are wound in ordinary fashion with half core as a mandrel.
(e) Laced-joint core.   Core is continuously wound from strip, annealed, every third leaf

If H_r is obtained from a constant d-c current in one winding of the transformer, the resultant incremental permeability μ_i''' over

$$\Delta B = B_m - B_r'''$$

is

$$\mu_i''' = \frac{B_m - (H_c - H_r)\mu_o}{H_r + H_c + \dfrac{B_m}{\mu_o}}. \tag{6}$$

It is also possible to express μ_i''' in terms of μ_{max} if Eq. (5) is substituted in Eq. (6).

For materials such as the permalloys, where a reverse current may be advantageously used, μ_o is usually very high and a suitable value for the reverse field H_r, in order to obtain a high μ_i'' or μ_i''' is $H_c < H_r < 2H_c$. Values of H_r greater than $2H_c$ are, of course, advantageous if they can be obtained. From the idealized loop of Fig. 15·4 it may be seen that, if

$$H_r \approx H_c + \frac{B_{sat}}{\mu_o},$$

the highest possible value of μ_i''' is obtained. This highest value of μ_i''' equals μ_{max}, which is approximately equal to $\mu_o/(1 + f)$.

Geometrical Core Shapes and Types of Construction That Have Been Evolved.—A number of methods of constructing cores have been evolved by various British and American manufacturers. These arrangements of core material are described and numbered in Fig. 15·5. With cores that contain no gap (that is, cores of either lap-joint or continuous-strip construction) it is necessary to have a reverse magnetic field H_r if ΔB is to be fairly high. Under these conditions, it is desirable that the magnetic material have a low H_c in order that the H_r available between pulses or from a d-c winding may reduce the remanence to a low or negative value. If the core is an unbreakable closed magnetic circuit, it is necessary to wind the coils by hand with a bobbin, or on a machine with a circular shuttle.

---

cut as it is disassembled.   The pieces are then reassembled into the Cu coils.   This core has a poor space factor.

(*f*) Long strips are laced into completed coils.   This method is tedious for thin laminations and large transformers.

(*g*) Core is continuously wound with extra window length, annealed, and cut at one end. The core is inserted into Cu coils and the ends of the magnetic strip are interleaved to form a lap joint.

(*h*) Alternate-stacked lap joint.

(*i*) Same as (*h*) except that the laminations are all similarly stacked to give a butt joint.

(*j*) U-U punchings, lap joint.

(*k*) U-I or L-L punchings with lap joint.

(*l*) U-I punchings with butt joints.

(*m*) E-E stacked, butt joints.

(*n*) Four I's stacked, lap joint.

Iron-dust cores for pulse transformers have, in general, proved inferior to laminated cores because of their large inherent effective gap, and hence their low effective permeability.

The magnetic materials manufactured in the United States and the United Kingdom, together with the types of pulse-transformer cores in which the materials have been used, are listed in Tables 15·1 and 15·2.

TABLE 15·1.—CORE MATERIALS MANUFACTURED AND USED IN THE U.S.A.

Material	Type of core	Type of inter-laminar insulation	Material manufacturer	Core manufacturer	Principal users of cores	Pulse-power range in which cores are generally used
78% Ni, 3% Mo, 19% Fe, Permalloy 0.0012 in.	(a)	SiO₂ dust deposited by cataphoresis process	Western Electric Co.	Western Electric Co.	Western Electric Co.	10–100 kw
45% Ni, 55% Fe, Permalloy 0.002 in.	(a), (b), (c), (d)	SiO₂ dust deposited by cataphoresis; or mica dust	Western Electric Co.	Western Electric Co.	Western Electric Co.	100 kw-1 Mw
45% Ni, 55% Fe, Permalloy 0.002 in.	(a), (b), (c), (d)	Mica dust	Carpenter	Magnetic Metals Co.	Western Electric Co.	100 kw-1 Mw
45% Ni, 55% Fe, Permalloy 0.002 in.	(e), (f), (g), experimental	Oxide	Carpenter	Magnetic Metals Co.	Radiation Laboratory	100 kw-1 Mw
45% Ni, 3% Si, 52% Fe, Silicon Nicaloi 0.002 in. and 0.004 in.	(e), (j), and (l)	Chrome silicate, colloidal silica	Allegheny Ludlum	General Electric Co	General Electric Co.	0.1 kw-1 Mw
45% Ni, 3% Mo, 52% Fe, Monimax 0.002 in, 0.003 in, and 0.004 in.	(e), (i), (j); type C in experimental quantity only	Oxide	Allegheny Ludlum	General Electric Co.	General Electric Co.	0.1 kw-1 Mw
3% Si, 97% Fe, Si Steel 0.003 in.	(e),(l),(j); type (c) and (e) in experimental quan.	Oxide and powder (MgO)	Allegheny Ludlum	General Electric Co.	General Electric Co.	10 kw-0.5 Mw
3% Si, 97% Fe, Hipersil .003 in. Oriented 0.002 in. 0.001 in.	(e)	Carlite coating (iron phosphate)	American Rolling Mill Co.	Westinghouse Electric Corporation	Westinghouse Electric Corporation, General Electric Co., Raytheon, Utah, and others	1 kw-3 Mw 25 kw-10 Mw 0.1 kw-1 Mw 0.1 kw-10 kw

TABLE 15·2.—CORE MATERIALS MANUFACTURED AND USED IN GREAT BRITAIN

Material	Type of core	Type of inter-laminar insulation	Material manufacturer	Core manufacturer	Principal users of cores
Radiometal 0.004 in.	(h)	Oxide; sometimes lacquer as well	Magnetic and Electric Alloys	Magnetic and Electric Alloys	The General Electric Co. Ltd. (GEC) British Thompson Huston Co. Ltd. (BTH)
Radiometal 0.004 in.	(h)	Paper interleaved	Magnetic and Electric Alloys	Magnetic and Electric Alloys	BTH
Radiometal 0.004 in.	(n)	. . . .	Telegraph Construction and Maintenance Co., Ltd.	. . . .	Metropolitan-Vickers Electric Co., Ltd. (METV)
Radiometal 0.002 in.	(e)	Oxide	. . . .	. . . .	BTH
Radiometal 0.002 in.	(a)	Lacquer	. . . .	. . . .	BTH
Radiometal 0.005 in	. . . .	Varnish	. . . .	. . . .	GEC
Rhometal 0.004 in.	(h)	Oxide	Magnetic and Electric Alloys	Magnetic and Electric Alloys	GEC
Rhometal 0.004 in.	(n)	. . . .	. . . .	. . . .	E. C. Cole Ltd.
Rhometal 0.004 in.	(n)	Oxide	Magnetic and Electric Alloys	Magnetic and Electric Alloys	GEC
Rhometal 0.004 in.	(n) or (e)	. . . .	. . . .	. . . .	METV
Rhometal 0.003 in.	(g) (n); (c) experimental only	. . . .	. . . .	. . . .	METV
Rhometal 0.002 in.	(a)	Lacquer	. . . .	. . . .	BTH
4 % Si, 96 % Fe, 0.007 in. 0.014 in.	(n) (n)	. . . .	. . . .	. . . .	METV METV
Stalloy 0 014 in.	(n)	. . . .	. . . .	. . . .	METV

Equation (13·20) shows that, in order to make the value of $(\alpha + \beta)_{opt}$ low (that is, to make the efficiency high), the effective pulse permeability μ_e should be made a maximum. As is shown later, μ_e depends upon the pulse duration, the thickness of the laminations, and the values of the resistivity and the permeability μ_i of the material. Other things being equal, it is of advantage in the design of a transformer to select the core material and type of core that provide the highest value of μ_i. There is, however, a dependence of $(\Delta \bar{B})_{opt}$ on load impedance, power level, wire size, and μ_e [see Eq. (13·17)]; also, the value of μ_i for a given core depends markedly on ΔB.

A workable procedure in the choice of core material and core for a pulse transformer is to estimate a reasonable value for μ_e, and from this estimate to determine the approximate value of $(\Delta \bar{B})_{\text{opt}}$ by the use of Eq. (13·17), past experience, and extrapolation from previous successful designs. The core material and structure giving the highest μ_i for this ΔB are then selected.

For regenerative-pulse-generator and interstage transformers operating at pulse powers of the order of magnitude of 0.5 kw, $(\Delta \bar{B})_{\text{opt}}$ is of the order of magnitude of 1000 gauss. For pulse transformers operating at pulse powers of the order of magnitude of 0.001 kw, $(\Delta \bar{B})_{\text{opt}}$ is much less than 1000 gauss. For the transformers that operate at very low values

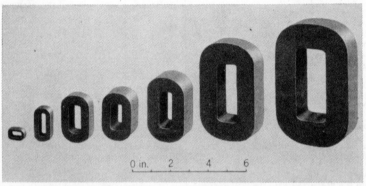

FIG. 15·6.—An assortment of widely used 0.002-in. Hipersil pulse-transformer cores.

of $\Delta \bar{B}$, it is advantageous to use cores without any gaps and with the steepest incremental B-H loops (see Figs. 15·1 and 15·2), which are found in materials of low H_c and high μ_o (that is, the permalloys).

For transformers that operate at high power levels $(\Delta \bar{B})_{\text{opt}}$ is of the order of magnitude of 8000 gauss. If sufficient reverse current is available, the highest value of μ_i can usually be attained by using a permalloy core with no gap. If these cores are continuously wound from ribbon, the winding of the coils for the transformer must be performed with a shuttle. This departure from the simple normal practice of coil winding and the fact that the core window cannot be used so economically if shuttle winding is required may in some cases induce the designer to choose a core with a gap.

The designer is obliged to choose a structure that contains a gap if insufficient reverse current is available. The advantage that the materials with very low H_c and very high μ_o (that is, the permalloys) have over oriented silicon steel in ungapped structures is largely lost in gapped structures, and silicon steel gains some advantage in gapped structure because of its higher B_{sat}. Efficient transformers can, however, be built with both types of materials with the various gapped structures illustrated in Fig. 15·5.   From the point of view of the ease of construction of the

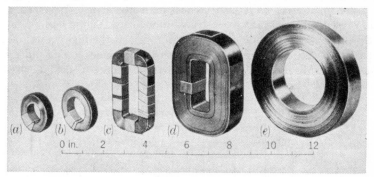

Fig. 15·7.—Various uncut Ni steel pulse-transformer cores. (a), (b), and (c) 0.001-in. Mo permalloy cores. (d) and (e) 0.002-in. 45-permalloy cores.

transformer, of a high available ΔB, a reasonably high value of μ_i, a high space factor, the availability of light gauge materials in large quantities, and the uniformity in the completed product, the type C core (Fig. 15·5) utilizing 0.002-in. Hipersil has been an extremely useful pulse-transformer core. An assortment of widely used sizes of 0.002-in. Hipersil cores is shown in Fig. 15·6. Various 0.001-in. Mo Permalloy and 0.002-in. 45-Permalloy uncut cores are shown in Fig. 15·7. Several 0.004-in. silicon Nicaloi punchings and one 0.003-in. Monimax punching widely used in pulse transformers are shown in Fig. 15·8.

Standard Tests on Core Materials and Cores.—There has been an effort on the part of the agencies interested in pulse transformers and on the part of

Fig. 15·8.—Various nickel steel punchings. Light-colored punchings are of 0.004-in. silicon Nicaloi, the dark punching of 0.003-in. Monimax.

industries manufacturing them to formulate a set of standard tests on pulse-transformer cores and core materials to facilitate the comparison of the various cores. This set of standard tests for pulse-transformer cores is set forth in the Radiation Laboratory Report No. 722.[1]

[1] W. H. Bostick, "Pulse Transformer Committee Standard Test Methods for Pulse Transformer Cores," RL Report No. 722, May 5, 1945.

The measuring techniques given in that report are described in Sec. 15·2.

Results of Tests on Various Core Materials.—In Table 15·3 are listed the results of a series of systematic measurements made in 1944 on several widely used materials for pulse-transformer cores manufactured in the U. S.[1] These results show that Hipersil excels at the high values of $\Delta\bar{B}$, and that the Ni steels are better at the lower values. The pulse performance of Mo Permalloy when a reverse magnetic field is used is especially notable.

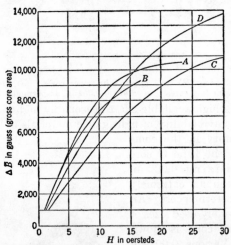

Fig. 15·9.—Loci of the tips of pulse *B-H* loops taken on butt-joint cores, with 1-μsec pulses.
    Curve *A* is for Monimax 0.003-in., ½ in. by ½ in. leg section.
    Curve *B* is for silicon Nicaloi 0.003 in., ½ in. by ½ in. leg section.
    Curve *C* is for silicon Nicaloi 0.004 in., ½ in. by ¾ in. leg section.
    Curve *D* is for Hipersil 0.002 in., ½ in. by ¾ in. leg section.

In Fig. 15·9 are shown the loci of the tips of *B-H* loops obtained with 1-μsec pulses for several cores constructed of punched laminations with butt joints and for a type C Hipersil core. Again it may be seen that Hipersil excels at the high flux densities whereas some of the nickel steels appear slightly better at lower flux densities.

Actual photographs of pulse *B-H* loops are shown in Fig 15·10.

The d-c and pulsed *B-H* loops shown in Fig. 15·11 are representative of the performance of British pulse-transformer cores, which were made, for the most part, of nickel steel. The construction of "synthesized" pulsed *B-H* loops shown in Fig. 15·11 will be described in Sec. 15·4.

---

[1] Although more accurate measurements have subsequently been made, the measurements listed in Table 15·3 provide a reliable basis for a comparison of the various core materials.

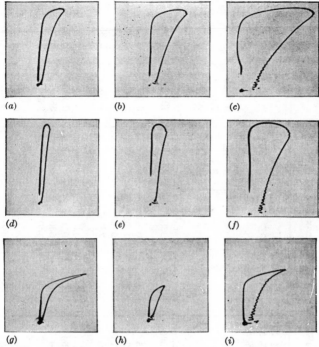

Fig. 15·10.—Photographs of oscilloscope traces of pulse *B-H* loops at various pulse durations. *B* is vertical and *H* is horizontal.

Core Material	V kv	N turns	$\dfrac{d\bar{B}}{dt}$ gauss sec^{-1}	τ μsec.	$\Delta\bar{B}$ gauss	ΔH at $t = \tau$ oersteds	$\mu_e = \dfrac{\Delta\bar{B}}{\Delta H}$ max
(a) 0.003 unoriented	5.72	200	10^9	10.25	10,250	19	540
(b) 0.003 "	8.58	100	3×10^9	3.33	10,000	27	370
(c) 0.003 "	14.3	50	10^{10}	1.05	10,500	52	200
(d) 0.002 oriented	5.72	200	10^9	10.25	10,250	6.4	1600
(e) 0.002 "	8.58	100	3×10^9	3.33	10,000	11	900
(f) 0.002 "	14.3	50	10^{10}	1.05	10,500	31	340
(g) 0.001 unoriented	5.72	200	10^9	7.00	7,000	27	260
(h) 0.001 "	8.58	100	3×10^9	1.30	4,000	9	440
(i) 0.001 "	14.3	50	10^{10}	0.75	7,500	21	350

Space factors

0.001-in. cores........................... 0.85

0.002-in. and 0.003 in..................... 0.95

2¼-*in. window cores*

$A = 2.86$ cm^2

$l = 17$ cm

15·2. Pulse Magnetization. *Electromagnetic Treatment of the Magnetization of the Core.*—The theoretical expression for the inductance and magnetic field of a coil of given length and diameter involves Nagaoka's constant, which depends upon the ratio of length to diameter of the coil. However, if the coil is wound in the form of a toroid, its inductance is

$$L = \frac{4\pi N^2 A}{10^9 l} \qquad \text{henrys,}$$

TABLE 15·3.—D-c AND PULSE DATA ON SEVERAL WIDELY USED CORE MATERIALS MANUFACTURED IN THE U.S.A.

Material	GE Si Nicaloi (B9W)		GE Monimax		WE Mo Permalloy	Westinghouse oriented Hipersil	
			Uncut core	Cut core*	Uncut core	Uncut core	Cut core
Constitution	42.65% Ni 0.40% Mn 0.34% Al 3% Si	42.4% Ni 3.33% Mn 0.75% Al	47% Ni 3% Mo		79% Ni 4% Mo	3.25% Si	
Thickness of lamination, in.	0.0025	0.004	0.0025		0.0012	0.0025	
Specific gravity	7.9	7.9	8.45		8.7	7.6	
Resistivity in microhm-cm	85	85	73		46	50–55	
D-c magnetization data							
μ_{max}	7650	37,000	21,900	2680*	79,650	12,200	6180
H in oersteds at							
$B = 1000$ gauss	0.18	0.05	0.09	0.41*	0.03	0.20	0.33
$B = 5000$	1.02	0.13	0.24	1.92*	0.065	0.46	0.83
$B = 10,000$	....	3.71	3.17	9.0*	....	0.85	1.71
$B = 12,500$	....	....	13.8	22.4*	....	1.45	2.85
B in gauss at $H = 25$	9800	11,950	13,400	12,900	8880	17,400	16,500
At $B = 5000$ gauss							
H_c in oersteds	0.195	0.059	0.11	0.13	0.045	0.273	0.257
B_r in gauss	2750	4300	3580	530	3970	3360	2100
Loss in ergs/cm³/cycle (60 cycles)	265	89	120	140	40	280	420
At $B = 10,000$ gauss							
H_c in gauss oersteds	....	0.08	0.13	0.20	....	0.38	0.45
B_r in gauss	....	7250	5500	950	....	8080	4700
Loss in ergs/cm³/cycle	....	390	475	520	....	820	1450

Material	GE Si Nicaloi (B9W)		GE Monimax		WE Mo Permalloy	Westinghouse oriented Hipersil	
Pulse magnetization data							
$\tau = 1\mu sec$							
For $H_r = 0$							
H in oersteds at $\Delta\bar{B} = 5000$ gauss	7.1	45.0	5.9	7.2*	....	30.0	7.0
at $\Delta\bar{B} = 7500$	22.5	....	11.6	11.6*	....	....	10.2
at $\Delta\bar{B} = 10,000$	....	....	33.3	16.25*	....	....	14.3
For $H_r = 0.5$ oersteds							
H in oersteds at $\Delta\bar{B} = 5000$ gauss	4.5	4.3	2.6	7.1*	1.0	4.8	5.2
at $\Delta\bar{B} = 7500$	6.9	7.5	4.1	10.8*	1.75	6.5	7.5
at $\Delta\bar{B} = 10,000$	9.7	11.3	5.8	14.8*	2.7	8.5	9.9
at $\Delta\bar{B} = 12,500$	13.0	15.6	7.6	19.1*	3.7	10.1	12.5
at $\Delta B = 15,000$	....	....	9.8				
For $H_r = H_c$							
H in oersteds at $\Delta\bar{B} = 5000$ gauss	5.25	8.1	3.2	6.65*	1.1	5.25	5.75
at $\Delta\bar{B} = 10,000$	....	....	7.2	15.4*	....	8.4	10.1
Loss in ergs/cm³/pulse							
at $\Delta\bar{B} = 5000$	1080	2160	685	985*	240	950	1125
at $\Delta B = 10,000$	....	....	2115	3840*	....	2840	4120

Tests were performed on strip-wound ring samples ¼ in. by ¼ in. in cross section, and with an inside diameter of 2 in. All results are reported on the basis of net core area. Measurements were made under the direction of W. Morrill of the General Electric Company, Pittsfield, Mass, 1944.

* Because of faulty cutting, the gap in this core was considerably larger than optimum.

and the magnetic field inside the coil is

$$H = \frac{4\pi N i}{10 l} \qquad \text{oersteds,} \qquad (7)$$

where l is the mean magnetic-path length of the toroid in centimeters, A is the cross-sectional area of the toroid in square centimeters, and i is the

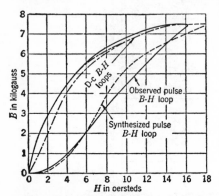

current in amperes. If a toroida core of effective permeability μ_e is inserted in this toroid, the inductance becomes

$$L = \frac{4\pi N^2 A \mu_e}{10^9 l}, \qquad (8)$$

and, since no free magnetic poles are formed, the magnetic field H inside the coil is unchanged.

If a coil is wound on the to-roidal core so that only a fraction of l is covered, and if $\mu_e \gg 1$, most of the magnetic flux is still constrained to remain in the core. The field H is still approximately constant in magnitude and parallel to the center line of the toroid throughout the whole of the core,

Fig. 15·11.—Experimental and synthe-sized pulse *B-H* loops for British Rhometal, No 8 punchings, oxidized and sprayed with lacquer; nominal thickness 0.004 in.; core in the form of two E's with 0.001 in. butt joint gap in each leg. $\Delta \bar{B} = 7500$ gauss, $\tau = 1.0$ μsec.

as it is when the coil completely encloses the core. Hence, Eqs. (7) and (8) are good approximations for the inductance and magnetic field of such a core and coil.

Under pulse conditions the effective permeability μ_e of the magnetic material is, because of eddy currents, different from μ, the intrinsic permeability of the material itself. It is, therefore, of importance to study the relationship between μ_e and μ.

Relationship of V to $\bar{B}$; Faraday's Law.—At any point within the coil, or within the toroidal core if there is a core, the following equations (in mks units) of Maxwell are applicable:

$$\nabla \times \mathbf{E} + \frac{\partial \mathbf{B}}{\partial t} = 0,$$

or

$$\int\int_A \nabla \times \mathbf{E} \cdot d\mathbf{S} + \int\int_A \frac{\partial \mathbf{B}}{\partial t} \cdot d\mathbf{S} = 0,$$

where A is the area of the coil. By Stokes's theorem, the emf per turn, in mks units, is

$$\oint_C \mathbf{E}\, d\mathbf{s} = -\int\int_A \frac{\partial \mathbf{B}}{\partial t} \cdot d\mathbf{S} = -A\frac{d\bar{B}}{dt}, \tag{9}$$

where C is the perimeter of A and where the average flux density over the area A is

$$\bar{B} = \frac{1}{A}\int\int_A \mathbf{B} \cdot d\mathbf{S}.$$

If $\bar{B}$ is expressed in gauss and A in square centimeters, and if the coil has N turns, the total voltage impressed across the coil may be written, in cgs units, as

$$V = -\frac{NA}{10^8}\frac{d\bar{B}}{dt} \qquad \text{volts.}$$

Since V is constant throughout the pulse for the idealized pulse,

$$\bar{B} = \int_0^B d\bar{B} = -\frac{10^8}{NA}\int_0^t V\, dt = -\frac{10^8 V t}{NA} \qquad \text{gauss;} \tag{10}$$

that is, $\bar{B}$ increases linearly with respect to time throughout the pulse if V remains constant regardless of the quality of the core material or whether there is any core at all.   The value of $\bar{B}$ at the time $t = \tau$ is denoted by the symbol $\Delta\bar{B}$.

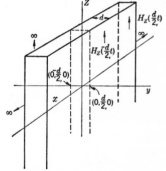

FIG. 15·12.—Idealization of a lamination in a pulse-transformer core.

Development of the Diffusion Equations. It is now assumed that a toroidal core occupies most of the coil area, and that μ_e is sufficiently high to constrain practically all of the magnetic flux in the core.   Then the area A is, for all practical purposes, equal to the net area of the core.   It is also assumed that the magnetic field impressed at the surface of the core does not vary along l and is everywhere parallel to the center line of the core.   The problem is to find the magnetic field (see Fig. 15·12)

$$H_z\left(\frac{d}{2}, t\right) = H_z\left(-\frac{d}{2}, t\right)$$

which, when applied to the surface of the core material, gives an average induction throughout the core of

$$\bar{B} = \frac{-10^8 V t}{NA} \qquad \text{gauss.}$$

It is apparent at the outset that the core material must be in the form of thin insulated laminations if eddy currents are to be held to a reasonably low value.   Figure 15·12 shows such a lamination in which the width of the lamination in the x direction is practically infinite compared with the thickness d.   The z direction is assumed to be along the center line of the core, and any current that flows in the coil produces a magnetic field in the z direction only.   It is assumed that this magnetic field $H_z(y,t)$ does not vary with the coordinates x or z.

The following Maxwell's equations in the mks system of units may be employed:

$$\nabla \times \mathbf{E} + \frac{\partial \mathbf{B}}{\partial t} = 0,$$

and

$$\nabla \times \mathbf{H} - \frac{\partial \mathbf{D}}{\partial t} = \sigma_1 \mathbf{E}.$$

In any known core material σ_1 is large and $\epsilon_1/\epsilon_0 = 1$, where ϵ_1 and ϵ_0 are respectively the dielectric constants, in mks units, of the material and of free space.   Conduction currents are therefore so much more important than displacement currents that it is possible to neglect the term $\partial \mathbf{D}/\partial t$. The symbol μ_1 is used to denote the permeability of the material in mks units.   Also, it is assumed that the permeability μ (μ_1 in mks units) of the core material is constant over the range of induction through which the core is to be operated.   Then

$$\mathbf{B} = \mu_1 \mathbf{H},$$

$$-\nabla \times \mathbf{E} = \mu_1 \frac{\partial \mathbf{H}}{\partial t},$$

and

$$\nabla \times \mathbf{H} = \sigma_1 \mathbf{E},$$

where

$$H_x = H_y = 0.$$

Since

$$\nabla \times \mathbf{H} = \begin{vmatrix} \mathbf{i} & \mathbf{j} & \mathbf{k} \\ \dfrac{\partial}{\partial x} & \dfrac{\partial}{\partial y} & \dfrac{\partial}{\partial z} \\ 0 & 0 & H_z \end{vmatrix} = \mathbf{i}\,\frac{\partial H_z}{\partial y} - \mathbf{j}\,\frac{\partial H_z}{\partial x},$$

and

$$\frac{\partial H_z}{\partial x} = 0,$$

then

$$\mathbf{i}\,\frac{\partial H_z}{\partial y} = \mathbf{i}\sigma_1 E_x,$$

and
$$E_y = E_z = 0.$$

Then

$$\nabla \times \mathbf{E} = \begin{vmatrix} \mathbf{i} & \mathbf{j} & \mathbf{k} \\ \dfrac{\partial}{\partial x} & \dfrac{\partial}{\partial y} & \dfrac{\partial}{\partial z} \\ E_x & 0 & 0 \end{vmatrix} = \mathbf{j}\,\frac{\partial E_x}{\partial z} - \mathbf{k}\,\frac{\partial E_x}{\partial y},$$

and since

$$\frac{\partial E_x}{\partial z} = 0,$$

$$\mathbf{k}\,\frac{\partial E_x}{\partial y} = \mathbf{k}\mu_1\,\frac{\partial H_z}{\partial t}.$$

The two equations

and

$$\left. \begin{aligned} \frac{\partial H_z}{\partial y} &= \sigma_1 E_x \\[2mm] \frac{\partial E_x}{\partial y} &= \mu_1\,\frac{\partial H_z}{\partial t} \end{aligned} \right\} \tag{11}$$

upon differentiation and subtraction yield the following diffusion equations:

and

$$\left. \begin{aligned} \frac{\partial^2 H_z}{\partial y^2} &= \mu_1\sigma_1\,\frac{\partial H_z}{\partial t}, \\[2mm] \frac{\partial^2 E_x}{\partial y^2} &= \mu_1\sigma_1\,\frac{\partial E_x}{\partial t}. \end{aligned} \right\} \tag{12}$$

Solution of the Diffusion Equations.—The solution[1] of Eq. (12) may be written as the sum of $H_a(y,t)$, a "steady-state" term or particular integral, and $H_b(y,t)$, a transient term or complementary function (H_a and H_b are in the z direction, but the subscripts z have been dropped for brevity of notation). The average value of $H_a(y,t)$ across the lamination is assumed equal to $(\Delta \bar{H}/\tau)t$, where $\Delta \bar{H}$ is the mean impressed field in the core at the end of the pulse of duration τ.

[1] This treatment follows that given in the following references:

L. W. Redfearn, "The Effective Permeability and Eddy Current Loss for Magnetic Material under Linear Magnetization," Metropolitan-Vickers Electric Co., Ltd., Report No. C.287, Feb., 1942.

C. R. Dunham, C. C. Hall, K. A. MacFadyen, "Calculation of Eddy Currents in Pulse Transformer Cores," The General Electric Co., Ltd., Report No. 8350, May 8, 1944.

For other treatments that reach the same solution, see L. A. MacColl, Bell Telephone Laboratories, Inc., and T. D. Holstein, "Skin Effect in Pulse-Transformer Cores," Westinghouse Research Laboratories, Report No. SR-170, Feb. 22, 1943.

Equation (9) when integrated over the area S (instead of A), as shown in Fig. 15·13, yields for the steady state

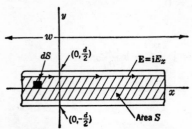

FIG. 15·13.—Path of integration for obtaining the steady-state distribution of E_x and H_z.

$$2wE_x = \int\int_S \frac{\partial \mathbf{B}}{\partial t} \cdot d\mathbf{S} = 2wy\frac{d\bar{B}}{dt},$$

since

$$\left|\frac{\partial \mathbf{B}}{\partial t}\right| = \frac{d\bar{B}}{dt}$$

when the eddy currents have attained a fixed pattern, that is, when the steady state has been attained.

Then

$$E_x = y\frac{d\bar{B}}{dt}$$

and the steady-state magnetic field associated with this E_x can be obtained by integrating Eq. (10) directly since the steady state E_x no longer involves t. Thus, the steady-state magnetic field associated with E_x is

$$H_a = \int dH_a = \sigma_1\frac{d\bar{B}}{dt}\int y\,dy = \text{constant}_1 y^2 + \text{constant}_2,$$

and the complete steady-state term or particular integral may be written

$$H_a = \frac{\Delta\bar{H}}{\tau}(\underbrace{t}_{1} + \underbrace{A_0 + A_2 y^2}_{2}), \qquad (13)$$

where Term 1 takes care of the constant rate of increase in H_a averaged throughout the lamination, and Term 2 takes care of the spacial distribution of magnetic field resulting from the steady-state pattern of eddy currents.

A substitution of Eq. (13) in Eq. (12) yields

$$A_2 = \frac{\mu_1\sigma_1}{2}.$$

Also,

$$\frac{2}{d}\int_0^{\frac{d}{2}} H_a\,dy = \frac{\Delta\bar{H}t}{\tau},$$

and hence

$$A_0 = \frac{-\mu_1\sigma_1 d^2}{24}.$$

Then

$$H_a = \frac{\Delta \bar{H} t}{\tau} + \frac{\mu_1 \sigma_1 \Delta \bar{H}}{2\tau} \left(y^2 - \frac{d^2}{12} \right). \tag{14}$$

It is apparent that the transient term or complementary function H_b has its maximum at $y = 0$ and decays exponentially with time. A solution that meets these conditions is

$$H_b = e^{-pt} \cos qy.$$

Substitution in Eq. (12) yields

$$p = \frac{q^2}{\mu_1 \sigma_1}.$$

Furthermore, the transient term must make no net contribution to the mean value of the magnetic field across the lamination because it has already been assumed that the average value of H_a over the lamination increases linearly with time. Then

$$\int_0^{d/2} e^{-pt} \cos qy \, dy = 0,$$

and hence

$$q = \frac{2n\pi}{d},$$

where n is any positive integer. Thus

$$p = \frac{4n^2\pi^2}{\mu_1 \sigma_1 d^2},$$

and the nth transient term may be written

$$H_b = a_n e^{-\frac{4n^2\pi^2 t}{\mu_1 \sigma_1 d^2}} \cos \frac{2n\pi y}{d}.$$

The full transient term may then be written

$$H_b = \frac{\mu_1 \sigma_1 \Delta \bar{H}}{2\tau} \sum_{n=1}^{\infty} a_n e^{-\frac{4n^2\pi^2 t}{\mu_1 \sigma_1 d^2}} \cos \frac{2n\pi y}{d},$$

and the total solution may be written

$$H_s(y,t) = \frac{\Delta \bar{H} t}{\tau} + \frac{\mu_1 \sigma_1 \Delta \bar{H}}{2\tau} \left[y^2 - \frac{d^2}{12} + \sum_{n=1}^{\infty} a_n e^{-\frac{4n^2\pi^2 t}{\mu_1 \sigma_1 d^2}} \cos \frac{2n\pi y}{d} \right]. \tag{15}$$

For the determination of a_n, the condition that $H_s(y,0) = 0$ for all values of y is applied. Hence.

$$y^2 - \frac{d^2}{12} + \sum_{n=1}^{\infty} a_n \cos \frac{2n\pi y}{d} = 0,$$

and

$$a_n = -\frac{2}{d} \int_{-\frac{d}{2}}^{\frac{d}{2}} \left(y^2 - \frac{d^2}{12} \right) \cos \frac{2n\pi y}{d} \, dy.$$

Integration by parts yields

$$a_n = -\frac{d^2}{n^2 \pi^2} \cos n\pi = -\frac{d^2 (-1)^n}{n^2 \pi^2}.$$

Hence, the complete solution is

$$H_z(y,t) = \frac{\Delta \bar{H} t}{\tau} + \frac{\mu_1 \sigma_1 \, \Delta \bar{H}}{2\tau} \left[y^2 - \frac{d^2}{12} \right.$$

$$\left. - \frac{d^2}{\pi^2} \sum_{n=1}^{\infty} \frac{(-1)^n}{n^2} e^{-\frac{4n^2 \pi^2 t}{\mu_1 \sigma_1 d^2}} \cos \frac{2n\pi y}{d} \right] \qquad \text{webers/meter}^2. \quad (16)$$

For the value of

$$H_z \left(\frac{d}{2}, t \right) = H_z \left(-\frac{d}{2}, t \right)$$

the symbol H is used.   Then

$$H = \frac{\Delta \bar{H} t}{\tau} + \frac{\mu_1 \sigma_1 d^2 \, \Delta \bar{H}}{12\tau} \left[1 - \frac{6}{\pi^2} \sum_{n=1}^{\infty} \frac{1}{n^2} e^{-\frac{4n^2 \pi^2 t}{\mu_1 \sigma_1 d^2}} \right] \qquad \text{webers/meter}^2, \quad (17)$$

or, in cgs units,

$$H = \frac{\Delta \bar{H} t}{\tau} + \frac{10^{-9} \pi \mu d^2 \, \Delta \bar{H}}{3\rho\tau} \left[1 - \frac{6}{\pi^2} \sum_{n=1}^{\infty} \frac{1}{n^2} e^{-\frac{10^9 n^2 \pi \rho t}{\mu d^2}} \right] \qquad \text{oersteds}, \quad (18a)$$

where ρ is the resistivity of the magnetic material.   The field H may be expressed as

$$H = \Delta \bar{H} \left\{ \frac{t}{\tau} + \frac{T}{\tau} \left[1 - \frac{6}{\pi^2} \sum_{n=1}^{\infty} \frac{1}{n^2} e^{-\frac{n^2 \pi^2 t}{3T}} \right] \right\}$$

$$\text{webers/meter}^2 \text{ or oersteds}, \quad (18b)$$

or

$$H = \Delta \bar{H} \frac{t}{\tau} \left[1 + \Phi \left(\frac{T}{t} \right) \right] \qquad \text{webers/meter}^2 \text{ or oersteds}, \quad (19)$$

where, in mks units,

$$T = \frac{\mu_1 \sigma_1 d^2}{12} \quad \text{seconds}$$

or, in cgs units,

$$T = \frac{10^{-9}\pi\mu d^2}{3\rho} \quad \text{seconds,}$$

and

$$\Phi\left(\frac{T}{t}\right) = \frac{T}{t}\left[1 - \frac{6}{\pi^2}\sum_{n=1}^{\infty}\frac{1}{n^2}e^{-\frac{n^2\pi^2 t}{3T}}\right].$$

The variation of $\Phi(T/t)$ with (T/t) is plotted in Fig. 15·14.

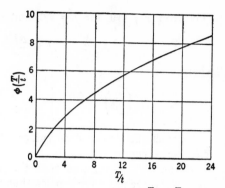

FIG. 15·14.—Plot of $\Phi\dfrac{T}{t}$ vs. $\dfrac{T}{t}$.

The average flux density $\bar{B}$ throughout the lamination is

$$\bar{B} = \frac{\mu\,\Delta\bar{H}t}{\tau} \quad \text{gauss.}$$

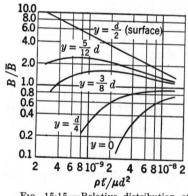

FIG. 15·15.—Relative distribution of flux density in a lamination for a rectangular voltage pulse applied at a time $t = 0$, where $\bar{B}$ increases linearly with time, and ρ = resistivity of the lamination in ohm-cm, d = the thickness of lamination in inches, t = time in seconds, y = distance from the midplane of the lamination in inches, and μ = average d-c incremental permeability over ΔB.

The relationships expressed by Eq. (16) are exhibited graphically in Fig. 15·15[1] where $B/\bar{B}$ is plotted against $\rho t/\mu d^2$ for various distances from the midplane of the lamination. The effective permeability

$$\mu_e \equiv \frac{\bar{B}}{H} = \frac{\mu}{1 + \Phi\left(\dfrac{T}{t}\right)}. \quad (20)$$

A graphical representation of μ_e is also given in Fig. 15·20.

The function $H_z(y,t)$ in Eq. (15) may be written as the sum of $\Delta\bar{H}t/\tau$ the value of the magnetic field if eddy currents were not present, plus an additional field needed to negate the effect of the eddy-current magnetic field, $H_e(y,t)$, where

$$H_e(y,t) = \frac{\mu_1\sigma_1\,\Delta\bar{H}}{2\tau}\left[y^2 - \frac{d^2}{12} - \frac{d^2}{\pi^2}\sum_{n=1}^{\infty}\frac{(-1)^n}{n^2}e^{-\frac{4n^2\pi^2 t}{\mu_1\sigma_1 d^2}}\cos\frac{2n\pi y}{d}\right]. \quad (21)$$

[1] A. G. Ganz, "Applications of Thin Permalloy Tape in Wide Band Telephone and Pulse Transformers," *Trans. Amer. Inst. Elect. Engrs.*, **65**, 177 (1946).

Then from Eq. (19) for $y = d/2$ and $y = -d/2$,

$$H = \frac{\Delta \bar{H} t}{\tau} + H_e, \tag{22}$$

where

$$H_e \equiv H_e\left(\frac{d}{2}, t\right) = \frac{\Delta \bar{H} T}{\tau}\left[1 - \frac{6}{\pi^2}\sum_{n=1}^{\infty}\frac{1}{n^2}e^{-\frac{n^2\pi^2 t}{3T}}\right] = \frac{\Delta \bar{H} t}{\tau}\,\Phi\left(\frac{T}{t}\right). \tag{23}$$

Plots of the steady-state values (that is, when $t \gg T$) of $H_z(y,t)$ and $E_x(y)$ are given in Fig. 15·16.

Under the assumption that the core is made of perfect magnetic material, there are no free poles that tend to demagnetize the core. At the end of the pulse, when $t = \tau$, the voltage V that was applied to the

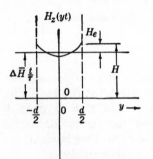 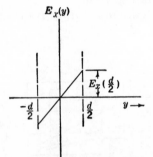

(a) H_z, where $H_e = \dfrac{\Delta \bar{H} T}{\tau} = \dfrac{\mu_{10}\sigma_1 d^2 \Delta \bar{H}}{12\tau}$

$\qquad = \dfrac{10^{-9}\pi\mu d^2 \Delta \bar{H}}{3\rho\tau}$ oersteds.

(b) E_x, where $E_x\left(\dfrac{d}{2}\right) = \dfrac{\mu_1 \Delta \bar{H} d}{2\tau}$ volts (mks)

$\qquad = \dfrac{10^{-8}\mu \Delta \bar{H} d}{2\tau}$ volts (cgs).

webers/meter²

FIG. 15·16.—Steady-state field distributions in the lamination.

coil is removed, the eddy-current magnetic field decays, and the core eventually arrives at the state where

$$H_z(y,t) = \Delta \bar{H} = \frac{\Delta \bar{B}}{\mu}.$$

The decay of the eddy-current field may readily be calculated if it is assumed, as a boundary condition, that at $t = \tau$ the eddy-current field

$$H_{ze}(y,\tau) = \frac{\mu_1\sigma_1 \Delta \bar{H}}{2\tau}\left(y^2 - \frac{d^2}{12}\right),$$

that is, that the transient term in Eq. (15) is equal to zero. The diffusion Eq. (12) may now be solved for $H_{ze}(y, t - \tau)$ with the same substitutions that were made to obtain the transient term in Eq. (16). Then, in mks units,

$$H_{ze}(y,\, t-\tau) = \frac{\mu_1\sigma_1\,\Delta\bar{H}d^2}{2\tau\pi^2} \sum_{n=1}^{\infty} \frac{(-1)^n}{n^2} e^{-\frac{4n^2\pi^2(t-\tau)}{\mu_1\sigma_1 d^2}} \cos\frac{2n\pi y}{d} \quad \text{webers/meter}^2,$$

$$H_{ze}\left(\frac{d}{2},\, t-\tau\right) = H_{ze}\left(-\frac{d}{2},\, t-\tau\right) \equiv H_e(t-\tau)$$

$$= \frac{6\mu_1\sigma_1 d^2\,\Delta\bar{H}}{12\tau\pi^2} \sum_{n=1}^{\infty} \frac{1}{n^2} e^{-\frac{4n^2\pi^2(t-\tau)}{\mu_1\sigma_1 d^2}}$$

$$= \Delta\bar{H}\left[\frac{T}{\tau} - \frac{T}{\tau}\left(1 - \frac{6}{\pi^2}\sum_{n=1}^{\infty}\frac{1}{n^2} e^{-\frac{n^2\pi^2(t-\tau)}{3T}}\right)\right]$$

$$= \frac{\Delta\bar{H}(t-\tau)}{\tau}\left[\frac{T}{t-\tau} - \frac{T}{t-\tau}\left(1 - \frac{6}{\pi^2}\sum_{n=1}^{\infty}\frac{1}{n^2} e^{-\frac{n^2\pi^2(t-\tau)}{3T}}\right)\right]$$

$$= \Delta\bar{H}\left[\frac{T}{\tau} - \frac{t-\tau}{\tau}\Phi\left(\frac{T}{t-\tau}\right)\right] \quad \text{webers/meter}^2 \text{ or oersteds.}$$

Then

$$H_z\left(\frac{d}{2},\, t-\tau\right) = \Delta\bar{H} + H_e(t-\tau)$$

$$= \Delta H\left[1 + \frac{T}{\tau} - \frac{t-\tau}{\tau}\Phi\left(\frac{T}{t-\tau}\right)\right]. \quad (25)$$

A typical theoretical plot of H vs. t from Eqs. (19) and (25) is given in Fig. 15·17. Actually, however, the field H returns to a value much lower than $\Delta\bar{H}$ because of hysteresis effects, gaps in the core, and reverse fields between pulses.

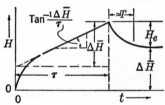

FIG. 15·17.—Typical theoretical plot of H vs. t.

It is to be remembered that, during the pulse, H is the magnetic field required at the surface of the laminations when the average induction $\bar{B}$ increases linearly with respect to time, that is, if a constant voltage V is suddenly applied across the coil. This magnetic field can be produced only by a magnetizing current i_m in the coil. Thus, during the pulse

$$i_m = \frac{10Hl}{4\pi N}.$$

If the core has a gap, free poles are formed which reduce the effective magnetic field at the surface of the laminations, and hence reduce in the core material itself the resultant $\bar{B}$ produced by a given i_m.

After the pulse when $\bar{B}$ (and hence H, also) decreases to some remanent value, the magnetic field in the core remains constant and greater than zero although the impressed magnetic field produced by i_m decreases to zero. Thus the values of $\bar{B}$, $\Delta\bar{B}$, $\bar{H}$, $\Delta\bar{H}$, and H defined herein are the incremental values above remanence, the remanent point being taken as the origin of the pulse B-H loop.

15·3. Energy Loss and Equivalent Circuits. *General Considerations of Energy Absorption and Storage in the Core.*—The electric field $E_x(y,t)$ associated with $H_z(y,t)$ may be obtained from Eqs. (11) and (15), and, in mks units, is given by the expression

$$E_x(y,t) = \frac{1}{\sigma_1}\frac{\partial H_z}{\partial y}$$

$$= \frac{\mu_1\,\Delta\bar{H}}{2\tau}\left[2y - \frac{2d}{\pi}\sum_{n=1}^{\infty}\frac{1}{n^2}e^{-\frac{4n^2\pi^2 t}{\mu_1\sigma_1 d^2}}\sin\frac{2n\pi y}{d}\right] \qquad \text{volts.} \quad (26)$$

At the surface of the lamination

$$E_x\left(\frac{d}{2},\,t\right) = \frac{\mu_1\,\Delta\bar{H}}{2\tau} \qquad \text{volts.}$$

Now,

$$\mathbf{i}E_x \times \mathbf{k}H_z = \mathbf{j}E_x H_z$$

is the Poynting vector, which represents the power per unit area flowing across any boundary plane $y = $ constant. The value of this vector at the surface of the lamination is denoted by

$$\mathbf{j}E_x\left(\frac{d}{2},\,t\right)H_z\left(\frac{d}{2},\,t\right)$$

and represents the instantaneous power per unit area flowing into the lamination. The energy per unit area that flows into a lamination during the pulse is, by Poynting's theorem,

$$\int_0^\tau E_x\left(\frac{d}{2},\,t\right)H_z\left(\frac{d}{2},\,t\right)dt = \int_0^\tau\left\{\int_{-\frac{d}{2}}^{\frac{d}{2}}\left[\underbrace{E_x^2(y,t)\sigma_1}_{1}\right.\right.$$

$$\left.\left.+ \underbrace{\epsilon_1 E_x(y,t)\frac{\partial E_x}{\partial t}}_{2} + \underbrace{\mu_1 H_z(y,t)\frac{\partial H_z}{\partial t}}_{3}\right]dy\right\}dt \qquad \text{joules.} \quad (27)$$

$$a,\ b,\ \text{and}\ c$$

Term 1 in the right-hand member of Eq. (27) represents the energy dissipated by eddy currents during the pulse. Term 2 is, for all practical purposes, equal to zero since displacement currents in the core material are negligible. Term 3 represents the energy stored in the magnetic field within the laminations during the pulse. Term 3*a*, the portion of Term 3 that represents the additional energy stored in the electromagnetic field associated with eddy currents, is dissipated in the form of eddy currents after the pulse during the establishment of an equal distribution of *B* throughout the lamination; that is, Term 3*a* is equal to

$$\int_\tau^\infty \left[\int_{-\frac{d}{2}}^{\frac{d}{2}} E_x^2(y,t)\sigma_1\, dy \right] dt \qquad \text{joules.}$$

In the case of the idealized core whose *B-H* loop is depicted in Fig. 15·18 the remainder of Term 3 (that is, 3*b* and 3*c*) equals $\mu_1(\Delta\bar{H})^2/2$ joules, a

quantity which is defined as W_m, the magnetic energy remaining in the core after the pulse. When the pulses are repeated, however, the magnetic field and flux density in the core must be returned to the starting point of the first pulse on the d-c or low-frequency hysteresis loop at the beginning of the next pulse. This return is accomplished by means of the fringing magnetic field resulting from the magnetic poles exposed at the faces of the gap, or by means of a reverse magnetic field obtained from a reverse current in a coil. Thus, part of this remainder 3*b* and 3*c* (defined as 3*b*) is returned to the circuit, part is dissipated in the

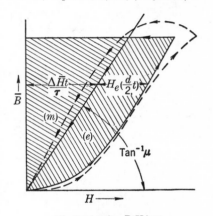

→ Idealized pulse *B-H* loop
--→ Actual pulse *B-H* loop

FIG. 15·18.—Idealized and actual pulse *B-H* loops.

core in the form of hysteresis (microscopic eddy-current) loss, and possibly a portion is dissipated in the core in the form of macroscopic eddy currents (these latter two energies comprise 3*c*). However, the energy 3*b* returned to the circuit may subsequently be returned wholly or in part to the core and dissipated there in the form of eddy currents or hysteresis loss. It is generally impossible to determine in advance how much of the energy 3*b* will eventually be dissipated in the circuit and how much will be dissipated in the core.

Calculation of Energy Dissipation in the Core.—If it is assumed (as it has been in the preceding sections) that the d-c incremental permeability over $\Delta\bar{B}$ is a constant, and that there are no hysteresis losses, it is possible to represent the behavior of such a core by the idealized pulse loop of Fig. 15·18. Area *e* represents the energy W_e dissipated in the core in the form of eddy currents, that is, Terms 1 and 3*a* in Eq. (27). Area *m* represents W_m, the energy returned to the circuit, that is, term 3*b* in Eq. (27). Term 3*c* in this idealized case equals zero. The sum of areas *m* and *e* represents the total energy delivered to the core during the pulse [that is, the term on the left-hand member of Eq. (27)]. The energy W_e represented by the area *e* in Fig. 15·18 is given in mks units by

$$W_e = \int_0^{\Delta \bar{B}} H_e \left(\frac{d}{2}, t \right) d\bar{B} \qquad \text{joules/meter}^3.$$

If the substitutions $t = \tau \bar{B}/\Delta \bar{B}$ and $\Delta \bar{H} = \Delta \bar{B}/\mu$ are performed in Eq. (23),

$$W_e = \int_0^{\Delta \bar{B}} \frac{\Delta \bar{B}}{\mu_1} \frac{T}{\tau} \left(1 - \frac{6}{\pi^2} \sum_{n=1}^{\infty} \frac{1}{n^2} e^{-\frac{n^2 \pi^2 \tau \bar{B}}{3T\Delta B}} \right) d\bar{B},$$

or

$$W_e = \frac{\Delta \bar{B}}{\mu_1} \frac{T}{\tau} \left[\Delta \bar{B} + \frac{18T\Delta \bar{B}}{\pi^4 \tau} \sum_{n=1}^{\infty} \frac{1}{n^4} \left(e^{-\frac{n^2 \pi^2 \tau}{3T}} - 1 \right) \right].$$

Since

$$\sum_{n=1}^{\infty} \frac{1}{n^4} = \frac{\pi^4}{90},$$

$$W_e = \frac{(\Delta \bar{B})^2 T}{\mu_1 \tau} \left[1 + \frac{18T}{\pi^4 \tau} \left(\sum_{n=1}^{\infty} \frac{1}{n^4} e^{-\frac{n^2 \pi^2 \tau}{3T}} - \frac{\pi^4}{90} \right) \right],$$

$$W_e = \frac{(\Delta \bar{B})^2 T}{\mu_1 \tau} \left[1 - \frac{T}{5\tau} \left(1 - \frac{90}{\pi^4} \sum_{n=1}^{\infty} \frac{1}{n^4} e^{-\frac{n^2 \pi^2 \tau}{3T}} \right) \right] \qquad \text{joules/meter}^3$$

or, in cgs units,

$$W_e = \frac{(\Delta \bar{B})^2 T}{4\pi \mu \tau 10^7} \left[1 - \frac{T}{5\tau} \left(1 - \frac{90}{\pi^4} \sum_{n=1}^{\infty} \frac{1}{n^4} e^{-\frac{n^2 \pi^2 \tau}{3T}} \right) \right] \qquad \text{ergs/cm}^3.$$

This equation may be written

$$W_e = \frac{(\Delta \bar{B})^2}{4\pi \mu 10^7} \frac{T}{\tau} \Psi \left(\frac{\tau}{T} \right). \tag{28}$$

The loss function $\Psi(\tau/T)$ has been plotted in Fig. 15·19.

The relationships expressed by Eqs. (21)[1] and (28) are exhibited

---

[1] A. G. Ganz, "Applications of Thin Permalloy Tape in Wide Band Telephone and Pulse Transformers," *Trans. Amer. Inst. Elect. Engrs.*, **65**, 177 (1946).

graphically also in Fig. 15·20 where, if the voltage is zero immediately after the pulse, the loss resulting from eddy currents [that is, Terms 1 and 3a of Eq. (27), or area W_e of Fig. 15·18] during and after the pulse, is given by

$$\text{Loss} = \frac{4.29 V^2 d^4 \mu_e}{10^9 N^2 A^2 \rho^2} G$$

$$\text{watt seconds/in.}^3/\text{pulse}$$

where

G is plotted in Fig. 15·20,

d = thickness of lamination in inches,

ρ = resistivity in ohm-centimeters,

μ = average d-c incremental permeability over ΔB,

N = number of turns on core,

A = cross-sectional area of core in square inches,

μ_e = effective permeability,

t = time in seconds, and

V = emf of the pulse in volts.

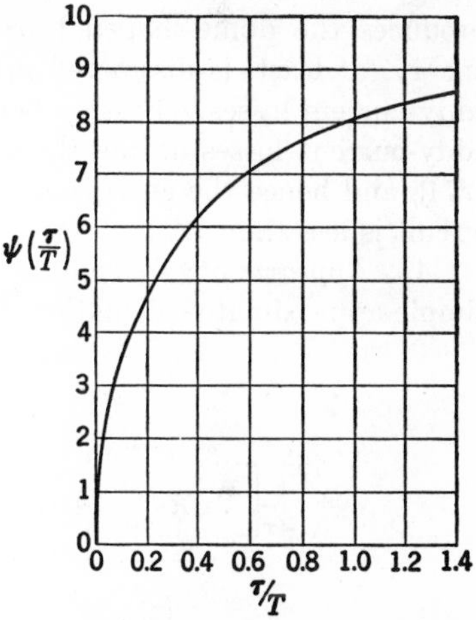

Also, in mks units,

FIG. 15·19.—Plot of the loss function $\Psi\left(\dfrac{\tau}{T}\right)$.

$$W_m = \int_0^{\Delta \bar{B}} \frac{\bar{B}}{\mu_1} d\bar{B} = \frac{(\Delta \bar{B})^2}{2\mu_1} \quad \text{joules/meter}^3$$

or, in cgs units,

$$W_m = \frac{(\Delta \bar{B})^2}{8\pi\mu 10^7} \quad \text{ergs/cm}^3. \quad (29)$$

If a fraction f of W_m is returned to and dissipated in the core, the total energy dissipated in the core per pulse is

$$W_{\text{total}} = \frac{(\Delta \bar{B})^2}{\mu_1} \left[\frac{f}{2} + \frac{T}{\tau} \Psi\left(\frac{\tau}{T}\right) \right] \quad \text{joules/meter}^3,$$

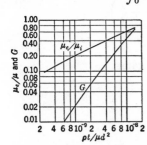

FIG. 15·20.—Plot of $\dfrac{\mu_e}{\mu}$ and the eddy-current loss during and after the pulse [that is, Terms 1 and 3a of Eq. (27), or the energy W_e represented by area e in Fig. 15·18].

or

$$W_{\text{total}} = \frac{(\Delta \bar{B})^2}{4\pi\mu 10^7} \left[\frac{f}{2} + \frac{T}{\tau} \Psi\left(\frac{\tau}{T}\right) \right] \quad \text{ergs/cm}^3.$$

Actually, however, μ is not constant during the pulse because of the finite coercive force and the saturation of the magnetic material. Hence, the initial rising portion of the experimental *B-H* loop differs somewhat from that of the theoretical loop, as shown in Fig. 15·18. Furthermore, because of the finite distributed capacitance of the pulse source and the coil on the core, the voltage pulse never ceases completely at $t = \tau$. The energy in this distributed capacitance flows into the core and thereby produces the dome-shaped top on the pulse loop. A portion of this energy, at least, is dissipated in the core in the form of hysteresis and eddy-current losses. Lastly, there are hysteresis losses and perhaps some eddy-current losses during the demagnetization [that is, term $3c$ in Eq. (27)], and hence the energy that actually remains to be returned to the circuit is less than W_m.

An Approximate Calculation of Energy Dissipated in the Core.—A simple approximate calculation of $W_m + W_e$ is possible because for cases

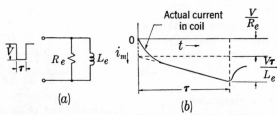

Fig. 15·21.—(a) Approximate equivalent circuit and (b) magnetizing current for a core.

where $t \gg T$ during the greater part of the pulse, and thus $0 < T/t < 2$, $\Phi(T/t) \approx T/t$ (see Fig. 15·14). Then

$$H \approx \Delta \bar{H} \frac{t}{\tau}\left(1 + \frac{T}{t}\right) = \frac{\Delta \bar{B}}{\mu}\frac{t}{\tau}\left(1 + \frac{T}{t}\right),$$

or

$$H \approx \frac{10^8 V}{\mu N A}\left(t + \frac{\pi \mu d^2 10^{-9}}{3\rho}\right) \qquad \text{gauss.}$$

Then

$$i_m = \frac{Vt}{L_e} + \frac{V}{R_e},$$

where

$$L_e = \frac{4\pi\mu N^2 A}{10^9 l} \qquad \text{henrys,} \tag{30}$$

and

$$R_e = \frac{12N^2 A\rho}{d^2 l} \qquad \text{ohms.} \tag{31}$$

The core can thus be represented by the approximate equivalent circuit of Fig. 15·21a, for which the magnetizing current i_m is plotted in Fig. 15·21b.

If it is assumed that a fraction f of W_m and, of course, all of W_e are eventually dissipated in the core,

$$W \approx fW_m + W_e = \frac{fV^2\tau^2}{2L_e} + \frac{V^2\tau}{R_e} = \frac{fV^2 10^9 l\tau^2}{8\pi N^2 A\mu} + \frac{V^2 d^2 l\tau}{12\rho N^2 A},$$

$$W \approx \frac{V^2 \tau l}{N^2 A}\left(\frac{10^9 f\tau}{8\pi\mu} + \frac{d^2}{12\rho}\right) \qquad \text{joules,}$$

or

$$W \approx \frac{Al(\Delta\bar{B})^2 f}{8\pi 10^7 \mu} + \frac{Ald^2(\Delta\bar{B})^2}{12\rho 10^{16}\tau}.$$

Then

$$W/\text{cm}^3/\text{pulse} \approx (\Delta\bar{B})^2\left(\frac{f}{8\pi\mu} + \frac{d^2}{12\rho 10^9\tau}\right) \qquad \text{ergs/cm}^3.$$

It should be remembered that these expressions for W are valid only if $0 < T/t < 2$ for the greater part of the pulse, that is, if $\tau \gg T$.

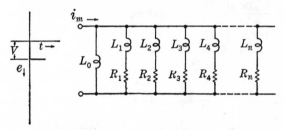

Fig. 15·22.—Accurate equivalent circuit for the core, where μ is constant.

An Accurate Equivalent Circuit for the Core.—If μ is assumed to be constant throughout the pulse (that is, if the pure hysteresis loss is zero and no saturation of the material occurs), the following expression, in cgs units, for i_m may be obtained from Eq. (19):

$$i_m = \frac{10l\,\Delta\bar{B}}{4\pi N\mu}\left[\frac{t}{\tau} + \frac{T}{\tau}\left(1 - \frac{6}{\pi^2}\sum_{n=1}^{\infty}\frac{1}{n^2}e^{-\frac{n^2\pi^2 t}{3T}}\right)\right] \qquad \text{amperes,}$$

or, with the substitution of Eq. (10), i_m may be given by

$$i_m = \frac{10^9 lV}{4\pi AN^2\mu}\left[t + T\left(1 - \frac{6}{n^2}\sum_{n=1}^{\infty}\frac{1}{n^2}e^{-\frac{n^2\pi^2 t}{3T}}\right)\right].$$

This expression for i_m suggests the equivalent circuit of Fig. 15·22, where a voltage V suddenly applied at the input terminals produces a current i'_m given by

$$i'_m = \frac{V}{L_0} + V\left[\frac{1}{R_1} - \frac{e^{-\frac{R_1}{L_1}t}}{R_1} + \frac{1}{R_2} - \frac{e^{-\frac{R_2}{L_2}t}}{R_2} + \frac{1}{R_3} - \frac{e^{-\frac{R_3}{L_3}t}}{R_3} + \cdots\right.$$

$$\left. + \frac{1}{R_n} - \frac{e^{-\frac{R_n}{L_n}t}}{R_n}\right], \qquad n \to \infty.$$

When $i_m = i'_m$, the circuit of Fig. 15·22 represents the core, if

$$L_0 = \frac{4\pi A \mu N^2}{10^9 l} \quad \text{henrys},$$

$$\frac{1}{R} = \frac{1}{R_1} + \frac{1}{R_2} + \frac{1}{R_3} + \cdots + \frac{1}{R_n} = \frac{10^9 l T}{4\pi A N^2 \mu} \quad \text{mhos},$$

$$\frac{1}{R_1} = \frac{10^9 T l}{4\pi A N^2 \mu} \frac{6}{\pi^2} \frac{1}{1^2} = \frac{1.5 \times 10^9 T}{\pi^3 A N^2 \mu} \quad \text{mhos},$$

$$\frac{1}{R_2} = \frac{1.5 \times 10^9 T l}{\pi^3 A N^2 \mu} \cdot \frac{1}{4} \quad \text{mhos},$$

$$\frac{1}{R_3} = \frac{1.5 \times 10^9 T l}{\pi^3 A N^2 \mu} \cdot \frac{1}{9} \quad \text{mhos},$$

$$\frac{1}{R_n} = \frac{1.5 \times 10^9 T l}{\pi^3 A N^2 \mu} \cdot \frac{1}{n^2} \quad \text{mhos},$$

and

$$\frac{R_n}{L_n} = \frac{n^2 \pi^2}{3T} \quad \text{sec}^{-1},$$

or

$$L_n = \frac{3 T R_n}{n^2 \pi^2} = \frac{3 T \pi A N^2 \mu}{1.5 \times 10^9 T l} = \frac{2\pi A N^2 \mu}{10^9 l} \quad \text{henrys}.$$

The actual value of the instantaneous d-c incremental permeability (that is, dB/dH) of the material over the range ΔB is never constant. The most accurate treatment of the magnetization of the core in the region below saturation assumes that there is a constant instantaneous d-c incremental permeability over ΔB, and that the value of this permeability is μ_o (see Fig. 15·2). The macroscopic eddy currents that flow may be accounted for by the foregoing electromagnetic treatment with the insertion of μ_o in the diffusion equations. The finite width of the d-c incremental loop may then be taken into account by the assumption of microscopic eddy currents, and additional LR-branches should be added in the equivalent circuit for the core in order to account for the effect of these microscopic eddy currents.[1] The effect of the reluctance of a gap in the magnetic circuit can be taken into account by adding to the field H, which is necessary to magnetize a material whose permeability is μ_o

[1] H. L. Rehkopf, "Equivalent Circuit of a Pulse Transformer Core," RL Report No. 666, Mar. 1945.

and the width of whose d-c *B-H* loop is $2H_c$, a field H_g [$= (l_g/l)\bar{B}$], which is necessary to magnetize the gap.

The effect of the finite width of the d-c *B-H* loop and also a small amount of saturation can be approximated by inserting in the solution of the diffusion equations the average incremental permeability μ_i of the material itself over the range ΔB (see Fig. 15·2) and then adding H_g to the resulting solution H.

A further approximation that is valid if the gap is small is to insert the average d-c incremental permeability μ_{ig} of the core (including gap) over the range ΔB in the solution of the diffusion equations and to assume that the resultant H is the entire magnetic field necessary to magnetize the core.

15·4. Additional Aspects of Pulse Magnetization. *Treatment of the Magnetization of the Core When $\mu = \mu_o = \infty$ and Saturation Occurs.*—If

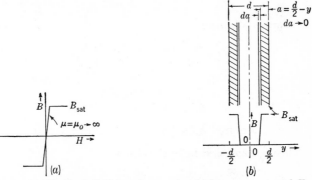

FIG. 15·23.—(*a*) Idealized *B-H* loop for a material of $\mu = \mu_o = \infty$ and $H_c = 0$. (*b*) Instantaneous distribution of flux density within the lamination for nonlinear magnetization where $\mu = \mu_o = \infty$ and $H_c = 0$.

μ or μ_1 is not assumed to be constant, an electromagnetic treatment is almost out of the question—except when the material is assumed to have infinite permeability but a finite value of B_{sat}. Under these conditions,[1] the lamination is divided at any instant during the pulse into outer surface sections that are saturated and an inner central section that is devoid of flux (see Fig. 15·23).

If the steep wavefront of flux density moves inward at a rate da/dt, the eddy current that flows in a lamination of length 1 cm, width 1 cm, and thickness d is

$$i_e = \frac{2\Delta B_{sat}\dfrac{da}{dt}}{10^8} \cdot \frac{a}{2\rho} \qquad \text{amperes,}$$

[1] A. G. Ganz, "Applications of Thin Permalloy Tape in Wide Band Telephone and Pulse Transformers," *Trans. A.I.E.E.*, **65**, 177 (1946).

where ΔB_{sat} is the change in B from starting point to B_{sat}, ($\Delta B_{sat} = B_{sat}$ if the lamination is unmagnetized at the beginning), and ρ is the resistivity of the lamination in ohm-cm.

Since the value of μ has been assumed to be infinite, the magnetic field at the surface is only that required to maintain i_e, that is,

$$H = \frac{4\pi}{10} i_e \qquad \text{oersteds.}$$

The change in average flux density at any moment is

$$\bar{B} = \frac{2a\Delta B_{sat}}{d};$$

whence

$$\mu_e = \frac{\bar{B}}{H} = \frac{2a\Delta B_{sat}}{d} \cdot \frac{10}{4\pi} \cdot \frac{10^8 \rho}{\Delta B_{sat} a \dfrac{da}{dt}} = \frac{10^9 \rho}{2\pi d \dfrac{da}{dt}}.$$

For a transformer winding

$$V = \frac{NA}{10^8} \frac{d\bar{B}}{dt} = \frac{2\Delta B_{sat}}{10^8} \frac{da}{dt} \frac{NA}{d}.$$

Then

$$\mu_e = \frac{10}{\pi} \rho \frac{\Delta B_{sat} NA}{V d^2}.$$

The time τ_o required to saturate the entire lamination is equal to $\dfrac{d}{2} \Big/ \dfrac{da}{dt}$. Then μ_e expressed in terms of τ_o is

$$\mu_e = \frac{10^9}{\pi} \frac{\rho \tau_o}{d^2}.$$

The maximum pulse duration that is capable of being passed by the transformer is equal to τ_o.

Since μ has been assumed to be infinite, no magnetic energy is stored in the core during the pulse. The energy dissipated per cubic centimeter per pulse by the eddy current during the pulse is given by

$$\text{energy loss/cm}^3\text{/pulse} = \frac{1}{8\pi} \cdot \frac{(\Delta \bar{B})^2}{\mu_e} \qquad \text{ergs/cm}^3\text{/pulse.}$$

The foregoing treatment is applicable to the magnetization of various permalloys under conditions of very high $d\bar{B}/dt$.

Theoretical Construction of Pulse Hysteresis Loops.—Under the assumption that the permeability used in the diffusion equation is constant and is equal to μ_i (or μ_{ig}), the average d-c incremental permeability over ΔB, it is possible to construct the ascending portion of pulse B-H loops from Eqs. (10) and (19), as has been done in Fig. 15·18.

It is possible, however, to construct pulse loops in such a way that their shape is more sensitive to the d-c properties of the core materials. If the eddy-current field H_e is calculated with the use of μ_i in the diffusion equation, and if this H_e is added to the magnetic field obtained from a d-c hysteresis loop over ΔB, there results a theoretical pulse loop that takes into account the coercive force and the saturation of the core material (for example, see Fig. 15·11).

The top of the loop and the beginning of the descending portion may be roughly constructed by assuming that H decreases very rapidly although $\bar{B}$ remains relatively stationary at the end of the pulse [see Eq. (25) and Fig. 15·17]. (Actually, $\bar{B}$ increases somewhat because the voltage pulse never drops to zero immediately at the end of the pulse. This increase in $\bar{B}$, as has already been stated, produces the dome on top of the pulse hysteresis loop.) For the constructed loop the value of H may thus be assumed to decrease rapidly along a line of roughly constant $\bar{B}$ until the magnetic field for this value of $\bar{B}$ on the descending portion of the d-c hysteresis loop is attained. Then $\bar{B}$ and H may be assumed to decrease along the path of the descending portion of the d-c hysteresis loop of the core. The rate of decrease along this path depends, of course, upon the constants of the circuit in which the pulse-transformer core is being measured.

A synthesized pulse B-H loop for a typical British core material has been constructed according to the foregoing procedure and is displayed in Fig. 15·11, together with the observed pulse B-H loop. In several such comparisons British observers report good agreement between theoretical and experimental pulse B-H loops.[1]

Experiments at the Radiation Laboratory, however, show the experimental values of μ_e to be substantially lower than the theoretical values when $\Delta\bar{H}$ is large compared with H_e, which is the condition under which the precision of the experiment for detecting variations in the intrinsic values of μ is the greatest. However, in experiments at very high values of $d\bar{B}/dt$ where any variations in the intrinsic values of μ that are due to a lag in the process of magnetization would be the greatest, H_e is comparable in size to $\Delta\bar{H}$, and the precision for detecting variations in μ is lower. These latter experiments nevertheless show better agreement between experimental and theoretical values of μ_e, despite the fact that, in these experiments, the values of magnetic fields at the surfaces of the laminations were so high that surface saturation could conceivably have reduced the effective value of μ for a portion of the core material.

[1] C. R. Dunham and C. C. Hall, "Air Gaps in Pulse Transformer Cores," The General Electric Co., Ltd., Report No. 8401, Feb. 11, 1944; C. R. Dunham, C. C. Hall, and K. A. MacFadyen, "Pulse Magnetization," The General Electric Co., Ltd. Report No. 8298, Sept. 24, 1943.

S. Siegel and H. L. Glick of the Westinghouse Research Laboratories report experiments in which cores were operated at values of B such that the permeability at the surfaces of the laminations were not reduced by any saturation effects. Their observed values of μ_e are also somewhat below the theoretical values.

Interlaminar eddy currents could, of course, account for the above

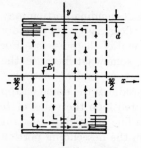

FIG. 15·24.—Plot of the electric field E within the core.

discrepancies, except that in all of the foregoing cases the interlaminar resistance was adequate. Inadequate knowledge of the lamination thickness or space factor might possibly be responsible for some of the discrepancies.

The discrepancies could also be explained by assuming that there is an intrinsic lag in the magnetization process. In view of the contradictory results of the British and American observers, however, it cannot be stated definitely that there is, in the process of magnetization, an intrinsic lag that produces an appreciable reduction in the observed μ_e under the pulse conditions of these experiments.

Interlaminar Resistance.—It would be unduly complex to calculate the interlaminar currents that flow during the buildup time of the intralaminar and interlaminar currents inasmuch as it is desired only to set a

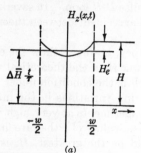

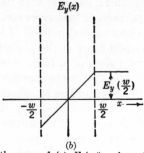

(a) (b)

FIG. 15·25.—Steady-state distribution throughout the core of (a) $H_z(x,t)$, where $H_e' = \dfrac{10^{-9}\mu\pi w^2 \Delta\bar{H}}{3\tau\left(\dfrac{r_s}{d}\right)}$ oersteds, and (b) $E_y(x)$, where $E_y\left(\dfrac{w}{2}\right) = \dfrac{10^{-8}\mu\Delta\bar{H}w}{2\tau}$ volts.

lower limit to the value that the interlaminar resistance may have. The distribution of $H_a(y,t)$ vs. y is given by Eq. (14) and is plotted in Fig. 15·16a for a time such that the transient term has become zero. The steady-state distribution of the electric field E_x vs. y may be obtained from Eq. (26) and is plotted in Fig. 15·16b.

If the core is made up of a stack of laminations w cm wide (see Fig.

15·24), whose interlaminar resistance between two laminations for an area of 1 cm² is r_s, the stack of laminations may be treated electromagnetically as is the single lamination. The magnetic and electric fields cannot penetrate the core very far by traveling in the y direction because of the shielding effect of the outside laminations. The fields can penetrate from the x direction, however, because of the fairly high resistivity r_s, and hence the flow of interlaminar currents is analogous in pattern to the flow of eddy currents within the laminations. The magnetic and electric fields corresponding to the steady state are then distributed within the core as shown in Fig. 15·25. The eddy-current field resulting from interlaminar currents is now given by

$$H'_e = \frac{10^{-9}\pi\mu w^2 \Delta \bar{H}}{3\tau \left(\dfrac{r_s}{d}\right)} \qquad \text{oersteds,}$$

where r_s/d, the "volume resistivity" of the core for interlaminar currents, takes the place of ρ in the expression for H_e in Fig. 15·16. Then

$$\frac{H'_e}{H_e} = \frac{w^2\rho}{r_s d}.$$

If the resistance $w\rho/d$ from side to side of a lamination 1 cm long and w cm wide is denoted by R_ρ and the interlaminar resistance r_s/w between two laminations w for one cm of their length is denoted by R_s,

$$\frac{H'_e}{H_e} = \frac{R_\rho}{R_s}.$$

In a typical Hipersil core

$$R_\rho = \frac{w\rho}{d} = \frac{2.54 \times 50 \times 10^{-6}}{0.0025 \times 2.54} = 2 \times 10^{-2} \text{ ohms.}$$

Experience has shown that in any well-insulated core

$$\frac{H'_e}{H_e} = \frac{R_\rho}{R_s} \leqq 0.1.$$

Then

$$R_s \geqq \frac{2 \times 10^{-2}}{10^{-1}} = 0.2 \text{ ohms.}$$

If, for example, $l = 10$ cm and the number of laminations in the stack is 250, the resistance across the stack should then be greater than

$$\frac{250 \times 0.2}{10} = 5 \text{ ohms.}$$

If it is assumed that within the core every point that lies on the y axis (see Fig. 15·24) remains at zero electrical potential, and that r_s is so high that no interlaminar eddy currents flow, the potential difference between two laminations at any point x, according to Fig. 15·16, is

$$v(x) = 2xE_x\left(\frac{d}{2}\right) = \frac{10^{-8}\mu\Delta\bar{H}xd}{\tau} \quad \text{volts.}$$

The maximum potential difference $v(w/2)$ occurs between two adjacent laminations at $x = w/2$ and $x = -w/2$, and

$$v\left(\frac{w}{2}\right) = \frac{10^{-8}\mu\Delta\bar{H}wd}{2\tau}.$$

For a typical pulse-transformer core,

$$\frac{\mu\Delta\bar{H}}{\tau} = 5 \times 10^9 \text{ gauss/sec,}$$
$$d = 0.0025 \times 2.54 = 0.00635 \text{ cm,}$$
$$w = 1 \times 2.54 = 2.54 \text{ cm,}$$

and

$$v\left(\frac{w}{2}\right) = 10^{-8} \times 5 \times 10^9 \times 6.35 \times 10^{-3} \times 2.53 = 0.8 \text{ volt.}$$

The interlaminar insulation must therefore be capable in this case of withstanding the small voltage stress of 0.8 volt.

The interlaminar insulation on thin-gauge Hipersil is a complex phosphate coating applied during the final annealing operation. The resulting "Carlite" coating is very thin ($\approx 10^{-5}$ in.) and has excellent insulating properties. On some core materials (which are usually in the form of punched laminations) the insulation is an oxide of iron formed by admitting a small amount of air to the steel at the end of the annealing process. This oxide coating, if applied skillfully, is exceedingly thin and is adequate for pulse transformers. The General Electric Company sometimes uses a chrome-silicate solution, which is baked onto the laminations by the anneal. The Western Electric Company, on the other hand, uses catephoresis, a process of depositing silicic acid particles on the strip steel by drawing the strip through a mixture of acetone and silicic acid immediately prior to winding the strip into a core and annealing it. Mica dust (which turns mainly into a complex of silicates upon being annealed) is sometimes used as a suspension in acetone and deposited on the strip, which is drawn through the liquid.

Various lacquers and varnishes have been tried on laminations, but have proved inferior because of the reduction of space factor in the resulting core.

15·5. Techniques for Measuring Core Performance.—As has already been shown, the value of μ_e depends upon pulse duration, lamination thickness, and resistivity, and upon μ_i, as it is defined by Figs. 15·2 and 15·3. For a given material the value of μ_e is affected by $\Delta \bar{B}$, the amount of gap in the core, and the value of the reverse magnetic field between pulses. Since μ_e depends upon so many parameters, it is necessary that manufacturers and users of pulse-transformer cores and core materials agree upon a set of standard methods for measuring and describing the properties of cores and core materials.[1]

It is not within the scope of this book to specify these standard test methods. There are, however, certain experimental techniques involved, which will now be described.

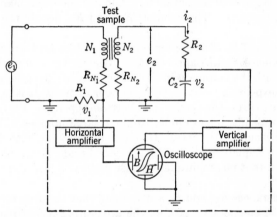

FIG. 15·26.—Circuit for viewing 60-cycle *B-H* loops on an oscilloscope.

Presentation of 60-cycle Hysteresis Loops on an Oscilloscope.—The circuit of Fig. 15·26, where $e_1 = \sqrt{2}\,E_{\text{rms}} \cos \omega t$ and $\omega = 2\pi \cdot 60$, may be used for the purpose of presenting 60-cycle hysteresis loops on an oscilloscope.
Since

$$e_2 = \frac{N_2 A}{10^8} \frac{dB}{dt},$$

$$B = \frac{10^8}{N_2 A} \int e_2\, dt.$$

If R_2 and C_2 are large, $i_2 = e_2/R_2$. Hence

$$\int \frac{i_2\, dt}{C_2} = \frac{e_2\, dt}{R_2 C_2} = v_2,$$

---

[1] W. H. Bostick, "Pulse Transformer Committee Standard Test Methods for Pulse Transformer Cores," RL Report No. 722, May 5, 1945.

and

$$\int e_2\,dt = R_2 C_2 v_2.$$

Then

$$B = \frac{10^8 R_2 C_2 v_2}{N_2 A} \qquad \text{gauss,}$$

and

$$H = \frac{4\pi N_1 i_m}{10l} = \frac{4\pi N_1 v_1}{10l R_1} \qquad \text{oersteds,}$$

where v_2 and v_1 are the deflecting voltage measured on a CRT screen, N_1 and N_2 are the numbers of turns on the coils, A is the cross-sectional area of the core in square centimeters, and l is the mean magnetic-path length in centimeters. The symbols R_{N_1} and R_{N_2} denote the resistance of the coils.

The resistance R_2 must be large enough not to load the circuit and hence not to increase $i_m R_1$ appreciably. The voltage e_2 must be large in comparison with the voltage v_2 in order that i_2 be limited primarily by R_2. Since it is inexpedient to use a large number of turns, it is necessary to use amplifiers to drive the vertical and horizontal plates of the oscilloscope tube. It is difficult, for example, to put a large number of turns on a continuously wound strip core. If the amplifiers built into the oscilloscope are not adequate, additional stages may be added externally. Care must be taken that no amplitude or phase distortion is introduced by the amplifiers.

If the resistances R_{N_1} and R_1 are so small that the drop $i_m(R_1 + R_{N_1})$ is negligible in comparison with e_1, the integrating $R_2 C_2$-circuit may be connected across the input circuit and the second winding may be omitted.

Appropriate circuit constants for use with a ring test sample having an interior diameter of $2\frac{1}{2}$ in. and a cross section of $\frac{1}{2}$ in. by $\frac{1}{2}$ in. may be estimated in the following manner:

First, the values $N_1 = N_2 = 100$ turns No. 20 (which have resistances $R_N = 0.2$ ohms), and $\Delta B = 10{,}000$ gauss are arbitrarily chosen. Next, a value of

$$e_2 = \Delta B N_2 A \omega \times 10^{-8} = 6 \text{ volts,}$$

and a value of $v_2 \approx 0.001\,e_2$ are chosen. Then

$$R_2 C_2 = e_2/(v_2 \omega) \approx 3 \text{ sec.}$$

Any values of R_2 and C_2 that satisfy this relation may be chosen, provided that (1) R_2 is large enough not to load the circuit appreciably, (2) R_2 is also large in comparison with the resistance of the winding, and yet small in comparison with the leakage resistance of the winding insulation, and

(3) C_2 is large in comparison with the stray capacitance to ground of R_2 and the oscilloscope input circuit. The following values are satisfactory:

$$R_2 = 1.5 \text{ megohms,}$$
$$C_2 = 2 \ \mu\text{f,}$$
$$v_2 = \frac{e_2}{R_2 C_2 \omega} \approx 5 \times 10^{-3} \text{ volts.}$$

The values of R_1 may be chosen arbitrarily—for example, the value of $R_1 = 0.3$ ohms is selected.
Then

$$e_1 = e_2 + (R_1 + R_{N_1})lH/(0.4\pi N_2) \approx 7 \text{ volts,}$$

for $H = 10$ oersteds, and

$$v_1 = R_1 lH/(0.4\pi N_1) \approx 0.5 \text{ volt,}$$

for $H = 10$ oersteds. The voltage sensitivities should be such as to give deflections of about 1-in:

Vertical sensitivity = 5×10^{-3} volt/in. (amplification $\approx 10,000/1$).
Horizontal sensitivity = 0.5 volt/in. (amplification $\approx 100/1$).

If 500 turns of No. 20 wire are used for N_1, and if e_1 is correspondingly increased, an error of less than 2 per cent is introduced by connecting the integrating circuit across the input circuit and omitting the second winding.

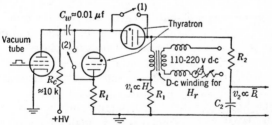

Fig. 15·27.—Circuit for obtaining pulse B-H loops with a hard-tube pulser.

The ring sample may conveniently be wound in the following manner. Each quadrant is wound with a single layer consisting of 25 turns of No. 20 wire, two in parallel. For the 60-cycle tests the windings of the four quadrants are connected in series to give two parallel 100-turn windings. For the pulse test the two windings in each quadrant may be connected in parallel; then the paralleled windings of two opposite quadrants may be connected in series to give a 50-turn winding for application of the pulse voltage, and the windings of the other two quadrants similarly connected for the d-c current that produces H_r (see Figs. 15·27 and 15·28).

Pulse Hysteresis Loops.—Pulse hysteresis loops may be taken conveniently with either a hard-tube pulser (Fig. 15·27) or a line-type pulser (Fig. 15·28). In some instances a vacuum diode is used in preference to a gas-filled tube in order to prevent distortion of the beginning of the pulse.

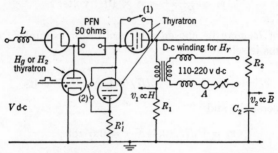

Fig. 15·28.—Circuit for obtaining pulse *B-H* loops with a line-type pulser.

With the circuits of Figs. 15·27 and 15·28, both the magnetizing current i_m and the magnetizing field H at the surface of the laminations are proportional to the voltage v_1 during the pulse as long as v_1 is small compared with V, that is,

$$H = \frac{4\pi N i_m}{10l} = \frac{4\pi N v_1}{10l R_1}.$$

where l is the mean magnetic-path length, and N is the number of turns

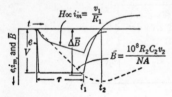

Fig. 15·29.—Traces of e, i_m, and $\bar{B}$ vs. t.

on the test coil. If v_1 is applied to the vertical deflecting plates of a synchroscope and the sweep to the horizontal plates, a curve of the general form indicated in Fig. 15·29 results.

If R_2 and C_2 are both large enough to make v_2 very small compared with V, the flux density averaged throughout the lamination may be expressed as follows:

$$\bar{B} = \frac{10^8 \int_0^t e\,dt}{NA} = \frac{10^8 \int_0^t i_2 R_2\,dt}{NA} = \frac{10^8 R_2 C_2 v_2}{NA}.$$

If v_2 is applied to the vertical deflecting plates of a synchroscope, $\bar{B}$ may be presented as shown in Fig. 15·29.

It is possible to present a pulse loop, as shown in Fig. 15·30, by applying v_1 to the horizontal plates and v_2 to the vertical plates of an oscilloscope. The dome-shaped top that often appears on pulse loops corresponds to the area under e for the interval $t_1 \leqq t \leqq t_2$ (see Fig. 15·29) during which e drops to zero. The integral

$$\int_{t_1}^{t_2} e \, dt$$

depends upon the characteristics of the pulse-forming network in a line-type pulser, upon the rate of cutoff of the switch tube in a hard-tube pulser, upon the stray capacitance to ground of pulser and test coil, and upon i_m at the time t_1. This integral also depends upon the magnitude and distribution of flux density within the laminations at the time t_1, upon the eddy currents in the laminations, and upon any external shunt resistances across the coil. If the value of the shunt resistance R_l (Fig. 15·27) is reduced, the voltage decreases more rapidly, the value of the integral is reduced, and the dome may be removed.

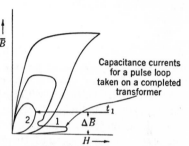

Fig. 15·30.—The appearance of various pulse B-H loops.

If the value of the integral is very large, the discontinuity in the pulse loop is not marked, and the oscilloscope trace has the appearance of loop 2, Fig. 15·30. Nevertheless, it is almost always possible to distinguish the point corresponding to t_1 on a pulse loop.

Some pulse transformers operate with little or no reverse magnetic field impressed on the core between pulses. If this operating condition is to be simulated in core testing, H_r must be made equal to zero. Hence, the circuit of Fig. 15·27 should be operated with switch (1) opened and switch (2) closed in order to permit the storage condenser to recharge through R_l between pulses. If the circuit of Fig. 15·28 is used, switch (1) should be opened and switch (2) should be closed to permit the recharging of the pulse-forming network. The resistance R_l' is inserted to effect a matching of the pulse-forming network during the pulse.

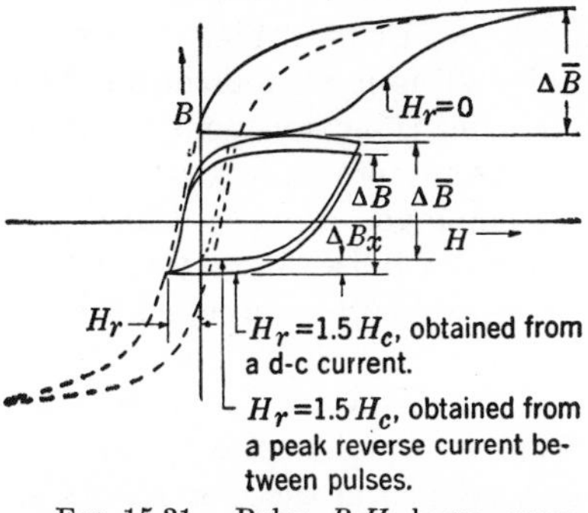

Fig. 15·31.—Pulse B-H loops superimposed on a d-c loop to show the difference between obtaining H_r from a peak reverse current between pulses and from a d-c current.

A pulse B-H loop taken with $H_r = 0$ is shown superimposed on the d-c loop of the core in Fig. 15·31.

Some pulse transformers that are operated in the stepdown position with a hard-tube pulser experience a small reverse field between pulses. The desired value of peak reverse field may be obtained for tests on cores by closing switch (1) and opening switch (2) in the circuit of Fig. 15·27, adjusting the number of turns on the coil, the storage capacitance C_w, and the charging resistance R_c. Since this process for obtaining H_r is somewhat tedious, it is sometimes advisable to employ an H_r produced by a d-c current, usually flowing through a separate winding, when testing the core.

The substitution of an H_r derived from a d-c current is only an approximation to the actual conditions experienced by the core in a pulser where the reverse field comes to a maximum between pulses and drops to zero at the beginning of the next pulse. These two methods of obtaining a reverse field produce a different operating point on the d-c loop (see Fig. 15·31). A value of H_r obtained from a d-c current should be a good approximation if H_c is small compared with the peak value of H at the end of the pulse (less than 10 per cent), and if ΔB_x (see Fig. 15·31) is small compared with ΔB (less than 10 per cent).

If $\Delta \bar{B}$ is large enough to take the material into the region of saturation, however, the difference in the peak values of H for the two methods of obtaining H_r may be considerable.

On the oscilloscope presentation of the pulse loop the swing ΔB_x is usually visible even though the integrating circuit, because of its short time constant, may not register accurately the magnitude of ΔB_x.

The core of a pulse transformer operated in a line-type pulser usually has an appreciable reverse field impressed on it, and in the core test the desired value of H_r can be obtained by using the circuit of Fig. 15·28 with switch (1) closed and switch (2) open, and by adjusting L and the number of turns on the sample core. If this adjustment is inconvenient, H_r may again be derived from a d-c current through another winding.

Obviously, a butt-joint core should be employed in pulse generators where the obtainable peak reverse field between pulses is very small or equal to zero. The gap in the average butt-joint core of oriented silicon steel is such that a reverse field which is approximately $0.5H_c$ of the material used for butt-joint cores is produced. Hence, in order that the remanence resulting from H be approximately equal to the remanence for a butt-joint core in pulse tests on uncut samples of these materials, it is recommended that a value of $H_r = 0.5H_c$ be used. However, the values of H for the resulting pulse loop on the uncut core are less than those for a butt-joint core by the field H necessary to magnetize the gap.

For applications of pulse transformers where the reverse field is appreciable, materials that have comparatively low H_c and no gaps in the core may advantageously be used. A transformer of these materials is generally designed to have a peak reverse field equal to or greater than $1.5H_c$ between pulses in the pulser generator, and hence it is recommended that a value of $H_r = 1.5H_c$ be used in the tests on these materials in the uncut-ring form.

For transformers that are normally operated in a pulser with a d-c current to reverse the field, H_r used in the measurement of the core should, of course, be derived from a d-c current.

In order to depict correctly the rising portion of the pulse loop it is desirable to reduce the effect of distributed-capacitance currents on the oscilloscope trace. In core tests such currents can be minimized by a suitable spacing between the test coil and core, a suggested minimum value being $\frac{1}{16}$ in. In measurements performed on completed transformers the circuit of Fig. 15·32 may be used to negate the effect of these currents. The capacitance C_D is approximately equal to the total distributed capacitance of the transformer referred to the primary, and L_L is approximately equal to the total leakage inductance referred to the primary. Some deviation from the nominal values of these circuit elements may be necessary for best results.

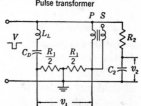

FIG. 15·32.—Circuit for canceling capacitance currents when pulse B-H loops of completed transformers are observed. The integrating circuit may be attached to either the primary or the secondary.

Numerous precautions must be taken with various elements of the measuring circuit of Fig. 15·27 in order to be certain that spurious results are not obtained. These precautions include the selection of a noninductive resistor R_1 and a resistor R_2 that is accurately constant with voltage. It is necessary that R_2, cable, and oscilloscope have very little capacitance to ground.

The pulser power required to test a given core at various values of $\Delta\bar{B}$ and τ may be determined approximately by the following method. The value of the constant voltage pulse is given by

$$V = 10^{-8}NA\Delta\bar{B}/\tau.$$

The value of the magnetizing current is given by

$$I = \frac{l\Delta H}{0.4\pi N} = \frac{l\Delta\bar{B}}{0.4\pi N\mu_e}.$$

Therefore the peak power drawn by the core at the end of the pulse is

$$VI = \frac{Al(\Delta\bar{B})^2 \cdot 10^{-7}}{4\pi\mu_e\tau} \quad \text{watts,}$$

where A is the cross-sectional area of the core in square centimeters, and l is the magnetic-path length in centimeters. The values of $\Delta\bar{B}$ and ΔH

in these relations are those for the time t_1 (Fig. 15·29), and μ_e is defined as the value of $\Delta\bar{B}/\Delta H$ at the time t_1.

This formula for peak power does not include the power dissipated in R_l (Fig. 15·27) or R_l' (Fig. 15·28). The value of R_l should be such that (1) the voltage does not change more than about 5 per cent from the beginning to the end of the pulse (during which time the magnetizing current is gradually increasing), and (2) the tail of the voltage pulse shows a fairly rapid fall and no long-period oscillations. A resistor of proper value may dissipate as much as half of the available pulse power of the pulser. Similar considerations apply in an even greater degree to R_l'. The resistor R_l' should be chosen to dissipate about 90 per cent of the rated pulse-power output of the line-type pulser, and the peak power supplied to the core must not exceed 20 per cent of this value.

The recurrence frequency at which a hard-tube pulser is operated should not exceed the value specified for the pulse duration at which it is being operated, and may be lower if convenient. The recurrence frequency at which a line-type pulser is operated should be the value specified for the particular pulse duration at which the pulser is being operated; deviation from this value may result in disruption of the network charging cycle.

As an example, it is required to estimate the pulser power and the appropriate circuit constants for testing a ring sample of 0.003-in. silicon steel with an internal diameter of $2\frac{1}{2}$ in. and a cross section of $\frac{1}{2}$ in. by $\frac{1}{2}$ in. at 10 kv and 0.5 μsec with a hard-tube pulser. The permeability of such a sample may be about 100 under these conditions.[1] The peak power to be supplied to the core is

$$P = \frac{Al(\Delta\bar{B})^2 \cdot 10^{-7}}{4\pi\mu_e\tau} = \frac{1.6 \cdot 24 \cdot 10^8 \cdot 10^{-7}}{4\pi \cdot 100 \cdot 0.5 \cdot 10^{-6}} = 620 \text{ kw.}$$

If another 400 kw is allowed for the dissipation in R_l, it is discovered that the pulse generator must deliver a peak power of 1 Mw. Hard-tube pulsers of this power rating usually deliver 40 amp at 25 kv. From these values the circuit constants may be calculated. Thus if the load resistance is assumed to be 1500 ohms, and V is 25 kv,

$$N = \frac{V\tau \cdot 10^8}{A \cdot \Delta\bar{B}} \approx 75 \text{ turns.}$$

[1] For typical values of the effective permeability of silicon steel cores, see H. L. Rehkopf, W. H. Bostick, and P. R. Gillette, "Pulse Transformer Core Material Measurements," RL Report No. 470, Dec. 10, 1943. The effective permeabilities of other materials may differ greatly from those for silicon steel; for example, continuous cores of 1-mil tape of some of the nickel-iron alloys with $H_r > 0$ may have much higher values.

Since a value of about 100 to 150 volts, or about $0.005V$, is desired for v_2 in order to give a reasonable deflection,

$$R_2C_2 = 200\tau = 10^{-4} \text{ sec.}$$

Any values of R_2 and C_2 that satisfy this relation may be chosen, provided that R_2 is large in comparison with the resistance of the winding insulation (and yet small in comparison with the leakage resistance of the winding), and that C_2 is large in comparison with the capacitance to ground of R_2 and the oscilloscope input circuit.   The values $R_2 = 10,000$ ohms and $C_2 = 0.01$ μf are satisfactory.   A value of 100 to 150 volts is also desired for v_1; therefore

$$R_1 = \frac{V_1}{I} = \frac{v_1V}{P} \approx 6 \text{ ohms.}$$

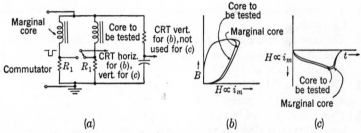

(a)   (b)   (c)

Fig. 15·33.—Comparison method for production testing of cores under pulse conditions with the use of a commutator. (a) Circuit. (b) Oscilloscope presentation of B-H loops of marginal core and core to be tested. (c) Synchroscope presentation of i_m vs. t curves.

As a second example, it is required to estimate the pulser power and the appropriate circuit constants for testing the same sample under the same conditions with a line-type pulser.   In order that the droop on the pulse not be excessive, the power of the pulse generator should be at least five times the peak power required by the core, or 3 Mw.   A line-type pulse generator of this power rating and designed to operate at an impedance level of 50 ohms is rated at 12.2 kv.   By a procedure similar to the foregoing, the following values are obtained:

$$R_l' = 55 \text{ ohms,}$$
$$V = 12.2 \text{ kv,}$$
$$N \approx 35 \text{ turns,}$$
$$R_2C_2 = 100\tau = 5 \times 10^{-5} \text{ sec,}$$
$$R_2 = 10,000 \text{ ohms,}$$
$$C_2 = 0.005 \ \mu\text{f,}$$

and

$$R_1 \approx 3 \text{ ohms.}$$

Lower-power equipment for testing is suitable for longer pulses (that is, in general, lower values of $d\bar{B}/dt$), and for cores with smaller air gaps (or no gaps), a reverse magnetic field, thinner material, and higher d-c permeability. Lower-power equipment can also be used under the above conditions with samples smaller than the one specified.

Production testing of cores can be performed conveniently by presenting simultaneously on an oscilloscope the pulse *B-H* loops or magnetizing currents of a core having the minimum acceptable μ_e and a core to be tested (see Fig. 15·33). For such comparison tests in a production line, the diodes and the circuit for reverse current may usually be omitted.

COIL MATERIAL

15·6. Insulation. *Types of Insulation and Their Characteristics.*— There are several insulation requirements for pulse transformer coils, namely:

1. The dielectric constant must be low in order to keep the value of C_D small.
2. The electric breakdown strength of the material itself must be high.
3. The material must be capable of operating successfully over a temperature range of $-40°C$ to $100°C$ or higher.
4. The interfacial dielectric strength of margins, or the "creep breakdown strength," must be high.
5. The material must have low water absorption if it is used without a hermetically sealed case since such absorption decreases the breakdown strength.
6. The "power factor" of the material must be low.
7. The insulation must be capable of being handled with sufficient ease to permit production of the transformers in large quantities.
8. Where voltages greater than 2 kv are encountered there must be no air pockets or voids in which corona can occur.

The Dry Type of Insulation.—For voltages in the range where corona is not likely to occur, that is, less than 2000 volts, many types of dry insulation (for example, paper sheet, formvar, cellulose acetate, impregnation with various varnishes) have been successfully used without special precautions for eliminating voids from the insulation. For operation at voltages at which corona occurs, the elimination of all voids is necessary if the transformer is to have long life.

Various solvent-bearing varnishes have been used as impregnants under vacuum in an effort to remove all voids in the insulation. In the United States, at least, these efforts have met with little success because (1) in the curing process the volatile solvent never escapes completely by diffusion, but boils to a certain extent and hence forms voids, and (2) the solvent that does escape by diffusion often does so after the varnish has become too rigid to collapse into the voids that are created. The British nevertheless report successful operation of trigger pulse transformers at 20 kv with glyptal varnish insulation.[1]

The difficulties in eliminating voids have been overcome to a great extent by General Electric Permafil and Westinghouse Fosterite, both of which are completely polymerizing varnishes that are used without solvents. These impregnants have the additional desirable properties for pulse-transformer insulation given in Table 15·4.

TABLE 15·4.—PROPERTIES OF SOLVENTLESS VARNISH, DRY-TYPE INSULATIONS

Property	Westinghouse Fosterite		GE Permafil	
	Resin	Resin plus paper pad	Resin	Resin plus paper pad
Electric strengh (high)	550 volts/mil at 22°C 400 volts/mil at 108°C	300 volts/mil		800 volts/mil (for a total pulse voltage of 50 kv applied at 125°C)
Power factor (low)....	0.002 at 100 cps	0.01 to 0.02 at 100 cps	0.02 to 0.03 at 1 Mc/sec for a sample ⅛ in. thick	
Moisture absorption (low)	0.2% wt increase in 24 hours 0.4% wt increase in 48 hours	0.11% wt increase in 24 hours 0.41% wt increase in 48 hours	0.1–0.2% by weight water absorption in 24 hours, saturation attained.	
Adhesiveness..........	good		good	
Cohesiveness..........	good		good	

The usual method of applying Fosterite is to dip one end of the coil (which may have insulation pads of Kraft paper, fiberglass, etc., depending upon the temperature requirements) into a viscous mixture of the resin plus inorganic filler (for example, SiO_2 or mica dust). The coil is then baked at about 130°C until the viscous mixture has hardened into a solid bottom (known as a cap)—a procedure which effectively

[1] L. W. Redfearn," Development of Pulse Transformers," Metropolitan-Vickers Electric Co., Ltd., Report No. C.334, September 1942.

transforms the coil into a concentric cup. This cuplike coil is then placed bottom down in a vacuum tank, the tank is evacuated to a pressure of about 1 cm of mercury, and the pure resin (no filler) is admitted to the tank under vacuum to such a height that the resin overflows the brim and fills the cup. The cup is then removed from the vacuum, care being taken to keep it upright, and placed in an oven and cured at about 130°C for several hours. The coil is then given a vacuum impregnation of the mixture of resin and filler and given a final baking at 130°C to 150°C for several hours.

The usual procedure for applying Permafil is to construct the coil in the form of a cup by cementing a bottom on the coil, to give the cup only one impregnation, and to cure for several hours with a starting temperature of 65°C and a finishing temperature of 125°C.

Transformers thus constructed of both these materials have passed successfully the immersion cycle specified in ARL-102A and successfully resisted humidity and corrosion without being hermetically sealed in a metal case.

Although Fosterite and Permafil are not fungicidal, they will not support fungus organisms. A fungicide coating such as Tuf-on 76F, containing penta-chlor-phenol, may be used when necessary.

Fosterite and Permafil and similar solventless varnishes are to be regarded as superimpregnants definitely superior to existing varnishes. They should find wide application on airborne equipment and test equipment. Fosterite and Permafil nevertheless absorb moisture and, for shipboard applications where prolonged exposure to high humidity without frequent opportunity for dehydration is probable, it is recommended that the transformers be hermetically sealed in metal cans.

Fosterite and Permafil have been successfully used on pulse transformers that operate at voltages up to 12 kv. It may be possible in the future to extend the safe operation of these or kindred materials to higher voltages.

For Fosterite and Permafil suitable limits on puncture stress and creep stress (here creep stress refers to a surface with air on one side and pad impregnated with resin on the other) are 200 volts/mil and 10 volts/mil, respectively.

A recently developed insulating material that is proving very useful in pulse transformers is Dupont Teflon, a polyfluoride material sold in tape form. Teflon has a dielectric constant of only 2 and a dielectric strength of about 2000 volts/mil. It can be used successfully with either oil or varnish impregnation and will withstand temperatures up to 250°C. Teflon tape is so "slippery" that it must be either bound or sewn into place on the transformer. Its use, therefore, has been confined to the relatively few applications where its electrical properties are particularly advantageous.

Oil-impregnated Paper Insulation.—The most suitable transformer insulation from the point of view of high dielectric strength, ease of construction, and long life at temperatures usually encountered, is dried cellulose fiber (usually Kraft paper) that is vacuum impregnated with refined dehydrated mineral oil in which there are practically no olefinic unsaturated hydrocarbons and only a small percentage of aromatic unsaturated hydrocarbons. The process of vacuum impregnation with oil eliminates all voids in the insulation. Refined dehydrated mineral oil itself has a high dielectric strength. Mineral oil has the added virtue that it can transfer heat rapidly by convection. Hence, for pulse transformers that operate at voltages of 5 kv and over, the use of oil and Kraft paper insulation has been standard practice in the United States since the first pulse transformers were made.[1]

In the design of pulse transformers the stress limits usually observed with vacuum-impregnated Kraft paper are as follows: puncture, 250 to 500 volts/mil; creep, 25 volts/mil.

A metal bellows or a corrugated diaphragm is usually used to accommodate the thermal expansions and contractions of the liquid in oil-filled transformers. Photographs of transformers with metal bellows are shown in Figs. 15·35, 15·36, 15·37, and 15·38 and 13·11; those with metal diaphragm are shown in Fig. 13·12.

Mechanism of Breakdown in Oil-impregnated Insulation.—Not much is understood in detail about the electrical breakdown of liquids and solids, but it is fairly certain that both puncture and creep breakdown occur as the result of the presence of some free electrons that move in the electric field, dissipate energy in the dielectric, and thereby raise other electrons to energy levels where they in turn become free electrons that also move in the electric field, dissipate more heat, and so on catastrophically. At the boundary of two substances, for example, mineral oil and mineral-oil-impregnated Kraft paper, there may be a layer of charge resulting from contact potential. Also, if the configuration of electric fields is such that there is a component of the electric-displacement vector normal to this surface, there is a surface charge density equal to the surface divergence of the electric-displacement vector. Furthermore, there is probably a discontinuity in moisture content and acidity, and in the mobility of ions at the surface, all of which may lead to surface

---

[1] Early in the history of pulse transformers the British used wax insulation as well as oil for voltages up to approximately 10 kv. This wax insulation gave some difficulty, and a change was made to oil. However, the difficulties with the wax insulation are reported to have been solved.

charges. It is very likely that the existence of these surface charges has a tendency to extend the total voltage applied across an interwinding pad along the surface of the margins until this total voltage is applied across a relatively small surficial distance across which breakdown occurs.

It has been demonstrated in tests made at the General Electric Company, Pittsfield, Mass . that, under both pulse and d-c conditions, the puncture breakdown strength of paper plus oil is somewhat greater if the paper plus oil contains some moisture in solution than if both constituents have been very thoroughly dehydrated. This effect is probably due to a more equal distribution of electrical stress throughout the insulating material—a distribution that is brought about by the few conducting ions released by the small amount of water. The presence of moisture in oil and paper, of course, increases the power factor at low frequencies.

Turn-to-turn insulation is never a serious problem since the turn-to-turn voltage on pulse transformers is almost always less than 1000 volts and usually less than 300 volts. Heavy formex or cotton-covered wire is adequate to withstand these voltages. In rare cases where the turn-to-turn voltage stress becomes very high the coil may be space-wound.

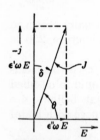

Fig. 15·34.— Vectors showing the relationship of the displacement current to the loss current.

The winding arrangement, thickness of pads, and length of creep on the margins must be so chosen that the transformer withstands the voltage and conforms to the general requirements of design set forth in Secs. 13·1 and 13·2.

Dielectric Constant and Power Factor.—When an electric field E is applied to a substance, a displacement current J results. This displacement current may be treated phenomenologically by the introduction of a dielectric constant ϵ where

$$J = \frac{\partial(\epsilon E)}{\partial t} = \epsilon \frac{\partial E}{\partial t} + E \frac{\partial \epsilon}{\partial t}.$$

If $E = E_0 e^{j\omega t}$,

$$\frac{\partial E}{\partial t} = j\omega E,$$

and

$$J = \left(\epsilon - \frac{j}{\omega}\frac{\partial \epsilon}{\partial t}\right)\frac{\partial E}{\partial t} = (\epsilon' - j\epsilon'')\frac{\partial E}{\partial t} = (j\epsilon'\omega + \epsilon''\omega)E,$$

where $\epsilon' = \epsilon$ = the dielectric constant of the material and

$$\epsilon'' = \frac{1}{\omega}\frac{\partial \epsilon}{\partial t}.$$

The loss tangent as shown in Fig. 15·34 is defined by

$$\tan \delta \equiv \frac{\text{loss current}}{\text{charging current}} = \frac{\epsilon''}{\epsilon'}.$$

$$= \frac{\dfrac{\epsilon'' E_0^2}{2}}{\dfrac{\epsilon' E_0^2}{2}} = \frac{\text{energy dissipated}}{\text{energy stored}}.$$

It may be seen from Fig. 15·34 that, for small values of δ, $\tan \delta \approx \cos \theta$, the power factor of the material.

To account for the magnitudes of ϵ' and $\tan \delta$ for a given material and for their variation with frequency, it is necessary to resort to an atomistic view of the processes of polarization. Such a discussion is beyond the scope of this volume.[1]

The fraction of the pulse power lost in the dielectric of the pulse transformer is very small, and errors in its computation are not serious. Therefore, a suitable average or upper limit to the loss tangent may be chosen for the range of dominant frequencies given by the Fourier analysis of the pulse. For example, for a 1-μsec pulse one might choose the value of the loss factor of the dielectric at 500 kc/sec in calculating the loss in the dielectric of the transformer. If the relationship,

$$\text{Loss tangent} = \frac{\text{energy dissipated}}{\text{energy stored}}$$

is used, it may be stated that the average power loss in the dielectric of a pulse transformer for ideal rectangular voltage pulses is

$$\tfrac{1}{2} C_D V^2 f_r \times \text{loss factor.}$$

Actually, there are oscillations on the tail of the voltage pulse with a magnetron load. These oscillations bring about further dissipation of energy in the dielectric.

Measurements on Insulating Materials.—The measurements of puncture and creep breakdown of insulating materials can, of course, be performed under pulse conditions as well as under 60-cycle or constant-voltage conditions. The measurements of dielectric constant and loss factor may be performed at various frequencies with well-known standard bridge-circuit techniques. Effective dielectric constant and loss factor could conceivably be measured under pulse conditions, but techniques for such measurements have not yet been developed.

---

[1] A. von Hippel and R. Breckenridge, "Interaction Between Electromagnetic Fields and Dielectric Materials," NDRC 14-122, M.I.T., January 1943.

FIG. 15·35.—A high-power magnetron plugged into the gasketed melamac well of a 10-Mw 1-μsec pulse transformer.

Bushings and Connectors.—Considerable attention must be paid to the proper choice of bushings and connectors in the casing of a pulse transformer. An example of a transformer having a gasketed melamacplastic socket into which a magnetron can be plugged is shown in Figs. 13·11c and 15·35, and one having a porcelain solder-seal socket is shown in Fig. 13·11a. This latter figure also illustrates the use of a connector socket employing porcelain insulation and solder-seal technique for a 50-ohm pulse cable. An airborne 250-kw 0.5- to 5.0-μsec pulse transformer having a magnetron-filament transformer that is attached to the high-voltage end of the secondary and enclosed in the high-voltage porcelain solder-seal bushing is shown in Fig. 15·36. Further use of porce-

FIG. 15·36.—An airborne 250-kw 0.5- to 5.0-sec pulse transformer with a filament transformer enclosed in the high-voltage porcelain solder-seal bushing.

lain solder-seal bushings is illustrated in the 35-kv trigger transformer shown in Fig. 15·37, and the use of cast-glass bushings on a 1.5-Mw 2.0-μsec transformer is illustrated in Fig. 15·38.

15·7. Wire.—Pulse transformers are wound with copper wire through which (in the ideal case) rectangular current pulses of short duration flow. It is therefore desirable to investigate the dissipation of energy in copper under these conditions.

Electromagnetic Treatment of a Rectangular Current Pulse in Copper.— The simplest calculation of pulse-energy loss in a conductor involves the current distribution in a solid semi-infinite in extent with the volume $y < 0$ occupied by free space and the volume $y > 0$ occupied by the solid medium, for example, copper. In copper the displacement currents are negligible compared with the conduction currents.[1] If the current density $j = ij_x$ is in the x direction only, the diffusion equations of (12) may be used, that is,

FIG. 15·37.—Porcelain solder-seal bushings on a 35-kv trigger transformer.

$$\frac{\partial^2 E_x}{\partial y^2} = \mu_1 \sigma_1 \frac{\partial E_x}{\partial t},$$

and   (29)

$$\frac{\partial^2 H_z}{\partial y^2} = \mu_1 \sigma_1 \frac{\partial H_z}{\partial t}.$$

A rectangular pulse of current of value I_0 may be represented by the boundary conditions

    1. $H_z(0, t < 0) = 0.$
    2. $H_z(0, 0 < t < \tau) = H_0 = I_0.$
    3. $H_z(0, \tau < t) = 0.$

[1] This treatment follows very closely that given in the following reference: L. W. Redfearn, "Skin Effects in Conductors with Single Rectangular Pulses of Current," Metropolitan-Vickers Electric Co., Ltd., Report No. C.530, May 1945.

The solution of the latter diffusion equation during the interval $0 < t < \tau$ may be made up of the sum of a steady-state solution H_{z_a} and a transient solution H_{z_b}. The general transient solution[1] of this equation may be written

$$H_{z_b} = \frac{1}{\sqrt{\pi}} \int_{-\infty}^{\infty} \Phi\left(y + 2\frac{\xi}{\mu_1\sigma_1}\right) e^{-\xi} \, d\xi,$$

where

$$\Phi(y, 0 < t < \tau) = H_0,$$
$$\Phi(y = 0, t < 0) = 0,$$
$$\Phi(y = 0, \tau < t) = 0.$$

FIG. 15·38.—Illustration of the use of cast-glass bushings on a 1.5-Mw 2.0-sec pulse transformer. The seal is accomplished by the adhesion of molten borosilicate glass to nickel iron.

and μ_1 and σ_1 are, respectively, the permeability and conductivity in mks units. The limits of integration may now be restricted so that, for the interval of time $0 < t < \tau$, the complete solution of H_z may be written

$$H_z = H_0\left(1 - \frac{2}{\sqrt{\pi}}\int_0^{\frac{y}{2}\sqrt{\frac{\mu_1\sigma_1}{t}}} e^{-\xi^2} \, d\xi\right), \qquad 0 < t < \tau. \qquad (30)$$

The complete solution of Eq. (29) for the time interval $\tau < t < \infty$, with the boundary condition that $H_z = 0$ at $y = 0$, is given by

[1] R. Frank und R. v. Mises, *Die Differential- und Integralgleichungen der Mechanik und Physik*, Vol. 2, F. Vieweg, Braunschweig, 1935, p. 534; W. E. Byerly, *Fourier's Series and Spherical, Cylindrical, and Ellipsoidal Harmonics*, Ginn, Boston, 1893, pp. 84–85.

$$H_z = \frac{2H_o}{\sqrt{\pi}} \int_{\frac{y}{2}\sqrt{\frac{\mu_1\sigma_1}{\tau}}}^{\frac{y}{2}\sqrt{\frac{\mu_1\sigma_1}{t-\tau}}} e^{-\xi^2}\, d\xi, \qquad \tau < t < \infty. \tag{31}$$

The rate of dissipation of power per unit area of surface is

$$p = \int_0^\infty \frac{j_x^2}{\sigma_1}\, dy = -\int_0^\infty \frac{j_x}{\sigma_1}\frac{\partial H_z}{\partial y}\, dy$$

since $j_x = \partial H_z/\partial y$. Integration by parts yields

$$p = -\frac{1}{\sigma_1}[H_z j_x]_0^\infty + \frac{1}{\sigma_1}\int_0^\infty H_z \frac{\partial j_x}{\partial y}\, dy.$$

Since

$$\frac{1}{\sigma_1}\frac{\partial j_x}{\partial y} = -\mu_1 \frac{\partial H_z}{\partial t}$$

and

$$H_z \text{ is } 0 \text{ at } y = \infty,$$

$$p = \frac{1}{\sigma_1}[H_z j_x]_0 - \mu_1 \int_0^\infty H_z \frac{\partial H_z}{\partial t}\, dy,$$

or

$$p = \frac{1}{\sigma_1}[H_z j_x]_0 - \frac{\mu_1}{2}\frac{\partial}{\partial t}\int_0^\infty H_z^2\, dy.$$

The energy loss associated with one pulse is

$$W = \int_0^\infty p\, dt = \frac{1}{\sigma_1}\int_0^\infty [H_z j_x]_0\, dt - \frac{\mu_1}{2}\int_0^\infty H_z^2\, dy.$$

The latter term is the difference in electromagnetic energy before and after the pulse and is equal to zero. Furthermore, since

$$H_z(0, 0 < t < \tau) = H_0,$$

and

$$H_z(0, \tau < t < \infty) = 0,$$

$$W = \frac{H_0}{\sigma_1}\int_0^\tau [j_x]_0\, dt = -\frac{H_0}{\sigma_1}\int_0^\tau \left[\frac{\partial H_z}{\partial y}\right]_{y=0} dt.$$

The differentiation of Eq. (30) yields

$$\left[\frac{\partial H_z}{\partial y}\right]_{y=0} = -H_0 \sqrt{\frac{\mu_1\sigma_1}{\pi t}} = -I_0 \sqrt{\frac{\mu_1\sigma_1}{\pi t}}.$$

Hence,

$$W = \frac{I_0^2}{\sigma_1}\sqrt{\frac{\mu_1}{\pi}}\int_0^\tau \sqrt{\frac{\sigma_1}{t}}\, dt = \frac{2I_0^2}{\sigma_1}\sqrt{\frac{\mu_1}{\pi}}\sqrt{\tau\sigma_1}.$$

The average rate of dissipation of power during the pulse is

$$\bar{p} = \frac{2I_0^2}{\sigma_1}\sqrt{\frac{\mu_1\sigma_1}{\pi\tau}}.$$

Hence, the effective depth of penetration of the pulse is

$$\Delta_p = \frac{1}{2} \sqrt{\frac{\tau \pi}{\sigma_1 \mu_1}}.$$

Since $\mu_1 = 4\pi \times 10^{-7}$ henrys/meter, and for copper $\sigma_1 = 10^8/1.87$ ohms^{-1} meter^{-1},

$$\Delta_p = \frac{1}{2} \sqrt{\frac{\tau' \times 10^{-6} \cdot \pi \cdot 1.87}{10^8 \cdot 4\pi \times 10^{-7}}} = \frac{1}{2} \sqrt{\tau' \cdot 4.675 \times 10^{-8}}$$

$$= \frac{2.16}{2} \sqrt{\tau'} \times 10^{-4} \text{ meters} \approx \sqrt{\tau'} \times 10^{-4} \text{ meters}$$

$$\approx \sqrt{\tau'} \times 10^{-2} \text{ cm},$$

where τ' is the pulse duration in μsec.

The effective skin depth Δ_ω for a sine wave of angular frequency $\omega = 2\pi f$ is

$$\Delta_\omega = \sqrt{\frac{2}{\mu_1 \sigma_1 \omega}}.$$

If the effective skin depth for a pulse is compared with that of a sine wave whose period is 2τ, $f = 1/2\tau$, $\omega = \pi/\tau$, and

$$\Delta_\omega = \sqrt{\frac{2\tau}{\mu_1 \sigma_1 \pi}}.$$

Thus, the ratio of the loss associated with a pulse current to the loss associated with a sine wave of the same effective value $[f = 1/(2\tau)]$ is equal to

$$\frac{\Delta_\omega}{\Delta_p} = \frac{2\sqrt{2}}{\pi} = 0.91. \tag{32}$$

The losses associated with pulse current are lower than those associated with the sinusoidal current because of the predominance of lower frequencies in the former. With the rounding-off of the corners on the pulse, the lower frequencies predominate to an even greater extent, and any loss calculations based on the substitution of a sinusoid ($f = 1/2\tau$) for a pulse yield an upper limit to the actual loss, even if the correction factor of 0.91 is used.

Consideration of the Proximity Effect.—The energy dissipated in copper wire when the wire is in the form of a transformer coil with single-layer-primary and single- or double-layer-secondary windings may readily be calculated from a flux plot, if it is assumed that the pulse duration is so short that there is practically no penetration of the copper by the magnetic field. The surface of the copper itself then coincides with a line of magnetic flux. The essential portion of such a flux plot for a typical pulse-transformer winding is given in Fig. 15·39. Some difficulties arise in constructing a flux plot in a region containing substances

of different dielectric constant.   Nevertheless this flux plot is accurate
enough for the purpose of computing the power loss in a winding.   From
this plot it can be calculated that the energy dissipated when the wire is
in the form of a coil with the linear winding space factor as shown in Fig.
15·39 and when the magnetic field corresponding to the pulse load current
exists on both the inside and outside surface of the winding is 1.34 times
the energy dissipated when the wire is isolated.   When the magnetic
field corresponding to the load pulse current exists on only the inside
or the outside of the winding, this "proximity factor" is $2 \times 1.36 = 2.7$.

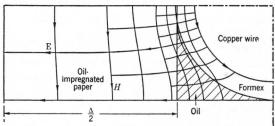

FIG. 15·39.—Flux plot showing lines of **E** and **H** for a typical pulse-transformer winding.
No. 25 quadruple formex wire, dia = 0.0219 in., bare Cu dia = 0.0179 in.   Spacing between
windings Δ = 0.040 in.

$$\text{Dielectric constants:} \begin{cases} \text{Formex} & 3.5 \ (0 \text{ to } 10^7 \text{ cycles/sec.}) \\ \text{Oil impregnated paper} & 3.5 \ (0 \text{ to } 10^7 \text{ cycles/sec.}) \\ \text{Oil} & 2.4 \ (0 \text{ to } 10^7 \text{ cycles/sec.}) \end{cases}$$

A consideration of the skin effect and the proximity factor enables one
to calculate the energy dissipated in single-layer or double-layer windings
during the pulse by the following formula:

$$W_p \approx \text{PF} \times I_0^2 R\tau \times \frac{d^2}{4(d\Delta - \Delta^2)} \approx \text{PF} \times I_0^2 R\tau \cdot \frac{d}{4\Delta} \qquad \text{joules,}$$

where PF is the proximity factor, I_o is the pulse current, R is the d-c
resistance of the winding, d is the diameter of the bare copper wire, and Δ
is the skin depth (in the same units as d).   The effective pulse current is
then given by

$$I_{\text{eff pulse}} = \sqrt{\frac{f_r W_p}{R}}.$$

It is obviously desirable to select a wire size such that d/Δ is held to a
reasonably small value (that is, less than 5).   Interleaving the primary
between two secondaries takes the factor of 2 out of the proximity factor
for the primary winding.   There may be more important winding considerations, however, which make it undesirable to interleave the primary.
   The configuration of electric and magnetic fields for multilayer and
duolateral windings is very difficult to reconstruct, and, in these more
complicated winding structures, the losses, which are usually considerably
higher than those given by a proximity factor of 1.34, can best be ascertained by measuring the Q's of the coils at the appropriate frequencies.

In many cases the pulse-transformer secondary carries the filament current as well as the pulse current, and the effective sum of these two currents, in general, should be kept so low that the effective current density in the wire does not exceed 5000 amp/in.[2] This limiting value of current density may be varied somewhat, however, depending upon the size of the transformer, the amount of copper in the coil, and the type of cooling used. The effective sum of pulse and filament currents may be calculated from the following expression:

$$I_{\text{eff. sum}} = \sqrt{I^2_{\text{eff. pulse}} + I^2_{\text{eff. filament}}}$$

Stored Energy Dissipated in the Windings.—A fraction of the energy stored in L_p, L_L, and C_D is, of course, dissipated in the winding after the pulse. It is impractical to attempt to develop any general relations governing this fraction of energy. However, calculations on one typical 120-kw 0.5- to 2.0-μsec transformer designed at the Radiation Laboratory show that, in the operation of a transformer on a magnetron load, the following conditions obtain:

1. The energy absorbed in the winding during the pulse is about 1 per cent of the input energy per pulse.
2. About 10 per cent of the energy stored in the leakage inductance during the pulse is dissipated in the winding after the pulse. This amount of dissipated energy is about 0.3 per cent of the output energy.
3. About 0.1 per cent of the energy stored in shunt inductance and distributed capacitance is dissipated in the winding after the pulse. This amount of dissipated energy is about 0.01 per cent of the input energy.
6. The total energy dissipation in the core is about 10 per cent of the input energy. Some of this energy is dissipated during the pulse, and the remainder is made up of energy stored in shunt inductance, distributed capacitance, and leakage inductance.
5. The loss in the dielectric may be about 0.1 per cent of the input energy.

Measurements on Power Loss in Pulse-transformer Windings.—It is possible to make calorimetric measurements on the power dissipated in the winding under pulse conditions by sending current pulses through a pulse-transformer coil (without the core) that is immersed in an oil-filled calorimeter. The calculated and calorimetrically measured values of the power dissipated in a pulse-transformer winding under pulse conditions are in sufficiently close agreement to justify the use of the foregoing calculations in the choice of wire sizes in the design of pulse transformers employing single-layer or double-layer windings.

APPENDIX A
MEASURING TECHNIQUES

By O. T. Fundingsland

The purpose of the following discussion is to present a summary of techniques developed specifically for measurements on power-pulse-generator circuits. The material is presented from a pragmatic engineering approach and is not intended as a rigorous and exhaustive treatment of fundamental principles. Although the techniques described here are capable of wide application in physics as well as in engineering, the range of measurements considered and most of the illustrations included are based chiefly on problems encountered in radar-transmitter development. Little attempt has been made either to refine these techniques beyond the immediate requirements, or to investigate the possibilities of other than the simple and direct methods that have proved capable of yielding sufficient information and have afforded adequate precision for good engineering practice.

In general, the peak and average values of voltages or currents can be measured either with the aid of appropriate circuits and meters of the moving-coil and moving-vane types, or by the use of a cathode-ray oscilloscope. The oscilloscopic methods are more suitable for measuring time intervals, instantaneous amplitudes, and instantaneous rates of change of voltage or current, for observing the qualitative nature of waveforms, and for obtaining permanent photographic records. The waveforms most commonly encountered in power-pulse generators include:

1. Repeating pulses having time durations from less than 0.1 μsec to more than 5 μsec, and with recurrence frequencies from less than 100 pps to more than 10,000 pps. The pulses encountered in practice are not truly rectangular:[1] they may have abrupt irregularities and other anomalous variations which comprise significant frequencies up to 50 or 100 Mc/sec. Pulse rise times as short as 0.01 μsec have been observed.

2. Sawtooth and repeating sinusoidal voltage waves with periods ranging from less than 100 μsec to more than 10,000 μsec. Such waveforms are encountered in the charging circuits of line-type pulse generators.

[1] See Chaps. 2 and 7 for photographs of sample waveforms.

661

3. Sine waves from 60 cycles/sec to 100 Mc/sec.

4. Sporadic transients, both synchronous and nonsynchronous, having durations as short as 0.01 μsec.

The pulse voltages in radar-transmitter applications range from less than 1 kv to more than 100 kv, and the pulse currents vary from 1 ma to 1000 amp.   The required time resolutions range from 10^{-2} sec to 10^{-8} sec. In some cases a time resolution of the order of magnitude of 10^{-9} sec is desirable for precise measurements of pulse duration or time jitter, or for checking the relations between the applied voltage and the buildup of current in a pulser load such as an oscillator.

In addition to time and amplitude measurements on voltage and current waves, it is often desirable to measure r-f pulse-voltage envelopes of microwaves generated by a magnetron or some other type of oscillator load, and also to observe the output r-f spectrum of a pulsed oscillator. Details regarding r-f envelope and spectrum measurements[1] are beyond the scope of this appendix and are described elsewhere in the Radiation Laboratory Series.[2]   However, since the behavior of the oscillator and the nature of its r-f output during pulse modulation constitute an important criterion of pulser performance in such a transmitting system, both r-f envelope viewers and spectrum analyzers are often necessary in connection with the design of pulse-generators, and hence are described briefly in Sec. A·6.

OSCILLOSCOPIC METHODS

A·1. Signal Presentation. *Oscilloscopes and Synchroscopes.*—The most common and widely applicable type of indication on the screen of a cathode-ray tube is a plot of the desired electrical signal against a linear time base.   With an electrostatic tube this plot is obtained by applying a sawtooth voltage to one pair of deflection plates and the signal to the

---

[1] "Model P-4E Synchroscope and R. F. Envelope Indicator," prepared by Group 55, RL Report No. M-124, June 18, 1943.

P. A. Cole, J. B. H. Kuper, and K. R. More, "Lighthouse R. F. Envelope Indicator," RL Report No. 542, Apr. 7, 1944.

Instruction Manual, "Spectrum Analyzer (Type 103) for Pulsed Oscillators at 3,000 Mc/sec, "RL Report Np. M-115, Nov. 18, 1942.

R. T. Young, Jr., "Fourier Analysis of Pulses with Frequency Shifts During the Pulse," RL Report No. 52-5, Jan. 30, 1943.

R. T. Young, Jr., "Frequency and Spectrum Characteristics of Standard Magnetrons and the Effect of Change of Shape of Current Pulse," RL Report No. 52-6, Mar. 12, 1943.

G. N. Glasoe, "Pulse Shapes and RF Spectra for Combinations of Stromberg-Carlson Mark I and Mark II Modulators with 2J22, 2J21, and 725A Magnetrons," RL Report No. 518, Mar. 17, 1944.

[2] Volume 23, Chap. 7.

other pair of plates.   If the signal is a rectangular pulse of about 1-μsec duration it is desirable to have a sweep speed of about 1 in./μsec in order to present the pulse on the cathode-ray-tube screen in a manner satisfactory for pulse-shape analysis.   For shorter and longer pulses the sweep speed should be correspondingly faster or slower.   The measurements of the pulses common to microwave-radar applications require the use of sweep speeds ranging from a tenth of an inch or less to several inches per microsecond.   The high sweep speeds used in the observation of pulse characteristics have necessitated the use of cathode-ray tubes with electrostatic deflection in preference to tubes of the magnetic-deflection type.

Ordinary oscilloscopes may be used to observe short pulses if certain modifications are made and the proper precautions are observed.   In particular, the stray capacitance and inductance associated with long connecting leads must be minimized, and the problem of shielding becomes important.   When pulses that have a rise time of 0.1 μsec or less are to be observed, it is desirable to apply the signal directly to the deflection plates without any intermediate amplifier, in order to minimize distortion of the pulse shape as presented on the screen of the cathode-ray tube. Also, because of the high sweep speeds required, the intensification of the electron beam must be greater than is customary with ordinary oscilloscopes.   In order to prevent the burning of the material of the cathode-ray-tube screen, the intensification should be applied for a time not much longer than that required for the beam to sweep across the face of the tube.   One of the most important features of an oscilloscope that is satisfactory for the observation of recurrent pulses is that the sweep should be started at some definite time before the signal is applied to the deflection plates.   For pulsers that require an input triggering impulse, this feature can easily be obtained by initiating the trigger pulse and the sawtooth voltage from the same source.   When the interpulse interval is constant, it is necessary only to have an oscillator of the proper frequency arranged so as to initiate a sawtooth wave shortly before it initiates the trigger pulse for the pulser.   This type of oscilloscope operation is referred to as "synchronous."   When the interpulse interval is determined by the construction of the pulser, such as with a rotary-gap switch, it is necessary to start the oscilloscope sweep by means of the signal to be observed.   This latter arrangement is called "self-synchronous" operation and, because of the inherent delay in the start of the sweep, the first part of the signal does not appear as a deflection of the moving electron beam.   The way in which this difficulty may be partially overcome by the use of a delay line in series with the connection to the signal plates of the cathode-ray tube is pointed out later in this discussion.   When there is appreciable time jitter in the pulses under observation, as in the operation of a pulser with certain series-gap switches, the self-synchronous operation is employed in order to obtain a superposition of the successive pulses on the cathode-ray-tube (CRT) screen.

An oscilloscope constructed to provide the features mentioned above has been called a synchroscope.[1] It differs from conventional oscilloscopes principally in that it is particularly designed for the observation of short pulses, and hence utilizes fast sweeps that are synchronous with the signal to be observed. Several adjustments are incorporated for convenience, such as a means of varying the phase of the sweep and the signal, the amplitude and recurrence frequency of the output trigger pulses, and the electron-beam intensity.

Most conventional cathode-ray tubes used in synchroscopes have appreciable astigmatism and some nonuniformity in the deflection sensitivity over the face of the tube. When the focus is good, however, it is usually possible to measure the amplitude of 50- to 100-volt signals (1- to 2-in. deflection on a 5-in. tube) with a precision of ± 1 per cent by

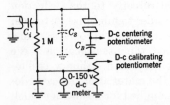

FIG. A·1.—Equivalent input circuit for a typical synchroscope.

applying a compensating d-c potential to the cathode-ray-tube plates to give null indication. This calibrating potential is usually applied between ground and the same plate to which the signal voltage is applied. The centering potential for the cathode-ray tube is applied to the opposite plate, which is maintained at r-f ground with a bypass capacitance C_B as shown in Fig. A·1. The input-coupling capacitance C_i, usually ≈ 0.01 μf, provides mutual d-c isolation between the deflection plates and the source of signal voltage. The 1-megohm resistance to ground prevents the accumulation of charge on the plates of the cathode-ray tube, and C_S represents the undesirable stray capacitance, including that of the deflection plates.

A high-speed oscilloscope that has linear sweeps up to 100 in./μsec and single-trace writing speeds up to 300 in./μsec has been designed and built at the Radiation Laboratory.[2] With this instrument, it is possible to measure, within ± 10 per cent, time differences of 10^{-9} sec on a given transient, and to photograph nonrepeating individual transients of short duration. These accomplishments are due in part to an improved high-voltage sealed-off cathode-ray tube (K1017), designed and built by the DuMont Laboratories, which has the following characteristics:

[1] A more complete discussion of the various types of synchroscopes is given in Chap. 7 of Vol. 22 of the Radiation Laboratory Series.

[2] Chapter 7, Vol. 22.

1. Electron transit time between deflecting plates $\approx 3 \times 10^{-10}$ sec.
2. Deflection sensitivity ≈ 180 volts/in.
3. Blue-sulphide screen (P11) that has low persistence and high photographic efficiency.
4. Sufficient trace intensity on the screen to record photographically a single-trace writing speed up to 300 in./μsec.
5. Negligible coupling between the deflecting plate systems at 1000 Mc/sec.

The high sweep speeds and excellent intensity control are obtained from special circuits using techniques derived from experience with radar pulsers.

This oscilloscope makes it possible to study the pulse-to-pulse variations caused by abnormal or anomalous load behavior such as magnetron sparking and mode-changing, and it is even possible to view directly the r-f envelopes of 3000-Mc/sec waves during the buildup of oscillations in an oscillator. Photographs of pulse traces obtained with this oscilloscope are reproduced in Fig. 10·18.

Sweep Calibrators.—One of the earliest methods of calibrating a linear sweep triggered at different recurrence frequencies was to shock-excite a fixed *LC*-circuit, which was coupled directly to the CRT plates, by means of the synchroscope trigger voltage. The early portion of the resulting sine wave (frequencies of 100 kc/sec to 1 Mc/sec) was distorted by the trigger voltage and, since the oscillations damped out quickly, it was difficult to obtain precise calibrations by this method. A calibrator whose output frequency depends upon high-*Q LC*-circuits has been devised that will produce several cycles with nearly constant amplitude. This circuit can be excited with a synchroscope trigger, and is designed to generate pulses of about 30 volts amplitude at recurrence frequencies of 200 kc/sec, 1 Mc/sec, or 5 Mc/sec. A calibrator of this type[1] should be checked occasionally against a crystal-controlled type J oscilloscope.

Another type of fast-sweep calibrator generates 30-volt range marks of 0.02-μsec duration at the base and with rise and fall times of about 0.003 μsec each that repeat at 0.1-μsec intervals. This calibrating unit also supplies a trigger voltage, synchronized with the range marks, which initiates the synchroscope sweep. Since this device is not designed for use with an external trigger, it cannot be synchronized and phased relative to another signal appearing simultaneously on the screen of the cathode-ray tube. However, these range marks can be superimposed with another signal on the screen by the method shown in Fig. A·2, although some caution is necessary to avoid interference. For example, if the sweep is triggered too soon by the calibrator, after or before it is

[1] Chap. 16, Vol. 21.

triggered by the internal circuit of the synchroscope, the sweep circuit may not have time to recover from the first excitation, and the calibration may be unreliable. The scheme is generally successful because the duty ratio of the pip generator is low and its recurrence frequency is usually incommensurate with that of the synchroscope trigger.

Voltage Dividers and Current-viewing Resistors.—For the observation or measurement of the pulse output from a pulser it is necessary to provide a means by which a voltage or current pulse may be applied as a signal to the deflecting plates of a cathode-ray tube. With a 5-in. tube a 1- to 1.5-in. deflection of the electron beam from the center of the circular screen can usually be used without serious distortion resulting from astigmatism. The maximum signal voltage applied to the deflect-

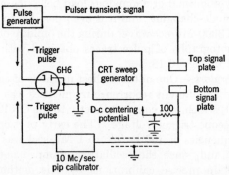

Fig. A·2.—Scheme for simultaneously presenting range marks and another signal on a synchroscope.

ing plates should therefore be about 50 to 100 volts for pulse observation. Since the pulse voltages of interest in connection with pulser measurements are generally many times greater than 100 volts, it is necessary to introduce some type of voltage divider between the pulser and the cathode-ray tube. A number of possible combinations of resistances and capacitances may be used as voltage dividers. Several of these are discussed in detail in Sec. A·2 with particular reference to their applicability to specific problems and to their inherent limitations.

The oscilloscopic presentation of a current pulse is obtained by introducing a resistor in series with the circuit and applying the voltage developed across this resistance by the pulse current to the deflection plates of the cathode-ray tube. Since such a resistor is usually introduced for the specific purpose of obtaining the amplitude-time trace of the pulse current on the screen of a cathode-ray tube for visual or photographic observation, it is commonly referred to as a "current-viewing" resistor. The value of the resistance used for this purpose depends on the maximum current-pulse amplitude and, for most pulser measurements, is generally less than 20 ohms.   The problems associated with the use of current-viewing resistors are also discussed in Sec. A·2.

In order to obtain an oscilloscopic presentation of a voltage or a current pulse that is a true picture of the amplitude-time variation, the stray inductances and capacitances introduced by the connecting leads should be negligibly small.   The ideal arrangement, therefore, would be to connect the deflecting plates directly to the voltage divider or to the current-viewing resistor with leads of negligible length.   In practical cases, however, this is generally not possible, and it is necessary to introduce a cable between the signal source and the deflecting plates of the cathode-ray tube.   The problems associated with the use of such a cable are discussed in Sec. A·2.

A voltage divider or current-viewing resistor must meet certain general requirements in order to be satisfactory for the observation and measurement of pulser characteristics.   These requirements may be stated as follows:

1. The input impedance of a voltage divider must be so high and the resistance of a current-viewing resistor must be so low that no appreciable disturbance is introduced in the circuit on which measurements are being made.
2. The circuit must have a uniform transient response over a wide band of frequencies, that is, it must not cause appreciable distortion of the waveforms under investigation.
3. The output impedance must be low compared with the input impedance of the cathode-ray-tube deflecting plates, and should be equal to or less than the cable surge impedance for all applications where impedance-matching is important.
4. The electrical characteristics of the voltage divider or current-viewing resistor must not vary with voltage, temperature, and time beyond the limits of the accuracy desired in the measurements.
5. The divider or resistor should, preferably, be capable of precise calibration with standard laboratory methods and apparatus.

Although no practical unit has yet been designed that fulfills all of these requirements and is adaptable for a wide range of measurements, several types have been designed to meet satisfactorily the needs of specific applications.

A·2. Pulse Measurements.   *The Parallel RC-divider.*—High-impedance voltage dividers designed for parallel connection to a pulser are generally comprised of noninductive resistors and high-quality condensers.   When the connecting leads are kept short and the ground connections are made directly to the chassis of the pulser, the inductance can be neglected for practical analyses. A voltage divider consisting of a pair of parallel RC-combinations is shown diagramatically in Fig. A·3.

FIG. A·3.—Parallel *RC*-divider circuit for pulse-voltage measurements with a synchroscope.

An analysis of the response of this circuit to an applied step-voltage V indicates the effects of the parameters on the signal voltage that is applied to the deflecting plates of the cathode-ray tube. The differential equation for the voltage v_2 after the switch S is closed can be set up by Kirchhoff's laws, and the general solution is found to be

$$\frac{v_2}{V} = \frac{R_2}{R_1 + R_2} + \left(\frac{C_1}{C_1 + C_2} - \frac{R_2}{R_1 + R_2}\right) e^{-\frac{t}{R_{11}C_{11}}},$$

where

$$R_{11} = \frac{R_1 R_2}{R_1 + R_2}$$

and

$$C_{11} = C_1 + C_2.$$

If $R_1 C_1 = R_2 C_2$,

$$\frac{R_2}{R_1 + R_2} = \frac{C_1}{C_1 + C_2}$$

and

$$\frac{v_2}{V} = \frac{R_2}{R_1 + R_2} = \frac{C_1}{C_1 + C_2},$$

giving a perfect voltage divider whose ratio is the same at all frequencies, that is, for all values of t. If $R_1 C_1 < R_2 C_2$,

$$\frac{R_2}{R_1 + R_2} > \frac{C_1}{C_1 + C_2}$$

and v_2 builds up exponentially with a time constant $= R_{11}C_{11}$ (see Fig. A·4a). If $R_1 C_1 > R_2 C_2$,

$$\frac{R_2}{R_1 + R_2} < \frac{C_1}{C_1 + C_2}$$

and v_2 decreases exponentially (see Fig. A·4b). Resistance dividers and capacitance dividers are special cases of this general *RC*-divider.

The Resistance Divider.—Two noninductive resistors connected in series form a voltage divider that is simple and convenient for pulse-voltage observations. If care is exercised in the construction of such a divider, the stray capacitance can be kept small and the time constants for the response curves shown in Fig. A·4 will be small. The ratio of voltage division for a resistance divider can be determined with high precision by ordinary Wheatstone-bridge measurements. Wire-wound resistors with a resistance of about 1000 ohms that are capable of withstanding 10,000-volt pulses of 1-μsec duration at recurrence frequencies of 1000 pps are commercially available. These resistors have L/R time constants of less than 0.003 μsec and negligible distributed capacitance, that is, they have reactance that is small and essentially proportional to frequency up to more than 10 Mc/sec. Since wire-wound resistors of less than 100 ohms with time constants equal to or less than 0.003 μsec are difficult to obtain commercially, it is better to use a coaxial carbon-on-ceramic resistor (see the discussion on current-viewing resistors at the end of Sec. A·2) in the low-voltage section. For a voltage division of about 100 to 1, a 1000-ohm resistance is commonly used in series with a 10-ohm resistance. Such dividers generally do not have the high input impedance desirable for circuit measurements and hence are retained only as standards against which capacitance dividers, which have a wider application, can be calibrated by direct comparison under pulse conditions.

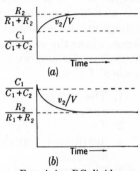

FIG. A·4.—RC-divider response curves, (a) $R_1C_1 < R_2C_2$, (b) $R_1C_1 > R_2C_2$.

This calibration is accomplished by substituting the standard resistance divider for the load in a pulse-generator circuit and connecting the capacitance divider of unknown ratio in parallel with it. Using null indication, the signal amplitudes of the two dividers can be compared with a probable error of less than ± 1 per cent. For best results, the ratio of the resistance divider should be adjusted to give nearly the same signal amplitude as the capacitance divider to be calibrated. Also, it is advisable to use a pulser that delivers a pulse with a flat top in order to minimize errors caused by the limited frequency response of the viewing system and by the observer. When considered with the cable and the oscilloscope input circuit, a resistance divider is really a parallel RC-divider for which C_1 is considered negligible; thus, a resistance divider does not give a true picture of the leading portion of fast-rising or short pulses if the CRT input capacitance is appreciable.

Transmission Cable and Impedance-matching.—Usually, the physical arrangement of an experimental setup makes it very inconvenient, if not impossible, to employ a voltage divider or a current-viewing resistor that is built into a synchroscope with negligibly short connecting leads to the CRT plates. In practice, therefore, a short length of shielded coaxial transmission cable is commonly used. A typical sample of such a cable has a characteristic impedance of 70 to 100 ohms, a capacitance of 12 to 14 $\mu\mu f$ per foot, and a velocity of electromagnetic-wave propagation of 700 to 800 ft/μsec. Low-impedance cables are preferred in order to minimize the effect of the input capacitance of the CRT deflecting plates.

To avoid undesirable reflections that tend to confuse the true signal appearing on the CRT screen, the cable impedance must be matched into the viewing system either at the CRT or at the divider. This matching imposes certain restrictions on the design of a divider, and the method used depends upon the particular type. In principle, however, the matching problem can be demonstrated by considering a simple voltage divider consisting of two pure resistances R_1 and R_2 connected in series, where the value R_2 is less than the cable surge impedance Z_0, and $R_1 \gg R_2$. To simplify the discussion, further idealizing assumptions are made as follows:

1. The voltage wave impressed upon the divider is a perfectly rectangular pulse.
2. The synchroscope input impedance is infinite. In particular, the distributed capacitance, including that of the CRT plates, is negligible.
3. The characteristic or surge impedance of the cable is a pure resistance, constant throughout the range of significant frequencies in the pulse. In other words, the cable is distortionless.
4. Losses in the cable are negligible.
5. The ratio of the divider is so high that the impedance of the high-voltage section can be considered infinite compared with the impedance of the low-voltage section. The pulse-generator circuit is thus undisturbed by the effects of mismatch between the divider and the cable; hence, the low-voltage section and the cable are fed by a constant-current source during the pulse

Figures A·5 and A·6 show two methods of obtaining a satisfactory matched condition.

If there is exact shunt termination at the synchroscope, that is, if $R_0 = Z_0$, no reflection occurs and the signal on the cathode-ray tube is at all times a true reproduction of the pulse voltage. However, the effective ratio of the divider is increased because the resistance of the low-voltage section is now the parallel value of R_2 and Z_0, or of R_2 and R_0.

With series matching by $R_m = Z_0 - R_2$ as shown in Fig. A·6, the wave initiated at the cable input is

$$v_c = \frac{Z_0 R_2 I}{R_2 + R_m + Z_0},$$

where I is the total current flowing through R_1 during the pulse.

The wave v_c traverses the cable toward the cathode-ray tube, where it is reflected without change in polarity from an essentially open circuit. When the reflected wave returns to the divider, it sees a matched load, $R_m + R_2 = Z_0$, and no further reflection occurs.   The cable is now fully

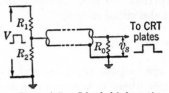

FIG. A·5.—Ideal high-ratio resistance divider and cable matched with a shunt resistor $R_0 = Z_0$ at the CRT input, $v_s =$

$$\frac{R_2 R_0}{R_1 R_2 + R_2 R_0 + R_0 R_1} V.$$

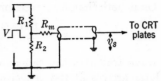

FIG. A·6.—Ideal high-ratio resistance divider and cable matched with a series resistor $R_m = Z_0 - R_2$ at the divider, $v_s = \dfrac{R_2}{R_1 + R_2} V.$

charged and the total current I flows through R_2.   While the cable is becoming charged, the current flow is divided and the voltage v_2 across R_2 is

$$v_2 = \frac{I(R_m + Z_0)R_2}{R_2 + R_m + Z_0}.$$

After the cable becomes fully charged, the voltage across R_2 is $v_2' = R_2 I$. During the entire pulse, the voltage at the cathode-ray tube, although delayed by the one-way transit time, has the constant value

$$v_s = 2v_c = \frac{2I R_2 Z_0}{R_2 + R_m + Z_0} = v_2';$$

or exact matching, $R_m + R_2 = Z_0$.

Either of these methods for matching the cable impedance is satisfactory for any length of cable. It should be noted that, for low divider ratios where the value of R_1 is not large compared with R_2, the matching problem becomes more complicated and the values of R_1, the internal impedance of the pulse-generator circuit, and the load impedance must also be considered in order to determine the correct value of R_m. In most applications $R_1 \geqq 10R_2$, and these considerations are of secondary importance.

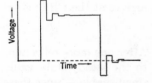

(a) $R_2 < Z_0$, $R_m = 0$, $R_0 = \infty$.

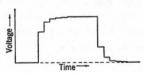

(b) $R_2 > Z_0$, $R_m = 0$, $R_0 = \infty$.

FIG. A·7.—Voltage pulses with cable improperly matched; cable transit time short compared with the pulse duration.

When the cable is improperly matched and the transit time of the cable is short compared with the pulse duration, the pulse signal viewed on the CRT screen may appear as the waveforms sketched in Fig. A·7, depending upon the relative values of Z_0, R_2, and the matching resistor. If the cable is long, successive reflections occur after the pulse.

As a numerical example, consider a length of cable that has a two-way transit time of 0.01 μsec and a surge impedance of 100 ohms. Let $R_2 = 50$ ohms and assume a constant current of 1 amp flowing through R_1. Omit both matching resistors. At the initial instant,

$$v_2 = \frac{100 \cdot 50 \cdot 1}{50 + 100} = 33.3 \text{ volts.}$$

This wave traverses the cable toward the cathode-ray tube and 0.005 μsec later arrives at the deflecting plates, where it is reflected without change in polarity. Hence, the initial value of v_s is 66.6 volts. When the reflected wave returns to the divider, it sees a mismatched receiver and a second wave,

$$v_2' = \frac{R_2 - Z_0}{R_2 + Z_0} = \frac{-50}{150} (33.3) = -11.1 \text{ volts,}$$

is reflected into the cable. When the v_2' wave arrives at the cathode-ray tube, 0.01 μsec after the arrival of the initial wavefront, another reflection occurs, and the deflecting voltage drops to

$$v_s' = 66.6 - 22.2 = 44.4 \text{ volts.}$$

After another interval of 0.01 μsec, a wave v_2'', reflected from the divider, arrives at the CRT; $v_2'' = +3.7$ volts and

$$v_s'' = 2(33.3 - 11.1 + 3.7) = 51.8 \text{ volts.}$$

After one more reflection, the voltage at the cathode-ray tube is so near to the steady-state value of 50 volts that no more reflections are distinguishable. Since these reflections recur at intervals of 0.01 μsec, they appear as high-frequency fuzz on the leading portion of the pulse unless a very fast sweep is used on the synchroscope. On a 0.1-μsec pulse viewed with a fast sweep, they appear more nearly like the idealized waveform sketched in Fig. A·7. In practice, the pulses often rise so slowly that when the mismatch is not great most of the reflections are dissipated during the rise. If R_2 is much smaller or if the cable is longer, however, the time required to dissipate these reflections may be an appreciable fraction of the pulse duration, and it is difficult to measure the true amplitude of the pulse. In this example, if a series matching resistor $R_m = 50$ ohms is used, the deflecting voltage during the entire pulse is 50 volts, but when a shunt matching resistor $R_0 = 100$ ohms is used, the deflecting voltage at all times is

$$v_s = \frac{50 \cdot 100 \cdot 1}{50 + 100} = 33.3 \text{ volts.}$$

When it is necessary to use a value of R_2 larger than Z_0, it is not possible to match the cable by ordinary means because the use of a shunt matching resistor R_0 reduces the voltage at the CRT, and thus nullifies the advantage gained by increasing R_2.

Capacitance Divider.—The most widely used pulse-voltage divider consists of a pair of condensers in series, the one of smaller capacitance C_1 having a high voltage rating, and being preferably of the vacuum type for the best quality and the least corona trouble. The photograph in Fig. A·8 shows the type of shielded construction used at the Radiation Laboratory with an Eimac VC12-32 vacuum condenser, rated at 32 kv, r-f voltage. Such a capacitance divider can usually be made to satisfy the requirement for high input impedance, where the pulse-generator load is of the order of magnitude of 1000 ohms or less, by using a high-voltage capacitance of the order of magnitude of 15 $\mu\mu f$ or less. Since a capacitance divider is inherently a pure reactance, however, it tends to form a resonant circuit with the inductance of the connecting leads, and may introduce undesirable high-frequency oscillations on the leading

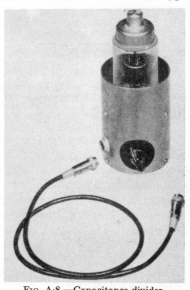

Fig. A·8.—Capacitance divider.

portion of the voltage pulse. These oscillations place a serious limitation on the measurement of extremely short pulses (of durations less than 0.1 μsec) and on the observation of the starting behavior of an oscillator load such as a magnetron.

With a capacitance divider, shunt termination of the cable cannot be used because it has the effect of producing an unbalanced RC-divider, differentiating the pulse and giving a signal similar to that sketched in Fig. A·9. For the same reason, a capacitance divider can be used only with an unterminated cable whose transit time is very short compared with the pulse duration. If the cable is just a little too long, the differentiating effect may not be so pronounced, but the droop during the pulse may cause appreciable error in measurements of pulse amplitude, as shown in Fig. A·10.

While the cable is becoming charged, the loading effect on C_2 is the same as if a resistor Z_0 were connected directly across C_2, and the voltage v_2 falls with a time constant equal to $Z_0(C_1 + C_2)$. For a 100-ohm cable and typical values of $C_1 = 12$ $\mu\mu$f and $C_2 = 1200$ $\mu\mu$f, this time constant is about 0.12 μsec. With a 12-ft length of cable having a two-way transit time of the order of magnitude of 0.03 μsec, v_2 falls to about 0.7 of its initial value while the cable is becoming charged. Furthermore, with mismatch at both ends of the cable, an open circuit at the cathode-ray tube, and pure reactance at the divider, a series of undesirable reflections appear on the pulse.

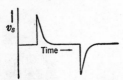

Fig. A·9.—Differentiated rectangular pulse as seen on the CRT screen of a synchroscope when a capacitance divider is used with a cable terminated in $R_0 = Z_0$.

Fig. A·10.—Drooping pulse resulting from the use of a cable with a transit time comparable to the pulse duration.

It is also evident that a divider containing reactance cannot be matched perfectly to a cable for all frequencies. Some form of compensating circuit might be used, but for most practical purposes fairly good results have been obtained with capacitance dividers by inserting a resistor, $R_m \approx Z_0$, in series with the cable input, as shown in Fig. A·11. This resistor serves a three-fold purpose. It introduces a voltage drop in the initial wave entering the cable, so that $v_c = v_2/2$. Hence, when v_c is reflected from the open-circuited end of the cable and returns to the divider, the cable is charged to a potential nearly equal to the voltage on C_2 at that instant. Secondly, the current flowing out of C_2 to charge the cable is reduced by a factor of two, and this reduction correspondingly lessens the droop in v_2. Finally, the resistor R_m effectively matches the cable impedance for the initial wavefront reflection from the cathode-ray tube. This statement is approximately true only because the reactance of C_2 is negligible compared with Z_0 for the higher frequencies in the Fourier spectrum of the pulse, that is, for those frequencies whose periods are comparable to the transit time of short lengths of cable. For a divider ratio of 100/1 or higher, the value of C_2 is about 1000 $\mu\mu$f, corresponding to a reactance of less than 1.5 ohms at 100 Mc/sec. For lower frequencies where the reactance is higher the mismatch is greater, but R_m helps to dissipate the reflections quickly. For frequencies of a few megacycles per second, which contribute significantly to the main portion

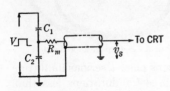

Fig. A·11.—Capacitance divider approximately matched to a cable by a series resistor $R_m = Z_0$; $v_s = \dfrac{C_1}{C_1 + C_2 + C_c + C_s}$.

of the pulse, the effect of R_m in the circuit is negligible, and the short lengths of cable must be considered essentially as a lumped capacitance, which is included with the CRT input capacitance C_s as part of C_2 in calibrating the divider. A capacitance divider should therefore be calibrated with the particular cable and cathode-ray tube with which it is to be used for measurements.

When very long pulses are observed with a low-ratio divider, the value of the low-voltage capacitance required may be so small that the charge leaking off during the pulse through the 1-megohm resistor to ground in the synchroscope causes an apparent droop in the voltage pulse that appears on the CRT screen. The magnitude of this droop can be estimated by again considering the relation between the pulse duration and the time constant of an equivalent unbalanced RC-divider. In this case, $R_1 = \infty$ and $R_2 = 1$ megohm. If $C_1 = 12\ \mu\mu f$ and $C_2 = 240\ \mu\mu f$, the time constant is 240 μsec for a divider ratio of 20/1. For a 10-μsec pulse duration, this time constant would cause a droop of the order of magnitude of 5 per cent. In some cases, this droop can be minimized by increasing the resistance in the synchroscope to 10 megohms, but this increase is not always feasible. Also, if both the low-voltage and the high-voltage capacitance are increased, the condition for negligible circuit loading may not be met adequately.

To avoid the last-mentioned limitation of capacitance dividers for measurements on long pulses and other low fre-
quency waveforms where the bleeding-off time constant is not sufficiently great to prevent distortion, the "balanced" parallel RC-divider may be used. It is demonstrated at the beginning of this section that, when $R_1C_1 = R_2C_2$, this divider theoretically has a uniform frequency response over an infinite band. In practice, the distributed capacitance of a high-voltage wire-wound resistor is appreciable but difficult to evaluate, and, in order to obtain a satisfactory balance, it is often necessary

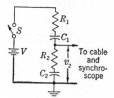

Fig. A·12.—Series RC-divider circuit for pulse-voltage measurements with a synchroscope.

to use lower values of resistance, or higher values of capacitance, than the circuit-loading requirement permits.

Series RC-divider.—Figure A·12 shows a fourth type of RC-divider for pulse-voltage measurements that has the same limitations as a pure capacitance divider for long pulse durations and with respect to the impedance-matching of the cable. For short pulse durations and for the study of the leading edge, however, this series RC-divider has a considerable advantage over the capacitance divider because it is not a pure reactance and therefore does not introduce oscillations into the load circuit of the pulse generator. An analysis of the circuit shows that the condition under which the divider ratio is independent of frequency is again $R_1C_1 = R_2C_2$.

Current-pulse-viewing Resistors.—Pulse currents in magnetron oscillators and in pulse-generator switch tubes that range from less than ten amperes to several hundred amperes have been observed to rise to full value in less than 0.01 μsec. Precise measurements of such rapidly rising high currents are especially difficult to accomplish. The first require-

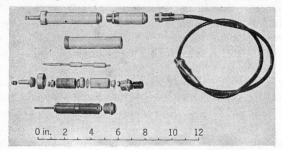

FIG. A·13.—Coaxial current-viewing resistor.

ment is that the viewing resistor itself must have negligible inductance. Even a carbon resistor 1 in. long has enough self-inductance to produce an $L\, dI/dt$ voltage comparable to its IR drop, and thus, in some applications, causes a spurious spike to appear on the pulse. Early experiments at the Radiation Laboratory indicated that a considerable improvement

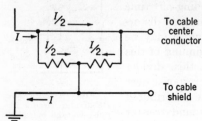

FIG. A·14.—Schematic diagram showing the directions of current flow in BTL coaxial noninductive resistors.

in the quality of the response could be obtained with a coaxial resistor, which was simply a coaxial cylinder filled with lampblack and clay. However, these hastily made units were unstable with changes in temperature and voltage. The problem was presented to engineers of the Bell Telephone Laboratories, who then designed a unit consisting of a pair of ceramic cylinders, carbon coated on the inside surface, and mounted in a convenient metallic assembly with corrugated spring contacts and cable connectors on either end.

Another mounting for these carbon-on-ceramic cylinders is provided by a telephone plug on one end and a cable connector on the other (see Fig. A·13). When so mounted, these resistors are found to have an inductance of less than 0.01 μh, and usually show a change of resistance with temperature and voltage of less than 2 per cent when the average-power rating of 15 watts is not exceeded and when the maximum pulse voltage is less than 150 volts. The two cylindrical elements in a single unit have nearly equal resistance values. The pulse current enters through the phone plug and divides equally; one half flows along the inner surface of the first cylinder toward the midpoint of the metal housing, and the other half flows in the center conductor toward the remote end of the unit and returns along the inner surface of the second cylinder toward the midpoint of the metal housing. The ground return is made through the outer metal cylinder from the midpoint of its length to the phone-jack, which is mounted directly on the chassis of the pulse generator. Thus the two cylinders are effectively connected in parallel, and the current flow is such that a high degree of flux cancellation is accomplished (see Fig. A·14). These units are available in resistance values from less than 0.5 ohm to more than 100 ohms. The series of pulse current photographs in Fig. A·15 shows the relative qualities of several types of noninductive resistors for oscilloscopic presentation of current pulses. When ordinary resistors were used, the connecting leads were made as short as possible in order to minimize the inductance. Figure A·15a through f show a 0.5-μsec pulse generated by a hard-tube pulser on a resistance load. The voltage pulse viewed with a capacitance divider is included for comparison. For this relatively slow-rising current pulse the small ($\frac{1}{2}$-in.) ordinary carbon-ceramic resistor appears almost as noninductive as the BTL coaxial unit. The three noninductive wirewound samples were selected at random from three different manufacturers and are not necessarily the best obtainable. The pulse photographs in Fig. A·15h through l show the same resistors used to view a magnetron current pulse that rises and falls more rapidly. The difference in quality between the BTL coaxial unit and the ordinary carbon-ceramic resistor becomes apparent in this comparison.

The problem of cable-matching with a current-viewing resistor is essentially the same as with a resistance divider. When the internal impedance of the pulser is low and the value of resistance used for viewing the current is comparable to the dynamic impedance of the load, the best results can be obtained only with shunt termination of the cable at the synchroscope. If series matching is used in this case, the sudden increase in the voltage across the viewing resistor that occurs when the initial wavefront returns from the open end of the cable at the synchroscope may effect an appreciable change in load current. A detailed analysis of this case cannot be based on the assumption that $R_1 \gg R_2$, but must include an equivalent circuit for the load and the pulser.

V-I Plots.—For some applications it is convenient to disconnect the d-c centering potential and the time-base sweep circuit of the synchroscope, and to present another signal on the second pair of CRT plates. In this way a systematic plot of the resultant signal on the screen is

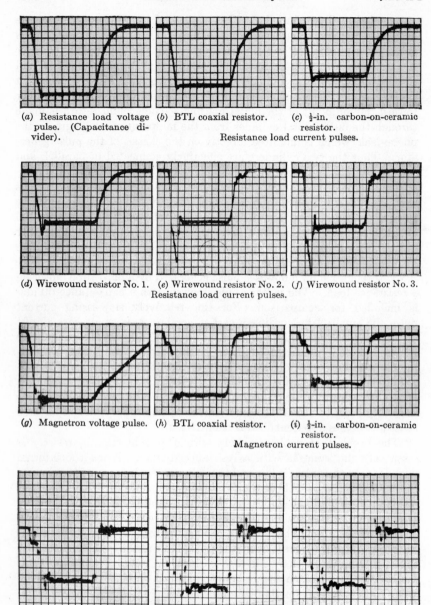

(a) Resistance load voltage pulse. (Capacitance divider).

(b) BTL coaxial resistor.

(c) ½-in. carbon-on-ceramic resistor.

Resistance load current pulses.

(d) Wirewound resistor No. 1.

(e) Wirewound resistor No. 2.

(f) Wirewound resistor No. 3.

Resistance load current pulses.

(g) Magnetron voltage pulse.

(h) BTL coaxial resistor.

(i) ½-in. carbon-on-ceramic resistor.

Magnetron current pulses.

(j) Wirewound resistor No. 1.

(k) Wirewound resistor No. 2.

(l) Wirewound resistor No. 3

Magnetron current pulses.

Fig. A·15.—Comparison of inductive effects in various current-viewing resistors.

obtained. This type of indication is useful for obtaining the pulse
voltage-current characteristics of nonlinear-impedance devices such as
surge-limiting diodes, pulse-generator switch tubes, and magnetrons.
Figure A·16 shows schematically the relative point-by-point correlation
of an idealized voltage-current plot of a pulsed magnetron with the
corresponding voltage and current pulses as they would appear on a
linear time base. The current flowing between the times t_0 and t_2 is due
to charging the capacitance associated with the magnetron input circuit
during the rise of voltage, the current maximum at t_1 corresponding to

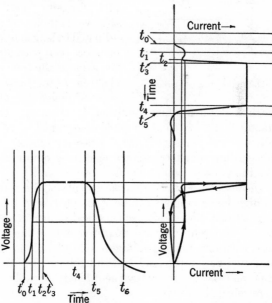

FIG. A·16.—Schematic diagram showing the correlation of an idealized voltage-current plot
of a pulsed magnetron with the corresponding voltage and current pulses.

the maximum value of dv/dt. The magnetron conduction current rises
between t_2 and t_3 during the buildup of the oscillations, and remains
nearly constant from t_3 to t_4 while the magnetron oscillates steadily.
The current between t_4 and t_5 corresponds to the initial part of the voltage
fall that occurs while the oscillations in the magnetron are dying out.
With a line-type pulser, the initial rate of fall of voltage $(t_4 - t_5)$ is slow,
and the voltage-current relations are the same as those that would be
obtained from a steady-state point-by-point plot of the voltage and
current. However, with a hard-tube pulser that has low internal
impedance, the initial rate of fall of voltage may be high enough to
produce an appreciable capacitive current of opposite sign, and the slope
of the *V-I* plot during the fall, corresponding to the time interval from

t_4 to t_5, may not be a true indication of the dynamic impedance of the magnetron. The magnitude of the discharging capacitive current from t_5 to t_6 is considerably less than the charging capacitive current because the rate of fall of the voltage is much slower than its rate of rise.

Photographs of typical *V-I* traces of a pulsed magnetron are included in Chap. 7 and in Vol. 6, Chap. 16.[1] By conducting two signals from the same voltage divider through different cables to the two sets of deflection plates of the cathode-ray tube, the two identical signals can be plotted against one another, and the two samples of cable can be adjusted in length until the difference between their delay times is the same as the transit time of the electron beam between the two sets of deflecting plates in the

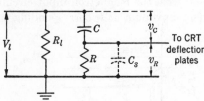

Fig. A·17.—Differentiating *RC*-circuit.

cathode-ray tube. When this condition is obtained, the resultant trace is a straight line oriented at an angle determined by relative deflection sensitivities of the two sets of CRT deflecting plates. Other useful information regarding magnetron starting can be obtained by plotting the current or the voltage against dv/dt.

Voltage Differentiator.—Precise measurements of the rate of rise and rate of fall of high-voltage pulses can be accomplished with the aid of the differentiating *RC*-circuit, shown schematically in Fig. A·17, and a synchroscope. This circuit converts measurements of the rate of change of voltage into measurements of a voltage amplitude. The differentiating circuit is connected across the load and the voltage v_R is transmitted to CRT deflecting plates through a convenient length of cable. The values of R and C are selected so that—

1. The voltage $v_R \ll v_C$ for the highest rates of change to be measured, that is, for the highest significant frequencies in the Fourier spectrum of the applied pulse.
2. The loading effect on the pulse-generator circuit is small.
3. The reactance of distributed capacitance across R and of the CRT input capacitance is high compared with R for all significant frequencies in the derivative.

When these conditions are fulfilled,

$$v_R = Ri = RC \frac{dv_C}{dt} \approx RC \frac{dv_l}{dt},$$

[1] For a more detailed discussion of this method of indication, see R. C. Fletcher and F. F. Rieke, "Mode Selection in Magnetrons," RL Report No. 809, Sept. 28, 1945.

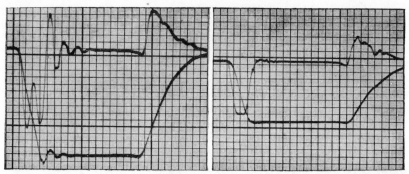

(*a*), (*b*). Voltage pulses and corresponding time derivatives superimposed on the screen of a cathode-ray tube by the use of a mechanical commutator.

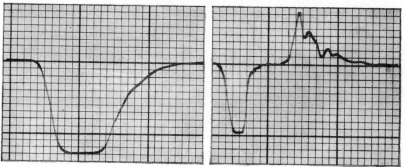

(*c*) Voltage pulse.

(*d*) Time derivative of (*c*) observed with short leads and matched cable.

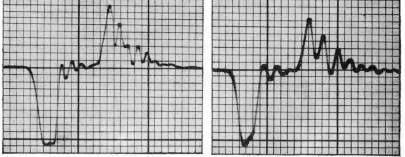

(*e*) Time derivative of (*c*) observed with short leads and mismatched cable.

(*f*) Time derivative of (*c*) observed with long leads and mismatched cable.

FIG. A·18.—Voltage pulses and time derivatives.

$$\frac{dv_l}{dt} \approx \frac{v_R}{RC},$$ (1)

where v_R is in volts, R in ohms, C in farads, and dv_l/dt in volts/sec.

Photographs of the oscilloscope traces for negative voltage pulses and the corresponding derivatives are shown in Fig. A·18.   These pulses were generated by a hard-tube pulser with a 1000-ohm resistance load.   Figures A·18a and b show the voltage pulse and the derivative observed simultaneously with a synchroscope by means of a mechanical commutator. With reasonable precautions, measurements of the rate-of-rise of voltage by the differentiating method are capable of much higher precision and accuracy than measurements of $\Delta v_l/\Delta t$, where Δv_l is the voltage change

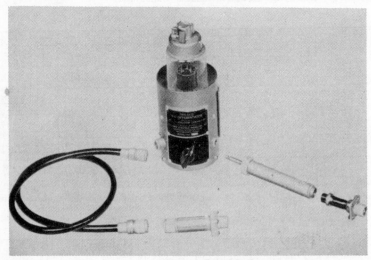

FIG. A·19.—RC-differentiator.

in a corresponding increment of time Δt.   The differentiating circuit also provides a method of distinguishing between real and spurious oscillations (or cable reflections) in a pulse-viewing system comprised of an RC-divider, a cable, and a synchroscope.

Certain precautions are necessary in the construction and the use of a differentiating RC-circuit.   The inductance of R and the connecting leads must be as low as possible to insure a true RC-response to the impressed voltage.   The BTL coaxial current-viewing resistors, having inductance ≤ 0.01 μh, are satisfactory.   The effect of long connecting leads is observable in the photograph of Fig. A·18f.

The cable impedance should be matched with a shunt resistor, R_0, at the synchroscope in preference to a series resistor at the cable input.

In this case R [Eq. (1)] should be replaced by $R' = \dfrac{RR_0}{R + R_0}$. If the cable impedance is matched with a series resistor R_m at the cable input, an appreciable distortion that results from the time constant $R_m C_s$ for the charging of the synchroscope input capacitance may be introduced. Figures A·18e and f show the effect of improper cable-matching.

To eliminate high-frequency pickup by the low-voltage section, a shielded type of construction should be used. A differentiator using an Eimac VC12-32 vacuum condenser and a BTL coaxial noninductive resistor is shown in Fig. A·19. For qualitative observations in which some inaccuracy can be tolerated for the sake of convenience, several ordinary carbon resistors ranging in value from 25 ohms to 100 ohms may be incorporated with a convenient switching arrangement as in the model made by Sylvania.

The input capacitance C_s of the synchroscope is effectively lumped across R, and must be below the limits specified in the following analysis (see Fig. A·17). This capacitance tends to bypass the higher frequencies of the derivative v_R, and therefore C_s should be made as small as possible. The effect of C_s on v_R is indicated by an examination of the response to the leading portion of a

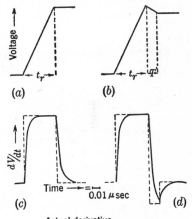

---- Actual derivative
—— v_R (response of differentiating circuit, Fig. A 17) $C = 15\ \mu\mu\text{f}$, $R = 50$ ohms, $C_s = 75\ \mu\mu\text{f}$

Fig. A·20.—Hypothetical voltage pulses and corresponding time derivatives.

(a) Trapezoidal voltage wave front.
(b) Trapezoidal voltage wave front with a spike.
(c) Time derivative of (a).
(d) Time derivative of (b).

trapezoidal voltage pulse applied to R_l. It is assumed that the voltage impressed on the differentiating circuit is of the form

$$v_l(t)_{0 \leq t \leq tr} = \frac{V_l}{t_r}\, t,$$
$$v_l(t)_{t \geq tr} = V_l,$$

where t_r is the time of rise of the voltage pulse. For the time interval $0 \leq t \leq t_r$,

$$v_R = \frac{CRV_l}{t_r}\left[1 - e^{-\frac{t}{RC_{11}}}\right] \tag{2}$$

where $C_{11} = C + C_s$, and for $t \geqq t_r$

$$v_R = \frac{CRV_l}{t_r}\left[1 - e^{-\frac{t_r}{RC_{11}}}\right]e^{-\frac{(t-t_r)}{RC_{11}}}.$$

Figure A·20 shows a graph of the applied trapezoidal voltage wave front, its actual time derivative, and the

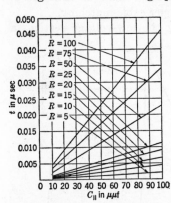

response v_R of a differentiating circuit with typical parameters. Also plotted are a trapezoidal wave front with a spike, its corresponding derivative, and v_R.

These hypothetical pulses and derivatives are plotted to demonstrate the type of distortion that is caused by C_s shunting R. The time constant RC_{11} should be held to a minimum for the best response of the differentiating circuit to sudden changes in the impressed voltage.

Fig. A·21.—Graph for estimating the maximum permissible value of C_{11} for k equal to one per cent.

From Eq. (2) a simple quantitative expression can be derived for determining the maximum permissible value of C_{11} for any desired fidelity of response to a linearly rising voltage.   For example, in order for $v_R/(RC)$ to be within 1 per cent of dv_l/dt,

$$e^{-\frac{t}{RC_{11}}} \leqq 0.01.$$

This relation requires that

$$t \geqq RC_{11} \ln 100$$

and

$$t \geqq 4.6RC_{11}.$$

Figure A·21 is a graph of t versus C_{11} for various values of R.   This graph shows the time that is required after closing the switch for v_R to approach within one per cent of the true derivative, for any combination of R and C_{11}.   If greater tolerance in the accuracy of v_R is permitted, for example, K per cent, the values of t are given by the product of

$$\left[1 - \frac{(\ln K)}{4.6}\right]$$

and the corresponding values of t for $K = 1$ per cent in Fig. A·21.

The photographs of Fig. A·22 show 0.1-μsec voltage pulses and the derivatives obtained with a resistance load and a magnetron load on a hard-tube pulser.   The response of the differentiator to the spikes and to the small oscillations on the voltage pulses is observable in these photographs.

From the photographs of Fig. A·18a and b, where the differentiator response and the traces of the applied voltage pulse are superimposed, it might be inferred that the output voltage from the differentiator rises more rapidly than does the input voltage.   This illusion appears because a voltage divider was used to obtain the voltage-pulse trace; in this case the divider ratio was about 150/1.   Actually, the rate of change of the

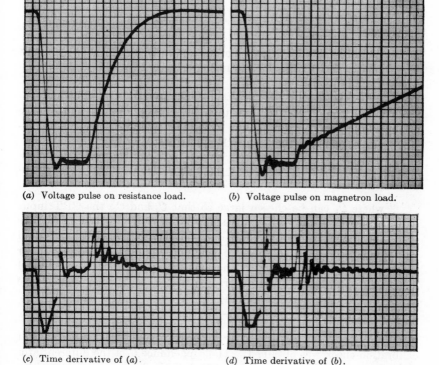

(a) Voltage pulse on resistance load.   (b) Voltage pulse on magnetron load.

(c) Time derivative of (a).   (d) Time derivative of (b).

Fig. A·22.—Oscilloscope traces of short pulses and their time derivatives.   Sweep speed: 10 div = 0.2 μsec.

voltage, v_R, is less than that of the applied voltage, as is evident from the differentiation of Eq. (2).   Since C_s is never zero, the value of dv_R/dt is less than V_l/t_r by the factor $C/(C + C_s)$.

The calibration of an RC-differentiator may be accomplished by one of the following three methods:

1. By the direct measurement of R and C.   For many applications the value of C is about 15 μμf or less.   Accurate measurements of such small capacitances are possible with a high-precision bridge, for example, the General Radio Twin-T, but elaborate precautions

must be observed and corrections must be made for lead inductance and stray capacitance to ground resulting from the large physical size of the high-voltage condenser.

2. By the measurement of Δv_l and Δt on a linearly rising portion of a pulse, using an accurately calibrated high-speed sweep. The values of Δv_l, Δt, and the corresponding v_R may be substituted into Eq. (1), to give

$$RC = \frac{v_R \Delta t}{\Delta v_l}.$$

Some modifications may be necessary in the pulse-generator circuit in order to obtain a linearly rising pulse that is suitable for calibration purposes.

3. By the removal of the resistor R and the substitution of a capacitance C_x. The unit can then be calibrated as a capacitance divider against a standard resistance divider under pulse conditions. The divider ratio thus determined is equal to

$$\frac{C + C_x + C_s + C_c}{C}$$

where C_x can be chosen large so that C_s and C_c, the CRT input capacitance and cable capacitance respectively, constitute less than 10 per cent of the numerator. Then C_x can be removed and measured easily on a bridge, and the values of C_s and C_c either measured or estimated. The value of C can then be calculated with a probable error no greater than the algebraic sum of the errors in measurement of the divider ratio and of $C_x + C_s + C_c$. This method of calibration is the most reliable.

Figure A·18*b* shows a linearly rising pulse on which an excellent calibration check was obtained. The capacitance C of the differentiator was measured on a General Radio 821-A Twin-T precision bridge, with necessary corrections for leads, capacitance to ground, etc. The average of several readings was 13.3 ± 0.2 $\mu\mu$f. A Wheatstone-bridge measurement of R' gave 19.97 ohms as the parallel value of R and R_0. The vertical-deflection sensitivity on the CRT screen was 5.50 ± 0.05 volts per small division. The voltage pulse was obtained from a capacitance divider with a ratio of 163/1, determined by comparison with a standard noninductive-resistance divider under pulse conditions. The estimated maximum error of this calibration was ± 1 per cent. The CRT sweep calibration indicated by a 10-Mc/sec sine wave (crystal-controlled oscillator) was

$$0.0208 \pm 0.004 \ \mu\text{sec}$$

per small division. To determine $\Delta v_l/\Delta t$, an enlarged photograph was made of the oscilloscope trace, and a straightedge was laid along the linear portion of the leading edge of the voltage pulse. The slope of this line in divisions (the average of several readings) was 3.6. Hence,

$$\frac{\Delta v_l}{\Delta t} = 3.6 \left[\frac{5.5 \times 163}{0.0208 \times 10^{-6}} \right] = 155 \text{ kv/}\mu\text{sec.}$$

The maximum amplitude of v_R was observed to be 7.4 divisions. By substituting into Eq. (1) there is obtained

$$\frac{dv_l}{dt} = \frac{7.4 \times 5.5}{20 \times 13.3 \times 10^{-12}} = 153 \text{ kv/}\mu\text{sec.}$$

A·3. Practical Considerations in Making Pulse Measurements.
Pulse Shape.—The number of pulse shapes actually encountered in practical circuit work is legion and the irregularities in the shape of the pulses to be measured complicate the interpretation and specification of measurements of both amplitude and duration. A good oscilloscopic viewing system provides flexibility for instantaneous or average amplitude measurements and qualitative information regarding the shape of a pulse. The relatively slow rise and fall and the rounded corners of most pulses observed

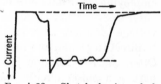

FIG. A·23.—Sketch of an irregularly shaped current pulse.

in practice are reproduced faithfully with pulse-viewing systems in which the design features of an ideal viewing system may only partially be fulfilled. The problem of verifying the relation

$$I_{av} = \tau f_r I_l,$$

expressing conservation of charge, may be taken as an example of the importance of pulse shape in the interpretation of the quantities involved. In this relation I_{av} is the average d-c current read by a meter in series with a rectifying load, I_l is the pulse current amplitude, τ is the pulse duration, and f_r is the number of pulses per second. In a circuit where the current pulse is of an irregular shape similar to that sketched in Fig. A·23 the fundamental question is how to measure τ and I_l in order most truly to represent an equivalent rectangular pulse. In this particular case such an equivalent pulse is any rectangular pulse whose area is equal to that of the irregularly shaped pulse. Although this definition of the equivalent pulse permits several values of I_l and τ, a commonly accepted procedure is to measure the amplitude of the average height of the pulse, corresponding to an imaginary line drawn through the top, and to take the pulse duration at one half of this amplitude. This procedure satisfies the law of conservation of charge, but when the peak instantaneous or pulse power, the total energy per pulse, and the r-f spectrum must all be considered in determining an equivalent rectangular pulse, the problem becomes much more complicated (see Appendix B).

The irregularities in pulse shapes that are encountered make it apparent that the usefulness of metering circuits for determining pulse voltage or pulse current is limited to special applications where the shape is known and the nature of the metering-circuit response to the particular pulse shape being measured is known. Measurements by metering circuits that are sensitive to pulse shape can properly be interpreted only with the aid of auxiliary oscilloscopic measurements, as discussed in Sec. A·3.

Shielding.—The importance of the shielding of all components of a viewing system cannot be overemphasized. Voltage dividers should be constructed with the high-voltage section shielded from the low-voltage section wherever feasible. In a capacitance divider or a differentiator employing an Eimac vacuum condenser, it is preferable to connect the outer sleeve rather than the inner cylinder of the condenser to the high-voltage terminal, in order that the corona path from this terminal will be direct to ground and the inner cylinder will be shielded at low potential. Often the r-f radiation produced by a sudden surge of current in one part of a pulser circuit, such as when a magnetron starts to conduct, causes pickup on the deflecting plates of the cathode-ray tube, which may appear as high-frequency fuzz on the signal trace. It is sometimes very difficult to distinguish between spurious oscillations or reflections in the viewing system, r-f pickup from a source of interference, and oscillations that really are present in the circuit being measured. In a synchroscope it is extremely important to shield the sweep circuit and all connections to one set of deflecting plates from the other set of deflecting plates; otherwise, coupling between the circuits can cause "crosstalk" to appear on the signal. This crosstalk may appear as a steady backward motion of the sweep during the rise of the pulse, or it may appear as a to-and-fro oscillation of the sweep as the pulse rises or falls. Sometimes, even with the best shielding, it is necessary to add resistance suppressors directly at the deflecting plates. The distributed capacitance is usually adequate for filtering if 1000-ohm noninductive resistors are inserted in series with the plates.

Amplifiers.—In high-level work it is nearly always possible to obtain sufficient voltage amplitude for presentation of the signal directly on a CRT screen, and amplifiers are unnecessary. This is fortunate, because it is much easier to design and construct dividers with wide-band-transfer characteristics than to construct video amplifiers with adequate bandwidth.

Cable Properties and Delay Lines.—It is sometimes desirable to insert a fixed delay time in the signal presentation, for example, when the CRT sweep is initiated or triggered by the same pulse that is to be viewed as a signal, that is, when self-synchronous operation is required. When using a nonsynchronous pulser switch, such as a rotary spark gap, the signal cannot be synchronized on the cathode-ray tube except by this method. Unless the signal can be delayed by a few tenths of a microsecond after the sweep is triggered and the intensifier pulse initiated, however, the leading edge of the pulse is lost to view. The photographs in Fig. A·24a and b show a typical pulse on a resistance load as it would appear in ordinary synchronous operation with two different lengths of

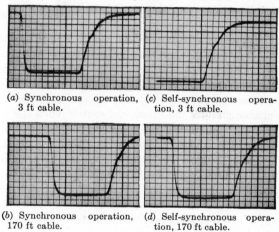

(a) Synchronous operation, 3 ft cable. (c) Self-synchronous operation, 3 ft cable.

(b) Synchronous operation, 170 ft cable. (d) Self-synchronous operation, 170 ft cable.

Fig. A·24.—Photographs of voltage pulses showing the delay in the start of the sweep in self-synchronous operation, and the effect of a long 100-ohm cable on the observed pulse shape.

cable. The traces shown in Fig. A·24c and d are for self-synchronous operation. It may be observed that the cable attenuation is not constant with frequency and that there is some distortion of the pulse. This distortion is particularly noticeable in the rounding of the leading top corner of the pulse and the slowing down of the rate of rise. There is also a slight decrease in the amplitude of the main part of the pulse that can be corrected by measuring the attenuation factor for a particular sample of cable, which is determined by the pulse amplitude at a point near the center of the top of the pulse. Usually, the attenuation factor for a 0.1-μsec pulse, when compared with the corresponding factor for longer pulses, shows greater losses for the shorter pulses. Lumped-parameter delay networks that produce less rounding of the leading edge of a given pulse, and that show less attenuation than a length of cable giving a corresponding delay time, have been designed and built, but the lumped-parameter networks usually introduce ripples and other irregularities because of the mismatch between sections. Unless the condensers are all carefully selected, the coils wound to very close tolerances, and the network constructed with a relatively large number of sections, it is usually preferable to have the greater, but smoother, distortion and attenuation produced by a cable, since there are fewer irregularities.

A·4. Voltage and Current Measurements in the Charging Circuit of a Line-type Pulser. *Forward Charging Voltage.*—In general, two types of measurements are made on the charging-voltage waves in a line-type pulse-generator circuit. With a relatively slow CRT sweep and a high-impedance balanced parallel RC-divider, one or more complete cycles of the charging voltage may be observed for waveform and amplitude measurements. With an expanded sweep the voltage across the switch immediately after the pulse discharge is observed to determine the magnitude of post-pulse inverse voltage across the switch or the pulse-forming network, and the nature of its removal from the network during the early portion of the recharging period. These latter data are especially significant in the study of the circuit behavior of a line-type pulser using d-c resonant charging and a unidirectional switch when the load impedance changes during a pulse or from pulse to pulse.

In measurements of charging voltage or inverse voltage, the time resolution required is nearly always large compared with the transit time of the short cables used with the dividers. The impedance-matching problem, therefore, becomes one of producing a balanced RC-divider when the cable is treated as a lumped capacitance in the circuit. Consider, for example, a d-c resonant-charging circuit in which the maximum forward voltage on the pulse-forming network is 8 kv and the average d-c charging current is about 40 ma. These values correspond to a pulse recurrence frequency of 500 pps with a 1-μsec 50-ohm network. To keep the average current through the divider less than 1 per cent of the charging current, its total d-c impedance must be at least 10 megohms. For a maximum signal of 80 volts at the CRT deflecting plates, the divider ratio should be about 100/1; therefore, the resistance of the low-voltage section of the divider must be about 100,000 ohms. Let $R_2 = 10^5$ ohms and assume that $C_c + C_s \approx 75 \ \mu\mu$f. The time constant R_2C_2 (Fig. A·3) is then equal to 7.5 μsec. In order to form a balanced parallel RC-divider, the distributed capacitance across the high-voltage resistor, $R_1 = 10$ megohms, must be about 0.75 $\mu\mu$f. Since it is difficult to evaluate the distributed capacitance, it is better, in practice, to add a lumped capacitance of about 12 to 25 $\mu\mu$f, such as a high-voltage vacuum condenser, in parallel with R_1 and then to increase C_2 correspondingly.

During the charging period the loading effect on the pulser circuit produced by this added capacitance (the sum of C_1 and C_2 in series) is usually negligible, but during the pulse this capacitance discharges through the pulser switch and, if C_1 is comparable to the storage capacitance of the pulse-forming network, the pulse current through the switch at the beginning of the pulse is appreciably increased.

By using a string of carbon resistors in the "stove-pipe" shielded arrangement shown in Fig. A·25, it is possible, without adding any additional capacitance and by using less than three feet of cable, to keep the effective time constant $R_{11}C_{11}$ less than 5 μsec. In this way an oscilloscopic presentation of the d-c resonant-charging voltage wave that is satisfactory for the observation of the character of the general waveform and for the measurement of the maximum forward-voltage amplitude is obtained, but the voltage across the switch for a period of about 25 μsec after the pulse is not accurately reproduced.

Immediate Post-pulse Voltage.—To make precise measurements of the post-pulse voltage across the pulser switch (or pulse-forming network) on an expanded time base, the following two devices are used: a diode in series with a resistance divider, and an unbalanced RC-divider. For measurements of inverse post-pulse voltage only, a diode is connected in series with a resistance divider as shown in Fig. A·26. The diode prevents the current from flowing through the shunt path during the major portion of the charging interval while forward voltage exists across the pulser switch. The total resistance can therefore be much less than is required for a balanced RC-divider with no diode. However, the resistance must be high enough to prevent excessive post-pulse inverse currents from flowing through the pulse-transformer primary winding. Such inverse currents may influence flux reset in the pulse-transformer core or cause

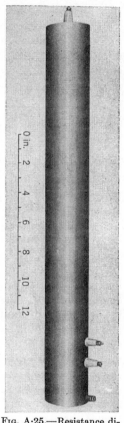

FIG. A·25.—Resistance divider.

the inverse voltage on the pulse-forming network to discharge too rapidly. In a thyratron pulser employing a 50-ohm pulse-forming network and a pulse transformer with a butt-joint core, a total resistance of 20,000 ohms or higher is usually satisfactory. Inverse voltage in a typical thyratron-pulser circuit may vary from a few hundred volts during normal operation to nearly the same magnitude as the peak forward voltage during abnormal load conditions, such as magnetron sparking. Hence, the desired divider ratios may vary from about 10/1 to 100/1 or more. As an example, assume a divider ratio of 11/1. With $R_1 = 20,000$ ohms (including effective diode resistance), R_2 should be about 2000 ohms. If the total capacitance of the cable and CRT input is 75 $\mu\mu$f, the effective time constant, neglecting distributed capacitance C_1 across R_1, is

$$R_2C_2 \approx 0.15 \ \mu\text{sec}.$$

This value is tolerable for most measurements of post-pulse voltage. For precise measurements of post-pulse voltage of either polarity, an unbalanced RC-divider circuit, shown in Fig. A·27, is used with a synchroscope. These measurements, however, are only reliable for a few microseconds after the pulse. The time constant $R_2(C_1 + C_2)$ is made

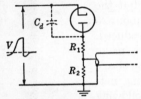

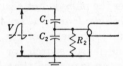

FIG. A·26.—Resistance divider used with diode for measurements of post-pulse inverse voltage across the pulser switch.

FIG. A·27.—Unbalanced RC-divider for measurements of post-pulse voltages of either polarity across the pulser switch.

long compared with the post-pulse interval of immediate interest, but short compared with the entire interpulse charging interval. Hence, the waveform of the forward charging voltage is distorted considerably, and, at the instant before the switch breaks down, the voltage appearing across R_2 (and at the cathode-ray tube) is zero. The divider responds as a capacitance divider that is reliable for a time short compared with the time constant $R_2(C_1 + C_2)$. The reference potential for determining whether the post-pulse voltage is positive or negative is not the actual zero voltage on the CRT deflecting plates, but rather it is the flat portion of the signal occurring during the pulse. This voltage is not a true zero reference because it is in error by the 100- to 200-volt drop that exists across the pulser switch during the pulse when it is in steady-state conduction.

METERING TECHNIQUES

A·5. Pulse Voltmeters.—Several types of pulse-voltmeter circuits have been designed in various laboratories both in this country and abroad. Included among the pulse-voltage indicators that have been reported[1] are balanced bridge circuits or feedback triode amplifiers used in conjunction with high-voltage-input diodes or with resistance or capacitance dividers, and at least one circuit based on an inverted-vacuum-tube principle. The discussion here, however, is confined to a relatively simple pulse-voltmeter circuit that has proved reliable and widely adaptable in pulse-generator work at the Radiation Laboratory and elsewhere, and that can be calibrated directly on d-c voltage. The type of pulse voltmeter described here is adaptable for measurements of approximately rectangular high-voltage pulses

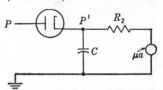

FIG. A·28.—Basic pulse-voltmeter circuit.

having amplitudes ranging up to 30 kv, durations greater than 0.1 μsec, and recurrence frequencies greater than about 100 pps.

The basic circuit of the pulse voltmeter used at the Radiation Laboratory is shown in Fig. A·28. The voltage of peak amplitude V_l to be measured is impressed between point P and ground. When the voltage at P is greater than the voltage V_C at P', the capacitance C charges up through the diode and V_C rises. However, C discharges continuously through R_2, so V_C falls during the interval when the voltage at P is less than V_C. With uniform regularly repeating pulses, V_C approaches an equilibrium state in which the rise produced by the charging through the diode is equal to the fall caused by the discharging through R_2. When the parameters are suitably chosen, the average potential V_a of C can be made very close to V_l, with the result that V_l is given approximately by the product of R_2 and the current indicated by the microammeter.

The following analysis of the circuit leads to an expression for the intrinsic error of the pulse-voltmeter indication in terms of the circuit parameters and the duty ratio of the voltage pulses to be measured. With the aid of this error equation, meters can be designed to give the least error for a particular operating condition. For example, when the

[1] The following references are typical but not all-inclusive:

R. O. McIntosh and J. W. Coltman, "Negative Peak Voltmeter," Westinghouse Research Laboratories, Research Report No. SR-108, Nov. 12, 1941.

"A Standard Voltmeter for Positive and Negative Pulses" U.S. Signal Corps Technical Memorandum No. SPSGS-TRB-3, Mar. 23, 1944.

E. C. S. Megaw, "Recording Pulse Peak Voltmeter for Magnetron Flashing Studies," General Electric Co., Ltd., Report No. 8492, June 4, 1944.

L. U. Hibbard, "Pulse Peak Kilovoltmeter," R.P. 213, Commonwealth of Australia, Council for Scientific and Industrial Research, Division of Radiophysics, Nov. 28, 1944.

R. Rudin, "Development in Peak Voltmeters and Ammeters for Use with Pulsed Magnetrons," BTL Report MM-44-140-68, Sept. 23, 1944.

duty ratio is 0.0002 or higher, parameters can be chosen such that the intrinsic error of the meter indication is less than two per cent. Practical design and operation problems are discussed, and a technique for viewing pulse-voltmeter operation is described.

The term "intrinsic error" is used throughout this discussion to mean the inherently negative error resulting from the impossibility of charging the condenser completely to the voltage of the applied pulses. This error is thus inherent in the circuit design, and is thus distinguished from practical errors produced by the change of

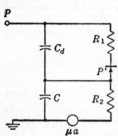

FIG. A·29.—Equivalent circuit for the pulse voltmeter of Fig. A·28.

components and the like. For example, errors of 2 to 10 per cent have been observed that were due to changes in the high resistance caused by heating from the nearby filament of the diode, and/or to inverse leakage current through the diode during the interval between pulses. A pulse voltmeter of this type, like most metering circuits, is sensitive to waveform, and measurements of irregularly shaped pulses can be interpreted properly only if the pulse voltmeter is used in conjunction with auxiliary filtering circuits and with adequate means for viewing both the applied voltage pulses and the pulse-voltmeter operation.

Analysis of Intrinsic Error.—An analysis of the pulse-voltmeter circuit can be made from the equivalent circuit shown in Fig. A·29. In this circuit the diode is represented as a perfect rectifier in series with a resistance

$$R_1 = \frac{V_p}{I_p},$$

where V_p is the tube drop corresponding to the plate current I_p. The capacitance C_d, introduced to represent the diode capacitance, is first assumed negligible, and its effect on the pulse-voltmeter response is treated separately. It is further assumed that the voltage waveform impressed on the pulse voltmeter consists of regularly spaced rectangular pulses as shown in Fig. A·30, with $T_r \gg \tau$. Also, the effect of the discharge

FIG. A·30.—Idealized rectangular voltage waveform.

of the capacitance C through R_2 is neglected in writing the equation for V_C during the pulse.

The waveform of the current through the diode during the pulse is closely approximated by a portion of an exponential charging curve as indicated in Fig. A·31. When the time constant R_1C is large compared with the pulse duration, the current at the beginning and at the end of the pulse does not differ greatly from the average pulse current I_p, and R_1 is very nearly constant. For long pulses where V_C approaches very near to V_l at the end of the pulse, the diode current and R_1 both vary appreciably during the pulse, but a precise knowledge of the magnitude of intrinsic error is of no value because, in this case, the error is less than the other errors inherent in practical design.

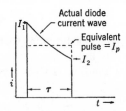

FIG. A·31.—Approximate shape of the current pulse in the diode of Fig. A·28.

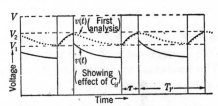

FIG. A·32.—Impressed voltage pulses and resulting voltage on the capacitance C of Fig. A·29 (distorted time scale).

The general shape of the waveform V_C at P' is that shown by the dotted line in Fig. A·32, and the equations describing the charging of C through R_1 during each pulse and the discharging of C through R_2 during each interpulse interval are

$$(V_l - V_2) = (V_l - V_1)e^{-\Delta}, \tag{3}$$

where

$$\Delta = \frac{\tau}{R_1C},$$

and

$$V_1 = V_2e^{-T}, \tag{4}$$

where

$$T = \frac{T_r}{R_2C}.$$

The notation is that of Fig. A·32. Solving Eqs. (3) and (4), V_1 and V_2 are given by

$$V_1 = \frac{V_l(1 - e^{-\Delta})}{e^T - e^{-\Delta}} \tag{5}$$

and

$$V_2 = \frac{V_l(1 - e^{-\Delta})}{(1 - e^{-\Delta - T})}. \tag{6}$$

These equations may be written

$$V_1 = V_l e^{-\frac{T}{2}} \frac{\sinh \frac{\Delta}{2}}{\sinh \frac{T + \Delta}{2}}, \tag{7}$$

and

$$V_2 = V_l e^{+\frac{T}{2}} \frac{\sinh \frac{\Delta}{2}}{\sinh \frac{T + \Delta}{2}}. \tag{8}$$

Thus, if T is small ($R_2 C \gg T_r$), both V_1 and V_2 are nearly equal to V_l, and the average value of V_c is very close to $\frac{1}{2}(V_1 + V_2)$.

The fractional intrinsic error, ϵ_s, in the meter reading is then given to a good approximation by

$$\epsilon_s = \frac{1}{V_l} (V_l - I_m R_2) = \frac{1}{V_l} \left[V_l - \frac{1}{2} (V_2 + V_1) \right]. \tag{9}$$

If Eqs. (7) and (8) are substituted into this expression, the following equation for ϵ_s in terms of the circuit parameters and the duty ratio is obtained:

$$\epsilon_s = 1 - \frac{\sinh \frac{\Delta}{2} \cosh \frac{T}{2}}{\sinh \frac{(T + \Delta)}{2}}, \tag{10}$$

which may be simplified to

$$\epsilon_s = \left(1 + \frac{\tanh \frac{\Delta}{2}}{\tanh \frac{T}{2}} \right)^{-1} = \left(1 + \frac{\tanh \frac{\tau}{2 R_1 C}}{\tanh \frac{T_r}{2 R_2 C}} \right)^{-1}. \tag{11}$$

When plotted as a function of C, ϵ_s varies in the manner indicated in Fig. A·33. The minimum value of ϵ_s is

$$\epsilon_{so} = \lim_{C \to \infty} \epsilon_s = \left(1 + \frac{\Delta}{T} \right)^{-1} = \left(1 + \frac{\tau R_2}{T_r R_1} \right)^{-1}. \tag{12}$$

Evidently, best results at any given duty ratio can be obtained with the maximum values of C and of R_2/R_1. It is usually possible to choose R_2 greater than $R_1 T_r / \tau$. Examination of the expression for ϵ_s reveals that ϵ_s is then less than or approximately equal to $1.1 \epsilon_{so}$ if C is greater than τ/R_1. Therefore, a simpler expression can be used for practical design and correction calculations, namely,

$$\epsilon_s \approx \left(1 + \frac{\tau R_2}{T_r R_1}\right)^{-1} \approx \frac{T_r R_1}{\tau R_2}, \tag{13}$$

where

$$C > \frac{\tau}{R_1} \qquad \text{and} \qquad \tau R_2 \gg T_r R_1.$$

The difference between the value given by the right-hand member of Eq. (13) and the value given by Eq. (11) is less than or approximately equal to 0.1 $(\epsilon_s - \epsilon_s^2)$.

It has been assumed in the above analysis that the capacitance of the diode has a negligible effect on pulse-voltmeter operation, which is equivalent to assuming that C_d/C is small compared with the fractional error in the meter reading. In some cases this is not true. As a result of capacitance-divider action between C and C_d, there are sudden approximately equal and opposite changes in V_C at the beginning and at the end of the period of diode conduction. The true waveform of V_C is therefore not that shown by the dotted line in Fig. A·32, but that shown by the solid line. The magnitude of the voltage change pro-

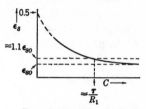

Fig. A·33.—The intrinsic error, ϵ_s, in the meter reading as a function of the capacitance C.

duced by the capacitance-divider effect is $C_d V_l/C$, and for low duty ratios the fractional error in the voltmeter reading is increased to

$$\epsilon \approx \frac{T_r R_1}{\tau R_2} + \frac{C_d}{C}, \tag{14}$$

where

$$C > \frac{\tau}{R_1} \qquad \text{and} \qquad R_2 \tau \gg T_r R_1.$$

If the voltage wave impressed on the pulse voltmeter has a backswing that is appreciable in magnitude and duration, the error contribution of the capacitance-divider effect is increased slightly.

The procedure for evaluating ϵ for a particular pulse-voltmeter reading, V_a, is shown by the following calculation of the error in a typical pulse voltmeter using a GL-8020 diode. If $V_a = 10^4$ volts, $R_2 = 500$ megohms, $C_d = 6$ $\mu\mu$f (including estimated circuit capacitance), $T_r = 2 \times 10^{-3}$ sec, $\tau = 0.5 \times 10^{-6}$ sec, and $C = 1000$ $\mu\mu$f, the pulse current through the diode is

$$I_p \approx \frac{V_a T_r}{R_2 \tau} \approx 0.080 \text{ amp.}$$

The diode resistance R_1 corresponding to this current is found from the diode-plate characteristic (Fig. A·34) to be 2120 ohms.   Since the conditions $C > \tau/R_1$ and $R_2\tau \gg T_r R_1$ are satisfied, ϵ is given by Eq. (14).

$$\epsilon = \frac{(2)(10^{-3})(2120)}{(5)(10^8)(0.5)(10^{-6})} + \frac{6(10^{-12})}{10^{-9}} = 0.023 = 2.3 \text{ per cent.}$$

The calculated and measured errors in typical pulse-voltmeter measurements are plotted in Fig. A·35 for various operating conditions.   The measured error was obtained by subtracting the pulse-voltmeter readings from those obtained with a synchroscope and a capacitance divider. The capacitance divider was calibrated (with an estimated maximum error of ± 1 per cent) against a standard resistance divider. The pulse-voltmeter was calibrated by a d-c voltage measured with a precision 0- to

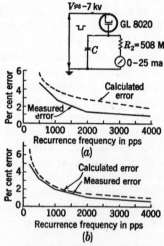

FIG. A·35.—Pulse-voltmeter error curves, (a) pulse duration: 0.11 μsec, $C = 0.00115$ μf, (b) pulse duration: 0.19 μsec, $C = 0.05$ μf.

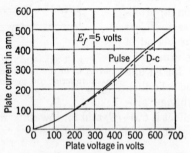

FIG. A·34.—Plate-current—plate-voltage characteristic of type GL-8020 diode.

1.0-ma meter and a standard 25-megohm multiplier.   The high-voltage source was connected to the point P' of the pulse voltmeter in order to avoid any errors caused by the power-supply ripple and the rectifying action of the diode.

Design and Operation.—Practical design considerations dictate that R_2 be made as large as possible, consistent with the current meters available.   For measuring voltages up to 12,500 volts, it is convenient to use a 0- to 25-μa meter with $R_2 = 500$ megohms.   For pulses from 0.1 μsec to 2.0 μsecs and duty ratios as low as 0.0002, the intrinsic error is less than 2 per cent for all values of C greater than 1000 $\mu\mu$f, provided that the values of R_1 and C_d for the diode are comparable to those for the GL-8020.   To extend the range up to 25,000 volts, a 0- to 50-μa meter may be used, or R_2 may be made equal to 1000 megohms.

Because of its high inverse-voltage rating (40 kv), the GL-8020 diode is preferred to other diodes that may have a lower tube drop. The WE-719A gave excellent results below 8 kv, but larger errors occurred at 10 kv or higher because of inverse leakage currents. This tube also has a larger value of C_d than the GL-8020.

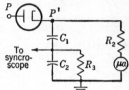

Useful qualitative information concerning pulse-voltmeter operation can be obtained from a simple scheme for viewing the incremental voltage on C during the pulse. The single capacitance C is replaced by two capacitances in series, C_1 and C_2 (see Fig. A·36), the latter being shunted by a resistance R_3 of such value that the time constant R_3C_2 is short compared with T_r, but very long compared with τ.

FIG. A·36.—Pulse-voltmeter with circuit for viewing the voltage on the capacitance C.

The synchroscope is connected across C_2, and the voltage divider thus created presents a signal voltage

$$v_s = \frac{C_1}{C_1 + C_2}\,(v_C - v_1),$$

which is a reasonably accurate representation of the incremental voltage waveform on C_1 when the diode is conducting. During the rise and fall of the applied voltage pulse, when the diode is not conducting, the signal is influenced by the capacitance C_d of the diode which, together with C_1 and C_2, acts as another voltage divider. In practice, the applied pulse is usually more nearly trapezoidal than rectangular in form, and typical signals appear as shown in the photographs in Fig. A·37. The curvature of the signal is a qualitative indication of the degree to which V_2 approaches V_l during the pulse, and the amplitude is an indication of the loss of voltage on C_1 during the interval between pulses. The incremental voltage signal becomes nearly flat on top if V_2 approaches very near to V_l.

For example, in Fig. A·37 trace a is the 0.25-μsec pulse (measured at the top) that was impressed on the pulse voltmeter. Traces b, c, and d indicate the effect of successively increasing recurrence frequencies, showing correspondingly decreasing errors. Traces b, f, and j show a comparison of the incremental voltages for a recurrence frequency of 500 pps with pulse durations increasing from 0.25 to 1.0 μsec. As the pulse duration increases, the signal becomes successively flatter, which shows a decreasing error in the meter indication.

An undesirable spike or, in some cases, high-frequency oscillations may be present on the leading edge of the voltage pulse that is to be measured. Such transients tend to cause the pulse-voltmeter reading to be too high, unless some form of filtering is employed. A simple remedy is to insert an extra resistance in series with the lead between the diode and the source of pulse voltage. The RC-filter comprised of this "despiking" resistor and the total capacitance to ground (capacitance C_s of the high-voltage-lead and the diode-plate connector added to the series value of C_d, C_1, and C_2) is very effective. However, great care

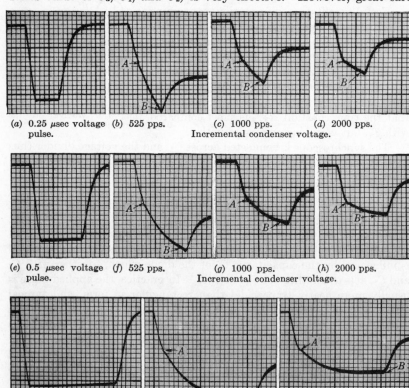

(a) 0.25 μsec voltage   (b) 525 pps.   (c) 1000 pps.   (d) 2000 pps.
    pulse.   Incremental condenser voltage.

(e) 0.5 μsec voltage   (f) 525 pps.   (g) 1000 pps.   (h) 2000 pps.
    pulse.   Incremental condenser voltage.

(i) 1 μsec voltage pulse.   (j) 525 pps.   (k) 1000 pps.
                                   Incremental condenser voltage.

FIG. A·37.—Negative voltage pulses impressed on a pulse voltmeter and the corresponding incremental voltages at various pulse durations and recurrence frequencies. The incremental voltage is shown by the trace between points (A) and (B).

must be taken to insert only the minimum additional resistance required for filtering, because any increase in R_1 raises the intrinsic error of the pulse voltmeter. It is helpful to employ the previously mentioned viewing scheme to insure that R_1 is not increased too much by the addition of the series despiking resistor. To ascertain whether or not the filtered pulse is "clean," a capacitance divider may be connected across the pulse voltmeter, as indicated in Fig. A·38, and the signal viewed on the screen of a cathode-ray tube.   Figure A·39 shows a representative pulse before and after filtering.

It must be noted that this divider actually becomes a part of the filter and, if it is removed after serving its viewing purpose, it should be replaced by an equivalent capacitance.   In some cases, it may prove more expedient to add a small amount of capacitance to ground in order to increase the filtering rather than to

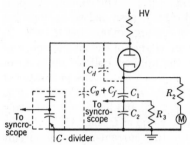

FIG. A·38.—Complete schematic diagram of diode pulse-voltmeter circuit, including despiking filter.

FIG. A·39.—Representative pulse before and after filtering.

add more resistance.   This practice also requires caution against loading the circuit whose voltage is being measured.   When the diode is reversed for reading negative pulses, the capacitance of the filament transformer becomes a part of the filter.

A·6. The Average-current Meter.—The obvious simple expedient for measuring average current in a pulse circuit is to connect a conventional current meter of suitable range in parallel with a large capacitance.   The magnitude of the capacitance required is determined by the internal impedance of the pulse generator, the pulse duration, the voltage-current characteristic of the load through which the pulse current flows, and certain physical properties of the meter.   To guard against disturbance of the pulse-generator circuit by an average-current-metering circuit that is connected in series with a nonlinear load, either the static or the dynamic impedance of the load (whichever is smaller) must be considered.   In practice, it is sometimes advisable to insert additional resistance and/or inductance in series with the meter as a further protection against surges of current that may

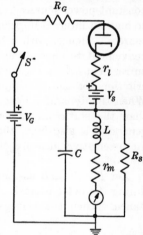

FIG. A·40.—Schematic diagram of pulse-discharging circuit including the equivalent circuit for a magnetron and an average-current meter.

injure it.   A resistor is usually connected in shunt with the meter to ground the load in case of meter burnout.

As a typical problem, consider the circuit shown in Fig. A·40.   The diode, the battery V_s, and the resistor r_l form the conventional equivalent circuit for a magnetron input.   The value V_s is the voltage intercept of a line tangent to the load voltage-current characteristic at the operating point (see Fig. A·41).   The dynamic imped-

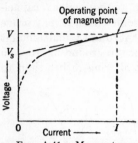

ance $r_l = \Delta V_l/\Delta I_l$ is assumed to be constant over a small operating range.   Let $R_l = V_l/I_l$ be the static impedance of the magnetron, and assume that the applied voltage pulse V_l of duration τ is supplied by a pulse generator of internal impedance R_G.   From Fig. A·41 it is evident that $r_l < R_l$, and hence it is necessary to determine a value of C that will make the

Fig. A·41.—Magnetron voltage-current characteristic under pulse conditions.

impedance of the current-metering circuit small compared with $r_l + R_G$ for the duration of the pulse.

Most hard-tube pulsers used in radar applications have relatively low internal impedances ($R_G \approx r_l$), and line-type pulsers have internal imped-ances of the same order of magnitude as the magnetron static impedance R_l.   For small changes in load impedance, therefore, hard-tube and line-type pulsers can be considered essentially as constant-voltage sources and constant-power sources, respectively.   Few, if any, pulse generators have so high an internal impedance that they are effectively constant-current sources.   Hence, with a load that has a low dynamic impedance, it is convenient to choose the ratio $\Delta I_l/I_l$, the fractional change (droop) in current caused by the increase in voltage on C during the pulse, as the criterion for the maximum tolerable disturbance of circuit behavior.   When the dynamic impedance of the load is high, perhaps even greater than the static impedance, and the internal impedance of the pulse generator is also high, the fractional change in load voltage may be a more sensitive measure of circuit disturbance caused by the metering unit.

Let $L = 0$, and assume that the charge flowing through the meter during the pulse is small compared with the charge stored in the capac-itance.   Then the voltage increment on C is given approximately by

$$\Delta v_C = \frac{I_l \tau}{C}, \qquad (15)$$

where I_l is the average magnitude of pulse current.

Actually, the voltage rise on C is appreciably less than the value indicated in Eq. (15), unless the time constant $r_m C$ is very large compared with the pulse duration τ.   However, Eq. (15) leads to a safe value for all cases, regardless of the value of r_m.

If a constant pulser voltage V_l is assumed, the decrease in load current caused by the voltage increment Δv_C is

$$\Delta I_l = \frac{\Delta v_C}{r_l + R_G}, \tag{16}$$

and, combining Eqs. (15) and (16),

$$C = \frac{\tau}{(r_l + R_G)} \frac{I_l}{\Delta I_l} \tag{17}$$

If the metering circuit is permitted to cause a 1 per cent change (droop) in the current, the minimum value of C is given by

$$C \approx \frac{100\tau}{r_l + R_G}, \tag{18}$$

As an example, let $\tau = 10^{-6}$ sec, $r_l = 100$ ohms, and $R_G = 150$ ohms. Then C must be at least 0.4 μf in order to insure that the ratio $\Delta I_l / I_l$ is less than 0.01. The value of R_s is not critical, but should be very large compared with r_m, unless the meter and shunt are calibrated together on direct current.

Although a value of C determined by Eq. (16) satisfies the criterion for the disturbance of the circuit behavior, it is also necessary to consider whether a capacitance of this value is sufficient to protect the meter adequately. The peak surge current through the meter during normal operation of pulser and load is

$$I_m \approx I_l \left(1 - e^{-\frac{\tau}{r_m C}}\right), \tag{19}$$

whereas the average value of direct current indicated by the meter is

$$I_{av} = I_l \tau f_r, \tag{20}$$

where f_r is the pulse recurrence frequency. The ratio sI_m / I_{av} is a measure of the overload imposed on the meter, where s is the fraction of the full-scale deflection indicated by the meter when it reads I_{av}, and is given by

$$S = \frac{sI_m}{I_{av}} = \frac{s\left(1 - e^{-\frac{\tau}{r_m C}}\right)}{\tau f_r} \tag{21}$$

For example, if $r_m = 10$ ohms, $C = 0.4$ μf, $\tau = 1.0$ μsec, $f_r = 1000$ pps, and the meter indicates a half-scale deflection, the calculated value of S is about 110. Although manufacturers' ratings generally do not include specifications of this surge ratio, experience has shown that it is advisable to keep the ratio considerably lower than 100. The magnitude of S may be lowered either by choosing a capacitance that is several times larger than the minimum value given by Eq. (18), or by adding a resistance in series with the meter to increase the effective value of r_m. Several current meters in common use with scales up to 15 ma, 25 ma, or 50 ma gave measured values of r_m ranging from 25 ohms to 2 ohms. The "thermal inertia" of the winding and the mechanical inertia of the movement of most conventional milliameters are appreciable, and surge ratios up to about 50 seem to be reasonably safe at short pulse durations of the order of magnitude of a microsecond or less. However, for long pulses or delicate meters, a surge ratio of 50 may be too high.

The quality of paper or electrolytic condensers used for high capacitances may be somewhat questionable. Consequently, to insure good high-frequency response to pulses with steep wavefronts, a second small capacitance of high quality, usually mica or silver ceramic, is sometimes connected in parallel with the larger condenser.

The use of an inductance in series with the meter should not be necessary during normal operation of a pulse generator with a stable load. In certain cases, however, instability of the load, for example, magnetron sparking, may result in abnormally large unpredictable surges of current. With a hard-tube pulser, the current during a magnetron spark is limited only by the emission of the pulser switch tube; occasionally the switch tube sparks also, allowing the current to become many times the normal value. In such cases an inductance is inserted in the metering circuit as shown in Fig. A·40 to provide added protection for the meter. To be effective, the time constant L/r_m should be large compared with the pulse duration. The values of r_m and R_s also should be chosen properly in order to prevent post-pulse oscillations in the meter circuit. To satisfy these conditions it may not be possible to make $R_s \gg r_m$. Hence, the entire unit should be calibrated on direct current.

A magnetron or an equivalent rectifying load does not conduct appreciably in either direction when the voltage across it is less than a threshold value V_s (see Fig. A·41). Therefore, since the voltage v_C on C is always small compared with V_s, the metering circuit may be isolated for an analysis to determine the conditions which must be fulfilled to prevent post-pulse oscillations.

The part of the circuit comprising C, r_m, L, and R_s of Fig. A·40 may be analyzed in the same manner as that used for the circuit of Fig. 2·22. In the latter case the Laplace-transform equation for the voltage across the shunt condenser was shown to be given by Eq. (2·36) and from this equation the condition for oscillation is determined. In the present case it is of interest to determine the value of R_s associated with the meter in Fig. A·40 which will make the circuit critically damped. This value of R_s must satisfy Condition 2 of Eq. (2·43), namely,

$$b = a^2 \tag{2·43}$$

where a and b are given by Eqs. (2·38) and (2·39) and in the notation of

Fig. A·40 these become,

$$2a = \frac{r_m}{L} + \frac{1}{R_s C}, \tag{22}$$

and

$$b = \frac{1}{LC} + \frac{r_m}{R_s LC}. \tag{23}$$

From Eqs. (22), (23), and Condition (2·43) there is obtained,

$$R_s = \frac{L}{C} \left(\frac{1}{r_m \pm 2\sqrt{\frac{L}{C}}} \right). \tag{24}$$

There are now two cases of interest depending on the value of r_m relative to $2\sqrt{L/C}$.

Case 1 . . . $r_m < 2\sqrt{L/C}$

Under this condition oscillations in the loop containing C, r_m, and L are possible for $R_s = \infty$, a familiar circumstance. Equation (24) gives one positive value and one negative value for R_s. The negative value has no significance in this problem for obvious reasons, and the positive value determines the only condition for critical damping. Any value of R_s less than this positive value will insure overdamping in this case.

Case 2 . . . $r_m > 2\sqrt{L/C}$

When this condition is satisfied the circuit is aperiodic with $R_s = \infty$. However, Eq. (24) reveals the interesting fact that R_s has two positive values when $r_m > 2\sqrt{L/C}$, and hence that the circuit is critically damped for two values of R_s. Oscillation is possible for any R_s between the two critical values. When the time constants $L/r_m = R_s C$, the circuit oscillates with its minimum period $T = 2\pi\sqrt{LC}$.

In designing a meter protective circuit where the values of C, r_m, and L have been chosen in accordance with Case 2, it is advisable to make R_s larger than the greater value determined by Eq. (24). In fact, R_s can be chosen large enough to obviate the necessity of calibrating the circuit as a whole.

To illustrate the above considerations two numerical examples are given:

1. Let $L = 1$ mh, $C = 2$ μf, and $r_m = 15$ ohms. Substituting these values into Eq. (24), the values of R_s are found to be,

$$R_s = 500/(15 \pm 10\sqrt{5})$$
$$= 13.4 \text{ or } -67.8 \text{ ohms}.$$

This example comes under Case 1 and the circuit is aperiodic for any value of R_s less than 13.4 ohms. The negative value is disregarded.

2. Using the same values of L and C, let $r_m = 25$ ohms. Then the two values of R_s are

$$R_s = 500/(25 \pm 10 \sqrt{5})$$
$$= 10.6 \text{ or } 189 \text{ ohms.}$$

This example is representative of Case 2. Any value of R_s greater than 189 ohms or less than 10.6 ohms will insure adequate damping, but the practical matter of calibration suggests a preferred value of $R_s \gg 25$ ohms. Note that $L/r_m = 40$ μsec, which indicates that the meter-current surge ratio is now reduced to less than 3 per cent of the ratio that exists when L is negligible in the circuit.

The principles outlined in this section have been written for a meter circuit connected directly in series with a pulse-generator load that acts as a rectifier. In some applications, it may be more convenient to connect the metering unit in some other position, for example, in series with a pulse transformer. When this is done, there is one further precaution that should be observed. There must be a proper rectifying element in series with the meter to eliminate the errors caused by interpulse currents that recharge either the stray capacitance or the pulse-generator storage condenser, and that have a net flow in the direction opposite to the pulse current. Another alternative is to connect the average-current meter into the pulse-generator circuit in such a way that only the charging current is measured. When the meter is thus isolated from the pulse current, the problem of meter protection is simplified, but the meter reading may not be a reliable indication of the actual load current because of shunt losses produced by the stray capacitance in the pulse-generator discharging circuit.

A·7. Auxiliary Measuring Techniques.—*R-f Envelope Viewer and Spectrum Analyzer.*—There are two methods that are most commonly used for examining the r-f pulse-voltage envelope. One method is to connect an r-f probe through a voltage divider to a square-law detector, and to feed the rectified voltage through a suitable video amplifier to the plates of the cathode-ray tube in a synchroscope.

The other method is to feed a relatively large portion of the r-f power into a lighthouse cavity detector[1] and to present the output rectified voltage directly on the plates of the cathode-ray tube of a synchroscope. This method is superior for precision laboratory measurements because no video amplifier is required, and because the response can be made reasonably good for frequencies up to about 50 Mc/sec as the bandwidth is determined chiefly by the resonant Q of the cavity and the distributed capacitance.

[1] P. A. Cole, J. B. H. Kuper, and K. R. More, "Lighthouse R.P. Envelope Indicator," RL Report No. 542, Apr. 7, 1944.

The type of spectrum analyzer developed at the Radiation Laboratory consists essentially of a narrow-band receiver with a square-law detector, an audio-frequency sawtooth-voltage source that frequency modulates the local oscillator and supplies the CRT sweep, and an oscilloscope. The local oscillator is of the cavity reflector type (usually a Klystron, a McNally tube, or a Shepherd tube) and has an approximately linear frequency response as a function of reflector voltage. The r-f power is supplied from a directional coupler or probe in the waveguide output of a magnetron (or other oscillator) through a suitable voltage divider. As the local-oscillator frequency varies, the CRT spot moves across the screen, and the power received during successive pulses causes the spot to trace a line-amplitude spectrum. Actually, this spectrum is very nearly the absolute value of the power spectrum. For pulses of duration shorter than 2 μsec, an r-f bandwidth of 10 kc/sec in the receiver of the spectrum analyzer is satisfactory. To obtain the best results with 5-μsec pulses, a considerably narrower band is required.[1]

A spectrum analyzer is used to determine whether or not pulses that droop, or are otherwise irregular in shape, cause serious frequency modulation of a pulsed oscillator. It is also used to measure the effective pulse duration, since the r-f bandwidth measured between pairs of minima on the spectrum is inversely proportional to the pulse duration of the current and the r-f envelope (see Appendix B). This application is especially important when very short pulse durations of less than 0.1 μsec are used, where it is difficult to produce good pulse shapes and to obtain reliable measurements of pulse duration with a linear time base, but where the width of the significant part of the r-f spectrum is greater than 10 Mc/sec.

Impulse Counting.—When abnormal load behavior, such as magnetron sparking, causes random pulse currents of abnormally high amplitude in a pulse-generator circuit, it is sometimes desirable to count the recurrences of all pulses having amplitudes exceeding a predetermined value. Conventional scaling circuits with minor circuit modifications and special

---

[1] For a detailed description of such a spectrum analyzer and operating instructions, see the instruction manual, "Spectrum Analyzer (Type 103) for Pulsed Oscillators at 3,000 Mc/sec," RL Report No. M-115, Nov. 18, 1942.

Criteria for evaluating pulse spectra for magnetrons are discussed in the following reports:

R. T. Young, Jr., "Fourier Analysis of Pulses with Frequency Shifts During the Pulse," RL Report No. 52-5, Jan. 30, 1943.

R. T. Young, Jr., "Frequency and Spectrum Characteristics of Standard Magnetrons and the Effect of Change of Shape of Current Pulse," RL Report No. 52-6, Mar. 12, 1943.

G. N. Glasoe, "Pulse Shapes and RF Spectra for Combinations of Stromberg-Carlson Mark I and Mark II Modulators with 2J22, 2J21, and 725A Magnetrons,"RL Report No. 518, Mar. 17, 1944.

shielding have been adapted for recording pulses of durations up to 5 μsec at recurrence frequencies of less than 1000 pps.

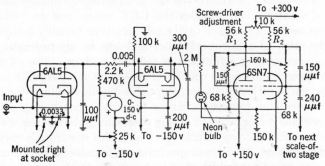

FIG. A·42.—Schematic diagram of a spark counter showing the input and the first stage.

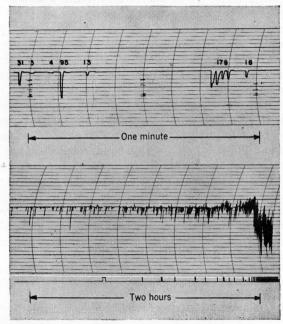

FIG. A·43.—Records of average magnetron current showing sparking as a function of time.

For counting magnetron sparks, it was found advisable to provide a bias threshold adjustment on the input stage. A "pulse-stretching" circuit was introduced at the output of the first diode to insure uniform sensitivity of the counter for pulse durations from about 0.1 μsec to 5 μsec. It was also necessary to insert a pulse-amplitude limiter at the input of the first scaling stage in order to prevent the second stage from being tripped directly by pulses of high amplitude at the first stage.   The input circuits and one stage of a typical scaling circuit are shown in Fig. A·42. The output of the last stage is usually connected to an electromechanical counter.

For indicating bursts of sparking recorded over longer periods of time a recording milliameter is useful.   Two sample records are shown on Fig. A·43.   On the upper strip the tape was run at high speed, and the approximate numbers of individual sparks per indicated burst are printed near the current peaks on the record.   The tape was moving from right to left and the current amplitude increased downward.   On the lower record, the tape was running much more slowly, as indicated, and the rate of sparking became excessive as the magnetron approached the end of life.   The bursts of sparking usually cause increases in current (downward), but there is evidence of magnetron mode-changing with occasional decreases in current (upward peaks), especially during the last hour of life.   The marks along the lower border of the tape were produced by connecting a second recording pen to the output of the electromechanical counter on a scale-of-16 pulse counter to indicate every 1600 sparks of the magnetron.

APPENDIX B

PULSE DURATION AND AMPLITUDE

By W. H. Bostick and J. V. Lebacqz

Among the most important parameters in the rating of pulse generators are pulse amplitude and pulse duration. In Chap. 1 it is stated that a pulse is the departure of some electrical quantity—voltage, current or power—from zero or from some equilibrium value. In general, the pulse is repeated at regular intervals, and for all practical considerations, the pulse duration is very short compared with the interpulse interval. There are a few exceptions, such as the "coded" pulses, in which a series of short pulses have a short time interval between them, but the code is repeated at relatively long time intervals.

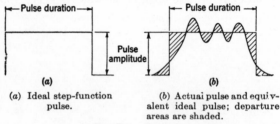

(a) Ideal step-function pulse.

(b) Actual pulse and equivalent ideal pulse; departure areas are shaded.

Fig. B·1.—Pulse shapes.

The concepts of pulse duration and pulse amplitude are very straightforward in the case of an ideal step-function pulse (Fig. B·1a); there can be no ambiguity in the definition of either, since the variable changes instantaneously from zero to a constant value that is the pulse amplitude and, after a time τ (the pulse duration) returns instantaneously to a value of zero. In practice, unfortunately, an ideal step-function pulse cannot be realized, and the value of pulse duration becomes indeterminate without an adequate definition. Since most pulsers have been designed to produce a pulse that approximates as closely as possible a step-function or rectangular pulse shape, it is only natural that, in the consideration of practical pulses, most of the definitions of pulse duration and pulse amplitude are in terms of an equivalent rectangular pulse.

There have been many attempts at definitions, and the problem is complicated by the fact that pulser loads can be either pure resistances or oscillators whose characteristics approximate those of a biased diode.

For instance, the pulse duration on a magnetron load has been variously defined as the duration of the voltage pulse at 90 per cent of the average maximum voltage amplitude, or as the duration of the current pulse at 50 per cent of the average maximum current amplitude. These definitions may be satisfactory in some cases, but the "average maximum current amplitude" of a current pulse that is in the general form of a half sine wave, for example, is meaningless.

The purpose of this appendix is to discuss several methods for determining average pulse amplitude and pulse duration that are based on equivalence of some quantities of the actual pulse and those of an assumed rectangular pulse. From the point of view of pulser output alone, the most important quantities are charge and energy; hence, an equivalent rectangular pulse constructed on the basis of equal charge—or average current—and equal energy per pulse can be used to define the pulse amplitude and duration.

In radar applications, however, one criterion of satisfactory operation of the transmitter is generally the width of the r-f spectrum. Since, for a rectangular pulse, there is a definite relationship between the pulse duration and the spectrum width at one-half power, the duration of a rectangular pulse equivalent to any actual pulse shape can be determined by r-f spectrum considerations. The second section of this appendix considers the possibility of the use of spectrum equivalence in determining pulse duration.

The equivalent rectangular pulses determined for a given pulse shape by different types of equivalence are not the same; the more nearly the actual pulse shape approximates a rectangular pulse, the more nearly equal are the values of pulse duration and amplitude obtained by the different methods of equivalence. If the difference in the results obtained by the different methods is appreciable, the choice of the definition is determined by considering the particular purpose for which the definition is being used.

B·1. Equivalent Rectangular Pulse by Conservation of Charge and Energy.—The general case of a load that can be represented by a biased diode is represented in Fig. B·2. If a current $i_l(t)$ flows in the load, the instantaneous power absorbed by the load is given by

$$p_l(t) = [V_s + r_l i_l(t)]i_l(t). \tag{1}$$

If only one pulse is assumed to be applied to this load, the equivalent rectangular pulse of current I_l, power P_l, and duration τ, is defined by an equation, for the conservation of energy,

$$P_l\tau = \int_{-\infty}^{\infty} p_l(t)\, dt \tag{2}$$

and an equation for conservation of charge,

$$I_l\tau = \int_{-\infty}^{\infty} i_l(t)\, dt,\qquad(3)$$

and by the load relation in Eq. (1), which is assumed to be valid for any

(a) Equivalent circuit.   (b) Voltage-current characteristics.

Fig. B·2.—Biased-diode load for pulser.

value of current.   The equivalent pulse voltage is then

$$V_l = \frac{P_l}{I_l}.$$

If the instantaneous power can be written

$$p_l(t) = P_l f(t)$$

and is zero at any time except when $0 < t < \tau_a$, Eq. (2) becomes

$$\tau = \int_0^{\tau_a} f(t)\, dt.\qquad(4)$$

Of course, P_l and I_l are not yet known, but they can be obtained by solving Eqs. (1), (2), and (3). Also, as it is assumed that Eq. (1) is valid for any value of current,

$$P_l = (V_s + r_l I_l)I_l,$$

or

$$I_l^2 + \frac{V_s}{r_l} I_l - \frac{P_l}{r_l} = 0,$$

or

$$I_l = -\frac{V_s}{2r_l} \pm \sqrt{\left(\frac{V_s}{2r_l}\right)^2 + \frac{P_l}{r_l}}.$$

Similarly,

$$i_l(t) = -\frac{V_s}{2r_l} \pm \sqrt{\left(\frac{V_s}{2r_l}\right)^2 + \frac{P_l}{r_l} f(t)}.$$

If these values are introduced in Eq. (3),

$$\left(\frac{V_s}{2r_l} \pm \sqrt{\left(\frac{V_s}{2r_l}\right)^2 + \frac{P_l}{r_l}}\right)\tau = \int_0^{\tau_a} \left(\frac{V_s}{2r_l} \pm \sqrt{\left(\frac{V_s}{2r_l}\right)^2 + \frac{P_l}{r_l} f(t)}\right) dt,\qquad(5)$$

or

$$\left(1 \pm \sqrt{1 + \frac{4P_l r_l}{V_s^2}}\right)\tau = \int_0^{\tau_a} \left(1 \pm \sqrt{1 + \frac{4P_l r_l}{V_s^2} f(t)}\right) dt. \tag{6}$$

Equations (6) and (4) each separately determine the pulse duration τ as a function of the assumed equivalent pulse power P_l; hence, after the integrations have been performed, values for τ and P_l can be obtained algebraically by solving Eqs. (4) and (6) simultaneously. For a pure-resistance load $V_s = 0$, and Eq. (5) becomes

$$\tau = \int_0^{\tau_a} \sqrt{f(t)}\, dt. \tag{7}$$

The above method of uniquely determining τ and P_l breaks down if the load resistance r_l becomes zero, for then Eqs. (2) and (3) are identical, and any pulse duration can satisfy the conditions of equivalence of energy and charge. This lack of uniqueness when $r_l = 0$ is a disadvantage of the foregoing method because most magnetrons have a small value of r_l, and the resulting power pulse is not very different from the current pulse. As a result, great care must be taken to obtain satisfactory accuracy in the determination of τ.

Three examples of the use of the above method are now given: the pulse duration and amplitude of a triangular and of a sinusoidal power pulse are given first, and a practical application to the determination of equivalent rectangular pulses of actual magnetron load pulse shapes follows.

Triangular Power Pulse on a Pure-resistance Load.—The instantaneous power during the first half of the pulse of Fig. B·3 is given by

$$p_l(t) = \frac{2P_m}{\tau_a} t;$$

hence,

$$f(t) = \frac{2P_m}{P_l \tau_a} t.$$

If $f(t)$ is introduced in Eq. (4),

$$\tau = \frac{4P_m}{P_l \tau_a} \int_0^{\tau_a/2} t\, dt = \frac{P_m}{2P_l} \tau_a,$$

and Eq. (7) gives

$$\tau = 2\sqrt{\frac{2P_m}{P_l \tau_a}} \int_0^{\tau_a/2} \sqrt{t}\, dt$$

$$= 2\sqrt{\frac{2P_m}{P_l \tau_a}} \frac{2}{3} t^{3/2} \Big|_0^{\tau_a/2} = \frac{2}{3}\sqrt{\frac{P_m}{P_l}} \tau_a.$$

If the two expressions for pulse duration are equated,

$$\frac{P_m}{2P_l} = \frac{2}{3}\sqrt{\frac{P_m}{P_l}},$$

or

$$P_l = \tfrac{9}{16}P_m$$

and

$$\tau = \tfrac{8}{9}\tau_a.$$

Sinusoidal Power Pulse on a Pure-resistance Load.—The expression for instantaneous power for the pulse of Fig. B·4 is

$$p_l(t) = P_m \sin\frac{\pi t}{\tau_a}.$$

Hence

$$f(t) = \frac{P_m}{P_l}\sin\frac{\pi t}{\tau_a}.$$

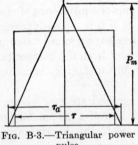

Fig. B·3.—Triangular power pulse.

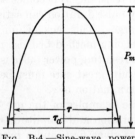

Fig. B·4.—Sine-wave power pulse.

The relations between the duration and amplitude of the equivalent rectangular pulse on a resistance load can again be obtained from Eqs. (4) and (7)

$$\tau = \frac{P_m}{P_l}\int_0^{\tau_a}\sin\frac{\pi t}{\tau_a}\,dt = \frac{P_m}{P_l}\frac{2\tau_a}{\pi},$$

$$\tau = \sqrt{\frac{P_m}{P_l}}\int_0^{\tau_a}\sqrt{\sin\frac{\pi t}{\tau_a}}\,dt = 1.194\frac{2\tau_a}{\pi}\sqrt{\frac{P_m}{P_l}}.$$

By equating these expressions for pulse duration, the relationship

$$P_l = \frac{P_m}{(1.194)^2} = 0.7P_m$$

is obtained.   Then

$$\tau = (1.194)^2\frac{2}{\pi}\tau_a = \frac{10}{11}\tau_a.$$

Pulses on Magnetron and Resistance Loads.—The above method permits the determination of the equivalent rectangular pulse for any pulse produced by an actual pulse-forming network.   As typical examples, consider the voltage and current pulse shape, and the power pulse shape

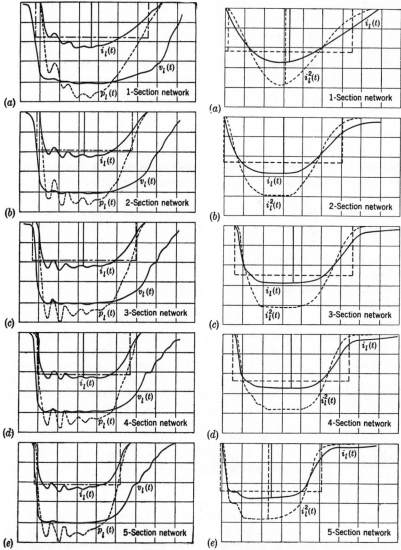

FIG. B·5.—Voltage, current, and computed power pulses in an HK7 magnetron, (a) with a 1-section pulse-forming network, (b) with a 2-section pulse-forming network, (c) with a 3-section pulse-forming network, (d) with a 4-section pulse-forming network, (e) with a 5-section pulse-forming network.

FIG. B·6.—Current and computed power pulses on resistance load, (a) with a 1-section pulse-forming network, (b) with a 2-section pulse-forming network, (c) with a 3-section pulse-forming network, (d), with a 4-section pulse-forming network, and (e) with a 5-section pulse-forming network.

obtained by calculation of the product of instantaneous observed pulse voltage and instantaneous observed pulse current shown in Fig. B·5 for one-, two-, three-, four-, and five-section networks operating into a magnetron load. The values of τ, I_l and P_l have been calculated for each case as follows, the only assumption being that the current is a single-valued function of voltage. First, the integrations indicated in Eqs. (2) and (3) are performed graphically. Then the ratio

$$\frac{P_l \tau}{I_l \tau} = V_l$$

is calculated. The value of I_l corresponding to this value of V_l may be obtained by finding a point on the voltage pulse at which the instantaneous voltage is equal to this value, and determining the value of instantaneous current at that instant from the corresponding current pulse. With the values of V_l and I_l known, the values of τ and P_l may be calculated readily. The equivalent rectangles thus determined are indicated in the Fig. B·5. All equivalent rectangles are so placed on the diagrams that a vertical line bisecting the rectangles will also bisect the area of the actual pulse shape.

Similar calculations have been carried through for the pulses produced on a pure-resistance load by the same networks. Instantaneous current and power pulse shapes, the latter obtained by squaring the instantaneous current, and the resulting equivalent rectangles, are shown in Fig. B·6.

B·2. Equivalent Rectangular Pulse by Minimum Departure Areas.— The method of minimum departure area is an attempt to predetermine an

FIG. B·7.—Determination of minimum departure areas for a triangular pulse.

equivalent rectangular pulse that has the same energy as the actual pulse and produces a spectrum distribution equal to that of the actual pulse over the most significant part of the spectrum, that is, down to at least the half-power point.

For simple pulse shapes, it can be shown that the spectrum distribution satisfies the above requirement if the rectangular pulse chosen is that for which the sum of the "departure areas" (see Fig. B·1b) is a minimum. The assumption is then made that, for any pulse shape obtained in practice, the rectangular pulse giving equality of energy and leading to the minimum total departure area also gives a frequency spectrum equal to that of the actual pulse over the most significant portion of the spectrum.

If one half of a symmetrical triangular power pulse (Fig. B·7) of maximum amplitude a and duration $2b$ at the base, and the equivalent rectangular pulse of amplitude h and duration $2c$ are considered, the condition of equal energy provides the relation

$$\frac{ab}{2} = ch.$$

The sum of the departure areas is given by

$$A = \frac{1}{2}\left[\frac{b}{a}(a - h)^2 + \frac{a}{b}(b - c)^2 + \frac{(ac - ab + bh)^2}{ab}\right]. \tag{9}$$

If the value $c = (ab)/(2h)$ is introduced in Eq. (9) and the terms are rearranged,

$$A = \frac{ab}{2}\left(\frac{a}{h}\right)^2\left[2\left(\frac{h}{a}\right)^4 - 4\left(\frac{h}{a}\right)^3 + 4\left(\frac{h}{a}\right)^2 - 2\frac{h}{a} + \frac{1}{2}\right].$$

By differentiating with respect to h and equating to zero, the values of h for which the area is a minimum are obtained.   Thus

$$\frac{dA}{dh} = \frac{b}{2}\left(\frac{a}{h}\right)^3\left[4\left(\frac{h}{a}\right)^4 - 4\left(\frac{h}{a}\right)^3 + 2\frac{h}{a} - 1\right] = 0,$$

and

$$4\left(\frac{h}{a}\right)^4 - 4\left(\frac{h}{a}\right)^3 + 2\left(\frac{h}{a}\right) - 1 = 0,$$

which can be rewritten

$$\left[2\left(\frac{h}{a}\right)^2 - 2\left(\frac{h}{a}\right) + 1\right]\left[2\left(\frac{h}{a}\right)^2 - 1\right] = 0,$$

and the solutions are

$$\frac{h}{a} = \pm\frac{1}{\sqrt{2}},$$

and

$$\frac{h}{a} = \frac{1 \pm \sqrt{-1}}{2}.$$

Obviously, only the real positive root is of interest in the discussion, or

$$\frac{h}{a} = 0.707.$$

Figure B·8 shows the calculated frequency spectrum for a symmetrical triangular pulse, and the theoretical spectra for several rectangular pulses of equal total energy, but of different ratios of amplitude to duration. It can readily be seen that the spectrum for the triangular pulse is superimposed on that of the rectangular pulse that has an amplitude 0.707 times that of the triangle from the maximum down to about 30 per cent of maximum power.

Similarly, it can be shown that the rectangular pulse for which the sum of the departure areas from a sinusoidal pulse is a minimum has an amplitude equal to 0.86 of the peak of the sine wave.   Referring to Fig. B·9, it is seen that again the equivalent rectangular pulse having an amplitude equal to 0.86 of the sine wave and the sinusoidal pulse have spectra that coincide down to about 25 per cent of the maximum.

Since the equivalent rectangles corresponding to a minimum total departure area for the hypothetical pulse shapes just discussed lead to a

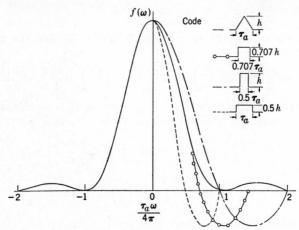

Fig. B·8.—Frequency spectrum distribution of a triangular pulse and rectangular pulses of equal area but varying height.

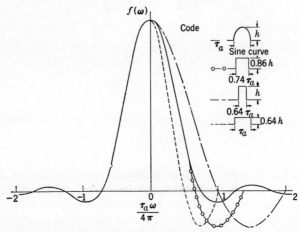

Fig. B·9.—Frequency spectrum distribution of a sinusoidal pulse and rectangular pulses of equal area but varying height.

spectrum distribution that is the same as that of the actual pulse over the most significant part of the spectrum, it seems reasonable to assume that the same will be true for any pulse shape encountered in practice because most actual pulses are more nearly rectangular or trapezoidal than those just considered.

The rectangular pulse equivalent in energy to any power pulse shape and giving the minimum departure area may be determined graphically by successive approximations.   First, the area of the rectangle is determined by integration of the actual power pulse (conservation of energy), and several likely equivalent pulses are drawn, until one is found for which

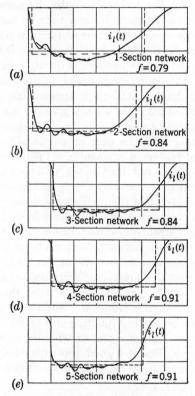

(a)

(b)

(c)

(d)

(e)

Fig. B·10.—Current pulses in an HK7 magnetron, the average current drawn through the oscillations, and the equivalent rectangular pulse from the method of minimum departure areas (a) with a 1-section pulse-forming network, (b) with a 2-section pulse-forming network, (c) with a 3-section pulse-forming network, (d) with a 4-section pulse-forming network, (e) with a 5-section pulse-forming network.

the sum of the departure areas is a minimum.   The process is tedious, but has been carried through for the five actual pulses already considered, and the resulting rectangular pulses are given in Fig. B·10.   It must be noted that the computations were based on current rather than on power pulse shapes, that is, on the assumption of conservation of charge, rather than conservation of energy.   This procedure is convenient because the current is easily measurable, and it can be justified on the basis that, for a magnetron, the variation of voltage is very small during the time of current flow; hence, the pulses of instantaneous current and power are very nearly proportional.

The ratio of the difference between the area of the pulse and the minimum sum of the departure areas to the area of the pulse may be defined as the form factor of the pulse. For a rectangular pulse, its value is, of course, one. For the triangular pulse discussed previously, it is 0.656. The value of the form factor can thus be used to indicate how closely a given pulse approximates a true rectangular pulse.

B·3. A Comparison of the Methods.—Appendix B has thus presented two fundamental methods of defining pulse duration and pulse amplitude. In the first method, the definition is based on the principle of conservation of energy and charge. Although unassailable from a theoretical standpoint, this method may not always give the best practical results. Two of its disadvantages have already been mentioned: the possibility of inaccuracy resulting from the near proportionality of the time functions for current and power on a magnetron load, and the fact that the pulse so determined does not lead to an r-f spectrum that is a good approximation of that of the actual pulse. In the rating of magnetron, the maximum pulse current of the oscillator is usually specified, and the above method of determining pulse amplitude and duration usually yields a rectangular current-pulse amplitude that is smaller than the instantaneous current of the actual pulse for a large fraction of the pulse duration. If the three-section network of Fig. B·5c is considered, for instance, it is seen that the equivalent rectangular current-pulse amplitude obtained is at least 10 per cent smaller than the actual current for about 60 per cent of the pulse duration. Since the maximum operating point of magnetrons is generally a function of both pulse current and pulse duration, there remains the question of whether or not the equivalent rectangular pulse is a sufficiently good approximation of the actual current pulse to be used in conjunction with the specification of the maximum operation point.

The method of the minimum departure areas, on the other hand, does not suffer from any of these drawbacks. For a magnetron load, it can be used with the assumption of either conservation of charge or conservation of energy, the two being very nearly equivalent for all practical purposes. The principal disadvantage is the time consumed in determining the pulse duration of any arbitrary pulse. The minimum departure area method should, nevertheless, be considered the most reliable and most accurate method of determining pulse duration. It may prove expedient, however, to use short-cut methods in many practical determinations of pulse duration and pulse amplitude. One such short-cut method has been used with good results that agree reasonably well with those obtained by the method of minimum departure areas. In this short-cut method, the current-pulse amplitude I_l is defined arbitrarily as the maximum value of an average curve drawn through the oscillations of the actual current pulse (see Fig. B·10). By the principle of conservation of charge, the pulse duration is found immediately as

$$\tau = \frac{\int_0^\infty i_l(t)\,dt}{I_l}.$$

This method is essentially equivalent to that mentioned earlier in the Appendix in which the duration of the current pulse is measured at 50 per cent of the average maximum amplitude. The new definition, however, specifies the amplitude more accurately and gives a value of pulse duration that is more independent of the actual current-pulse shape; it can readily be seen that the measurement at 50 per cent of the maximum amplitude corresponds exactly to conservation of charge in the case of a trapezoidal pulse shape, but not necessarily for any other pulse shape.

TABLE B·1.—PULSE DURATIONS

Method of computation	Rated pulse duration	Conservation of charge and energy		Conservation of energy, minimum departure areas			Conservation of charge, average maximum current	
		Resistance load τ/τ_a	Magnetron load τ/τ_a	Resistance load τ/τ_a	Magnetron load	Form factor	Resistance load	Magnetron load
Pulse shapes								
Triangular power pulse		$\frac{8}{9}$	......	0.707	......	0.656	......	......
Sine-wave power pulse		$\frac{10}{11}$	......	0.74	......	....	......	......
No. of network sections	$\tau_N = 2C_N Z_N$ μsec	τ_l, μsec	τ_l, μsec	....	τ_l, μsec	....	τ_l, μsec	τ_l, μsec
1	2.1	3.17	2.90	.....	2.48	0.79	1.79	2.23
2	2.1	3.02	2.45	.....	2.28	0.84	1.94	2.06
3	2.15	3.02	2.65	.....	2.32	0.89	2.11	2.14
4	2.11	3.00	2.38	.....	2.28	0.91	2.08	2.10
5	2.03	2.60	2.20	.....	2.05	0.91	2.00	2.02

Table B·1 gives the results obtained for pulse duration by the three methods outlined above—conservation of charge and energy; conservation of energy (or charge, if the current pulse is essentially proportional to the power pulse) and minimum departure area; average maximum current and conservation of charge; and the rated pulse duration,

$$\tau_N = 2C_N Z_N,$$

of the pulse-forming networks.   It may be noted that, on magnetron load, the pulse durations determined by the last two methods do not differ by more than 10 per cent, and that the pulse durations obtained by the short-cut method are the nearest to the rated values of the networks. One great advantage of the short-cut method is its simplicity compared with either of the other two.   Although it leads to values of pulse duration that are slightly small, it does, on the other hand, give values for pulse currents that are too large in the same proportion.   Since a small increase in current may be more detrimental to the oscillator than a similar increase in pulse duration, it is probably better, from a practical standpoint, to rate the pulser output on the basis of the third definition: less damage is likely to result to the magnetron from exceeding rated current, and, except for very nonrectangular pulses, the short-cut method provides a satisfactory definition of pulse amplitude and duration.

List of Symbols

In the table that follows are listed the more important and extensively used symbols appearing in this book. Many symbols used in particular developments have not been included in the list when their use is restricted to relatively few pages of the text.

ENGLISH LETTER SYMBOLS

Symbol	Description	Defined or First Used Page
A	Cross-sectional area of PT core	510
a	Thickness of layer of PT winding	513
B	Average magnetic induction	617
ΔB	Increment of average flux density above remanent value of B	537
B_c	Flux density in charging reactor	368
B_m	Some value of flux density less than B_{sat}	604
B_r	Remanent flux density	600
B_{rg}	Remanent flux density in PT core with gap	602
B_{sat}	Saturation flux density	600
C_C	Distributed capacitance of PT primary winding	79, 508
C_D	Same as C_C for PT secondary winding	79, 508
C_d	Capacitance of despiking network	437
C_{gp}	Plate-to-grid capacitance of a vacuum tube	576
C_l	Shunt capacitance due to a load	79
C_N	Energy storage capacitance of a PFN	127, 176
C_o	Capacitance between primary and secondary of PT	507
C_r	Capacitance of rth section of a PFN	187
C_s	Shunt capacitance	26
C_s	Energy storage capacitance in trigger generator	307
C_{sN}	Stray capacitance of a PFN	236
C_w	Energy storage capacitance	22
C_0	Capacitance of lossless transmission line	228
C_ν	Capacitance of section ν of a PFN (Guillemin theory)	192
d	Lamination thickness	637
E_b	A-c power supply voltage	382
E_{bb}	D-c power supply voltage	22
E_c	Grid bias voltage	25
E_{co}	Grid cut-off voltage	576
E_{g_1}	Control-grid voltage (vacuum tube)	91
E_{g_2}	Screen-grid voltage (vacuum tube)	91
e_g	Applied grid voltage	576
e_g'	$|e_g - E_{co}|$	576

Symbol	Description	Defined or First Used Page

e_l	Voltage across load.	563
$\mathbf{E}$	Electric field	618
f	B_r'/B_{sat}	603
f	τ/τ_{opt}	535
f_c	Cut-off frequency for low-pass filter	184
f_r	Pulse recurrence frequency	23
f_0	Resonant frequency of charging circuit of a line-type pulser	360
f_1	Factor depending on voltage distribution between primary and secondary of a PT	522
f_2	Factor relating L_L to PT winding arrangement	541
f_3, f_4	Proportionality factors	541
G_l	Load conductance	208
g_d	Shunt-diode conductance	44
g_l	Load conductance	28
g_p	Switch-tube conductance	28
g_s	Shunt conductance	34
H	Magnetizing force in PT	513
H_c	Coercive force	601
H_c	Magnetizing force in charging reactor	368
H_e	Eddy-current magnetic field	623
H_r	Reverse magnetic field	601
I_{av}	Average current	3
I_c	Pulse current in charging element	109
I_l	Pulse current in load	22
I_m	Magnetizing current	536
I_{max}	Maximum current during a pulse	51
I_P	Current in PT primary	71
I_p	Plate current in switch tube	22
I_p	Current in PT primary	513
I_{pulse}	Pulse current	3
I_{rms}	Effective current	61
I_S	Current in PT secondary	71
I_s	Current source replacing voltage source V_s	34
I_s	Pulse current in shunt impedance	109
I_s	Current in PT secondary	513
I_w	Current source replacing charged storage condenser	27
i_c	Instantaneous current in charging element	60
i_e	Eddy current	633
i_L	Instantaneous current in inductance	23
i_l	Instantaneous load current	23
i_m	Magnetizing current	625
i_p	Instantaneous plate current in switch tube	60
i_r	Current in rth section of PFN	180
i_s	Instantaneous current in shunt path	40
i_0	Initial current	62
i_ν	Current in mesh ν of PFN (Guillemin theory)	192

Symbol	Description	Defined or First Used Page
J	Displacement current	652
k	Coupling coefficient	506
L	Average peripheral spacing of moving electrodes of rotary spark gap	284
L_C	"Charging inductance" in series with distributed capacitance in PT	79, 508
L_c	Inductance of isolating element	62
L_c	Charging inductance in line-type pulser	357
L_D	Same as L_C for the other PT winding	79, 508
L_e	Effective shunt inductance in PT	79, 508
L_L	Leakage inductance in PT	79, 512
L_N	Inductance of a PFN	127
L_p	Primary inductance of PT	510
L_r	Inductance of rth section of PFN	187
L_r	Value of inductance for resonant charging	360
L_s	Shunt Inductance	39
L_w	Energy storage inductance	22
L_0	Total distributed inductance of lossless transmission line	209
L_v	Inductance of section v of PFN (Guillemin theory)	192
l	Mean magnetic path length	510
l_g	Length of gap in PT core	602
$\mathcal{L}$	Length of PT winding	513
M	Mutual inductance	505
N	Number of turns of PT coil	510
N_c	Number of turns on charging reactor	364
N_f	Number of fixed electrodes of rotary gap	282
N_p	Number of turns on PT primary	513
N_r	Number of moving electrodes of rotary gap	282
N_s	Number of turns on PT secondary	513
n	Voltage transformation ratio of a transformer	71
n	Number of meshes in a PFN	180
P_{av}	Average power	3
P_L	Overhead power loss in line-type pulser	249
P_l	Pulse power in a load	70
P_m	Maximum power during a pulse	714
P_N	Power input to PFN	392
P_p	Pulse power dissipated in switch tube	72
P_R	Power dissipated in isolating resistance	61
PFN	Pulse forming network	8
PRF	Pulse recurrence frequency	3
PT	Pulse transformer	
p	Laplace transform parameter	28
Q	Quality factor of a circuit	12, 360
Q_N	Charge on a PFN	176
q_N	Instantaneous charge on a PFN	356

LIST OF SYMBOLS

Symbol	Description	Defined or First Used Page

R_c Resistance of isolating element in charging circuit of a pulser....... 26, 357

R_d Resistance of despiking network.................................. 437

R_e Shunt resistance in PT.. 236, 508

R_G Internal resistance of voltage source............................. 501

R_g Isolating resistance in grid circuit of a vacuum tube................. 25

R_l Load resistance... 22

R_p Switch resistance plus series losses in PFN and PT.................. 236

R_s Resistance in parallel with pulser output.......................... 33

R_s r_s/w... 637

R_w Resistance of PT winding....... 508

R_ρ $w\rho/d$... 637

r_g Grid-to-cathode resistance of vacuum tube........................ 575

r_l Dynamic resistance of a load (magnetron or biased diode)............ 33

r_p Internal resistance of switch tube................................ 22

r_s Resistance between two laminations of PT core..................... 637

S_d Hypothetical switch in series with shunt diode...................... 44

S_l Hypothetical switch in series with diode load....................... 33

S_M Hypothetical switch in series with magnetron....................... 46

S_T Switch tube.. 27

T Symbol for a tube... 74

T $\dfrac{\mu_1\sigma_1 d^2}{12}$ using mks units or $\dfrac{10^{-9}\pi\mu d^2}{3\rho}$ using cgs units.................... 623

T_k Deionizing time... 487

T_r Pulse recurrence interval $(1/f_r)$................................. 3

t_r Rise time of a pulse... 537

$\mathfrak{U}$ Average circumference of layer of PT winding...................... 513

$V_{ba}(t)$ Voltage across output of hard-tube pulser......................... 27

$V_C(t)$ Time function of voltage across a capacitance...................... 53

V_G Source or generator voltage..................................... 532

V_g Pulse grid voltage... 25

V_{J_1} PFN voltage at end of a pulse due to impedance mismatch $= V_{N-1}$.... 419

V_l Pulse voltage across a load...................................... 22

V_{ln} Voltage of nth reflected pulse at the load......................... 418

V_M Observed value of V_{max}.. 297

V_{max} Maximum voltage across a series gap switch for which prefiring is negligible... 297

V_{min} Minimum voltage across a series gap switch for which misfiring is negligible... 298

V_N Initial voltage on a PFN... 176

V_{N_n} PFN voltage at end of nth charging period........................ 419

V_{N-n} PFN voltage at end of nth reflection............................. 418

V_P PT primary voltage... 71

V_p Voltage drop across switch tube................................. 22

$V(p)$ Laplace transform of $V(t)$...................................... 28

V_S PT secondary voltage... 71

Symbol	Description	Defined or First Used Page
V_S	Theoretical maximum value of V_{max}	297
V_s	Voltage at which conduction starts in an ideal diode; starting voltage of a magnetron	32
V_{start}	Minimum power supply voltage at which firing occurs for series gaps	298
V_w	Voltage source equivalent to charged energy storage condenser	27
V_w	Equilibrium value of storage condenser voltage	53
V_w'	Energy storage condenser voltage at the start of a particular pulse	53
V_0	Initial voltage on lossless transmission line	177
V_T	Equilibrium value of storage condenser voltage at the end of a pulse	53
V_T'	Energy storage condenser voltage at the end of a particular pulse	53
v_l	Instantaneous voltage across a load	237
v_p	Instantaneous-voltage drop across switch tube	60
W	Energy in magnetic field	513
W	Energy in a charged capacitance	519
W_e	Energy dissipated in PT core due to eddy currents	627
W_l	Energy dissipated in a load	226
W_m	Energy returned to the circuit from PT core	628
W_N	Energy stored in PFN	250
w	Width of core lamination	637
Y	Admittance $= 1/Z$	185
Y_N	Admittance of a PFN	208
Z_l	Load impedance	84
Z_N	Impedance of a PFN	129, 176
Z_p	Internal impedance of a pulser	85
Z_s	Impedance in parallel with pulser load	33
Z_T	Characteristic impedance of PT winding	523
Z_0	Characteristic impedance of a transmission line	84

GREEK LETTER SYMBOLS

Symbol	Description	Page
α	Shunt loss coefficient $= 1 + \dfrac{Z_N + R_p}{R_e}$	238
α	PT parameter	533
β	Series loss coefficient $= 1 + \dfrac{R_p}{Z_N}$	238
β	PT parameter	533
γ	Ratio of total load distributed capacitance to PFN capacitance	252
γ	$e^{-\frac{\pi}{2Q}}$	419
Γ_p	$1/L_p$	591
Γ_L	$1/L_L$	591
Δ	Distance between layers of PT winding	513
Δ_p	Skin depth	548
δ	One way transmission time for lossless transmission line	177, 524
δ	Loss tangent $= \tan \delta$	653

728   *LIST OF SYMBOLS*

Symbol	Description	Defined or First Used Page
ϵ	Dielectric constant	519
ϵ	Small positive voltage	576
ϵ_0	Dielectric constant of free space	618
ϵ_1	Dielectric constant of core material in mks units	618
η	Efficiency of a PT	71
η_b	Efficiency of power supply	249
η_c	Efficiency of charging circuit	249
η_d	Efficiency of discharging circuit	249
η_p	Efficiency of pulser circuit	249
η_t	Efficiency of a PT	236
η_0	Overall efficiency of a pulser	249
κ	Reflection coefficient	85, 419
μ	Amplification factor	91, 576
μ	Permeability	523
μ_e	Effective pulse permeability	510
μ_i	D-c incremental permeability	601
μ_{ig}	D-c incremental permeability for core with gap	601
μ_{max}	Maximum permeability	603
μ_o	Average permeability	601
μ_{og}	Average permeability for core with gap	601
μ_1	Permeability in mks units	618
ρ	Resistivity	511
σ	PT circuit parameter	564
σ_1	Conductivity of core material in mks units	618
τ	Pulse duration	3
τ_a	Duration of power pulse	714
τ_l	Pulse duration at the load	250
τ_{max}	Maximum pulse duration obtainable with a regenerative pulse generator	587
τ_N	Pulse duration produced by a PFN on a matched resistance load	250
τ_o	Time required to saturate a core lamination	634
ω	Circuit parameter	42
ω	Angular frequency of a-c voltage	177
ω	$\omega^2 = \omega_0^2 - a^2$	357
ω_a	Applied a-c angular frequency	367
ω_0	$\omega_0^2 = \dfrac{1}{L_c C_N}$	357

Index

A

A-c charging diode, 414–416
  general analysis of, 380–386
  nonresonant, 381, 385, 393–400
  resonant, 381, 385, 386–393
    average-current component in, 389
    charging-circuit efficiency in, 392
    circuit utilization factor in, 392
A-c charging transformers, linearity requirements for, 401
  practical, 400–407
A-c impedance, 177
Airborne radar systems, light-weight medium power pulser for, 140–152
Aluminum-cathode gap (see Fixed gap)
Amplitude jitter, 290, 331
Anger circuit, 468–471
Anode buildup, 320
Anode circuit, 344–349
  of hydrogen thyratrons, 344
Anode current, rate of rise of, 348
Anode voltage, forward, 346
  inverse, 346–348
Arnott, E. G. F., 321n., 324n.
Autotransformer, 512
Average current, 361, 467, 470, 483
Average-current component in a-c resonant charging, 389
Average-current measurements, 146
Average-current meter, 701–706
Average values of the transformer currents, 396

B

Backswing voltage, 43, 45, 50, 79, 88, 146, 154, 261, 509, 551, 569
Bell Telephone Laboratories, 104, 281, 295, 317, 321, 322, 328, 472–476

Bettler, P. C., 451n.
B-H loop, d-c, 612
  idealized, 633
  idealized and actual pulse, 627
  pulse, 612, 643
    circuit for, 641
B-H oscillograms, for a-c charging transformers, 403, 405, 406
  for d-c charging reactor, 369, 370
Bias, cutoff, for tetrode, 100
  for triode, 100
  negative, 92
Bias voltage, cutoff, 99
Biased diode, current-voltage characteristic of, 32, 231
Biased-diode load, 527
Blocking-oscillator driver, 124–132
Blocking-oscillator transformer, design of, 543–547
Blumlein circuit, 465–468
Bootstrap driver, 120–124, 138
Bostick, W. H., 611n., 639n.
Breakdown field of rotary gap, 291
Breakdown time of rotary gap, 275
Breakdown voltage, dynamic, of single fixed gap, 296
  static, of single fixed gap, 296
Bushings for pulse transformers, 654
Butt joint in core, 601, 644
Byerly, W. E., 656n.

C

Cable, matched, with a series resistor, 671
  with a shunt resistor, 671
  for pulse-forming network, 164
Cable impedance matching, 671
Cable-matching, 677
Cable properties and delay lines, 689
Capacitance divider, 673–675

Carslaw, H. S., 27*n*.
Cathode and anode erosion of fixed gap, 319–321
Cathode current, 148
Cathode erosion, 317, 320
Cathode follower, 121, 125
Cathode fatigue, 97
Cauer's extension of Foster's theorem, 194
Chaffee, E. L., 98*n*.
Characteristic current-voltage of a non-linear load, 110
Characteristic curves for triodes and tetrodes, 98–108
Characteristic impedance (*see* Impedance, characteristic)
Characteristics, grid-current–plate-voltage, 101–108
  idealized current-voltage, of a tetrode, 110
  plate-current–grid-voltage, 99–101
  plate-current–plate voltage, 101–108
Charging, of storage condenser, 51–69
  (*See also* A-c charging; D-c charging; Full-cycle charging; Half-cycle charging; Inductance charging; Linear charging; Recharging; Resonant charging)
Charging-circuit efficiency in a-c resonant charging, 392
Charging-circuit losses, 429
Charging circuits, of line-type pulser, 355–416
  miscellaneous, 414–416
Charging cycle, 358
Charging diode, 138, 361
  (*See also* Hold-off diode)
Charging efficiency, 392, 421
Charging element, inductance, 355
  resistance, 355
Charging inductance, 361, 455, 467, 483
  of a pulse transformer, 526–530
Charging period, 384
Charging reactor, 356
  coil design for, 372
  core design for, 372
  linearity of, 366
  sample design for, 376
  saturation of core, 364, 370
Charging transformer losses, 413

Charging transformers, a-c, (*see* A-c charging transformers)
Charging voltage, forward, measurement of, 690–692
Circuit (*see* type of circuit)
Circuit complexity, 16
Circuit utilization factor in a-c resonant charging, 392
Coding, pulse-, 131, 486
Coil design for d-c charging reactor, 372
Coil material for pulse transformers, 648–660
Cole, P. A., 662*n*., 706*n*.
Condenser, as energy reservoir, 21–23
  discharging of, 25–51
  storage, charging of, 51–69
    effect of inductance of isolating element on, 67
    voltage on, 77
Condenser voltage equilibrium, 53, 55
Connectors, for pulse transformers, 654
Conservation of charge, definition of equivalent rectangular pulse, 711–716
Conservation of energy, definition of equivalent rectangular pulse, 711–716
Core, accurate equivalent circuit for, 631
  with butt joints, 601, 644
  without butt joints, 600
  magnetization of, 633
Core design for d-c charging reactor, 372
Core material for pulse transformers, 599–648
  d-c data for, 614–615
  d-c properties of, 599–601
  pulse data for, 614–615
  standard tests on, 611
  thickness of, 599
Core performance, techniques for measuring, 639–648
Core saturation, 603*n*.
Core size, 538, 545
Coupling coefficient, 506
Craggs, J. D., 274*n*., 332
Crout, P. D., 528
Current, average (*see* Average current)
  effective (*see* Effective current)
Current-fed network (*see* Network)
Current modes in pulse transformer, 528

Current pulse, 175, 176, 666
  amplitude for, 69
Current pulse droop, 80, 88, 169, 568, 702
  (*See also* Pulse droop)
Current pulse rectangular in copper, 655–658
Current-pulse shapes, 186
Current-pulse-viewing resistors, 676
Current spike (*see* Spike, current)
Current-viewing resistors, 666
Current-voltage characteristics of a biased diode, 32, 231
CV85 trigatron, 332
CV125 trigatron, 332

D

Darlington circuit, 464
D-c charging, 356–380
  general analysis of, 356–363
D-c charging current from nonlinear charging reactor, 365
D-c charging reactors, design of, 372–380
  linearity requirements for, 364–366
  practical, 364–372
D-c charging voltage from nonlinear charging reactor, 365
D-c hysteresis loop, 605
  of a core, 600
  (*See also* B-H loop)
D-c incremental permeability, 601, 632, 634
D-c permeability, 510
D-c resonant charging, 360, 418
Deionization, 279
Deionization time, 336, 353
Delay line, 133, 158
Delay lines and cable properties, 689
Delay time, 351
Despiking circuit, 453
Despiking RC-network, 436
Diaplex, 215
Dielectric, dissipation factor of, 216
Dielectric constant and power factor, 652
Dielectric strength, 651
Dielectrics, 215
Diffusion equations, 656
  development of, 617–619
  solution of, 619–626
Dillinger, J. R., 312n., 320n., 324n., 327n., 335n.

Diode, biased (*see* Biased diode)
Discharging of storage condenser, 25–51
Discharging circuit, effect of, on pulse shape, 255–261
  efficiency of, 449
  general properties of, 225–233
  of line-type pulser, 225–272
Discharging efficiency, 466, 483
Discharging (pulse) interval, 54
Dissipation factor of dielectric, 216
Distributed capacitance, 516–522, 537
  effective, of pulse-transformer coils, measurement of, 521
  for a transformer, 507
Divider (*see* specific type of divider)
Donovan, A C., 367n.
Double-switch single-network circuit, 488–492
Drewell, P., 336n.
Driver, 119
  blocking-oscillator, 124–132
  bootstrap, 120–124, 138
  multivibrator, 132–139
  pulse-forming-network, 132–139
  regenerative, 124–134, 150
Driver circuits, 119–139, 157, 168
Dry type of insulation, 648–651
  solventless varnish for, 649
Dunham, C. R., 619n., 635n.
Duolaterally wound coil, 554
Dupont, 650
Duration (*see* Pulse duration)
Duty, 4
Duty cycle, 4
Duty ratio, 4
Dynamic resistance, 231
  of load, 3, 33, 78, 110

E

Eddy current, 620, 624, 636
  energy dissipated by, 626
Eddy current loss, 629
Effective current, 361
  in a-c resonant charging circuit, 390
  in transformer winding, 547
Effective current density, in transformer winding, 548
Effective values of the transformer currents, 396

Efficiency, 13, 534
  of hard-type pulser, 16
  of line-type pulser, 13, 16
  pulser, 244, 249–255, 462
    of line-type pulser, 249
    over-all, 249
    of rectifier circuit, 249
    total, 249
829 tetrode, 105, 123, 126, 132
884 tube, 123
8020 shunt diode, 154
Electrode material, for fixed gap, choice
    of, 317
  for rotary gaps, 280
Electrodes, fixed, 276
  moving, 276
  for rotary gaps, number of, 282
Energy, dissipated, in the core, calcula-
    tion, 627
      approximate, 630
    by eddy currents, 626
    in pulse-transformer windings, 660
  stored in magnetic field, 627
Energy density, average, in coil, 541
  in core, 541
Energy loss, 626–633
Energy reservoir, comparison of a con-
    denser and an inductance as, 23–25
  (*See also* Condenser; Inductance)
Energy transfer, maximum, 533
Equivalent circuit, for pulse-transformer
    core, 626–633
  (*See also* component for which equiv-
    alent circuit is given)
Erosion of electrodes of fixed gap, 319–
    321
Evans Signal Laboratory, 342*n*.

F

Fe-I gap, 328
5C22 thyratron, 138, 341, 455
5D21 tetrode, 100, 104, 132, 472
527 triode, 106
Fixed gap, aluminum-cathode, 298
    designs of, 321–323
  cathode and anode erosion of, 319–321
  cylindrical electrode, 295
  cylindrical-electrode aluminum-cath-
    ode, 318–327
  enclosed, 294–335

Fixed gap, iron-sponge mercury-cathode,
    327–332
  designs of, 328
  mercury-cathode, 295, 303
    (*See also* Series gap)
  static- and dynamic-breakdown volt-
    ages of a single, 296
  three-electrode, 332–335
    hydrogen-filled, 335
  types (*see* listing under O)
Fixed gap design, general considerations
    for, 316–318
Fixed gap dissipation, 324–326, 331
Fixed spark gap (*see* Fixed gap)
Fletcher, R. C., 680*n*.
Fluharty, R. G., 274*n*., 326*n*.
Flux density, 538
  distribution of, 623
  incremental, 537
Fluxplot, for typical pulse-transforming
    winding, 659
Fosterite, 557, 649, 650
Foster's reactance theorem, 193
Foster's theorem, Cauer's extension of,
    194
4C35 thyratron, 138, 341, 479
Fourier-series, 187
Frank, R., 656*n*.
Frequency response, of pulse transformer,
    591–598
  of transformer, oscilloscope presenta-
    tion of, 595
Full-cycle charging, 394–397, 449
Fundingsland, O. T., 443*n*.

G

Ganz, A. G., 623*n*., 628*n*., 633*n*.
Gap in the core, 601
  (*See also* Fixed gap; Rotary gap;
    Series gap)
Gap length of the core, optimum, 602–604
Gap restriking, 279
Gap spacing, 320
Gaps, number of, vs. voltage range, 300–
    302
Gardner, M. F., 27*n*.
Gas, for fixed gap, choice of, 316
  for rotary gaps, 280
Gas cleanup, 336
Gas pressure, 320
Gaseous-discharge switch, 10, 14, 175

GE 68G627 pulse transformer, 129, 150
General Electric Company, 355n., 373, 400–402, 408, 557, 559, 614–615, 638, 649
Geometry of fixed gap, determination of, 318
Germeshausen, K. J., 312n., 335n.
Gibbs phenomenon, 187
Gillette, P. R., 522n.
Glasoe, G. N., 662n., 707n.
Glick, H. L., 327n.
Goucher, F- S., 274n., 295n., 316n., 318n., 327n., 331n.
Grid, power dissipation in, 97
Grid circuit of hydrogen thyratron, 349–354
Grid current, 97
Grid drive, positive, 91
Grid-driving power, 157
Grid swing, 92, 119
Guillemin, E. A., 189n., 193n.
Guillemin networks, 200–203
  current-fed, 211–213
    type A, 212
    type B, 212
    type C, 212
    type F, 212
  voltage-fed, type A, 201
    type B, 201
    type C, 201
    type D, 201
    type E, 201
Guillemin's theory, 189–207

H

Half-cycle charging, 397–400
Half-wave single-phase charging, 476–478
Hanna, C. R., 377n.
Hard-tube pulser, 5, 6–8, 19–172
  application of pulse-shaping networks to, 165–172
  comparison of, with line-type pulser, 13–17
  high-power short-pulse, 160–165
  lightweight medium power, 140–152
  1Mw, 152–160
  output circuit of, 21–89
  required switch characteristics of, 90–98
  two arrangements of use of pulse transformer with, 74

Haynes, J. R., 295n., 303n.
Heat dissipation, 151, 459
Hibbard, L. U., 693n.
High-reactance transformers, design of, 407–414
Hipersil pulse-transformer cores, 610
Hold-off diode, 163, 381, 414–416, 456
  (*See also* Charging diode)
Hull, A. W., 274n.
Hydrogen thyratron, 335–354
  anode circuit of, 344
  control-grid characteristic in, 338
  grid circuit of, 349–354
  life of, 341
  operating characteristics of, 336–344
  operation of, 339
    series and parallel, 342
  tube characteristics of, 339
Hysteresis loop on an oscilloscope, 639–641
  (*See also* B-H loop)
Hysteresis loss, 627

I

I_p-V_p curve, 111–118
Ionization, residual, 297
Ionization time, 345
Impedance, a-c, 177
  characteristic, 176
    of pulse-forming network, 9, 129
  instantaneous, 437
  internal, of pulser, 4
  mismatch, 417
  of a network, measurement of, 221
Impedance characteristic, of a cable, 670
  of a pulse transformer, 522–526
Impedance-matching, 4, 9, 13, 16, 227
  cable, 671, 677
  to load, 70–76
  and transmission cable, 669–673
Impedance mismatch with long cable, reflection effects of, 84–89
Impedance transformation ratio, of transformer, 10
Inductance, as the energy reservoir, 23
Inductance charging, from an a-c source, 380–386
  (*See also* A-c charging)
  from d-c power supply, 356–380
  efficiency of, 363
Inductance measurements, 366–372

Inductive kicker, 305–307
Ingram, S. B., 295n.
Input capacitance of load, 536
Insulating materials, measurements on, 653
Insulation for pulse transformers, 648–655
Interlaminar insulation, 638
Interlaminar resistance, 636–638
Interpulse interval 16, 54, 119
Iron-sponge mercury-cathode gap (*see* Fixed gap)
Isolating element, 6, 12, 52
  average power dissipated in, 59
  effect of inductance of, on charging of storage condenser, 67
  high resistance as, 52–61
  inductance, 61–69, 145
  inductive resistor as, 61–69
  principal advantages of inductance as, 68
  resistance, 153

J

Jitter, time (*see* Time jitter)
Joos, G., 501n.

K

Keyers, 1
Kicker, inductive, 305–307
Kraft paper, 551
Krulikoski, S. J., 344n., 347n.

L

Laplace-transform method, 27, 175
Leading edge of pulse (*see* Pulse)
Leakage core, 400
  separate, 409
Leakage inductance, 506, 511–516
  calculation of, 512
  measurement of, 515
  of transformer, 400
Leakage-reactance-core gap, 411
Lebacqz, J. V., 274n., 468n.
Linear charging, 12, 361
Linearity requirements for a-c charging transformers, 401
Line-simulating network, 124, 180
  (*See also* Network)

Line-type pulse generator with a magnetron load, 573
Line-type pulser, 5, 8–12, 173–496
  characteristics of, 233–244
  charging circuit of, 355–416
  measurement in, 690
  comparison of, with hard-tube pulser, 13–17
  discharging circuit of, 225–272
  efficiency of, 13, 16, 249
  equivalent circuit, 236–238
  performance of, 417–447
  switches for, 234, 273–354
Line-type pulser characteristics, 233–244
Line-voltage variation, 117
Load, coupling to, 70–76
  direct-connected, 73
  duration of pulse at, 226
  dynamic resistance of, 3, 33, 78, 110
  energy dissipated in, 226
  linear, 3
  nonlinear, 3
  open circuit in (*see* Open circuit)
  pulse power in, 226
  resistance, 177
  short circuit in (*see* Short circuit)
  static resistance of, 3, 110
  transformer-coupled, 73
Load characteristics, effect of on pulser regulation, 108–118
Load current, change in, during a pulse, 58
  reducing the change in, 166
Load current variation, 117
Load dynamic resistance, 78
Load effect on pulser operation, 418–423
Load impedance, effects of change in, 417
Load line, 238–244
Load voltage, 469
Loss, series, 237, 238
  shunt, 238

M

MacColl, L. A., 619n.
MacFayden, K. A., 635n.
McIntosh, R. O., 693n.
Magnetic-path length, mean, 599
Magnetic shunt, 400
Magnetizing current, 522

Magnetron, current voltage characteristic of, 32, 702
  mode-changing of, 206, 417, 438–441
  mode-skipping, 439
  normal operation of, 435–438
  pushing figure of, 118
  sparking of, 425, 441–447, 707
Magnetron current, average, 146, 155, 253
Magnetron-input characteristics, 435
Magnetron load, 527
  pulser performance with, 435–447, 707
Marx circuit, 494
Maxwell's equations, 618
Measurement (*see* quantity measured)
Measuring techniques, 661–709
Mechanical-design considerations for rotary gaps, 283–289
Megaw, E. C. S., 693*n*.
Metering techniques in pulse measurements, 692–709
Mica, 215
Minimum departure areas, equivalent rectangular pulse by, 716–720
Mode changing of magnetrons, 206, 417, 438–441
Mode skipping, 438
Mode-skipping magnetron, *V-I* characteristics of, 439
Modulators, 1
Moody, F. N., 500*n*.
Motor, 285
Multiple-switch circuit for voltage multiplication, 494–496
Multiple-switch multiple-network circuit, 485–488
Multivibrator, biased, 132
Multivibrator driver, 132–139

N

Naval Research Laboratory, Anacostia, D.C., 171
Network, average power supplied by, 253
  current-fed, 8, 25, 135, 175, 207–213
  of equal capacitance per section, 196–200, 203–207
  Guillemin, 200–203, 211–213
  initial charge on, 176
  inverse voltage on, 427
  line-simulating, 124, 180

Network, mutual inductance, 199
  pulse-forming, 8, 175, 224, 225, 234, 356
    cable as, 164
    characteristic impedance of, 9, 129
    current-fed, 25
    voltage on, 454
  type A, 201, 212
  type B, 201, 212
  type C, 201, 212
  type D, 201, 205
  type E, 205, 213, 219
  type F, 201, 212
  voltage-fed, 8, 175, 189–207
Network attenuation, 222
Network capacitance, 454
Network-charging circuit, 12
Network coils, 213–215
  construction of, 221
Network condensers, 215–221
Network impedance, 176, 181
Network impedance function, 181
Network phase shift, 222
Network storage capacitance, 176
Network voltage, 358, 388, 395, 398, 424, 455
Networks, derived from a transmission line, 179–189
Nickel-steel pulse-transformer cores, 611
Nickel-steel punchings for pulse transformer cores, 611
Nonlinear circuits, 429–431
Nonlinear-inductance circuit, 471–476

O

Oil-impregnated paper, 215
Oil-impregnated paper insulation, 651
1B22 gap, 321, 322
1B29 gap, 321, 322
1B31 gap, 321, 322
1B34 gap, 322
1B41 gap, 322
  operating range for, 324
1B42 gap, 328
1B45 gap, 322
1B49 gap, 322
1-Mw hard-tube pulser, 152–160
Open-circuited lossless transmission line, 176
Open circuits, 431–435
  in load, 417

Operating characteristics, of aluminum-cathode gap, 323
of hydrogen thyratron, 336–344
of iron-sponge mercury-cathode gap, 329
Opposing-pin rotary gap, 287
Oscillations on top of the current pulse, 265
Oscilloscope, 662–665
high-speed, 664
use of in pulser measurements, 662–692
Oscilloscope presentation frequency response of transformer, 595
Output circuit of hard-tube pulser, 21–89, 141, 153, 160
basic, 21–25
with biased-diode load, 32–51
with high resistance as isolating element, 52–61
with inductance or inductive resistor as isolating element, 61–69
with a resistance load, 26–31
Output power regulation, 77
Overload relay, 433
Overshoots, 179, 187

P

Parabolic fall of pulse, 191
Parabolic rise of pulse, 191
Parallel-pin rotary gap, 287
Peak current, 470
Peak power, 69
of pulse, 3
Peek, F. W., 294n.
Performance, of high-power airborne pulser, 461–463
of high-power rotary gap pulser, 451
of line-type pulsers, 417–447
Permafil, 557, 649, 650
Permeability, d-c, 510
d-c incremental, 601, 632, 634
effective, of the core, 537
PFN (see Pulse-forming network)
Philco Corporation, 140
Plate-current–grid-voltage characteristics, 99–101
Post-pulse voltage, 691
Power, average, 466, 483
dissipated in shunt elements, 69
Power dissipation, 104

Power factor and dielectric constant, 652
Power input, average, 470
to pulser, 151
Power loss in pulse-transformer windings, 660
Power output, average, 470
of pulsers, 3
Power supply, 14, 455
average current, 149
voltage-doubler, 148
Power-supply voltage, 73, 77
Power transfer, 227, 232, 238–244
maximum, 500–503
Power transfer to the load, 69–89
Pre-fire, 297
PRF, 3, 123
Protection, of circuit elements, 433–435, 457
Protective measures, 151, 160, 431
Proximity effect, 547, 658–660
Pulse, backswing on tail, 569–571
change in load current during, 58
current, 3, 320
(See also Current pulse)
equivalent rectangular, by conservation of energy, 711–716
by minimum departure areas, 716–720
leading edge of, 2, 255–257
(See also Pulse, rise of)
parabolic fall of, 191
parabolic rise of, 191
peak power of, 3
rectangular, 177, 711–720
rise of, 2
on a magnetron load, 565–568
on a resistance load, 563–565
(See also Pulse, leading edge of)
sinusoidal power, 714
sinusoidal spectrum distribution, 718
top of, 2, 257
trailing edge of, 2, 258–261
(See also Pulse tail)
triangular power, 713
triangular spectrum distribution, 718
Pulse amplitude, 710–722
average, 69
definition of, 710
Pulse cable, 255, 231
between pulser and load, effect of, 271

Pulse characteristics, 98
(*See also* Characteristics)
of tubes of receiver type, 102
Pulse-coding (*see* Coding, pulse-)
Pulse current, 3, 320, 447
change in, 165
Pulse droop, 509, 568, 569, 674
(*See also* Current pulse droop)
Pulse duration, 2, 15, 119, 123, 136, 226, 236, 320, 447, 456, 534, 544, 710–722
change of, 16
continuously variable, from 0.5 μsec to 5 μsec, 158
definition of, 710
equivalent, 251, 710–722
maximum, 587, 634
range of, 127
from 0.1–0.5 μsec, 160
from 0.3 μsec to 0.15 μsec, 160
Pulse energy, 184
Pulse-forming network (*See* Network)
cable as, 164
Pulse-forming-network driver, 132–139
Pulse generator, basic circuit of, 5
regenerative, 124
Pulse generator output transformer, 500
Pulse hysteresis loop, 641–648
theoretical construction of, 634–636
(*See also* *B-H* loop)
Pulse magnetization, 613–626, 633–638
Pulse measurements, 667–687
Pulse plate current, 95
Pulse power, 3, 69, 238–244
Pulse-power output, of the driver, 119
vs. transmission-line voltage, 229
Pulse recurrence frequency (*see* PRF)
Pulse shape, 2, 13, 16, 179, 188, 190, 207, 220, 534, 687
computed and actual, 261–272
effect of discharging circuit on, 255–261
optimum, 552
on a resistance load, 573
(*See also* Wave shape)
Pulse shapes obtained from hard-tube pulser, calculations of, with biased-diode load, 33–51
with resistance load, 26–32
effect of measuring circuit on, 678
effect of pulse transformer and cable on, 81–84, 88

Pulse shapes obtained from hard-tube pulser, effect of shunt capacitance and load resistance, 31
examples of, magnetron (biased-diode) load, 38, 46–49
sloping top or droop, 51, 56–58
Pulse shapes obtained from line-type pulser, effect of cable on, 271, 272
effect of circuit parameters on, 262, 266–268, 440
effect of magnetron sparking on, 442
magnetron load, 271, 272, 715, 719
multiple pulses, 491, 493
with non-linear inductance switch, 472
with various types of PFN, resistance load, five-section, 183, 205, 715
one section, 203, 715
six-section, 188, 189
three-section, 204, 715
two-section, 204, 715
type E, 207, 220
Pulse shapes obtained from regenerative driver, 126, 128, 130
very short pulse duration, 165
Pulse shapes obtained from regenerative pulse generator, 590
Pulse-shaping circuit, 177, 473
Pulse tail, 2, 183, 189, 569
oscillations on, 571–573
(*See also* Pulse, trailing edge of)
Pulse top, on magnetron load, 569
on resistance load, 568
Pulse transformer, 9, 225, 235, 497–660
advantages of, 78
bushings for, 654
charging inductance of, 526–530
coil material for, 648–660
connectors for, 654
core materials for, 609
current modes in, 528
design, 532–562
methods for, 536–555
elementary theory of, 499–531
equivalent circuit, 508–510
values of elements, 510
frequency response of, 591–598
GE 68G627, 150
with hard-tube pulse generator, 566
insulation for, 648–655
iron-core, 124
with line-type pulse generator, 567

Pulse transformer, operating data for, 558
 power output, 511
  design of, 547–554
 power-transfer efficiency of, 71
 primary inductance, 510
 for regenerative pulse generator, 511
  design of, 543–547
 time delay in, 85, 272
 two arrangements for use with hard-tube pulser, 74
 typical design specifications for, 561
 typical designs, 555–562
 for very high resistance load, 554
 for very high voltages, 555
 winding schemes for, 517, 518
 wire for, 655–660
Pulse transformer cores, equivalent circuit for, 626–633
 various types of, 606
Pulse transformer coupling to load, 70–76
 effects of, 78–89
Pulse-transformer effect on pulse shapes, 563–575
Pulse transformer materials, 599–660
Pulse transformer parameters, effect on circuit behavior, 563–598
 effect on regenerative pulse generators, 575–591
Pulse voltage, 3, 537
 change in, 165
 rate of rise of, 77
Pulse voltmeters, 692–701
 intrinsic error of, 694–698
Pulsed bridge circuit, 222
Pulser circuit, direct connection, 70
Pulser-circuit efficiency, 470
Pulser design, switch-tube characteristics affecting, 93–98
Pulser efficiency (*see* Efficiency, pulser)
Pulser load line, 243
Pulser performance, with magnetron load, 435–447
Pulser power output, effect of stray capacitance on, 76
Pulser regulation (*see* Regulation, pulser)
Pulser switch (*see* Switch, pulser)
Pulser, coded, 486
 comparison of hard-tube and line-type, 13–17
 hard-tube (*see* Hard-tube pulsers)
 high-power airborne, 454–463

Pulser, high-power rotary-gap, 448–454
 performance of, 451
 light-weight, medium power, for airborne radar systems, 140–152
 line-type (*see* Line-type pulsers)
 Model 9, 152–160
 multiple-load, 480–483
 multiple-network, 463–468
 multiple-pulse line type, 484–494
 thyratron bridge, operating data for, 480
 vest-pocket, 140
Pulses, formation of, 175–179
 shaping of, 175–179
Pushing figure of magnetron, 118

Q

Q of charging circuit, 359

R

Radial-pin rotary gap, 287
Rate of rise, 689
 of trigger pulse, 350
 of voltage, 447
Rational-fraction expansions, 185
Rayleigh's principle, 179–183
RC-differentiator, calibration of, 685
RC divider, parallel, 667
RC-divider, series, 675
Recharging current, average, 154
Recharging path, inductance for, 39–51, 144
 resistance for, 33–39, 144, 163
Rectifying rotary gap, 476
Recurrence period, 358
 frequency, 123
Redfearn, L. W., 619n., 649n, 655n.
Reflection effects caused by impedance mismatch with long cable, 84–89
Reflections, 178, 670
Regenerative driver, 124–132, 150
Regenerative pulse generator, 575–591
 (*See also* Pulse transformer)
Regulation, 16, 77
 pulser, 244–249
  effect of switch-tube and load characteristics on, 108–118
  transient, 244
  against variations in load characteristics, 247–249
  against variations in network voltage, 245–247

Rehkopf, H. L., 446n., 632n., 646n.
Reignition voltage, 346
Relay (*see* type of relay)
Resistance charging, 487
Resistance divider, 668
Resonant charging, 12, 360, 381, 386–393, 418
Reverse current, 511
  effects of, 331
Reverse magnetic field, 605–607, 644
R-f envelope viewer, 706
Rieke, F. F., 165n.
Rise of pulse (*see* Pulse)
Rms current in a-c resonant charging circuit, 390
  in the transformer, 483
Roberts, D. T., 334n.
Rotary-gap efficiency, 289
Rotary-gap geometry, 276–280
Rotary-gap performance, 289–294
Rotary gaps, 273, 275–294
  breakdown field of, 291
  breakdown time of, 275
  electrical considerations in design of, 276–283
  mechanical design considerations, 283–289
  motor and housing, 285
  with holes in insulating disk, 287
  opposing-pin, 287
  parallel-pin, 287
  performance of, for d-c resonant charging, 291
    for a-c resonant charging, 291
  radial-pin, 287
  rotor, size of, 283
  types of, 286–289
Rotary spark gap (*see* Rotary gap)
Rudin, R., 693n.

S

Saturation, of reactor core, 364, 370
Screen-grid voltage, 108
Self-synchronous, 663
Series gap, 274
  division of voltage across, 312–315
  general operating characteristics of, 296–304
  two and three gap operation, 302–303
  (*See also* Fixed gap)
Series spark gap (*see* Series gap)

715 B tetrode, 104, 115, 126, 147
715 B tube, 115
Shielding, 688
Short circuit in the load, 248, 417, 423–431, 457
Shunt capacitance, 26, 30, 161, 251
Shunt diode, 44, 146, 154, 348, 426–429, 433, 443, 455
  8020, 154
Shunt inductance, 251
Shunt losses, 69
Siegel, S., 454n.
Signal presentation, 662–667
Single-switch multiple-network circuit, 492
6AG7 tube, 135
6C21 triode, 100, 106, 132, 157
6D21 tetrode, 100, 106, 163
6SN7 triode, 106
Skin depth, 659
Skin effect, 547
Slack, C. N., 274n., 316n.
Slater, J. C., 523n.
Spark gap, 175
  (*See also* Fixed gap; Rotary gap; Series gap)
Sparking, of magnetrons, 417, 425, 441–447, 707
Spectrum analyzer, 706
Spectrum distribution of pulses, 718
Spike, current, 188
  current pulse, 436, 567
  on top of the pulse, 102
Squirted flux, 530
Static resistance of load, 3, 110
Steady-state theory, 183–185
Storage condenser (*see* Condenser, storage)
Stray capacitance, 508
Stromberg-Carlson Company, 140, 141
Sullivan, H. J., 312n.
Sweep calibrator, 665
Sweep speeds, 663
Switch, average power dissipated in, 92
  bidirectional, 418, 424
  effective resistance of, 23
  gaseous-discharge, 10, 14, 175
  for line-type pulsers, 273–354
    requirements for, 273
  pulser, 5, 356
  unidirectional, 342, 418

Switch unidirectional, circuit using, 423
    vacuum tube, 6
    vacuum tubes as, 90–118
    resistance of, 7
    voltage drop in, 22
Switch characteristics required for hard-
    tube pulsers, 90–98
Switch operation, typical, 298–300
Switch resistance, effect of, 269
Switch tube, 225
    average power dissipated in, 22, 92
    characteristic curves for triode and
      tetrode, 98–108
    power dissipation in, 73
Switch-tube characteristics, affecting pul-
    ser design, 93–98
    effect of on pulser regulation, 108–118
Switch-tube current, 92
Switch-tube operation, above knee of
    I_p-V_p curve, 111–114
    below knee of I_p-V_p curve, 114–115
Switch-tube resistance, 78
Switch tubes, enclosed-gap types, 321,
    322, 328, 333
    hard-tube types, 95, 96
    hydrogen-thyratron types, 340, 341
    oxide-coated cathode, 93, 95
    sparking in, 93, 95
    thoriated tungsten cathode, 93, 95
Synchronous, 663
Synchroscope, 662–665
Synchroscope input impedance, 670

T

Tail-biting circuit, 133
Teflon, 650
Terman, F. E., 91*n*.
Tetrode, 92
    characteristic curves for, 98–108, 110
    3D21, 105, 115
    3E29, 135, 157
    5D21, 100, 104, 132, 472
    6D21, 100, 106, 163
    715 B, 104, 115, 126, 147
    829, 105, 123, 126, 132
Thermal relay, 434
Three-gap operation, 302
    possible circuits for, 303
Thyratron bridge, 478–480
Thyratrons, 175, 274
    hydrogen (*see* Hydrogen thyratron)

Thyratrons, 3C45, 138, 341
    4C35, 138, 341, 479
    5C22, 138, 341, 455
    mercury, 335
Thyrite, 429
Time jitter, 15, 16, 120, 129, 278, 284,
    295, 299, 326, 330, 334, 351, 471
Time lag, 275
Time of rise, 206
    of ripple, 206
    for the voltage pulse, 80, 683
Tonks, L., 274*n*.
Top of pulse (*see* Pulse)
Trailing edge of pulse (*see* Pulse)
Transformer, distributed capacitance for,
    507
    current, 574
    high-reactance (see High-reactance
      transformers)
    impedance-transformation ratio of, 10
    isolation, 512
    noninverting, 535
    pulse (*see* Pulse transformers)
    for regenerative pulse generator, 500
    stepdown, 510
    stepup, 510
    transmission delay of, 525
    voltage-transformation ratio of, 10
Transformer dissipation of energy in core,
    508
Transformer equivalent circuit, 503–508
Transformer theory, general, 499–510
Transformer voltage, 483
Transmission cable and impedance
    matching, 669–673
Transmission delay of a transformer, 525
Transmission line, 177
    lossless, 176, 226
    short-circuited, 209
Transmission-line admittance functions,
    185
Transmission-line capacitance, 228
Transmission-line impedance function,
    181
Transmission-line voltage vs. pulse-power
    output, 229
Transmission time, 177
Trapezoidal wave, 190
Trigatron, 295, 332
    CV85, 332
    CV125, 332

Trigger circuit, condenser-discharge, 307–311
  using a saturable-core transformer, 311
Trigger-coupling condensers, 297, 312, 314
Trigger generator, 304–312
Trigger pulse, 119
  rate of rise of, 350
Trigger voltage, 302, 330, 334
Triggering, parallel, 124
  series, 124
Triode, 92
  characteristic curves for, 98–108
  6C21, 100, 106, 132, 157
  6SN7, 106
  304TH, 100, 104, 123
  527, 106
Tube dissipation, 345
Tube drop, 345
  of hydrogen thyratrons, variation with time, 344
Tubes, of receiver type, pulse characteristics of, 102
  (*See also* specific type of tube)
Turns, number of, 538
2050 tube, 123
Two-gap operation, 302
Type A Guillemin network, 201, 212
Type B Guillemin network, 201, 212
Type C Guillemin network, 201, 212
Type D Guillemin network, 201, 205
Type E network, 205, 213, 219
Type F Guillemin network, 201, 212

U

Undercurrent relay, 433
U.S. Signal Corps, 693*n.*

V

V_{max}, definition of, 297
V_{min}, definition of, 297
V_{start}, definition of, 297
V-I plots, 675–680
Vacuum-tube switch (*see* Switch, vacuum-tube)
Varela, A. A., 171
Vershbow, A. E., 459*n.*
Voltage current characteristics of magnetron, 32, 702
Voltage differentiator, 680–687

Voltage distribution along the windings of transformer, 519
Voltage dividers, 666
  for series gaps, 312–315
Voltage-dividing resistors, 297, 312, 314
Voltage drop across three fixed spark gaps, 325
Voltage-doubler power supply, 148
Voltage-fed network, (*see* Network)
Voltage pulse, average amplitude for, 69
Voltage pulses, and time derivatives, 681
  short, and time derivatives, oscilloscope traces of, 685
Voltage range, of CV125, 334
  vs. number of gaps, 300–302
Voltage rate of rise, 447
Voltage stepup ratios, 396, 398, 420
Voltage supply, 16
  (*See also* Power supply)
Voltage-transformation ratio of transformer, 10
von Hippel, A., 653*n.*

W

Wave shape, charging current, for d-c charging, 362
  charging voltage, for d-c charging, 362
  in a-c charging, 408
  current, for a-c nonresonant charging, 399
    for a-c resonant charging, 389
  voltage, for a-c nonresonant charging, 399
    for a-c resonant charging, 389
  (*See also* Pulse shape)
Webster, A. G., 179*n.*
Western Electric Company, 560, 614, 615
Westinghouse Research Laboratories, 458–461, 463, 557, 559, 614, 615, 649
Whittaker, E. T., 185*n.*
Winding schemes for pulse transformers, 517, 518
Wire for pulse transformers, 655–660
Woodbury, R. B., 74*n.*, 102*n.*
WX3226 gaps, 299, 320–322
WX3240 gap, 320–322

Y

Young, R. T., Jr., 662*n.*, 707*n.*

Z

Zeidler, H. M., 589*n.*

CATALOGUE OF DOVER BOOKS

ENGINEERING AND TECHNOLOGY

General and mathematical

ENGINEERING MATHEMATICS, Kenneth S. Miller. A text for graduate students of engineering to strengthen their mathematical background in differential equations, etc. Mathematical steps very explicitly indicated. Contents: Determinants and Matrices, Integrals, Linear Differential Equations, Fourier Series and Integrals, Laplace Transform, Network Theory, Random Function . . . all vital requisites for advanced modern engineering studies. Unabridged republication. Appendices: Borel Sets; Riemann-Stieltjes Integral; Fourier Series and Integrals. Index. References at Chapter Ends. xii + 417pp. 6 x 8½.   S1121 Paperbound **$2.00**

MATHEMATICAL ENGINEERING ANALYSIS, Rufus Oldenburger. A book designed to assist the research engineer and scientist in making the transition from physical engineering situations to the corresponding mathematics. Scores of common practical situations found in all major fields of physics are supplied with their correct mathematical formulations—applications to automobile springs and shock absorbers, clocks, throttle torque of diesel engines, resistance networks, capacitors, transmission lines, microphones, neon tubes, gasoline engines, refrigeration cycles, etc. Each section reviews basic principles of underlying various fields: mechanics of rigid bodies, electricity and magnetism, heat, elasticity, fluid mechanics, and aerodynamics. Comprehensive and eminently useful. Index. 169 problems, answers. 200 photos and diagrams. xiv + 426pp. 5⅜ x 8½.   S919 Paperbound **$2.00**

MATHEMATICS OF MODERN ENGINEERING, E. G. Keller and R. E. Doherty. Written for the Advanced Course in Engineering of the General Electric Corporation, deals with the engineering use of determinants, tensors, the Heaviside operational calculus, dyadics, the calculus of variations, etc. Presents underlying principles fully, but purpose is to teach engineers to deal with modern engineering problems, and emphasis is on the perennial engineering attack of set-up and solve. Indexes. Over 185 figures and tables. Hundreds of exercises, problems, and worked-out examples. References. Two volume set. Total of xxxiii + 623pp. 5⅜ x 8.
S734 Vol I Paperbound **$1.85**
S735 Vol II Paperbound **$1.85**
The set **$3.70**

MATHEMATICAL METHODS FOR SCIENTISTS AND ENGINEERS, L. P. Smith. For scientists and engineers, as well as advanced math students. Full investigation of methods and practical description of conditions under which each should be used. Elements of real functions, differential and integral calculus, space geometry, theory of residues, vector and tensor analysis, series of Bessel functions, etc. Each method illustrated by completely-worked-out examples, mostly from scientific literature. 368 graded unsolved problems. 100 diagrams. x + 453pp. 5⅝ x 8⅜.   S220 Paperbound **$2.00**

THEORY OF FUNCTIONS AS APPLIED TO ENGINEERING PROBLEMS, edited by R. Rothe, F. Ollendorff, and K. Pohlhausen. A series of lectures given at the Berlin Institute of Technology that shows the specific applications of function theory in electrical and allied fields of engineering. Six lectures provide the elements of function theory in a simple and practical form, covering complex quantities and variables, integration in the complex plane, residue theorems, etc. Then 5 lectures show the exact uses of this powerful mathematical tool, with full discussions of problem methods. Index. Bibliography. 108 figures. x + 189pp. 5⅜ x 8.
S733 Paperbound **$1.35**

Aerodynamics and hydrodynamics

AIRPLANE STRUCTURAL ANALYSIS AND DESIGN, E. E. Sechler and L. G. Dunn. Systematic authoritative book which summarizes a large amount of theoretical and experimental work on structural analysis and design. Strong on classical subsonic material still basic to much aeronautic design . . . remains a highly useful source of information. Covers such areas as layout of the airplane, applied and design loads, stress-strain relationships for stable structures, truss and frame analysis, the problem of instability, the ultimate strength of stiffened flat sheet, analysis of cylindrical structures, wings and control surfaces, fuselage analysis, engine mounts, landing gears, etc. Originally published as part of the CALCIT Aeronautical Series. 256 illustrations. 47 study problems. Indexes. xi + 420pp. 5⅜ x 8½.
S1043 Paperbound **$2.25**

FUNDAMENTALS OF HYDRO- AND AEROMECHANICS, L. Prandtl and O. G. Tietjens. The well-known standard work based upon Prandtl's lectures at Goettingen. Wherever possible hydrodynamics theory is referred to practical considerations in hydraulics, with the view of unifying theory and experience. Presentation is extremely clear and though primarily physical, mathematical proofs are rigorous and use vector analysis to a considerable extent. An Engineering Society Monograph, 1934. 186 figures. Index. xvi + 270pp. 5⅜ x 8.
S374 Paperbound **$1.85**

Catalogue of Dover Books

FLUID MECHANICS FOR HYDRAULIC ENGINEERS, H. Rouse. Standard work that gives a coherent picture of fluid mechanics from the point of view of the hydraulic engineer. Based on courses given to civil and mechanical engineering students at Columbia and the California Institute of Technology, this work covers every basic principle, method, equation, or theory of interest to the hydraulic engineer. Much of the material, diagrams, charts, etc., in this self-contained text are not duplicated elsewhere. Covers irrotational motion, conformal mapping, problems in laminar motion, fluid turbulence, flow around immersed bodies, transportation of sediment, general charcteristics of wave phenomena, gravity waves in open channels, etc. Index. Appendix of physical properties of common fluids. Frontispiece + 245 figures and photographs. xvi + 422pp. 5⅜ x 8. S729 Paperbound **$2.25**

WATERHAMMER ANALYSIS, John Parmakian. Valuable exposition of the graphical method of solving waterhammer problems by Assistant Chief Designing Engineer, U.S. Bureau of Reclamation. Discussions of rigid and elastic water column theory, velocity of waterhammer waves, theory of graphical waterhammer analysis for gate operation, closings, openings, rapid and slow movements, etc., waterhammer in pump discharge caused by power failure, waterhammer analysis for compound pipes, and numerous related problems. "With a concise and lucid style, clear printing, adequate bibliography and graphs for approximate solutions at the project stage, it fills a vacant place in waterhammer literature," WATER POWER. 43 problems. Bibliography. Index. 113 illustrations. xiv + 161pp. 5⅜ x 8½. S1061 Paperbound **$1.65**

AERODYNAMIC THEORY: A GENERAL REVIEW OF PROGRESS, William F. Durand, editor-in-chief. A monumental joint effort by the world's leading authorities prepared under a grant of the Guggenheim Fund for the Promotion of Aeronautics. Intended to provide the student and aeronautic designer with the theoretical and experimental background of aeronautics. Never equalled for breadth, depth, reliability. Contains discussions of special mathematical topics not usually taught in the engineering or technical courses. Also: an extended two-part treatise on Fluid Mechanics, discussions of aerodynamics of perfect fluids, analyses of experiments with wind tunnels, applied airfoil theory, the non-lifting system of the airplane, the air propeller, hydrodynamics of boats and floats, the aerodynamics of cooling, etc. Contributing experts include Munk, Giacomelli, Prandtl, Toussaint, Von Karman, Klemperer, among others. Unabridged republication. 6 volumes bound as 3. Total of 1,012 figures, 12 plates. Total of 2,186pp. Bibliographies. Notes. Indices. 5⅜ x 8. S328-S330 Clothbound, The Set **$17.50**

APPLIED HYDRO- AND AEROMECHANICS, L. Prandtl and O. G. Tietjens. Presents, for the most part, methods which will be valuable to engineers. Covers flow in pipes, boundary layers, airfoil theory, entry conditions, turbulent flow in pipes, and the boundary layer, determining drag from measurements of pressure and velocity, etc. "Will be welcomed by all students of aerodynamics," NATURE. Unabridged, unaltered. An Engineering Society Monograph, 1934. Index. 226 figures, 28 photographic plates illustrating flow patterns. xvi + 311pp. 5⅜ x 8. S375 Paperbound **$1.85**

SUPERSONIC AERODYNAMICS, E. R. C. Miles. Valuable theoretical introduction to the supersonic domain, with emphasis on mathematical tools and principles, for practicing aerodynamicists and advanced students in aeronautical engineering. Covers fundamental theory, divergence theorem and principles of circulation, compressible flow and Helmholtz laws, the Prandtl-Busemann graphic method for 2-dimensional flow, oblique shock waves, the Taylor-Maccoll method for cones in supersonic flow, the Chaplygin method for 2-dimensional flow, etc. Problems range from practical engineering problems to development of theoretical results. "Rendered outstanding by the unprecedented scope of its contents . . . has undoubtedly filled a vital gap," AERONAUTICAL ENGINEERING REVIEW. Index. 173 problems, answers. 106 diagrams. 7 tables. xii + 255pp. 5⅜ x 8. S214 Paperbound **$1.45**

HYDRAULIC TRANSIENTS, G. R. Rich. The best text in hydraulics ever printed in English . . . by one of America's foremost engineers (former Chief Design Engineer for T.V.A.). Provides a transition from the basic differential equations of hydraulic transient theory to the arithmetic intergration computation required by practicing engineers. Sections cover Water Hammer, Turbine Speed Regulation, Stability of Governing, Water-Hammer Pressures in Pump Discharge Lines, The Differential and Restricted Orifice Surge Tanks, The Normalized Surge Tank Charts of Calame and Gaden, Navigation Locks, Surges in Power Canals—Tidal Harmonics, etc. Revised and enlarged. Author's prefaces. Index. xiv + 409pp. 5⅜ x 8½. S116 Paperbound **$2.50**

HYDRAULICS AND ITS APPLICATIONS, A. H. Gibson. Excellent comprehensive textbook for the student and thorough practical manual for the professional worker, a work of great stature in its area. Half the book is devoted to theory and half to applications and practical problems met in the field. Covers modes of motion of a fluid, critical velocity, viscous flow, eddy formation, Bernoulli's theorem, flow in converging passages, vortex motion, form of effluent streams, notches and weirs, skin friction, losses at valves and elbows, siphons, erosion of channels, jet propulsion, waves of oscillation, and over 100 similar topics. Final chapters (nearly 400 pages) cover more than 100 kinds of hydraulic machinery: Pelton wheel, speed regulators, the hydraulic ram, surge tanks, the scoop wheel, the Venturi meter, etc. A special chapter treats methods of testing theoretical hypotheses: scale models of rivers, tidal estuaries, siphon spillways, etc. 5th revised and enlarged (1952) edition. Index. Appendix. 427 photographs and diagrams. 95 examples, answers. xv + 813pp. 6 x 9. S791 Clothbound **$8.00**

FLUID MECHANICS THROUGH WORKED EXAMPLES, D. R. L. Smith and J. Houghton. Advanced text covering principles and applications to practical situations. Each chapter begins with concise summaries of fundamental ideas. 163 fully worked out examples applying principles outlined in the text. 275 other problems, with answers. Contents: The Pressure of Liquids on Surfaces; Floating Bodies; Flow Under Constant Head in Pipes; Circulation; Vorticity; The Potential Function; Laminar Flow and Lubrication; Impact of Jets; Hydraulic Turbines; Centrifugal and Reciprocating Pumps; Compressible Fluids; and many other items. Total of 438 examples. 250 line illustrations. 340pp. Index. 6 x 8⅞.   S981 Clothbound **$6.00**

THEORY OF SHIP MOTIONS, S. N. Blagoveshchensky. The only detailed text in English in a rapidly developing branch of engineering and physics, it is the work of one of the world's foremost authorities—Blagoveshchensky of Leningrad Shipbuilding Institute. A senior-level treatment written primarily for engineering students, but also of great importance to naval architects, designers, contractors, researchers in hydrodynamics, and other students. No mathematics beyond ordinary differential equations is required for understanding the text. Translated by T. & L. Strelkoff, under editorship of Louis Landweber, Iowa Institute of Hydraulic Research, under auspices of Office of Naval Research. Bibliography. Index. 231 diagrams and illustrations. Total of 649pp. 5⅜ x 8½.   Vol. I: S234 Paperbound **$2.00**
Vol. II: S235 Paperbound **$2.00**

THEORY OF FLIGHT, Richard von Mises. Remains almost unsurpassed as balanced, well-written account of fundamental fluid dynamics, and situations in which air compressibility effects are unimportant. Stressing equally theory and practice, avoiding formidable mathematical structure, it conveys a full understanding of physical phenomena and mathematical concepts. Contains perhaps the best introduction to general theory of stability. "Outstanding," Scientific, Medical, and Technical Books. New introduction by K. H. Hohenemser. Bibliographical, historical notes. Index. 408 illustrations. xvi + 620pp. 5⅜ x 8⅜.   S541 Paperbound **$2.95**

THEORY OF WING SECTIONS, I. H. Abbott, A. E. von Doenhoff. Concise compilation of subsonic aerodynamic characteristics of modern NASA wing sections, with description of their geometry, associated theory. Primarily reference work for engineers, students, it gives methods, data for using wing-section data to predict characteristics. Particularly valuable: chapters on thin wings, airfoils; complete summary of NACA's experimental observations, system of construction families of airfoils. 350pp. of tables on Basic Thickness Forms, Mean Lines, Airfoil Ordinates, Aerodynamic Characteristics of Wing Sections. Index. Bibliography. 191 illustrations. Appendix. 705pp. 5⅜ x 8.   S558 Paperbound **$3.25**

WEIGHT-STRENGTH ANALYSIS OF AIRCRAFT STRUCTURES, F. R. Shanley. Scientifically sound methods of analyzing and predicting the structural weight of aircraft and missiles. Deals directly with forces and the distances over which they must be transmitted, making it possible to develop methods by which the minimum structural weight can be determined for any material and conditions of loading. Weight equations for wing and fuselage structures. Includes author's original papers on inelastic buckling and creep buckling. "Particularly successful in presenting his analytical methods for investigating various optimum design principles," AERONAUTICAL ENGINEERING REVIEW. Enlarged bibliography. Index. 199 figures. xiv + 404pp. 5⅝ x 8⅜.   S660 Paperbound **$2.50**

Electricity

TWO-DIMENSIONAL FIELDS IN ELECTRICAL ENGINEERING, L. V. Bewley. A useful selection of typical engineering problems of interest to practicing electrical engineers. Introduces senior students to the methods and procedures of mathematical physics. Discusses theory of functions of a complex variable, two-dimensional fields of flow, general theorems of mathematical physics and their applications, conformal mapping or transformation, method of images, freehand flux plotting, etc. New preface by the author. Appendix by W. F. Kiltner. Index. Bibliography at chapter ends. xiv + 204pp. 5⅜ x 8½.   S1118 Paperbound **$1.50**

FLUX LINKAGES AND ELECTROMAGNETIC INDUCTION, L. V. Bewley. A brief, clear book which shows proper uses and corrects misconceptions of Faraday's law of electromagnetic induction in specific problems. Contents: Circuits, Turns, and Flux Linkages; Substitution of Circuits; Electromagnetic Induction; General Criteria for Electromagnetic Induction; Applications and Paradoxes; Theorem of Constant Flux Linkages. New Section: Rectangular Coil in a Varying Uniform Medium. Valuable supplement to class texts for engineering students. Corrected, enlarged edition. New preface. Bibliography in notes. 49 figures. xi + 106pp. 5⅜ x 8.   S1103 Paperbound **$1.25**

INDUCTANCE CALCULATIONS: WORKING FORMULAS AND TABLES, Frederick W. Grover. An invaluable book to everyone in electrical engineering. Provides simple single formulas to cover all the more important cases of inductance. The approach involves only those parameters that naturally enter into each situation, while extensive tables are given to permit easy interpolations. Will save the engineer and student countless hours and enable them to obtain accurate answers with minimal effort. Corrected republication of 1946 edition. 58 tables. 97 completely worked out examples. 66 figures. xiv + 286pp. 5⅜ x 8½.   S974 Paperbound **$1.85**

GASEOUS CONDUCTORS: THEORY AND ENGINEERING APPLICATIONS, J. D. Cobine. An indispensable text and reference to gaseous conduction phenomena, with the engineering viewpoint prevailing throughout. Studies the kinetic theory of gases, ionization, emission phenomena; gas breakdown, spark characteristics, glow, and discharges; engineering applications in circuit interrupters, rectifiers, light sources, etc. Separate detailed treatment of high pressure arcs (Suits); low pressure arcs (Langmuir and Tonks). Much more. "Well organized, clear, straightforward," Tonks, Review of Scientific Instruments. Index. Bibliography. 83 practice problems. 7 appendices. Over 600 figures. 58 tables. xx + 606pp. 5⅜ x 8. **S442 Paperbound $2.95**

INTRODUCTION TO THE STATISTICAL DYNAMICS OF AUTOMATIC CONTROL SYSTEMS, V. V. Solodovnikov. First English publication of text-reference covering important branch of automatic control systems—random signals; in its original edition, this was the first comprehensive treatment. Examines frequency characteristics, transfer functions, stationary random processes, determination of minimum mean-squared error, of transfer function for a finite period of observation, much more. Translation edited by J. B. Thomas, L. A. Zadeh. Index. Bibliography. Appendix. xxii + 308pp. 5⅜ x 8. **S420 Paperbound $2.25**

TENSORS FOR CIRCUITS, Gabriel Kron. A boldly original method of analyzing engineering problems, at center of sharp discussion since first introduced, now definitely proved useful in such areas as electrical and structural networks on automatic computers. Encompasses a great variety of specific problems by means of a relatively few symbolic equations. "Power and flexibility . . . becoming more widely recognized," Nature. Formerly "A Short Course in Tensor Analysis." New introduction by B. Hoffmann. Index. Over 800 diagrams. xix + 250pp. 5⅜ x 8. **S534 Paperbound $2.00**

SELECTED PAPERS ON SEMICONDUCTOR MICROWAVE ELECTRONICS, edited by Sumner N. Levine and Richard R. Kurzrok. An invaluable collection of important papers dealing with one of the most remarkable devolopments in solid-state electronics—the use of the **p-n** junction to achieve amplification and frequency conversion of microwave frequencies. Contents: General Survey (3 introductory papers by W. E. Danielson, R. N. Hall, and M. Tenzer); General Theory of Nonlinear Elements (3 articles by A. van der Ziel, H. E. Rowe, and Manley and Rowe); Device Fabrication and Characterization (3 pieces by Bakanowski, Cranna, and Uhlir, by McCotter, Walker and Fortini, and by S. T. Eng); Parametric Amplifiers and Frequency Multipliers (13 articles by Uhlir, Heffner and Wade, Matthaei, P. K. Tien, van der Ziel, Engelbrecht, Currie and Gould, Uenohara, Leeson and Weinreb, and others); and Tunnel Diodes (4 papers by L. Esaki, H. S. Sommers, Jr., M. E. Hines, and Yariv and Cook). Introduction. 295 Figures. xiii + 286pp. 6½ x 9¼. **S1126 Paperbound $2.25**

THE PRINCIPLES OF ELECTROMAGNETISM APPLIED TO ELECTRICAL MACHINES, B. Hague. A concise, but complete, summary of the basic principles of the magnetic field and its applications, with particular reference to the kind of phenomena which occur in electrical machines. Part I: General Theory—magnetic field of a current, electromagnetic field passing from air to iron, mechanical forces on linear conductors, etc. Part II: Application of theory to the solution of electromechanical problems—the magnetic field and mechanical forces in non-salient pole machinery, the field within slots and between salient poles, and the work of Rogowski, Roth, and Strutt. Formery titled "Electromagnetic Problems in Electrical Engineering." 2 appendices. Index. Bibliography in notes. 115 figures. xiv + 359pp. 5⅜ x 8½. **S246 Paperbound $2.25**

Mechanical engineering

DESIGN AND USE OF INSTRUMENTS AND ACCURATE MECHANISM, T. N. Whitehead. For the instrument designer, engineer; how to combine necessary mathematical abstractions with independent observation of actual facts. Partial contents: instruments & their parts, theory of errors, systematic errors, probability, short period errors, erratic errors, design precision, kinematic, semikinematic design, stiffness, planning of an instrument, human factor, etc. Index. 85 photos, diagrams. xii + 288pp. 5⅜ x 8. **S270 Paperbound $2.00**

A TREATISE ON GYROSTATICS AND ROTATIONAL MOTION: THEORY AND APPLICATIONS, Andrew Gray. Most detailed, thorough book in English, generally considered definitive study. Many problems of all sorts in full detail, or step-by-step summary. Classical problems of Bour, Lottner, etc.; later ones of great physical interest. Vibrating systems of gyrostats, earth as a top, calculation of path of axis of a top by elliptic integrals, motion of unsymmetrical top, much more. Index. 160 illus. 550pp. 5⅜ x 8. **S589 Paperbound $2.75**

MECHANICS OF THE GYROSCOPE, THE DYNAMICS OF ROTATION, R. F. Deimel, Professor of Mechanical Engineering at Stevens Institute of Technology. Elementary general treatment of dynamics of rotation, with special application of gyroscopic phenomena. No knowledge of vectors needed. Velocity of a moving curve, acceleration to a point, general equations of motion, gyroscopic horizon, free gyro, motion of discs, the damped gyro, 103 similar topics. Exercises. 75 figures. 208pp. 5⅜ x 8. **S66 Paperbound $1.65**

STRENGTH OF MATERIALS, J. P. Den Hartog. Distinguished text prepared for M.I.T. course, ideal as introduction, refresher, reference, or self-study text. Full clear treatment of elementary material (tension, torsion, bending, compound stresses, deflection of beams, etc.), plus much advanced material on engineering methods of great practical value: full treatment of the Mohr circle, lucid elementary discussions of the theory of the center of shear and the "Myosotis" method of calculating beam deflections, reinforced concrete, plastic deformations, photoelasticity, etc. In all sections, both general principles and concrete applications are given. Index. 186 figures (160 others in problem section). 350 problems, all with answers. List of formulas. viii + 323pp. 5⅜ x 8.   S755 Paperbound **$2.00**

PHOTOELASTICITY: PRINCIPLES AND METHODS, H. T. Jessop, F. C. Harris. For the engineer, for specific problems of stress analysis. Latest time-saving methods of checking calculations in 2-dimensional design problems, new techniques for stresses in 3 dimensions, and lucid description of optical systems used in practical photoelasticity. Useful suggestions and hints based on on-the-job experience included. Partial contents: strained and stress-strain relations, circular disc under thrust along diameter, rectangular block with square hole under vertical thrust, simply supported rectangular beam under central concentrated load, etc. Theory held to minimum, no advanced mathematical training needed. Index. 164 illustrations. viii + 184pp. 6⅛ x 9¼.   S720 Paperbound **$2.00**

APPLIED ELASTICITY, J. Prescott. Provides the engineer with the theory of elasticity usually lacking in books on strength of materials, yet concentrates on those portions useful for immediate application. Develops every important type of elasticity problem from theoretical principles. Covers analysis of stress, relations between stress and strain, the empirical basis of elasticity, thin rods under tension or thrust, Saint Venant's theory, transverse oscillations of thin rods, stability of thin plates, cylinders with thin walls, vibrations of rotating disks, elastic bodies in contact, etc. "Excellent and important contribution to the subject, not merely in the old matter which he has presented in new and refreshing form, but also in the many original investigations here published for the first time," NATURE. Index. 3 Appendixes. vi + 672pp. 5⅜ x 8.   S726 Paperbound **$2.95**

APPLIED MECHANICS FOR ENGINEERS, Sir Charles Inglis, F.R.S. A representative survey of the many and varied engineering questions which can be answered by statics and dynamics. The author, one of first and foremost adherents of "structural dynamics," presents distinctive illustrative examples and clear, concise statement of principles—directing the discussion at methodology and specific problems. Covers fundamental principles of rigid-body statics, graphic solutions of static problems, theory of taut wires, stresses in frameworks, particle dynamics, kinematics, simple harmonic motion and harmonic analysis, two-dimensional rigid dynamics, etc. 437 illustrations. xii + 404pp. 5⅜ x 8½. S1119 Paperbound **$2.00**

THEORY OF MACHINES THROUGH WORKED EXAMPLES, G. H. Ryder. Practical mechanical engineering textbook for graduates and advanced undergraduates, as well as a good reference work for practicing engineers. Partial contents: Mechanisms, Velocity and Acceleration (including discussion of Klein's Construction for Piston Acceleration), Cams, Geometry of Gears, Clutches and Bearings, Belt and Rope Drives, Brakes, Inertia Forces and Couples, General Dynamical Problems, Gyroscopes, Linear and Angular Vibrations, Torsional Vibrations, Transverse Vibrations and Whirling Speeds (Chapters on vibrations considerably enlarged from previous editions). Over 300 problems, many fully worked out. Index. 195 line illustrations. Revised and enlarged edition. viii + 280pp. 5⅜ x 8¾.   S980 Clothbound **$5.00**

THE KINEMATICS OF MACHINERY: OUTLINES OF A THEORY OF MACHINES, Franz Reuleaux. The classic work in the kinematics of machinery. The present thinking about the subject has all been shaped in great measure by the fundamental principles stated here by Reuleaux almost 90 years ago. While some details have naturally been superseded, his basic viewpoint has endured; hence, the book is still an excellent text for basic courses in kinematics and a standard reference work for active workers in the field. Covers such topics as: the nature of the machine problem, phoronomic propositions, pairs of elements, incomplete kinematic chains, kinematic notation and analysis, analyses of chamber-crank trains, chamber-wheel trains, constructive elements of machinery, complete machines, etc., with main focus on controlled movement in mechanisms. Unabridged republication of original edition, translated by Alexander B. Kennedy. New introduction for this edition by E. S. Ferguson. Index. 451 illustrations. xxiv + 622pp. 5⅜ x 8½.   S1124 Paperbound **$3.00**

ANALYTICAL MECHANICS OF GEARS, Earle Buckingham. Provides a solid foundation upon which logical design practices and design data can be constructed. Originally arising out of investigations of the ASME Special Research Committee on Worm Gears and the Strength of Gears, the book covers conjugate gear-tooth action, the nature of the contact, and resulting gear-tooth profiles of: spur, internal, helical, spiral, worm, bevel, and hypoid or skew bevel gears. Also: frictional heat of operation and its dissipation, friction losses, etc., dynamic loads in operation, and related matters. Familiarity with this book is still regarded as a necessary prerequisite to work in modern gear manufacturing. 263 figures. 103 tables. Index. x + 546pp. 5⅜ x 8½.   S1073 Paperbound **$2.75**

Optical design, lighting

THE SCIENTIFIC BASIS OF ILLUMINATING ENGINEERING, Parry Moon, Professor of Electrical Engineering, M.I.T. Basic, comprehensive study. Complete coverage of the fundamental theoretical principles together with the elements of design, vision, and color with which the lighting engineer must be familiar. Valuable as a text as well as a reference source to the practicing engineer. Partial contents: Spectroradiometric Curve, Luminous Flux, Radiation from Gaseous-Conduction Sources, Radiation from Incandescent Sources, Incandescent Lamps, Measurement of Light, Illumination from Point Sources and Surface Sources, Elements of Lighting Design. 7 Appendices. Unabridged and corrected republication, with additions. New preface containing conversion tables of radiometric and photometric concepts. Index. 707-item bibliography. 92-item bibliography of author's articles. 183 problems. xxiii + 608pp. 5⅜ x 8½. **S242 Paperbound $2.85**

OPTICS AND OPTICAL INSTRUMENTS: AN INTRODUCTION WITH SPECIAL REFERENCE TO PRACTICAL APPLICATIONS, B. K. Johnson. An invaluable guide to basic practical applications of optical principles, which shows how to set up inexpensive working models of each of the four main types of optical instruments—telescopes, microscopes, photographic lenses, optical projecting systems. Explains in detail the most important experiments for determining their accuracy, resolving power, angular field of view, amounts of aberration, all other necessary facts about the instruments. Formerly "Practical Optics." Index. 234 diagrams. Appendix. 224pp. 5⅜ x 8. **S642 Paperbound $1.65**

APPLIED OPTICS AND OPTICAL DESIGN, A. E. Conrady. With publication of vol. 2, standard work for designers in optics is now complete for first time. Only work of its kind in English; only detailed work for practical designer and self-taught. Requires, for bulk of work, no math above trig. Step-by-step exposition, from fundamental concepts of geometrical, physical optics, to systematic study, design, of almost all types of optical systems. Vol. 1: all ordinary ray-tracing methods; primary aberrations; necessary higher aberration for design of telescopes, low-power microscopes, photographic equipment. Vol. 2: (Completed from author's notes by R. Kingslake, Dir. Optical Design, Eastman Kodak.) Special attention to high-power microscope, anastigmatic photographic objectives. "An indispensable work," J., Optical Soc. of Amer. "As a practical guide this book has no rival," Transactions, Optical Soc. Index. Bibliography. 193 diagrams. 852pp. 6⅛ x 9¼. **Vol. 1 S366 Paperbound $2.95**
Vol. 2 S612 Paperbound $2.95

Miscellaneous

THE MEASUREMENT OF POWER SPECTRA FROM THE POINT OF VIEW OF COMMUNICATIONS ENGINEERING, R. B. Blackman, J. W. Tukey. This pathfinding work, reprinted from the "Bell System Technical Journal," explains various ways of getting practically useful answers in the measurement of power spectra, using results from both transmission theory and the theory of statistical estimation. Treats: Autocovariance Functions and Power Spectra; Direct Analog Computation; Distortion, Noise, Heterodyne Filtering and Pre-whitening; Aliasing; Rejection Filtering and Separation; Smoothing and Decimation Procedures; Very Low Frequencies; Transversal Filtering; much more. An appendix reviews fundamental Fourier techniques. Index of notation. Glossary of terms. 24 figures. XII tables. Bibliography. General index. 192pp. 5⅜ x 8. **S507 Paperbound $1.85**

CALCULUS REFRESHER FOR TECHNICAL MEN, A. Albert Klaf. This book is unique in English as a refresher for engineers, technicians, students who either wish to brush up their calculus or to clear up uncertainties. It is not an ordinary text, but an examination of most important aspects of integral and differential calculus in terms of the 756 questions most likely to occur to the technical reader. The first part of this book covers simple differential calculus, with constants, variables, functions, increments, derivatives, differentiation, logarithms, curvature of curves, and similar topics. The second part covers fundamental ideas of integration, inspection, substitution, transformation, reduction, areas and volumes, mean value, successive and partial integration, double and triple integration. Practical aspects are stressed rather than theoretical. A 50-page section illustrates the application of calculus to specific problems of civil and nautical engineering, electricity, stress and strain, elasticity, industrial engineering, and similar fields.—756 questions answered. 566 problems, mostly answered. 36 pages of useful constants, formulae for ready reference. Index. v + 431pp. 5⅜ x 8. **T370 Paperbound $2.00**

METHODS IN EXTERIOR BALLISTICS, Forest Ray Moulton. Probably the best introduction to the mathematics of projectile motion. The ballistics theories propounded were coordinated with extensive proving ground and wind tunnel experiments conducted by the author and others for the U.S. Army. Broad in scope and clear in exposition, it gives the beginnings of the theory used for modern-day projectile, long-range missile, and satellite motion. Six main divisions: Differential Equations of Translatory Motion of a projectile; Gravity and the Resistance Function; Numerical Solution of Differential Equations; Theory of Differential Variations; Validity of Method of Numerical Integration; and Motion of a Rotating Projectile. Formerly titled: "New Methods in Exterior Ballistics." Index. 38 diagrams. viii + 259pp. 5⅜ x 8½. **S232 Paperbound $1.75**

Catalogue of Dover Books

LOUD SPEAKERS: THEORY, PERFORMANCE, TESTING AND DESIGN, N. W. McLachlan. Most comprehensive coverage of theory, practice of loud speaker design, testing; classic reference, study manual in field. First 12 chapters deal with theory, for readers mainly concerned with math. aspects; last 7 chapters will interest reader concerned with testing, design. Partial contents: principles of sound propagation, fluid pressure on vibrators, theory of moving-coil principle, transients, driving mechanisms, response curves, design of horn type moving coil speakers, electrostatic speakers, much more. Appendix. Bibliography. Index. 165 illustrations, charts. 411pp. 5⅜ x 8. **S588 Paperbound $2.25**

MICROWAVE TRANSMISSION, J. C. Slater. First text dealing exclusively with microwaves, brings together points of view of field, circuit theory, for graduate student in physics, electrical engineering, microwave technician. Offers valuable point of view not in most later studies. Uses Maxwell's equations to study electromagnetic field, important in this area. Partial contents: infinite line with distributed parameters, impedance of terminated line, plane waves, reflections, wave guides, coaxial line, composite transmission lines, impedance matching, etc. Introduction. Index. 76 illus. 319pp. 5⅜ x 8. **S564 Paperbound $1.50**

MICROWAVE TRANSMISSION DESIGN DATA, T. Moreno. Originally classified, now rewritten and enlarged (14 new chapters) for public release under auspices of Sperry Corp. Material of immediate value or reference use to radio engineers, systems designers, applied physicists, etc. Ordinary transmission line theory; attenuation; capacity; parameters of coaxial lines; higher modes; flexible cables; obstacles, discontinuities, and injunctions; tunable wave guide impedance transformers; effects of temperature and humidity; much more. "Enough theoretical discussion is included to allow use of data without previous background," Electronics. 324 circuit diagrams, figures, etc. Tables of dielectrics, flexible cable, etc., data. Index. ix + 248pp. 5⅜ x 8. **S459 Paperbound $1.65**

RAYLEIGH'S PRINCIPLE AND ITS APPLICATIONS TO ENGINEERING, G. Temple & W. Bickley. Rayleigh's principle developed to provide upper and lower estimates of true value of fundamental period of a vibrating system, or condition of stability of elastic systems. Illustrative examples; rigorous proofs in special chapters. Partial contents: Energy method of discussing vibrations, stability. Perturbation theory, whirling of uniform shafts. Criteria of elastic stability. Application of energy method. Vibrating systems. Proof, accuracy, successive approximations, application of Rayleigh's principle. Synthetic theorems. Numerical, graphical methods. Equilibrium configurations, Ritz's method. Bibliography. Index. 22 figures. ix + 156pp. 5⅜ x 8. **S307 Paperbound $1.50**

ELASTICITY, PLASTICITY AND STRUCTURE OF MATTER, R. Houwink. Standard treatise on rheological aspects of different technically important solids such as crystals, resins, textiles, rubber, clay, many others. Investigates general laws for deformations; determines divergences from these laws for certain substances. Covers general physical and mathematical aspects of plasticity, elasticity, viscosity. Detailed examination of deformations, internal structure of matter in relation to elastic and plastic behavior, formation of solid matter from a fluid, conditions for elastic and plastic behavior of matter. Treats glass, asphalt, gutta percha, balata, proteins, baker's dough, lacquers, sulphur, others. 2nd revised, enlarged edition. Extensive revised bibliography in over 500 footnotes. Index. Table of symbols. 214 figures. xviii + 368pp. 6 x 9¼. **S385 Paperbound $2.45**

THE SCHWARZ-CHRISTOFFEL TRANSFORMATION AND ITS APPLICATIONS: A SIMPLE EXPOSITION, Miles Walker. An important book for engineers showing how this valuable tool can be employed in practical situations. Very careful, clear presentation covering numerous concrete engineering problems. Includes a thorough account of conjugate functions for engineers—useful for the beginner and for review. Applications to such problems as: Stream-lines round a corner, electric conductor in air-gap, dynamo slots, magnetized poles, much more. Formerly "Conjugate Functions for Engineers." Preface. 92 figures, several tables. Index. ix + 116pp. 5⅜ x 8½. **S1149 Paperbound $1.25**

THE LAWS OF THOUGHT, George Boole. This book founded symbolic logic some hundred years ago. It is the 1st significant attempt to apply logic to all aspects of human endeavour. Partial contents: derivation of laws, signs & laws, interpretations, eliminations, conditions of a perfect method, analysis, Aristotelian logic, probability, and similar topics. xviii + 424pp. 5⅜ x 8. **S28 Paperbound $2.00**

SCIENCE AND METHOD, Henri Poincaré. Procedure of scientific discovery, methodology, experiment, idea-germination—the intellectual processes by which discoveries come into being. Most significant and most interesting aspects of development, application of ideas. Chapters cover selection of facts, chance, mathematical reasoning, mathematics, and logic; Whitehead, Russell, Cantor; the new mechanics, etc. 288pp. 5⅜ x 8. **S222 Paperbound $1.35**

FAMOUS BRIDGES OF THE WORLD, D. B. Steinman. An up-to-the-minute revised edition of a book that explains the fascinating drama of how the world's great bridges came to be built. The author, designer of the famed Mackinac bridge, discusses bridges from all periods and all parts of the world, explaining their various types of construction, and describing the problems their builders faced. Although primarily for youngsters, this cannot fail to interest readers of all ages. 48 illustrations in the text. 23 photographs. 99pp. 6⅛ x 9¼. **T161 Paperbound $1.00**

Technological, historical

A DIDEROT PICTORIAL ENCYCLOPEDIA OF TRADES AND INDUSTRY, Manufacturing and the Technical Arts in Plates Selected from "L'Encyclopédie ou Dictionnaire Raisonné des Sciences, des Arts, et des Métiers" of Denis Diderot. Edited with text by C. Gillispie. This first modern selection of plates from the high point of 18th century French engraving is a storehouse of valuable technological information to the historian of arts and science. Over 2000 illustrations on 485 full-page plates, most of them original size, show the trades and industries of a fascinating era in such great detail that the processes and shops might very well be reconstructed from them. The plates teem with life, with men, women, and children performing all of the thousands of operations necessary to the trades before and during the early stages of the industrial revolution. Plates are in sequence, and show general operations, closeups of difficult operations, and details of complex machinery. Such important and interesting trades and industries are illustrated as sowing, harvesting, beekeeping, cheesemaking, operating windmills, milling flour, charcoal burning, tobacco processing, indigo, fishing, arts of war, salt extraction, mining, smelting, casting iron, steel, extracting mercury, zinc, sulphur, copper, etc., slating, tinning, silverplating, gilding, making gunpowder, cannons, bells, shoeing horses, tanning, papermaking, printing, dyeing, and more than 40 other categories. Professor Gillispie, of Princeton, supplies a full commentary on all the plates, identifying operations, tools, processes, etc. This material, presented in a lively and lucid fashion, is of great interest to the reader interested in history of science and technology. Heavy library cloth. 920pp. 9 x 12. **T421 Two volume set $18.50**

CHARLES BABBAGE AND HIS CALCULATING ENGINES, edited by P. Morrison and E. Morrison. Babbage, leading 19th century pioneer in mathematical machines and herald of modern operational research, was the true father of Harvard's relay computer Mark I. His Difference Engine and Analytical Engine were the first machines in the field. This volume contains a valuable introduction on his life and work; major excerpts from his autobiography, revealing his eccentric and unusual personality; and extensive selections from "Babbage's Calculating Engines," a compilation of hard-to-find journal articles by Babbage, the Countess of Lovelace, L. F. Menabrea, and Dionysius Lardner. 8 illustrations, Appendix of miscellaneous papers. Index. Bibliography. xxxviii + 400pp. 5⅜ x 8. **T12 Paperbound $2.00**

HISTORY OF HYDRAULICS, Hunter Rouse and Simon Ince. First history of hydraulics and hydrodynamics available in English. Presented in readable, non-mathematical form, the text is made especially easy to follow by the many supplementary photographs, diagrams, drawings, etc. Covers the great discoveries and developments from Archimedes and Galileo to modern giants—von Mises, Prandtl, von Karman, etc. Interesting browsing for the specialist; excellent introduction for teachers and students. Discusses such milestones as the two-piston pump of Ctesibius, the aqueducts of Frontius, the anticipations of da Vinci, Stevin and the first book on hydrodynamics, experimental hydraulics of the 18th century, the 19th-century expansion of practical hydraulics and classical and applied hydrodynamics, the rise of fluid mechanics in our time, etc. 200 illustrations. Bibliographies. Index. xii + 270pp. 5¾ x 8. **S1131 Paperbound $2.00**

BRIDGES AND THEIR BUILDERS, David Steinman and Sara Ruth Watson. Engineers, historians, everyone who has ever been fascinated by great spans will find this book an endless source of information and interest. Dr. Steinman, recipient of the Louis Levy medal, was one of the great bridge architects and engineers of all time, and his analysis of the great bridges of history is both authoritative and easily followed. Greek and Roman bridges, medieval bridges, Oriental bridges, modern works such as the Brooklyn Bridge and the Golden Gate Bridge, and many others are described in terms of history, constructional principles, artistry, and function. All in all this book is the most comprehensive and accurate semipopular history of bridges in print in English. New, greatly revised, enlarged edition. 23 photographs, 26 line drawings. Index. xvii + 401pp. 5⅜ x 8. **T431 Paperbound $2.00**

Prices subject to change without notice.

Dover publishes books on art, music, philosophy, literature, languages, history, social sciences, psychology, handcrafts, orientalia, puzzles and entertainments, chess, pets and gardens, books explaining science, intermediate and higher mathematics, mathematical physics, engineering, biological sciences, earth sciences, classics of science, etc. Write to:

Dept. catrr.
Dover Publications, Inc.
180 Varick Street, N.Y. 14, N.Y.